经典原版书库

离散数学及其应用

（英文精编版·第6版）

Discrete Mathematics and Its Applications

(Sixth Edition)

（美）Kenneth H. Rosen 著

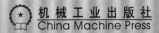

机械工业出版社
China Machine Press

本书版权登记号：图字：**01-2010-1530**

图书在版编目（CIP）数据

离散数学及其应用 (英文精编版·第 6 版) / (美) 罗森 (Rosen, K. H.) 著. —北京: 机械工业出版社, 2010.9

（经典原版书库）

书名原文：Discrete Mathematics and Its Applications, Sixth Edition

ISBN 978-7-111-31329-8

Ⅰ. 离…　Ⅱ. 罗…　Ⅲ. 离散数学-英文　Ⅳ. O158

中国版本图书馆 CIP 数据核字(2010)第 136920 号

机械工业出版社 (北京市西城区百万庄大街 22 号　邮政编码　100037)
责任编辑：白　宇
北京京北印刷有限公司印刷
2010 年 10 月第 1 版第 1 次印刷
170mm×242mm　•　29 印张
标准书号：ISBN 978-7-111-31329-8
定价：55.00 元

凡购本书，如有缺页、倒页、脱页，由本社发行部调换

客服热线: (010) 88378991；88361066

购书热线: (010) 68326294；88379649；68995259

投稿热线: (010) 88379604

读者信箱: hzjsj@hzbook.com

Adapter's Forword

Purpose

The original of *Discrete Mathematics and its Applications* is intended for one-term or two-term introductory courses of Discrete Mathematics taken by students from wide variety of majors, including computer science, mathematics, engineering and etc. It's an excellent textbook written by Prof. Kenneth H. Rosen and has been widely used in over 600 institutions around the world.

The sixth edition gives a focused introduction to the primary themes of the Discrete Mathematics course and demonstrates the relevance and practicality of Discrete Mathematics to a wide variety of real-world applications. All the topics, examples, references and exercises are quite helpful to the students.

In recent years, bilingual teaching has been encouraged in universities and colleges in China. More and more Chinese instructors and students are getting interested in this book. However, as a textbook, over 800 original pages make Chinese students find it difficult to read. In order to introduce this book to more Chinese college students, we tried to maintain the author's writing style and omitted some contents to adapt for the Chinese students' English reading ability. The compressed version fits into the syllabus of undergraduate course, and reduce students' reading burden as well.

What is Compressed

Since some contents in the original are taught in some other courses, such as Number theory, Discrete Probability, Induction and Recursion, Boolean Algebra and Finite-state Machine, we removed them which were in the original book as Chapter 3, Chapter 4, Chapter 6, Chapter 11 and Chapter 12. As a result, Logic and Proofs, Sets, Functions, Relations, Graphs, Trees, Counting and Advanced Counting Techniques are reserved in the compressed version.

There are over 3800 exercises in the original textbook, posing various types of questions. Some of them are designed for basic skill development, some are in intermediate level and some are more difficult and challenging. In order to keep the original feature of the book, we removed the even-number questions of the remained Chapters, so that the questions with different difficulties are reserved. The historical information for the background of many topics is also removed, so as to reduce the reading burden of students.

Some concepts are given in the exercises. It is difficult for students to comprehend because of the simplicity of the descriptions, such as the concepts about the Normal and Canonical forms for a proposition. So we have added the detail description about them in Chapter 1.

Acknowledgments

I would like to thank Kenneth H. Rosen, the author of the original book, and McGraw-Hill, the original publisher, who authorized us to compress the original book. It is their understanding and generosity that make it possible for more Chinese students to enjoy this distinguished book.

Thanks to everyone at China Machine Press who has put into great effort to make this cooperation possible.

Thanks to my colleague Jie Yang who has given precious comments for the work.

The compression is made based on my teaching experiences, and the syllabus of Discrete Mathematics course for undergraduate students. It is certainly wild open for discussions on further improvements. Your comments and suggestions are extremely important, and we would be highly appreciated.

Qiong Chen
South China University of Technology
(csqchenscut.edu.cn)

Preface

In writing this book, I was guided by my long-standing experience and interest in teaching discrete mathematics. For the student, my purpose was to present material in a precise, readable manner, with the concepts and techniques of discrete mathematics clearly presented and demonstrated. My goal was to show the relevance and practicality of discrete mathematics to students, who are often skeptical. I wanted to give students studying computer science all of the mathematical foundations they need for their future studies. I wanted to give mathematics students an understanding of important mathematical concepts together with a sense of why these concepts are important for applications. And most importantly, I wanted to accomplish these goals without watering down the material.

For the instructor, my purpose was to design a flexible, comprehensive teaching tool using proven pedagogical techniques in mathematics. I wanted to provide instructors with a package of materials that they could use to teach discrete mathematics effectively and efficiently in the most appropriate manner for their particular set of students. I hope that I have achieved these goals.

I have been extremely gratified by the tremendous success of this text. The many improvements in the sixth edition have been made possible by the feedback and suggestions of a large number of instructors and students at many of the more than 600 schools where this book has been successfully used. There are many enhancements in this edition. The companion website has been substantially enhanced and more closely integrated with the text, providing helpful material to make it easier for students and instructors to achieve their goals.

This text is designed for a one- or two-term introductory discrete mathematics course taken by students in a wide variety of majors, including mathematics, computer science, and engineering. College algebra is the only explicit prerequisite, although a certain degree of mathematical maturity is needed to study discrete mathematics in a meaningful way.

Goals of a Discrete Mathematics Course

A discrete mathematics course has more than one purpose. Students should learn a particular set of mathematical facts and how to apply them; more importantly, such a course should teach students how to think logically and mathematically. To achieve these goals, this text stresses mathematical reasoning and the different ways problems are solved. Five important themes are interwoven in this text: mathematical reasoning, combinatorial analysis, discrete structures, algorithmic thinking, and applications and modeling. A successful discrete mathematics course should carefully blend and balance all five themes.

1. *Mathematical Reasoning:* Students must understand mathematical reasoning in order to read, comprehend, and construct mathematical arguments. This text starts with a discussion of mathematical logic, which serves as the foundation for the subsequent discussions of methods of proof. Both the science and the art of constructing proofs are addressed. The technique of mathematical induction is stressed through many different types of examples of such proofs and a careful explanation of why mathematical induction is a valid proof technique.

2. *Combinatorial Analysis:* An important problem-solving skill is the ability to count or enumerate objects. The discussion of enumeration in this book begins with the basic techniques of counting. The stress is on performing combinatorial analysis to solve counting problems and analyze algorithms, not on applying formulae.

3. *Discrete Structures:* A course in discrete mathematics should teach students how to work with discrete structures, which are the abstract mathematical structures used to represent discrete objects and relationships between these objects. These discrete structures include sets, permutations, relations, graphs, trees, and finite-state machines.

4. *Algorithmic Thinking:* Certain classes of problems are solved by the specification of an algorithm. After an algorithm has been described, a computer program can be constructed implementing it. The mathematical portions of this activity, which include the specification of the algorithm, the verification that it works properly, and the analysis of the computer memory and time required to perform it, are all covered in this text. Algorithms are described using both English and an easily understood form of pseudocode.

5. *Applications and Modeling:* Discrete mathematics has applications to almost every conceivable area of study. There are many applications to computer science and data networking in this text, as well as applications to such diverse areas as chemistry, botany, zoology, linguistics, geography, business, and the Internet. These applications are natural and important uses of discrete mathematics and are not contrived. Modeling with discrete mathematics is an extremely important problem-solving skill, which students have the opportunity to develop by constructing their own models in some of the exercises.

Special Features

Accessibility   This text has proved to be easily read and understood by beginning students. There are no mathematical prerequisites beyond college algebra for almost all of this text. Students needing extra help will find tools on the MathZone companion website for bringing their mathematical maturity up to the level of the text. The few places in the book where calculus is referred to are explicitly noted. Most students should easily understand the pseudocode used in the text to express algorithms, regardless of whether they have formally studied programming languages. There is no formal computer science prerequisite.

Each chapter begins at an easily understood and accessible level. Once basic mathematical concepts have been carefully developed, more difficult material and applications to other areas of study are presented.

Flexibility   This text has been carefully designed for flexible use. The dependence of chapters on previous material has been minimized. Each chapter is divided into sections of approximately the same length, and each section is divided into subsections that form natural blocks of material for teaching. Instructors can easily pace their lectures using these blocks.

Writing Style   The writing style in this book is direct and pragmatic. Precise mathematical language is used without excessive formalism and abstraction. Care has been taken to balance the mix of notation and words in mathematical statements.

Mathematical Rigor and Precision   All definitions and theorems in this text are stated extremely carefully so that students will appreciate the precision of language and rigor needed in mathematics. Proofs are motivated and developed slowly; their steps are all carefully justified. The axioms used in proofs and the basic properties that follow from them are explicitly described in an appendix, giving students a clear idea of what they can assume in a proof. Recursive definitions are explained and used extensively.

Worked Examples   Examples are used to illustrate concepts, relate different topics, and introduce applications. In most examples, a question is first posed, then its solution is presented with the appropriate amount of detail.

Applications   The applications included in this text demonstrate the utility of discrete mathematics in the solution of real-world problems. This text includes applications to a wide variety of areas, including computer science, data networking, psychology, chemistry, engineering, linguistics, biology, business, and the Internet.

Algorithms   Results in discrete mathematics are often expressed in terms of algorithms; hence, key algorithms are introduced in each chapter of the book. The computational complexity of the algorithms in the text is also analyzed at an elementary level.

Key Terms and Results   A list of key terms and results follows each chapter. The key terms include only the most important that students should learn, not every term defined in the chapter.

Exercises   There are exercises in the text, with many different types of questions posed. There is an ample supply of straightforward exercises that develop basic skills, a large number of intermediate exercises, and many challenging exercises. Exercises are stated clearly and unambiguously, and all are carefully graded for level of difficulty. Exercise sets contain special discussions that develop new concepts not covered in the text, enabling students to discover new ideas through their own work.

Exercises that are somewhat more difficult than average are marked with a single star *; those that are much more challenging are marked with two stars **. Exercises whose solutions require calculus are explicitly noted. Exercises that develop results used in the text are clearly identified with the symbol ☞. Answers or outlined solutions to exercises are provided at the back of the text. The solutions include proofs in which most of the steps are clearly spelled out.

Review Questions   A set of review questions is provided at the end of each chapter. These questions are designed to help students focus their study on the most important concepts and techniques of that chapter. To answer these questions students need to write long answers, rather than just perform calculations or give short replies.

Computer Projects   Each chapter is followed by a set of computer projects. The computer projects tie together what students may have learned in computing and in discrete mathematics. Computer projects that are more difficult than average, from both a mathematical and a programming point of view, are marked with a star, and those that are extremely challenging are marked with two stars.

Computations and Explorations   A set of computations and explorations is included at the conclusion of each chapter. These exercises are designed to be completed using existing software tools, such as programs that students or instructors have written or mathematical computation packages such as Maple or Mathematica. Many of these exercises give students the opportunity to uncover new facts and ideas through computation. (Some of these exercises are discussed in the *Exploring Discrete Mathematics with Maple* companion workbook available online.)

Writing Projects   Each chapter is followed by a set of writing projects. To do these projects students need to consult the mathematical literature. Some of these projects are historical in nature and may involve looking up original sources. Others are designed to serve as gateways to new topics and ideas. All are designed to expose students to ideas not covered in depth in the text. These projects tie mathematical concepts together with the writing process and help expose students to possible areas for future study. (Suggested references for these projects can be found online or in the printed *Student's Solutions Guide*.)

Suggested Readings   A list of suggested readings for each chapter is provided in a section at the end of the text. These suggested readings include books at or below the level of this text, more difficult books, expository articles, and articles in which discoveries in discrete mathematics were originally published. Some of these publications are classics, published many years ago, while others have been published within the last few years.

Ancillaries

Student's Solutions Guide   This student manual, available separately, contains full solutions to all odd-numbered problems in the exercise sets. These solutions explain why a particular method is used and why it works. For some exercises, one or two other possible approaches are described to show that a problem can be solved in several different ways. Suggested references for the writing projects found at the end of each chapter are also included in this volume. Also included are a guide to writing proofs and an extensive description of common mistakes students make in discrete mathematics, plus sample tests and a sample crib sheet for each chapter designed to help students prepare for exams.

(ISBN-10: 0-07-310779-4)   (ISBN-13: 978-0-07-310779-0)

Instructor's Resource Guide   This manual, available by request for instructors, contains full solutions to even-numbered exercises in the text. Suggestions on how to teach the material in each chapter of the book are provided, including the points to stress in each section and how to put the material into perspective. It also offers sample tests for each chapter and a test bank containing over 1300 exam questions to choose from. Answers to all sample tests and test bank questions are included. Finally, several sample syllabi are presented for courses with differing emphasis and student ability levels, and a complete section and exercise migration guide is included to help users of the fifth edition update their course materials to match the sixth edition.

(ISBN-10: 0-07-310781-6)   (ISBN-13: 978-0-07-310781-3)

Instructor's Testing and Resource CD   An extensive test bank of more than 1300 questions using Brownstone Diploma testing software is available by request for use on Windows or Macintosh systems. Instructors can use this software to create their own tests by selecting questions of their choice or by random selection. They can also sort questions by section, difficulty level, and type; edit existing questions or add their own; add their own headings and instructions; print scrambled versions of the same test; export tests to word processors or the Web; and create and manage course grade books. A printed version of this test bank, including the questions and their answers, is included in the *Instructor's Resource Guide*.

(ISBN-10: 0-07-310782-4)   (ISBN-13: 978-0-07-310782-0)

Acknowledgments

I would like to thank the many instructors and students at a variety of schools who have used this book and provided me with their valuable feedback and helpful suggestions. Their input has made this a much better book than it would have been otherwise. I especially want to thank Jerrold Grossman, John Michaels, and George Bergman for their technical reviews of the sixth edition and their "eagle eyes," which have helped ensure the accuracy of this book. I also appreciate the help provided by all those who have submitted comments via the website.

   I thank the reviewers of this sixth and the five previous editions. These reviewers have provided much helpful criticism and encouragement to me. I hope this edition lives up to their high expectations.

Reviewers for the Sixth Edition

Charles Ashbacher,
  Mount Mercy College

Ian Barland,
  Rice University

George Bergman,
  University of California, Berkeley

David Berman,
  University of North Carolina, Wilmington

Miklós Bóna,
  University of Florida

Greg Cameron,
  Brigham Young University

John Carter,
  University of Toronto

Greg Chapman,
  Cosumnes River College

Chao-Kun Cheng,
  Virginia Commonwealth University

Thomas Cooper,
  Georgia Perimeter College, Lawrenceville

Beverly Diamond,
  College of Charleston

Thomas Dunion,
  Atlantic Union College

Bruce Elenbogen,
  University of Michigan, Dearborn

Herbert Enderton,
  University of California, Los Angeles

Anthony Evans,
  Wright State University

Prosenjit Bose,
Carleton University

Kirby Brown,
Polytechnic University

Michael Button,
The Master's College

Stephanie Fitchett,
Florida Atlantic University

Jerry Fluharty,
Eastern Shore Community College

Joel Fowler,
*Southern Polytechnic State
University*

William Gasarch,
University of Maryland

Sudpito Ghosh,
Colorado State University

Jerrold Grossman,
Oakland University

Ruth Haas,
Smith College

Patricia Hammer,
Hollins University

Keith Harrow,
Brooklyn College

Bert Hartnell,
St. Mary's University

Julia Hassett,
Oakton College

Kavita Hatwal,
Portland Community College

John Helm,
Radford University

Arthur Hobbs,
Texas A&M University

Fannie Howell,
Roanoke High School

Wei Hu,
Houghton College

Nan Jiang,
University of South Dakota

Margaret Johnson,
Stanford University

Martin Jones,
College of Charleston

Tim Kearns,
*California Polytechnic State
University, San Luis Obispo*

Barbara Cortzen,
DePaul University

Daniel Cunningham,
Buffalo State College

George Davis,
University of Georgia

Jonathan Knappenberger,
LaSalle University

Ed Korntved,
Northwest Nazarene University

Przemo Kranz,
University of Mississippi

Loredana Lanzani,
University of Arkansas

Yoonjin Lee,
Smith College

Miguel Lerma,
Northwestern University

Jason Levy,
University of Hawaii

Lauren Lilly,
Tabor College

Ekaterina Lioutikova,
Saint Joseph College

Vladimir Logvinenko,
De Anza College

Joan Lukas,
University of Massachusetts, Boston

Lester McCann,
University of Arizona

Jennifer McNulty,
University of Montana

John G. Michaels,
SUNY Brockport

Michael Oppedisano,
Morrisville State College

Michael O'Sullivan,
San Diego State University

Charles Parry,
Virginia Polytechnic Institute

Linda Powers,
Virginia Polytechnic Institute

Dan Pritikin,
Miami University

Anthony Quas,
University of Memphis

Eric Rawdon,
Duquesne University

Kim Factor,
Marquette University

William Farmer,
McMaster University

Li Feng,
Albany State University

Henry Ricardo,
Medgar Evers College

Oskars Rieksts,
Kutztown University

Stefan Robila,
Montclair State University

Chris Rodger,
Auburn University

Robert Rodman,
North Carolina State University

Shai Simonson,
Stonehill College

Barbara Smith,
Cochise College

Wasin So,
San Jose State University

Diana Staats,
Dutchess Community College

Lorna Stewart,
University of Alberta

Bogdan Suceava,
*California State University,
Fullerton*

Kathleen Sullivan,
Seattle University

Laszlo Szekely,
University of South Carolina

Daniel Tauritz,
University of Missouri, Rolla

Don VanderJagt,
Grand Valley State University

Fran Vasko,
Kutztown University

Susan Wallace,
University of North Florida

Zhenyuan Wang,
University of Nebraska, Omaha

Tom Wineinger,
*University of Wisconsin,
Eau Claire*

Charlotte Young,
South Plains College

Reviewers of Previous Editions

Eric Allender,
Rutgers University

Stephen Andrilli,
La Salle University

Kendall Atkinson,
University of Iowa, Iowa City

Zhaojun Bai,
University of California, Davis

Jack R. Barone,
Baruch College

Klaus Bichteler,
University of Texas, Austin

Alfred E. Borm,
Southwest Texas State University

Ken W. Bosworth,
University of Maryland

Lois Brady,
*California Polytechnic State
University, San Luis Obispo*

Scott Buffett,
University of New Brunswick

Russell Campbell,
University of Northern Iowa

E. Rodney Canfield,
University of Georgia

Kevin Carolan,
Marist College

Tim Carroll,
Bloomsburg University

Kit C. Chan,
Bowling Green State University

Allan C. Cochran,
University of Arkansas

Peter Collinge,
Monroe Community College

Ron Davis,
Millersville University

Nachum Dershowitz,
*University of Illinois,
Urbana–Champaign*

Thomas Dowling,
The Ohio State University

Patrick C. Fischer,
Vanderbilt University

Jane Fritz,
University of New Brunswick

Ladnor Geissinger,
University of North Carolina

Jonathan Goldstine,
Pennsylvania State University

Paul Gormley,
Villanova University

Brian Gray,
Howard Community College

Jonathan Gross,
Columbia University

Laxmi N. Gupta,
Rochester Institute of Technology

Daniel Gusfield,
University of California, Davis

David F. Hayes,
San Jose State University

Xin He,
SUNY at Buffalo

Donald Hutchison,
Clackamas Community College

Kenneth Johnson,
North Dakota State University

Daniel Somerville,
University of Massachusetts, Boston

Patrick Tantalo,
University of California, Santa Cruz

David Jonah,
Wayne State University

Akihiro Kanamori,
Boston University

W. Thomas Kiley,
George Mason University

Takashi Kimura,
Boston University

Nancy Kinnersley,
University of Kansas

Gary Klatt,
University of Wisconsin

Nicholas Krier,
Colorado State University

Lawrence S. Kroll,
San Francisco State University

Shui F. Lam,
*California State University,
Long Beach*

Robert Lavelle,
Iona College

Harbir Lamba,
George Mason University

Sheau Dong Lang,
University of Central Florida

Cary Lee,
Grossmont Community College

Yi-Hsin Liu,
University of Nebraska, Omaha

Stephen C. Locke,
Florida Atlantic University

George Luger,
University of New Mexico

David S. McAllister,
North Carolina State University

Robert McGuigan,
Westfield State College

Michael Maller,
Queens College

Ernie Manes,
University of Massachusetts

Francis Masat,
Glassboro State College

J. M. Metzger,
University of North Dakota

Thomas D. Morley,
Georgia Institute of Technology

D. R. Morrison,
University of New Mexico

Philip D. Tiu,
Oglethorpe University

Lisa Townsley-Kulich,
Illinois Benedictine College

Ho Kuen Ng,
San Jose State University

Timothy S. Norfolk, Sr.
University of Akron

Truc T. Nguyen,
Bowling Green State University

George Novacky,
University of Pittsburgh

Jeffrey Nunemacher,
Ohio Wesleyan University

Jaroslav Opatrny,
Concordia University

Jonathan Pakianathan,
University of Rochester

Thomas W. Parsons,
Hofstra University

Mary K. Prisco,
University of Wisconsin, Green Bay

Halina Przymusinska,
*California Polytechnic State
University, Pomona*

Don Reichman,
*Mercer County Community
College*

Harold Reiter,
University of North Carolina

Adrian Riskin,
Northern Arizona State University

Amy L. Rocha,
San Jose State University

Janet Roll,
University of Findlay

Matthew J. Saltzman,
Clemson University

Alyssa Sankey,
Slippery Rock University

Dinesh Sarvate,
College of Charleston

Michael J. Schlosser,
The Ohio State University

Steven R. Seidel,
Michigan Technological University

Douglas Shier,
Clemson University

Alistair Sinclair,
University of California, Berkeley

Carl H. Smith,
University of Maryland

Hunter S. Snevily,
University of Idaho

Thomas Upson,
Rochester Institute of Technology

Roman Voronka,
New Jersey Institute of Technology

Bharti Temkin,
Texas Tech University

George Trapp,
West Virginia University

James Walker,
University of South Carolina

Wallace Terwilligen,
Bowling Green State University

David S. Tucker,
Midwestern State University

Anthony S. Wojcik,
Michigan State University

I would like to thank the staff of McGraw-Hill for their strong support of this project. In particular, thanks go to Liz Haefele, Publisher, for her backing; to Liz Covello, Senior Sponsoring Editor, for her advocacy and enthusiasm; and to Dan Seibert, Developmental Editor, for his dedication and attention. I would also like to thank the original editor, Wayne Yuhasz, whose insights and skills helped ensure the book's success, as well as all the other previous editors of this book.

To the staff involved in the production of this sixth edition, I offer my thanks to Peggy Selle, Lead Project Manager; Michelle Whitaker, Senior Designer; Jeff Huettman, Lead Media Producer; Sandy Schnee, Senior Media Project Manager; Melissa Leick, Supplements Coordinator; and Kelly Brown, Executive Marketing Manager. I am also grateful to Jerry Grossman, who checked the entire manuscript for accuracy; Rose Kramer and Gayle Casel, the technical proofreaders; Pat Steele, the manuscript copyeditor; and Georgia Mederer, who checked the accuracy of the solutions in the *Student's Solutions Guide* and *Instructor's Resource Guide*.

Kenneth H. Rosen

To the Student

What is discrete mathematics?   Discrete mathematics is the part of mathematics devoted to the study of discrete objects. (Here *discrete* means consisting of distinct or unconnected elements.) The kinds of problems solved using discrete mathematics include:

- How many ways are there to choose a valid password on a computer system?
- What is the probability of winning a lottery?
- Is there a link between two computers in a network?
- How can I identify spam e-mail messages?
- How can I encrypt a message so that no unintended recipient can read it?
- What is the shortest path between two cities using a transportation system?
- How can a list of integers be sorted so that the integers are in increasing order?
- How many steps are required to do such a sorting?
- How can it be proved that a sorting algorithm correctly sorts a list?
- How can a circuit that adds two integers be designed?
- How many valid Internet addresses are there?

You will learn the discrete structures and techniques needed to solve problems such as these.

More generally, discrete mathematics is used whenever objects are counted, when relationships between finite (or countable) sets are studied, and when processes involving a finite number of steps are analyzed. A key reason for the growth in the importance of discrete mathematics is that information is stored and manipulated by computing machines in a discrete fashion.

Why Study Discrete Mathematics?   There are several important reasons for studying discrete mathematics. First, through this course you can develop your mathematical maturity: that is, your ability to understand and create mathematical arguments. You will not get very far in your studies in the mathematical sciences without these skills.

Second, discrete mathematics is the gateway to more advanced courses in all parts of the mathematical sciences. Discrete mathematics provides the mathematical foundations for many computer science courses including data structures, algorithms, database theory, automata theory, formal languages, compiler theory, computer security, and operating systems. Students find these courses much more difficult when they have not had the appropriate mathematical foundations from discrete math. One student has sent me an e-mail message saying that she used the contents of this book in every computer science course she took!

Math courses based on the material studied in discrete mathematics include logic, set theory, number theory, linear algebra, abstract algebra, combinatorics, graph theory, and probability theory (the discrete part of the subject).

Also, discrete mathematics contains the necessary mathematical background for solving problems in operations research (including many discrete optimization techniques), chemistry, engineering, biology, and so on. In the text, we will study applications to some of these areas.

Many students find their introductory discrete mathematics course to be significantly more challenging than courses they have previously taken. One reason for this is that one of the primary goals of this course is to teach mathematical reasoning and problem solving, rather than a discrete set of skills. The exercises in this book are designed to reflect this goal. Although there are plenty of exercises in this text similar to those addressed in the examples, a large percentage of the exercises require original thought. This is intentional. The material discussed in the text provides the tools needed to solve these exercises, but your job is to successfully apply these tools using your own creativity. One of the primary goals of this course is to learn how to attack problems that may be somewhat different from any you may have previously seen. Unfortunately, learning how to solve only particular types of exercises is not sufficient for success in developing the problem-solving skills needed in subsequent courses and professional work. This text addresses many different topics, but discrete mathematics is an extremely diverse and large area of study. One of my goals as an author is to help you develop the skills needed to master the additional material you will need in your own future pursuits.

The Exercises   I would like to offer some advice about how you can best learn discrete mathematics (and other subjects in the mathematical and computing sciences). You will learn the most by actively working exercises. I suggest that you solve as many as you possibly can. After working the exercises your instructor has assigned, I encourage you to solve additional exercises such as those in the exercise sets following each section of the text and in the supplementary exercises at the end of each chapter. (Note the key explaining the markings preceding exercises.)

Key to the Exercises

No marking	A routine exercise
*	A difficult exercise
**	An extremely challenging exercise
☞	An exercise containing a result used in the book (The Table below shows where each of these exercises are used.)
(*Requires calculus*)	An exercise whose solution requires the use of limits or concepts from differential or integral calculus

The best approach is to try exercises yourself before you consult the answer section at the end of this book. Note that the odd-numbered exercise answers provided in the text are answers only and not full solutions; in particular, the reasoning required to obtain answers is omitted in these answers. The *Student's Solutions Guide*, available separately, provides complete, worked solutions to all odd-numbered exercises in this text. When you hit an impasse trying to solve an odd-numbered exercise, I suggest you consult the *Student's Solutions Guide* and look for some guidance as to how to solve the problem. The more work you do yourself rather than passively reading or copying solutions, the more you will learn. The answers and solutions to the even-numbered exercises are intentionally not available from the publisher; ask your instructor if you have trouble with these.

Web Resources   You are strongly encouraged to take advantage of additional resources available on the Web, especially those on the MathZone companion website for this book found at www.mhhe.com/rosen. You will find many Extra Examples designed to clarify key concepts; Self Assessments for gauging how well you understand core topics; Interactive Demonstration Applets exploring key algorithms and other concepts; a Web Resources Guide containing an extensive selection of links to external sites relevant to the world of discrete mathematics; extra explanations and practice to help you master core concepts; added instruction on writing proofs and on avoiding common mistakes in discrete mathematics; in-depth discussions of important applications; and guidance on utilizing Maple software to explore the computational aspects of discrete mathematics. Places in the text where these additional online resources are available are identified in the margins by special icons. You will also find NetTutor, an online tutorial service that you can use to receive help from tutors either via real-time chat or via messages. For more details on these online resources, see the description of the MathZone companion website immediately preceding this "To the Student" message.

The Value of This Book   My intention is to make your investment in this text an excellent value. The book, the associated ancillaries, and MathZone companion website have taken many years of effort to develop and refine. I am confident that most of you will find that the text and associated materials will help you master discrete mathematics. Even though it is likely that you will not cover some chapters in your current course, you should find it helpful—as many other students have—to read the relevant sections of the book as you take additional courses. Most of you will return to this book as a useful tool throughout your future studies, especially for those of you who continue in computer science, mathematics, and engineering. I have designed this book to be a gateway for future studies and explorations, and I wish you luck as you begin your journey.

Kenneth H. Rosen

LIST OF SYMBOLS

TOPIC	SYMBOL	MEANING
LOGIC	$\neg p$	negation of p
	$p \wedge q$	conjunction of p and q
	$p \vee q$	disjunction of p and q
	$p \oplus q$	exclusive or of p and q
	$p \rightarrow q$	the implication p implies q
	$p \leftrightarrow q$	biconditional of p and q
	$p \equiv q$	equivalence of p and q
	$\mathbf{T}$	tautology
	$\mathbf{F}$	contradiction
	$P(x_1, \ldots, x_n)$	propositional function
	$\forall x\, P(x)$	universal quantification of $P(x)$
	$\exists x\, P(x)$	existential quantification of $P(x)$
	$\exists! x\, P(x)$	uniqueness quantification of $P(x)$
	$\therefore$	therefore
	$p\{S\}q$	partial correctness of S
SETS	$x \in S$	x is a member of S
	$x \notin S$	x is not a member of S
	$\{a_1, \ldots, a_n\}$	list of elements of a set
	$\{x \mid P(x)\}$	set builder notation
	$\mathbf{N}$	set of natural numbers
	$\mathbf{Z}$	set of integers
	$\mathbf{Z}^+$	set of positive integers
	$\mathbf{Q}$	set of rational numbers
	$\mathbf{R}$	set of real numbers
	$S = T$	set equality
	$\emptyset$	the empty (or null) set
	$S \subseteq T$	S is a subset of T
	$S \subset T$	S is a proper subset of T
	$|S|$	cardinality of S
	$P(S)$	the power set of S
	$(a_1, \ldots, a_n)$	n-tuple
	(a, b)	ordered pair
	$A \times B$	Cartesian product of A and B
	$A \cup B$	union of A and B
	$A \cap B$	intersection of A and B
	$A - B$	the difference of A and B
	$\overline{A}$	complement of A
	$\displaystyle\bigcup_{i=1}^{n} A_i$	union of $A_i, i = 1, 2, \ldots, n$
	$\displaystyle\bigcap_{i=1}^{n} A_i$	intersection of $A_i, i = 1, 2, \ldots, n$
	$A \oplus B$	symmetric difference of A and B

TOPIC	SYMBOL	MEANING
FUNCTIONS	$f(a)$	value of the function f at a
	$f:A \rightarrow B$	function from A to B
	$f_1 + f_2$	sum of the functions f_1 and f_2
	$f_1 f_2$	product of the functions f_1 and f_2
	$f(S)$	image of the set S under f
	$\iota_A(s)$	identity function on A
	$f^{-1}(x)$	inverse of f
	$f \circ g$	composition of f and g
	$\lfloor x \rfloor$	floor function of x
	$\lceil x \rceil$	ceiling function of x
	a_n	term of $\{a_i\}$ with subscript n
	$\sum_{i=1}^{n} a_i$	sum of $a_1, a_2, \ldots, a_n$
	$\sum_{\alpha \in S} a_\alpha$	sum of a_α over $\alpha \in S$
	$\prod_{i=1}^{n} a_n$	product of $a_1, a_2, \ldots, a_n$
	$f(x)$ is $O(g(x))$	$f(x)$ is big-O of $g(x)$
	$n!$	n factorial
	$f(x)$ is $\Omega(g(x))$	$f(x)$ is big-Omega of $g(x)$
	$f(x)$ is $\Theta(g(x))$	$f(x)$ is big-Theta of $g(x)$
	$\sim$	asymptotic
	$\min(x, y)$	minimum of x and y
	$\max(x, y)$	maximum of x and y
	$\approx$	approximately equal to
INTEGERS	$a \mid b$	a divides b
	$a \nmid b$	a does not divide b
	$a \textbf{ div } b$	quotient when a is divided by b
	$a \textbf{ mod } b$	remainder when a is divided by b
	$a \equiv b \pmod{m}$	a is congruent to b modulo m
	$a \not\equiv b \pmod{m}$	a is not congruent to b modulo m
	$\gcd(a, b)$	greatest common divisor of a and b
	$\text{lcm}(a, b)$	least common multiple of a and b
	$(a_k a_{k-1} \cdots a_1 a_0)_b$	base b representation
MATRICES	$[a_{ij}]$	matrix with entries a_{ij}
	$\mathbf{A} + \mathbf{B}$	matrix sum of $\mathbf{A}$ and $\mathbf{B}$
	$\mathbf{AB}$	matrix product of $\mathbf{A}$ and $\mathbf{B}$
	$\mathbf{I}_n$	identity matrix of order n
	$\mathbf{A}^t$	transpose of $\mathbf{A}$
	$\mathbf{A} \vee \mathbf{B}$	join of $\mathbf{A}$ and $\mathbf{B}$
	$\mathbf{A} \wedge \mathbf{B}$	the meet of $\mathbf{A}$ and $\mathbf{B}$
	$\mathbf{A} \odot \mathbf{B}$	Boolean product of $\mathbf{A}$ and $\mathbf{B}$
	$\mathbf{A}^{[n]}$	nth Boolean power of $\mathbf{A}$

TOPIC	SYMBOL	MEANING
COUNTING	$P(n, r)$	number of r-permutations of a set with n elements
	$C(n, r)$	number of r-combinations of a set with n elements
	$\binom{n}{r}$	binomial coefficient n choose r
	$C(n; n_1, n_2, \ldots, n_m)$	multinomial coefficient
	$p(E)$	probability of E
	$p(E \mid F)$	conditional probability of E given F
	$E(X)$	expected value of the random variable X
	$V(X)$	variance of the random variable X
	C_n	Catalan number
	$N(P_{i_1} \cdots P_{i_n})$	number of elements having properties $P_{i_j}, j = 1, \ldots, n$
	$N(P'_{i_1} \cdots P'_{i_n})$	number of elements not having properties $P_{i_j}, j = 1, \ldots, n$
	D_n	number of derangements of n objects
RELATIONS	$S \circ R$	composite of the relations R and S
	R^n	nth power of the relation R
	R^{-1}	inverse relation
	s_C	select operator for condition C
	$P_{i_1, i_2, \ldots, i_m}$	projection
	$J_p(R, S)$	join
	Δ	diagonal relation
	R^*	connectivity relation of R
	$[a]_R$	equivalence class of a with respect to R
	$[a]_m$	congruence class modulo m
	(S, R)	poset consisting of the set S and partial ordering R
	$a \prec b$	a is less than b
	$a \succ b$	a is greater than b
	$a \preccurlyeq b$	a is less than or equal to b
	$a \succcurlyeq b$	a is greater than or equal to b
GRAPHS AND TREES	(u, v)	directed edge
	$G = (V, E)$	graph with vertex set V and edge set E
	$\{u, v\}$	undirected edge
	$\deg(v)$	degree of the vertex v
	$\deg^-(v)$	in-degree of the vertex v
	$\deg^+(v)$	out-degree of the vertex v
	K_n	complete graph on n vertices
	C_n	cycle of size n
	W_n	wheel of size n
	Q_n	n-cube
	$K_{m,n}$	complete bipartite graph of size m, n

TOPIC	SYMBOL	MEANING
GRAPHS AND TREES (cont.)	$G_1 \cup G_2$	union of G_1 and G_2
	$a, x_1, \ldots, x_{n-1}, b$	path from a to b
	$a, x_1, \ldots, x_{n-1}, a$	circuit
	r	number of regions of the plane
	$\deg(R)$	degree of the region R
	n	number of vertices of a rooted tree
	i	number of internal vertices of a rooted tree
	l	number of leaves of a rooted tree
	m	greatest number of children of an internal vertex in a rooted tree
	h	height of a rooted tree
BOOLEAN ALGEBRA	$\overline{x}$	complement of the Boolean variable x
	$x + y$	Boolean sum of x and y
	$x \cdot y$ (or xy)	Boolean product of x and y
	B	$\{0, 1\}$
	F^d	dual of F
	$x \mid y$	x NAND y
	$x \downarrow y$	x NOR y
		inverter
		OR gate
		AND gate
LANGUAGES AND FINITE-STATE MACHINES	λ	the empty string
	xy	concatenation of x and y
	$l(x)$	length of the string x
	w^R	reversal of w
	(V, T, S, P)	phrase-structure grammar
	S	start symbol
	$w \rightarrow w_1$	production
	$w_1 \Rightarrow w_2$	w_2 is directly derivable from w_1
	$w_1 \overset{*}{\Rightarrow} w_2$	w_2 is derivable from w_1
	$< A >::=< B > c \mid d$	Backus-Naur form
	(S, I, O, f, g, s_0)	finite-state machine with output
	s_0	start state
	AB	concatenation of the sets A and B
	A^*	Kleene closure of A
	(S, I, f, s_0, F)	finite-state machine with no output
	(S, I, f, s_0)	Turing machine

Contents

Chapter 1

The Foundations: Logic and Proofs

The rules of logic specify the meaning of mathematical statements. For instance, these rules help us understand and reason with statements such as "There exists an integer that is not the sum of two squares" and "For every positive integer n, the sum of the positive integers not exceeding n is $n(n+1)/2$." Logic is the basis of all mathematical reasoning, and of all automated reasoning. It has practical applications to the design of computing machines, to the specification of systems, to artificial intelligence, to computer programming, to programming languages, and to other areas of computer science, as well as to many other fields of study.

To understand mathematics, we must understand what makes up a correct mathematical argument, that is, a proof. Once we prove a mathematical statement is true, we call it a theorem. A collection of theorems on a topic organize what we know about this topic. To learn a mathematical topic, a person needs to actively construct mathematical arguments on this topic, and not just read exposition. Moreover, because knowing the proof of a theorem often makes it possible to modify the result to fit new situations, proofs play an essential role in the development of new ideas. Students of computer science often find it surprising how important proofs are in computer science. In fact, proofs play essential roles when we verify that computer programs produce the correct output for all possible input values, when we show that algorithms always produce the correct result, when we establish the security of a system, and when we create artificial intelligence. Automated reasoning systems have been constructed that allow computers to construct their own proofs.

In this chapter, we will explain what makes up a correct mathematical argument and introduce tools to construct these arguments. We will develop an arsenal of different proof methods that will enable us to prove many different types of results. After introducing many different methods of proof, we will introduce some strategy for constructing proofs. We will introduce the notion of a conjecture and explain the process of developing mathematics by studying conjectures.

1.1 Propositional Logic

Introduction

The rules of logic give precise meaning to mathematical statements. These rules are used to distinguish between valid and invalid mathematical arguments. Because a major goal of this book is to teach the reader how to understand and how to construct correct mathematical arguments, we begin our study of discrete mathematics with an introduction to logic.

In addition to its importance in understanding mathematical reasoning, logic has numerous applications in computer science. These rules are used in the design of computer circuits, the construction of computer programs, the verification of the correctness of programs, and in many other ways. Furthermore, software systems have been developed for constructing proofs automatically. We will discuss these applications of logic in the upcoming chapters.

Propositions

Our discussion begins with an introduction to the basic building blocks of logic—propositions. A **proposition** is a declarative sentence (that is, a sentence that declares a fact) that is either true or false, but not both.

Example 1   All the following declarative sentences are propositions.
1. Washington,D.C., is the capital of the United States of America.
2. Toronto is the capital of Canada.
3. $1 + 1 = 2$.
4. $2 + 2 = 3$.

Propositions 1 and 3 are true, whereas 2 and 4 are false.   ◄

Some sentences that are not propositions are given in Example 2.

Example 2   Consider the following sentences.
1. What time is it?
2. Read this carefully.
3. $x + 1 = 2$.
4. $x + y = z$.

Sentences 1 and 2 are not propositions because they are not declarative sentences. Sentences 3 and 4 are not propositions because they are neither true nor false. Note that each of sentences 3 and 4 can be turned into a proposition if we assign values to the variables. We will also discuss other ways to turn sentences such as these into propositions in Section 1.3.   ◄

We use letters to denote **propositional variables** (or **statement variables**), that is, variables that represent propositions, just as letters are used to denote numerical variables. The conventional letters used for propositional variables are $p, q, r, s, \ldots$. The **truth value** of a proposition is true, denoted by T, if it is a true proposition and false, denoted by F, if it is a false proposition.

The area of logic that deals with propositions is called the **propositional calculus** or **propositional logic.** It was first developed systematically by the Greek philosopher Aristotle more than 2300 years ago.

We now turn our attention to methods for producing new propositions from those that we already have. These methods were discussed by the English mathematician George Boole in 1854 in his book *The Laws of Thought*. Many mathematical statements are constructed by combining one or more propositions. New propositions, called **compound propositions,** are formed from existing propositions using logical operators.

Definition 1   Let p be a proposition. The *negation of p*, denoted by $\neg p$ (also denoted by $\overline{p}$), is the statement
    "It is not the case that p."
The proposition $\neg p$ is read "not p." The truth value of the negation of p, $\neg p$, is the opposite of the truth value of p.

Example 3   Find the negation of the proposition
    "Today is Friday."
and express this in simple English.
Solution: The negation is
    "It is not the case that today is Friday."
This negation can be more simply expressed by
    "Today is not Friday,"
or   ◄
    "It is not Friday today."

Example 4   Find the negation of the proposition
    "At least 10 inches of rain fell today in Miami."
and express this in simple English.
Solution: The negation is
    "It is not the case that at least 10 inches of rain fell today in Miami."

This negation can be more simply expressed by

"Less than 10 inches of rain fell today in Miami."   ◄

Remark: Strictly speaking, sentences involving variable times such as those in Examples 3 and 4 are not propositions unless a fixed time is assumed. The same holds for variable places unless a fixed place is assumed and for pronouns unless a particular person is assumed. We will always assume fixed times, fixed places, and particular people in such sentences unless otherwise noted.

Table 1 displays the **truth table** for the negation of a proposition p. This table has a row for each of the two possible truth values of a proposition p. Each row shows the truth value of $\neg p$ corresponding to the truth value of p for this row.

The negation of a proposition can also be considered the result of the operation of the **negation operator** on a proposition. The negation operator constructs a new proposition from a single existing proposition. We will now introduce the logical operators that are used to form new propositions from two or more existing propositions. These logical operators are also called **connectives.**

TABLE 1 The Truth Table for the Negation of a Proposition.	
p	$\neg p$
T	F
F	T

Definition 2   Let p and q be propositions. The *conjunction* of p and q, denoted by $p \wedge q$, is the proposition "p and q." The conjunction $p \wedge q$ is true when both p and q are true and is false otherwise.

Table 2 displays the truth table of $p \wedge q$. This table has a row for each of the four possible combinations of truth values of p and q. The four rows correspond to the pairs of truth values TT, TF, FT, and FF, where the first truth value in the pair is the truth value of p and the second truth value is the truth value of q.

Note that in logic the word "but" sometimes is used instead of "and" in a conjunction. For example, the statement "The sun is shining, but it is raining" is another way of saying "The sun is shining and it is raining." (In natural language, there is a subtle difference in meaning between "and" and "but"; we will not be concerned with this nuance here.)

Example 5   Find the conjunction of the propositions p and q where p is the proposition "Today is Friday" and q is the proposition "It is raining today."

Solution: The conjunction of these propositions, $p \wedge q$, is the proposition "Today is Friday and it is raining today." This proposition is true on rainy Fridays and is false on any day that is not a Friday and on Fridays when it does not rain.   ◄

Definition 3   Let p and q be propositions. The *disjunction* of p and q, denoted by $p \vee q$, is the proposition "p or q." The disjunction $p \vee q$ is false when both p and q are false and is true otherwise.

Table 3 displays the truth table for $p \vee q$.

The use of the connective *or* in a disjunction corresponds to one of the two ways the word *or* is used in English, namely, in an inclusive way. A disjunction is true when at least one of the two propositions is true. For instance, the inclusive or is being used in the statement

"Students who have taken calculus or computer science can take this class."

Here, we mean that students who have taken both calculus and computer science can take the class, as well as the students who have taken only one of the two subjects. On the other hand, we are using the exclusive or when we say

TABLE 2 The Truth Table for the Conjunction of Two Propositions.		
p	q	$p \wedge q$
T	T	T
T	F	F
F	T	F
F	F	F

TABLE 3 The Truth Table for the Disjunction of Two Propositions.		
p	q	$p \vee q$
T	T	T
T	F	T
F	T	T
F	F	F

"Students who have taken calculus or computer science, but not both, can enroll in this class." Here, we mean that students who have taken both calculus and a computer science course cannot take the class. Only those who have taken exactly one of the two courses can take the class.

Similarly, when a menu at a restaurant states, "Soup or salad comes with an entrée," the restaurant almost always means that customers can have either soup or salad, but not both. Hence, this is an exclusive, rather than an inclusive, or.

Example 6   What is the disjunction of the propositions p and q where p and q are the same propositions as in Example 5?

Solution: The disjunction of p and q, $p \vee q$, is the proposition

"Today is Friday or it is raining today."

This proposition is true on any day that is either a Friday or a rainy day (including rainy Fridays). It is only false on days that are not Fridays when it also does not rain.   ◄

As was previously remarked, the use of the connective *or* in a disjunction corresponds to one of the two ways the word *or* is used in English, namely, in an inclusive way. Thus, a disjunction is true when at least one of the two propositions in it is true. Sometimes, we use *or* in an exclusive sense. When the exclusive or is used to connect the propositions p and q, the proposition "p or q (but not both)" is obtained. This proposition is true when p is true and q is false, and when p is false and q is true. It is false when both p and q are false and when both are true.

Definition 4   Let p and q be propositions. The *exclusive or* of p and q, denoted by $p \oplus q$, is the proposition that is true when exactly one of p and q is true and is false otherwise.

The truth table for the exclusive or of two propositions is displayed in Table 4.

Conditional Statements

We will discuss several other important ways in which propositions can be combined.

Definition 5   Let p and q be propositions. The *conditional statement* $p \rightarrow q$ is the proposition "if p, then q." The conditional statement $p \rightarrow q$ is false when p is true and q is false, and true otherwise. In the conditional statement $p \rightarrow q$, p is called the *hypothesis* (or *antecedent* or *premise*) and q is called the *conclusion* (or *consequence*).

The statement $p \rightarrow q$ is called a conditional statement because $p \rightarrow q$ asserts that q is true on the condition that p holds. A conditional statement is also called an **implication.**

The truth table for the conditional statement $p \rightarrow q$ is shown in Table 5. Note that the statement $p \rightarrow q$ is true when both p and q are true and when p is false (no matter what truth value q has).

Because conditional statements play such an essential role in mathematical reasoning, a variety of terminology is used to express $p \rightarrow q$. You will encounter most if not all of the following ways to express this conditional statement:

"if p, then q"   "p implies q"
"if p, q"   "p only if q"
"p is sufficient for q"   "a sufficient condition for q is p"
"q if p"   "q whenever p"
"q when p"   "q is necessary for p"
"a necessary condition for p is q"   "q follows from p"
"q unless $\neg p$"

TABLE 4 The Truth Table for the Exclusive Or of Two Propositions.		
p	q	$p \oplus q$
T	T	F
T	F	T
F	T	T
F	F	F

TABLE 5 The Truth Table for the Conditional Statement $p \to q$.		
p	q	$p \to q$
T	T	T
T	F	F
F	T	T
F	F	T

A useful way to understand the truth value of a conditional statement is to think of an obligation or a contract. For example, the pledge many politicians make when running for office is

"If I am elected, then I will lower taxes."

If the politician is elected, voters would expect this politician to lower taxes. Furthermore, if the politician is not elected, then voters will not have any expectation that this person will lower taxes, although the person may have sufficient influence to cause those in power to lower taxes. It is only when the politician is elected but does not lower taxes that voters can say that the politician has broken the campaign pledge. This last scenario corresponds to the case when p is true but q is false in $p \to q$.

Similarly, consider a statement that a professor might make:

"If you get 100% on the final, then you will get an A."

If you manage to get a 100% on the final, then you would expect to receive an A. If you do not get 100% you may or may not receive an A depending on other factors. However, if you do get 100%, but the professor does not give you an A, you will feel cheated.

Many people find it confusing that "p only if q" expresses the same thing as "if p then q." To remember this, note that "p only if q" says that p cannot be true when q is not true. That is, the statement is false if p is true, but q is false. When p is false, q may be either true or false, because the statement says nothing about the truth value of q. A common error is for people to think that "q only if p" is a way of expressing $p \to q$. However, these statements have different truth values when p and q have different truth values.

The word "unless" is often used to express conditional statements. Observe that "q unless $\neg p$" means that if $\neg p$ is false, then q must be true. That is, the statement "q unless $\neg p$" is false when p is true and q is false, but it is true otherwise. Consequently, "q unless $\neg p$" and $p \to q$ always have the same truth value.

We illustrate the translation between conditional statements and English statements in Example 7.

Example 7   Let p be the statement "Maria learns discrete mathematics" and q the statement "Maria will find a good job." Express the statement $p \to q$ as a statement in English.

Solution: From the definition of conditional statements, we see that when p is the statement "Maria learns discrete mathematics" and q is the statement "Maria will find a good job," $p \rightarrow q$ represents the statement

"If Maria learns discrete mathematics, then she will find a good job."

There are many other ways to express this conditional statement in English. Among the most natural of these are:

"Maria will find a good job when she learns discrete mathematics."

"For Maria to get a good job, it is sufficient for her to learn discrete mathematics."

and

"Maria will find a good job unless she does not learn discrete mathematics."   ◄

Note that the way we have defined conditional statements is more general than the meaning attached to such statements in the English language. For instance, the conditional statement in Example 7 and the statement

"If it is sunny today, then we will go to the beach."

are statements used in normal language where there is a relationship between the hypothesis and the conclusion. Further, the first of these statements is true unless Maria learns discrete mathematics, but she does not get a good job, and the second is true unless it is indeed sunny today, but we do not go to the beach. On the other hand, the statement

"If today is Friday, then $2 + 3 = 5$."

is true from the definition of a conditional statement, because its conclusion is true. (The truth value of the hypothesis does not matter then.) The conditional statement

"If today is Friday, then $2 + 3 = 6$."

is true every day except Friday, even though $2 + 3 = 6$ is false.

We would not use these last two conditional statements in natural language (except perhaps in sarcasm), because there is no relationship between the hypothesis and the conclusion in either statement. In mathematical reasoning, we consider conditional statements of a more general sort than we use in English. The mathematical concept of a conditional statement is independent of a cause-and-effect relationship between hypothesis and conclusion. Our definition of a conditional statement specifies its truth values; it is not based on English usage. Propositional language is an artificial language; we only parallel English usage to make it easy to use and remember.

The if-then construction used in many programming languages is different from that used in logic. Most programming languages contain statements such as **if** p **then** S, where p is a proposition and S is a program segment (one or more statements to be executed). When execution of a program encounters such a statement, S is executed if p is true, but S is not executed if p is false, as illustrated in Example 8.

Example 8   What is the value of the variable x after the statement

$$\textbf{if } 2 + 2 = 4 \textbf{ then } x := x + 1$$

if $x = 0$ before this statement is encountered? (The symbol $:=$ stands for assignment. The statement $x := x + 1$ means the assignment of the value of $x + 1$ to x.)

Solution: Because $2 + 2 = 4$ is true, the assignment statement $x := x + 1$ is executed. Hence, x has the value $0 + 1 = 1$ after this statement is encountered.   ◄

Converse, Contrapositive, and Inverse   We can form some new conditional statements starting with a conditional statement $p \rightarrow q$. In particular, there are three related conditional statements that occur so often that they have special names. The proposition $q \rightarrow p$ is called the **converse** of $p \rightarrow q$. The **contrapositive** of $p \rightarrow q$ is the proposition $\neg q \rightarrow \neg p$. The proposition $\neg p \rightarrow \neg q$ is called the **inverse** of $p \rightarrow q$. We will see that of these three conditional statements formed from $p \rightarrow q$, only the contrapositive always has the same truth value as $p \rightarrow q$.

We first show that the contrapositive, $\neg q \rightarrow \neg p$, of a conditional statement $p \rightarrow q$ always has the same truth value as $p \rightarrow q$. To see this, note that the contrapositive is false only when $\neg p$

is false and $\neg q$ is true, that is, only when p is true and q is false. We now show that neither the converse, $q \rightarrow p$, nor the inverse, $\neg p \rightarrow \neg q$, has the same truth value as $p \rightarrow q$ for all possible truth values of p and q. Note that when p is true and q is false, the original conditional statement is false, but the converse and the inverse are both true.

When two compound propositions always have the same truth value we call them **equivalent,** so that a conditional statement and its contrapositive are equivalent. The converse and the inverse of a conditional statement are also equivalent, as the reader can verify, but neither is equivalent to the original conditional statement. (We will study equivalent propositions in Section 1.2.) Take note that one of the most common logical errors is to assume that the converse or the inverse of a conditional statement is equivalent to this conditional statement.

We illustrate the use of conditional statements in Example 9.

Example 9   What are the contrapositive, the converse, and the inverse of the conditional statement

"The home team wins whenever it is raining."?

Solution: Because "q whenever p" is one of the ways to express the conditional statement $p \rightarrow q$, the original statement can be rewritten as

"If it is raining, then the home team wins."

Consequently, the contrapositive of this conditional statement is

"If the home team does not win, then it is not raining."

The converse is

"If the home team wins, then it is raining."

The inverse is

"If it is not raining, then the home team does not win."

Only the contrapositive is equivalent to the original statement.   ◄

Biconditionals   We now introduce another way to combine propositions that expresses that two propositions have the same truth value.

Definition 6   Let p and q be propositions. The *biconditional statement* $p \leftrightarrow q$ is the proposition "p if and only if q." The biconditional statement $p \leftrightarrow q$ is true when p and q have the same truth values, and is false otherwise. Biconditional statements are also called *bi-implications*.

The truth table for $p \leftrightarrow q$ is shown in Table 6. Note that the statement $p \leftrightarrow q$ is true when both the conditional statements $p \rightarrow q$ and $q \rightarrow p$ are true and is false otherwise. That is why we use the words "if and only if" to express this logical connective and why it is symbolically written by combining the symbols $\rightarrow$ and $\leftarrow$. There are some other common ways to express $p \leftrightarrow q$:

TABLE 6 The Truth Table for the Biconditional $p \leftrightarrow q$.		
p	q	$p \leftrightarrow q$
T	T	T
T	F	F
F	T	F
F	F	T

"p is necessary and sufficient for q"
"if p then q, and conversely"
"p iff q."

The last way of expressing the biconditional statement $p \leftrightarrow q$ uses the abbreviation "iff" for "if and only if." Note that $p \leftrightarrow q$ has exactly the same truth value as $(p \rightarrow q) \wedge (q \rightarrow p)$.

Example 10   Let p be the statement "You can take the flight" and let q be the statement "You buy a ticket." Then $p \leftrightarrow q$ is the statement

"You can take the flight if and only if you buy a ticket."

This statement is true if p and q are either both true or both false, that is, if you buy a ticket and can take the flight or if you do not buy a ticket and you cannot take the flight. It is false when p

and q have opposite truth values, that is, when you do not buy a ticket, but you can take the flight (such as when you get a free trip) and when you buy a ticket and cannot take the flight (such as when the airline bumps you).   ◄

Implicit use of biconditionals   You should be aware that biconditionals are not always explicit in natural language. In particular, the "if and only if" construction used in biconditionals is rarely used in common language. Instead, biconditionals are often expressed using an "if, then" or an "only if" construction. The other part of the "if and only if" is implicit. That is, the converse is implied, but not stated. For example, consider the statement in English "If you finish your meal, then you can have dessert." What is really meant is "You can have dessert if and only if you finish your meal." This last statement is logically equivalent to the two statements "If you finish your meal, then you can have dessert" and "You can have dessert only if you finish your meal." Because of this imprecision in natural language, we need to make an assumption whether a conditional statement in natural language implicitly includes its converse. Because precision is essential in mathematics and in logic, we will always distinguish between the conditional statement $p \rightarrow q$ and the biconditional statement $p \leftrightarrow q$.

Truth Tables of Compound Propositions

We have now introduced four important logical connectives—conjunctions, disjunctions, conditional statements, and biconditional statements—as well as negations. We can use these connectives to build up complicated compound propositions involving any number of propositional variables. We can use truth tables to determine the truth values of these compound propositions, as Example 11 illustrates. We use a separate column to find the truth value of each compound expression that occurs in the compound proposition as it is built up. The truth values of the compound proposition for each combination of truth values of the propositional variables in it is found in the final column of the table.

Example 11   Construct the truth table of the compound proposition

$$(p \vee \neg q) \rightarrow (p \wedge q).$$

Solution: Because this truth table involves two propositional variables p and q, there are four rows in this truth table, corresponding to the combinations of truth values TT, TF, FT, and FF. The first two columns are used for the truth values of p and q, respectively. In the third column we find the truth value of $\neg q$, needed to find the truth value of $p \vee \neg q$, found in the fourth column. The truth value of $p \wedge q$ is found in the fifth column. Finally, the truth value of $(p \vee \neg q) \rightarrow (p \wedge q)$ is found in the last column. The resulting truth table is shown in Table 7.   ◄

TABLE 7 The Truth Table of $(p \vee \neg q) \rightarrow (p \wedge q)$.

p	q	$\neg q$	$p \vee \neg q$	$p \wedge q$	$(p \vee \neg q) \rightarrow (p \wedge q)$
T	T	F	T	T	T
T	F	T	T	F	F
F	T	F	F	F	T
F	F	T	T	F	F

Precedence of Logical Operators

We can construct compound propositions using the negation operator and the logical operators defined so far. We will generally use parentheses to specify the order in which logical operators in a compound proposition are to be applied. For instance, $(p \vee q) \wedge (\neg r)$ is the conjunction of $p \vee q$ and $\neg r$. However, to reduce the number of parentheses, we specify that the negation operator is applied before all other logical operators. This means that $\neg p \wedge q$ is the conjunction of $\neg p$ and q, namely, $(\neg p) \wedge q$, not the negation of the conjunction of p and q, namely $\neg(p \wedge q)$.

Another general rule of precedence is that the conjunction operator takes precedence over the disjunction operator, so that $p \wedge q \vee r$ means $(p \wedge q) \vee r$ rather than $p \wedge (q \vee r)$. Because this rule may be difficult to remember, we will continue to use parentheses so that the order of the disjunction and conjunction operators is clear.

Finally, it is an accepted rule that the conditional and biconditional operators $\rightarrow$ and $\leftrightarrow$ have lower precedence than the conjunction and disjunction operators, $\wedge$ and $\vee$. Consequently, $p \vee q \rightarrow r$ is the same as $(p \vee q) \rightarrow r$. We will use parentheses when the order of the conditional operator and

TABLE 8
Precedence of Logical Operators.

Operator	Precedence
$\neg$	1
$\wedge$	2
$\vee$	3
$\rightarrow$	4
$\leftrightarrow$	5

biconditional operator is at issue, although the conditional operator has precedence over the biconditional operator. Table 8 displays the precedence levels of the logical operators, $\neg$, $\wedge$, $\vee$, $\rightarrow$, and $\leftrightarrow$.

Translating English Sentences

There are many reasons to translate English sentences into expressions involving propositional variables and logical connectives. In particular, English (and every other human language) is often ambiguous. Translating sentences into compound statements (and other types of logical expressions, which we will introduce later in this chapter) removes the ambiguity. Note that this may involve making a set of reasonable assumptions based on the intended meaning of the sentence. Moreover, once we have translated sentences from English into logical expressions we can analyze these logical expressions to determine their truth values, we can manipulate them, and we can use rules of inference (which are discussed in Section 1.5) to reason about them.

To illustrate the process of translating an English sentence into a logical expression, consider Examples 12 and 13.

Example 12 How can this English sentence be translated into a logical expression?

"You can access the Internet from campus only if you are a computer science major or you are not a freshman."

Solution: There are many ways to translate this sentence into a logical expression. Although it is possible to represent the sentence by a single propositional variable, such as p, this would not be useful when analyzing its meaning or reasoning with it. Instead, we will use propositional variables to represent each sentence part and determine the appropriate logical connectives between them. In particular, we let a, c, and f represent "You can access the Internet from campus," "You are a computer science major," and "You are a freshman," respectively. Noting that "only if" is one way a conditional statement can be expressed, this sentence can be represented as

$$a \rightarrow (c \vee \neg f).$$ ◄

Example 13 How can this English sentence be translated into a logical expression?

"You cannot ride the roller coaster if you are under 4 feet tall unless you are older than 16 years old."

Solution: Let q, r, and s represent "You can ride the roller coaster," "You are under 4 feet tall," and "You are older than 16 years old," respectively. Then the sentence can be translated to

$$(r \wedge \neg s) \rightarrow \neg q.$$

Of course, there are other ways to represent the original sentence as a logical expression, but the one we have used should meet our needs. ◄

System Specifications

Translating sentences in natural language (such as English) into logical expressions is an essential part of specifying both hardware and software systems. System and software engineers take requirements in natural language and produce precise and unambiguous specifications that can be used as the basis for system development. Example 14 shows how compound propositions can be used in this process.

Example 14   Express the specification "The automated reply cannot be sent when the file system is full" using logical connectives.

Solution: One way to translate this is to let p denote "The automated reply can be sent" and q denote "The file system is full." Then $\neg p$ represents "It is not the case that the automated reply can be sent," which can also be expressed as "The automated reply cannot be sent." Consequently, our specification can be represented by the conditional statement $q \rightarrow \neg p$.   ◄

System specifications should be **consistent,** that is, they should not contain conflicting requirements that could be used to derive a contradiction. When specifications are not consistent, there would be no way to develop a system that satisfies all specifications.

Example 15   Determine whether these system specifications are consistent:

"The diagnostic message is stored in the buffer or it is retransmitted."

"The diagnostic message is not stored in the buffer."

"If the diagnostic message is stored in the buffer, then it is retransmitted."

Solution: To determine whether these specifications are consistent, we first express them using logical expressions. Let p denote "The diagnostic message is stored in the buffer" and let q denote "The diagnostic message is retransmitted." The specifications can then be written as $p \vee q$, $\neg p$, and $p \rightarrow q$. An assignment of truth values that makes all three specifications true must have p false to make $\neg p$ true. Because we want $p \vee q$ to be true but p must be false, q must be true. Because $p \rightarrow q$ is true when p is false and q is true, we conclude that these specifications are consistent because they are all true when p is false and q is true. We could come to the same conclusion by use of a truth table to examine the four possible assignments of truth values to p and q.   ◄

Example 16   Do the system specifications in Example 15 remain consistent if the specification "The diagnostic message is not retransmitted" is added?

Solution: By the reasoning in Example 15, the three specifications from that example are true only in the case when p is false and q is true. However, this new specification is $\neg q$, which is false when q is true. Consequently, these four specifications are inconsistent.   ◄

Boolean Searches

Logical connectives are used extensively in searches of large collections of information, such as indexes of Web pages. Because these searches employ techniques from propositional logic, they are called **Boolean searches.**

In Boolean searches, the connective *AND* is used to match records that contain both of two search terms, the connective *OR* is used to match one or both of two search terms, and the connective *NOT* (sometimes written as *AND NOT*) is used to exclude a particular search term. Careful planning of how logical connectives are used is often required when Boolean searches are used to locate information of potential interest. Example 17 illustrates how Boolean searches are carried out.

Example 17   **Web Page Searching**   Most Web search engines support Boolean searching techniques, which usually can help find Web pages about particular subjects. For instance, using Boolean searching to find Web pages about universities in New Mexico, we can look for pages matching NEW *AND* MEXICO *AND* UNIVERSITIES. The results of this search will include those pages that contain the three words NEW, MEXICO, and UNIVERSITIES. This will include all of the pages of interest, together with others such as a page about new universities in Mexico.

(Note that in Google, and many other search engines, the word "AND" is not needed, although it is understood, because all search terms are included by default.) Next, to find pages that deal with universities in New Mexico or Arizona, we can search for pages matching (NEW *AND* MEXICO *OR* ARIZONA) *AND* UNIVERSITIES. (*Note:* Here the *AND* operator takes precedence over the *OR* operator. Also, in Google, the terms used for this search would be NEW MEXICO *OR* ARIZONA.) The results of this search will include all pages that contain the word UNIVERSITIES and either both the words NEW and MEXICO or the word ARIZONA. Again, pages besides those of interest will be listed. Finally, to find Web pages that deal with universities in Mexico (and not New Mexico), we might first look for pages matching MEXICO *AND* UNIVERSITIES, but because the results of this search will include pages about universities in New Mexico, as well as universities in Mexico, it might be better to search for pages matching (MEXICO *AND* UNIVERSITIES) *NOT* NEW. The results of this search include pages that contain both the words MEXICO and UNIVERSITIES but do not contain the word NEW. (In Google, and many other search engines, the word "NOT" is replaced by a minus sign "−". In Google, the terms used for this last search would be MEXICO UNIVERSITIES − NEW.)   ◄

Logic Puzzles

Puzzles that can be solved using logical reasoning are known as **logic puzzles.** Solving logic puzzles is an excellent way to practice working with the rules of logic. Also, computer programs designed to carry out logical reasoning often use well-known logic puzzles to illustrate their capabilities. Many people enjoy solving logic puzzles, which are published in books and periodicals as a recreational activity.

We will discuss two logic puzzles here. We begin with a puzzle that was originally posed by Raymond Smullyan, a master of logic puzzles, who has published more than a dozen books containing challenging puzzles that involve logical reasoning.

Example 18   In [Sm78] Smullyan posed many puzzles about an island that has two kinds of inhabitants, knights, who always tell the truth, and their opposites, knaves, who always lie. You encounter two people A and B. What are A and B if A says "B is a knight" and B says "The two of us are opposite types"?

Solution: Let p and q be the statements that A is a knight and B is a knight, respectively, so that $\neg p$ and $\neg q$ are the statements that A is a knave and B is a knave, respectively.

We first consider the possibility that A is a knight; this is the statement that p is true. If A is a knight, then he is telling the truth when he says that B is a knight, so that q is true, and A and B are the same type. However, if B is a knight, then B's statement that A and B are of opposite types, the statement $(p \wedge \neg q) \vee (\neg p \wedge q)$, would have to be true, which it is not, because A and B are both knights. Consequently, we can conclude that A is not a knight, that is, that p is false.

If A is a knave, then because everything a knave says is false, A's statement that B is a knight, that is, that q is true, is a lie, which means that q is false and B is also a knave. Furthermore, if B is a knave, then B's statement that A and B are opposite types is a lie, which is consistent with both A and B being knaves. We can conclude that both A and B are knaves.   ◄

We pose more of Smullyan's puzzles about knights and knaves in Exercises 28–30 at the end of this section. Next, we pose a puzzle known as the **muddy children puzzle** for the case of two children.

Example 19   A father tells his two children, a boy and a girl, to play in their backyard without getting dirty. However, while playing, both children get mud on their foreheads. When the children stop playing, the father says "At least one of you has a muddy forehead," and then asks the children to answer "Yes" or "No" to the question: "Do you know whether you have a muddy forehead?" The father asks this question twice. What will the children answer each time this question is asked, assuming that a child can see whether his or her sibling has a muddy forehead, but cannot see his or her own forehead? Assume that both children are honest and that the children answer each question simultaneously.

Solution: Let s be the statement that the son has a muddy forehead and let d be the statement that the daughter has a muddy forehead. When the father says that at least one of the two children has a muddy forehead, he is stating that the disjunction $s \lor d$ is true. Both children will answer "No" the first time the question is asked because each sees mud on the other child's forehead. That is, the son knows that d is true, but does not know whether s is true, and the daughter knows that s is true, but does not know whether d is true.

After the son has answered "No" to the first question, the daughter can determine that d must be true. This follows because when the first question is asked, the son knows that $s \lor d$ is true, but cannot determine whether s is true. Using this information, the daughter can conclude that d must be true, for if d were false, the son could have reasoned that because $s \lor d$ is true, then s must be true, and he would have answered "Yes" to the first question. The son can reason in a similar way to determine that s must be true. It follows that both children answer "Yes" the second time the question is asked.   ◄

Logic and Bit Operations

Computers represent information using bits. A **bit** is a symbol with two possible values, namely, 0 (zero) and 1 (one). This meaning of the word bit comes from *binary digit*, because zeros and ones are the digits used in binary representations of numbers. The well-known statistician John Tukey introduced this terminology in 1946. A bit can be used to represent a truth value, because there are two truth values, namely, *true* and *false*. As is customarily done, we will use a 1 bit to represent true and a 0 bit to represent false. That is, 1 represents T (true), 0 represents F (false). A variable is called a **Boolean variable** if its value is either true or false. Consequently, a Boolean variable can be represented using a bit.

Computer **bit operations** correspond to the logical connectives. By replacing true by a one and false by a zero in the truth tables for the operators $\land$, $\lor$, and $\oplus$, the tables shown in Table 9 for the corresponding bit operations are obtained. We will also use the notation *OR, AND,* and *XOR* for the operators $\lor, \land$, and $\oplus$, as is done in various programming languages.

Truth Value	Bit
T	1
F	0

TABLE 9 Table for the Bit Operators *OR, AND,* and *XOR.*

x	y	$x \lor y$	$x \land y$	$x \oplus y$
0	0	0	0	0
0	1	1	0	1
1	0	1	0	1
1	1	1	1	0

Information is often represented using bit strings, which are lists of zeros and ones. When this is done, operations on the bit strings can be used to manipulate this information.

Definition 7 A *bit string* is a sequence of zero or more bits. The *length* of this string is the number of bits in the string.

Example 20   101010011 is a bit string of length nine.   ◄

We can extend bit operations to bit strings. We define the **bitwise *OR*, bitwise *AND*,** and **bitwise *XOR*** of two strings of the same length to be the strings that have as their bits the *OR*, *AND*, and *XOR* of the corresponding bits in the two strings, respectively. We use the symbols

$\lor$, $\land$, and $\oplus$ to represent the bitwise *OR*, bitwise *AND*, and bitwise *XOR* operations, respectively. We illustrate bitwise operations on bit strings with Example 21.

Example 21   Find the bitwise *OR*, bitwise *AND*, and bitwise *XOR* of the bit strings 01 1011 0110 and 11 0001 1101. (Here, and throughout this book, bit strings will be split into blocks of four bits to make them easier to read.)

Solution: The bitwise *OR*, bitwise *AND*, and bitwise *XOR* of these strings are obtained by taking the *OR*, *AND*, and *XOR* of the corresponding bits, respectively. This gives us

$$
\begin{array}{lll}
01 & 1011 & 0110 \\
11 & 0001 & 1101 \\
\hline
11 & 1011 & 1111 & \text{bitwise } OR \\
01 & 0001 & 0100 & \text{bitwise } AND \\
10 & 1010 & 1011 & \text{bitwise } XOR
\end{array}
$$

◄

Exercises

1. Which of these sentences are propositions? What are the truth values of those that are propositions?

   a) Boston is the capital of Massachusetts.   b) Miami is the capital of Florida.

   c) $2 + 3 = 5$ d) $5 + 7 = 10$ e) $x + 2 = 11$ f) Answer this question

2. What is the negation of each of these propositions?

   a) Today is Thursday.   b) There is no pollution in New Jersey.

   c) $2 + 1 = 3$.   d) The summer in Maine is hot and sunny.

3. Let p and q be the propositions "Swimming at the New Jersey shore is allowed" and "Sharks have been spotted near the shore," respectively. Express each of these compound propositions as an English sentence.

   a) $\neg q$ b) $p \land q$ c) $\neg p \lor q$ d) $p \to \neg q$ e) $\neg q \to p$ f) $\neg p \to \neg q$ g) $p \leftrightarrow \neg q$ h) $\neg p \land (p \lor \neg q)$

4. Let p and q be the propositions

      p : It is below freezing.

      q : It is snowing.

   Write these propositions using p and q and logical connectives.

   a) It is below freezing and snowing.

   b) It is below freezing but not snowing.

   c) It is not below freezing and it is not snowing.

   d) It is either snowing or below freezing (or both).

   e) If it is below freezing, it is also snowing.

   f) It is either below freezing or it is snowing, but it is not snowing if it is below freezing.

   g) That it is below freezing is necessary and sufficient for it to be snowing.

5. Let p and q be the propositions

      p : You drive over 65 miles per hour.

      q : You get a speeding ticket.

   Write these propositions using p and q and logical connectives.

   a) You do not drive over 65 miles per hour.

   b) You drive over 65 miles per hour, but you do not get a speeding ticket.

   c) You will get a speeding ticket if you drive over 65 miles per hour.

   d) If you do not drive over 65 miles per hour, then you will not get a speeding ticket.

   e) Driving over 65 miles per hour is sufficient for getting a speeding ticket.

   f) You get a speeding ticket, but you do not drive over 65 miles per hour.

   g) Whenever you get a speeding ticket, you are driving over 65 miles per hour.

6. Let p, q, and r be the propositions

p : Grizzly bears have been seen in the area.

q : Hiking is safe on the trail.

r : Berries are ripe along the trail.

Write these propositions using p, q, and r and logical connectives.

a) Berries are ripe along the trail, but grizzly bears have not been seen in the area.

b) Grizzly bears have not been seen in the area and hiking on the trail is safe, but berries are ripe along the trail.

c) If berries are ripe along the trail, hiking is safe if and only if grizzly bears have not been seen in the area.

d) It is not safe to hike on the trail, but grizzly bears have not been seen in the area and the berries along the trail are ripe.

e) For hiking on the trail to be safe, it is necessary but not sufficient that berries not be ripe along the trail and for grizzly bears not to have been seen in the area.

f) Hiking is not safe on the trail whenever grizzly bears have been seen in the area and berries are ripe along the trail.

7. Determine whether each of these conditional statements is true or false.

a) If $1 + 1 = 2$, then $2 + 2 = 5$.

b) If $1 + 1 = 3$, then $2 + 2 = 4$.

c) If $1 + 1 = 3$, then $2 + 2 = 5$.

d) If monkeys can fly, then $1 + 1 = 3$.

8. For each of these sentences, determine whether an inclusive or an exclusive or is intended. Explain your answer.

a) Coffee or tea comes with dinner.

b) A password must have at least three digits or be at least eight characters long.

c) The prerequisite for the course is a course in number theory or a course in cryptography.

d) You can pay using U.S. dollars or euros.

9. For each of these sentences, state what the sentence means if the or is an inclusive or (that is, a disjunction) versus an exclusive or. Which of these meanings of or do you think is intended?

a) To take discrete mathematics, you must have taken calculus or a course in computer science.

b) When you buy a new car from Acme Motor Company, you get $2000 back in cash or a 2% car loan.

c) Dinner for two includes two items from column A or three items from column B.

d) School is closed if more than 2 feet of snow falls or if the wind chill is below -100.

10. Write each of these statements in the form "if p, then q" in English. [*Hint:* Refer to the list of common ways to express conditional statements.]

a) It snows whenever the wind blows from the northeast.

b) The apple trees will bloom if it stays warm for a week.

c) That the Pistons win the championship implies that they beat the Lakers.

d) It is necessary to walk 8 miles to get to the top of Long's Peak.

e) To get tenure as a professor, it is sufficient to be world-famous.

f) If you drive more than 400 miles, you will need to buy gasoline.

g) Your guarantee is good only if you bought your CD player less than 90 days ago.

h) Jan will go swimming unless the water is too cold.

11. Write each of these propositions in the form "p if and only if q" in English.

a) If it is hot outside you buy an ice cream cone, and if you buy an ice cream cone it is hot outside.

b) For you to win the contest it is necessary and sufficient that you have the only winning ticket.

c) You get promoted only if you have connections, and you have connections only if you get promoted.

d) If you watch television your mind will decay, and conversely.

e) The trains run late on exactly those days when I take it.

12. State the converse, contrapositive, and inverse of each of these conditional statements.

    a) If it snows today, I will ski tomorrow.

    b) I come to class whenever there is going to be a quiz.

    c) A positive integer is a prime only if it has no divisors other than 1 and itself.

13. How many rows appear in a truth table for each of these compound propositions?

    a) $p \to \neg p$ b) $(p \lor \neg r) \land (q \lor \neg s)$ c) $q \lor p \lor \neg s \lor \neg r \lor \neg t \lor u$ d) $(p \land r \land t) \leftrightarrow (q \land t)$

14. Construct a truth table for each of these compound propositions.

    a) $p \land \neg p$ b) $p \lor \neg p$ c) $(p \lor \neg q) \to q$ d) $(p \lor q) \to (p \land q)$ e) $(p \to q) \leftrightarrow (\neg q \to \neg p)$

    f) $(p \to q) \to (q \to p)$

15. Construct a truth table for each of these compound propositions.

    a) $(p \lor q) \to (p \oplus q)$ b) $(p \oplus q) \to (p \land q)$ c) $(p \lor q) \oplus (p \land q)$ d) $(p \leftrightarrow q) \oplus (\neg p \leftrightarrow q)$

    e) $(p \leftrightarrow q) \oplus (\neg p \leftrightarrow \neg r)$ f) $(p \oplus q) \to (p \oplus \neg q)$

16. Construct a truth table for each of these compound propositions.

    a) $p \to \neg q$ b) $\neg p \leftrightarrow q$ c) $(p \to q) \lor (\neg p \to q)$ d) $(p \to q) \land (\neg p \to q)$

    e) $(p \leftrightarrow q) \lor (\neg p \leftrightarrow q)$ f) $(\neg p \leftrightarrow \neg q) \leftrightarrow (p \leftrightarrow q)$

17. Construct a truth table for each of these compound propositions.

    a) $p \to (\neg q \lor r)$ b) $\neg p \to (q \to r)$ c) $(p \to q) \lor (\neg p \to r)$

    d) $(p \to q) \land (\neg p \to r)$ e) $(p \leftrightarrow q) \lor (\neg q \leftrightarrow r)$ f) $(\neg p \leftrightarrow \neg q) \leftrightarrow (q \leftrightarrow r)$

18. Construct a truth table for $(p \leftrightarrow q) \leftrightarrow (r \leftrightarrow s)$.

19. Find the bitwise *OR*, bitwise *AND*, and bitwise *XOR* of each of these pairs of bit strings.

    a) 101 1110, 010 0001   b) 1111 0000, 1010 1010

    c) 00 0111 0001, 10 0100 1000   d) 11 1111 1111, 00 0000 0000

Fuzzy logic is used in artificial intelligence. In fuzzy logic, a proposition has a truth value that is a number between 0 and 1, inclusive. A proposition with a truth value of 0 is false and one with a truth value of 1 is true. Truth values that are between 0 and 1 indicate varying degrees of truth. For instance, the truth value 0.8 can be assigned to the statement "Fred is happy," because Fred is happy most of the time, and the truth value 0.4 can be assigned to the statement "John is happy," because John is happy slightly less than half the time.

20. The truth value of the negation of a proposition in fuzzy logic is 1 minus the truth value of the proposition. What are the truth values of the statements "Fred is not happy" and "John is not happy"?

21. The truth value of the disjunction of two propositions in fuzzy logic is the maximum of the truth values of the two propositions. What are the truth values of the statements "Fred is happy, or John is happy" and "Fred is not happy, or John is not happy"?

*22. The nth statement in a list of 100 statements is "Exactly n of the statements in this list are false."

    a) What conclusions can you draw from these statements?

    b) Answer part (a) if the nth statement is "At least n of the statements in this list are false."

    c) Answer part (b) assuming that the list contains 99 statements.

23. Each inhabitant of a remote village always tells the truth or always lies. A villager will only give a "Yes" or a "No" response to a question a tourist asks. Suppose you are a tourist visiting this area and come to a fork in the road. One branch leads to the ruins you want to visit; the other branch leads deep into the jungle. A villager is standing at the fork in the road. What one question can you ask the villager to determine which branch to take?

24. Express these system specifications using the propositions p "The message is scanned for viruses" and q "The message was sent from an unknown system" together with logical connectives.

    a) "The message is scanned for viruses whenever the message was sent from an unknown system."

    b) "The message was sent from an unknown system but it was not scanned for viruses."

    c) "It is necessary to scan the message for viruses whenever it was sent from an unknown system."

    d) "When a message is not sent from an unknown system it is not scanned for viruses."

25. Are these system specifications consistent? "The system is in multiuser state if and only if it is operating normally. If the system is operating normally, the kernel is functioning. The kernel is not functioning or the system is in interrupt mode. If the system is not in multiuser state, then it is in interrupt mode. The system is not in interrupt mode."

26. Are these system specifications consistent? "The router can send packets to the edge system only if it supports the new address space. For the router to support the new address space it is necessary that the latest software release be installed. The router can send packets to the edge system if the latest software release is installed, The router does not support the new address space."

27. What Boolean search would you use to look for Web pages about beaches in New Jersey? What if you wanted to find Web pages about beaches on the isle of Jersey (in the English Channel)?

Exercises 28–29 relate to inhabitants of the island of knights and knaves created by Smullyan, where knights always tell the truth and knaves always lie. You encounter two people, A and B. Determine, if possible, what A and B are if they address you in the ways described. If you cannot determine what these two people are, can you draw any conclusions?

28. A says "At least one of us is a knave" and B says nothing.

29. A says "We are both knaves" and B says nothing.

Exercises 30–32 are puzzles that can be solved by translating statements into logical expressions and reasoning from these expressions using truth tables.

30. Steve would like to determine the relative salaries of three coworkers using two facts. First, he knows that if Fred is not the highest paid of the three, then Janice is. Second, he knows that if Janice is not the lowest paid, then Maggie is paid the most. Is it possible to determine the relative salaries of Fred, Maggie, and Janice from what Steve knows? If so, who is paid the most and who the least? Explain your reasoning.

31. A detective has interviewed four witnesses to a crime. From the stories of the witnesses the detective has concluded that if the butler is telling the truth then so is the cook; the cook and the gardener cannot both be telling the truth; the gardener and the handyman are not both lying; and if the handyman is telling the truth then the cook is lying. For each of the four witnesses, can the detective determine whether that person is telling the truth or lying? Explain your reasoning.

32. Solve this famous logic puzzle, attributed to Albert Einstein, and known as the **zebra puzzle.** Five men with different nationalities and with different jobs live in consecutive houses on a street. These houses are painted different colors. The men have different pets and have different favorite drinks. Determine who owns a zebra and whose favorite drink is mineral water (which is one of the favorite drinks) given these clues: The Englishman lives in the red house. The Spaniard owns a dog. The Japanese man is a painter. The Italian drinks tea. The Norwegian lives in the first house on the left. The green house is immediately to the right of the white one. The photographer breeds snails. The diplomat lives in the yellow house. Milk is drunk in the middle house. The owner of the green house drinks coffee. The Norwegian's house is next to the blue one. The violinist drinks orange juice. The fox is in a house next to that of the physician. The horse is in a house next to that of the diplomat. [*Hint:* Make a table where the rows represent the men and columns represent the color of their houses, their jobs, their pets, and their favorite drinks and use logical reasoning to determine the correct entries in the table.]

1.2   Propositional Equivalences

Introduction

An important type of step used in a mathematical argument is the replacement of a statement with another statement with the same truth value. Because of this, methods that produce propositions with the same truth value as a given compound proposition are used extensively in the construction of mathematical arguments. Note that we will use the term "compound proposition" to refer to an expression formed from propositional variables using logical operators, such as $p \wedge q$.

We begin our discussion with a classification of compound propositions according to their possible truth values.

Definition 1   A compound proposition that is always true, no matter what the truth values of the propositions that occur in it, is called a *tautology*. A compound proposition that is always false is called a *contradiction*. A compound proposition that is neither a tautology nor a contradiction is called a *contingency*.

Tautologies and contradictions are often important in mathematical reasoning. Example 1 illustrates these types of compound propositions.

TABLE 1 Examples of a Tautology and a Contradiction.			
p	$\neg p$	$p \vee \neg p$	$p \wedge \neg p$
T	F	T	F
F	T	T	F

TABLE 2   De Morgan's Laws.
$\neg(p \wedge q) \equiv \neg p \vee \neg q$
$\neg(p \vee q) \equiv \neg p \wedge \neg q$

Example 1   We can construct examples of tautologies and contradictions using just one propositional variable. Consider the truth tables of $p \vee \neg p$ and $p \wedge \neg p$, shown in Table 1. Because $p \vee \neg p$ is always true, it is a tautology. Because $p \wedge \neg p$ is always false, it is a contradiction.   ◄

Logical Equivalences

Compound propositions that have the same truth values in all possible cases are called **logically equivalent**. We can also define this notion as follows.

Definition 2   The compound propositions p and q are called *logically equivalent* if $p \leftrightarrow q$ is a tautology. The notation $p \equiv q$ denotes that p and q are logically equivalent.

Remark: The symbol $\equiv$ is not a logical connective and $p \equiv q$ is not a compound proposition but rather is the statement that $p \leftrightarrow q$ is a tautology. The symbol $\Leftrightarrow$ is sometimes used instead of $\equiv$ to denote logical equivalence.

One way to determine whether two compound propositions are equivalent is to use a truth table. In particular, the compound propositions p and q are equivalent if and only if the columns giving their truth values agree. Example 2 illustrates this method to establish an extremely important and useful logical equivalence, namely, that of $\neg(p \vee q)$ of $\neg p \wedge \neg q$. This logical equivalence is one of the two **De Morgan laws**, shown in Table 2, named after the English mathematician Augustus De Morgan, of the mid-nineteenth century.

Example 2   Show that $\neg(p \vee q)$ and $\neg p \wedge \neg q$ are logically equivalent.

Solution: The truth tables for these compound propositions are displayed in Table 3. Because the truth values of the compound propositions $\neg(p \vee q)$ and $\neg p \wedge \neg q$ agree for all possible combinations of the truth values of p and q, it follows that $\neg(p \vee q) \leftrightarrow (\neg p \wedge \neg q)$ is a tautology and that these compound propositions are logically equivalent.   ◄

TABLE 3 Truth Tables for $\neg(p \vee q)$ and $\neg p \wedge \neg q$.						
p	q	$p \vee q$	$\neg(p \vee q)$	$\neg p$	$\neg q$	$\neg p \wedge \neg q$
T	T	T	F	F	F	F
T	F	T	F	F	T	F
F	T	T	F	T	F	F
F	F	F	T	T	T	T

Example 3   Show that $p \to q$ and $\neg p \vee q$ are logically equivalent.

Solution: We construct the truth table for these compound propositions in Table 4. Because the truth values of $\neg p \vee q$ and $p \to q$ agree, they are logically equivalent.   ◄

TABLE 4 Truth Tables for $\neg p \vee q$ and $p \to q$.

p	q	$\neg p$	$\neg p \vee q$	$p \to q$
T	T	F	T	T
T	F	F	F	F
F	T	T	T	T
F	F	T	T	T

We will now establish a logical equivalence of two compound propositions involving three different propositional variables p, q, and r. To use a truth table to establish such a logical equivalence, we need eight rows, one for each possible combination of truth values of these three variables. We symbolically represent these combinations by listing the truth values of p, q, and r, respectively. These eight combinations of truth values are TTT, TTF, TFT, TFF, FTT, FTF, FFT, and FFF; we use this order when we display the rows of the truth table. Note that we need to double the number of rows in the truth tables we use to show that compound propositions are equivalent for each additional propositional variable, so that 16 rows are needed to establish the logical equivalence of two compound propositions involving four propositional variables, and so on. In general, 2^n rows are required if a compound proposition involves n propositional variables.

Example 4   Show that $p \vee (q \wedge r)$ and $(p \vee q) \wedge (p \vee r)$ are logically equivalent. This is the *distributive law* of disjunction over conjunction.

Solution: We construct the truth table for these compound propositions in Table 5. Because the truth values of $p \vee (q \wedge r)$ and $(p \vee q) \wedge (p \vee r)$ agree, these compound propositions are logically equivalent.   ◄

TABLE 5 A Demonstration That $p \vee (q \wedge r)$ and $(p \vee q) \wedge (p \vee r)$ Are Logically Equivalent.

p	q	r	$q \wedge r$	$p \vee (q \wedge r)$	$p \vee q$	$p \vee r$	$(p \vee q) \wedge (p \vee r)$
T	T	T	T	T	T	T	T
T	T	F	F	T	T	T	T
T	F	T	F	T	T	T	T
T	F	F	F	T	T	T	T
F	T	T	T	T	T	T	T
F	T	F	F	F	T	F	F
F	F	T	F	F	F	T	F
F	F	F	F	F	F	F	F

Table 6 contains some important equivalences. *In these equivalences, **T** denotes the compound proposition that is always true and **F** denotes the compound proposition that is always false. We also display some useful equivalences for compound propositions involving conditional statements and biconditional statements in Tables 7 and 8, respectively. The reader is asked to verify the equivalences in Tables 6–8 in the exercises at the end of the section.

---

*Readers familiar with the concept of a Boolean algebra will notice that these identities are a special case of identities that hold for any Boolean algebra. Compare them with set identities in Table 1 in Section 2.2.

The associative law for disjunction shows that the expression $p \vee q \vee r$ is well defined, in the sense that it does not matter whether we first take the disjunction of p with q and then the disjunction of $p \vee q$ with r, or if we first take the disjunction of q and r and then take the disjunction of p with $q \vee r$. Similarly, the expression $p \wedge q \wedge r$ is well defined. By extending this reasoning, it follows that $p_1 \vee p_2 \vee \cdots \vee p_n$ and $p_1 \wedge p_2 \wedge \cdots \wedge p_n$ are well defined whenever $p_1, p_2, \ldots, p_n$ are propositions. Furthermore, note that De Morgan's laws extend to

$$\neg(p_1 \vee p_2 \vee \cdots \vee p_n) \equiv (\neg p_1 \wedge \neg p_2 \wedge \cdots \wedge \neg p_n)$$

and

$$\neg(p_1 \wedge p_2 \wedge \cdots \wedge p_n) \equiv (\neg p_1 \vee \neg p_2 \vee \cdots \vee \neg p_n).$$

TABLE 6 Logical Equivalences.

Equivalence	Name
$p \wedge T \equiv p$ $p \vee F \equiv p$	Identity laws
$p \vee T \equiv T$ $p \wedge F \equiv F$	Domination laws
$p \vee p \equiv p$ $p \wedge p \equiv p$	Idempotent laws
$\neg(\neg p) \equiv p$	Double negation law
$p \vee q \equiv q \vee p$ $p \wedge q \equiv q \wedge p$	Commutative laws
$(p \vee q) \vee r \equiv p \vee (q \vee r)$ $(p \wedge q) \wedge r \equiv p \wedge (q \wedge r)$	Associative laws
$p \vee (q \wedge r) \equiv (p \vee q) \wedge (p \vee r)$ $p \wedge (q \vee r) \equiv (p \wedge q) \vee (p \wedge r)$	Distributive laws
$\neg(p \wedge q) \equiv \neg p \vee \neg q$ $\neg(p \vee q) \equiv \neg p \wedge \neg q$	De Morgan's laws
$p \vee (p \wedge q) \equiv p$ $p \wedge (p \vee q) \equiv p$	Absorption laws
$p \vee \neg p \equiv T$ $p \wedge \neg p \equiv F$	Negation laws

TABLE 7 Logical Equivalences Involving Conditional Statements.

$$p \rightarrow q \equiv \neg p \vee q$$
$$p \rightarrow q \equiv \neg q \rightarrow \neg p$$
$$p \vee q \equiv \neg p \rightarrow q$$
$$p \wedge q \equiv \neg(p \rightarrow \neg q)$$
$$\neg(p \rightarrow q) \equiv p \wedge \neg q$$
$$(p \rightarrow q) \wedge (p \rightarrow r) \equiv p \rightarrow (q \wedge r)$$
$$(p \rightarrow r) \wedge (q \rightarrow r) \equiv (p \vee q) \rightarrow r$$
$$(p \rightarrow q) \vee (p \rightarrow r) \equiv p \rightarrow (q \vee r)$$
$$(p \rightarrow r) \vee (q \rightarrow r) \equiv (p \wedge q) \rightarrow r$$

TABLE 8 Logical Equivalences Involving Biconditionals.

$$p \leftrightarrow q \equiv (p \rightarrow q) \wedge (q \rightarrow p)$$
$$p \leftrightarrow q \equiv \neg p \leftrightarrow \neg q$$
$$p \leftrightarrow q \equiv (p \wedge q) \vee (\neg p \wedge \neg q)$$
$$\neg(p \leftrightarrow q) \equiv p \leftrightarrow \neg q$$

Using De Morgan's Laws

The two logical equivalences known as De Morgan's laws are particularly important. They tell us how to negate conjunctions and how to negate disjunctions. In particular, the equivalence $\neg(p \vee q) \equiv \neg p \wedge \neg q$ tells us that the negation of a disjunction is formed by taking the conjunction of the negations of the component propositions. Similarly, the equivalence $\neg(p \wedge q) \equiv \neg p \vee \neg q$ tells us that the negation of a conjunction is formed by taking the disjunction of the negations of the component propositions. Example 5 illustrates the use of De Morgan's laws.

Example 5 Use De Morgan's laws to express the negations of "Miguel has a cellphone and he has a laptop computer" and "Heather will go to the concert or Steve will go to the concert."

Solution: Let p be "Miguel has a cellphone" and q be "Miguel has a laptop computer." Then "Miguel has a cellphone and he has a laptop computer" can be represented by $p \wedge q$. By the first of De Morgan's laws, $\neg(p \wedge q)$ is equivalent to $\neg p \vee \neg q$. Consequently, we can express the negation of our original statement as "Miguel does not have a cellphone or he does not have a laptop computer."

Let r be "Heather will go to the concert" and s be "Steve will go to the concert." Then "Heather will go to the concert or Steve will go to the concert" can be represented by $r \vee s$. By the second of De Morgan's laws, $\neg(r \vee s)$ is equivalent to $\neg r \wedge \neg s$. Consequently, we can express the negation of our original statement as "Heather will not go to the concert and Steve will not go to the concert." ◄

Constructing New Logical Equivalences

The logical equivalences in Table 6, as well as any others that have been established (such as those shown in Tables 7 and 8), can be used to construct additional logical equivalences. The reason for this is that a proposition in a compound proposition can be replaced by a compound proposition that is logically equivalent to it without changing the truth value of the original compound proposition. This technique is illustrated in Examples 6–8, where we also use the fact that if p and q are logically equivalent and q and r are logically equivalent, then p and r are logically equivalent.

Example 6   Show that $\neg(p \rightarrow q)$ and $p \wedge \neg q$ are logically equivalent.

Solution: We could use a truth table to show that these compound propositions are equivalent (similar to what we did in Example 4). Indeed, it would not be hard to do so. However, we want to illustrate how to use logical identities that we already know to establish new logical identities, something that is of practical importance for establishing equivalences of compound propositions with a large number of variables. So, we will establish this equivalence by developing a series of logical equivalences, using one of the equivalences in Table 6 at a time, starting with $\neg(p \rightarrow q)$ and ending with $p \wedge \neg q$. We have the following equivalences.

$$
\begin{aligned}
\neg(p \rightarrow q) &\equiv \neg(\neg p \vee q) && \text{by Example 3} \\
&\equiv \neg(\neg p) \wedge \neg q && \text{by the second De Morgan law} \\
&\equiv p \wedge \neg q && \text{by the double negationlaw}
\end{aligned}
$$
◄

Example 7   Show that $\neg(p \vee (\neg p \wedge q))$ and $\neg p \wedge \neg q$ are logically equivalent by developing a series of logical equivalences.

Solution: We will use one of the equivalences in Table 6 at a time, starting with $\neg(p \vee (\neg p \wedge q))$ and ending with $\neg p \wedge \neg q$. (*Note:* we could also easily establish this equivalence using a truth table.) We have the following equivalences.

$$
\begin{aligned}
\neg(p \vee (\neg p \wedge q)) &\equiv \neg p \wedge \neg(\neg p \wedge q) && \text{by the second De Morgan law} \\
&\equiv \neg p \wedge [\neg(\neg p) \vee \neg q] && \text{by the first De Morgan law} \\
&\equiv \neg p \wedge (p \vee \neg q) && \text{by the double negation law} \\
&\equiv (\neg p \wedge p) \vee (\neg p \wedge \neg q) && \text{by the second distributive law} \\
&\equiv \mathbf{F} \vee (\neg p \wedge \neg q) && \text{because } \neg p \wedge p \equiv \mathbf{F} \\
&\equiv (\neg p \wedge \neg q) \vee \mathbf{F} && \text{by the commutative law for disjunction} \\
&\equiv \neg p \wedge \neg q && \text{by the identity law for } \mathbf{F}
\end{aligned}
$$

Consequently $\neg(p \vee (\neg p \wedge q))$ and $\neg p \wedge \neg q$ are logically equivalent. ◄

Example 8   Show that $(p \wedge q) \rightarrow (p \vee q)$ is a tautology.

Solution: To show that this statement is a tautology, we will use logical equivalences to demonstrate that it is logically equivalent to $\mathbf{T}$. (*Note:* This could also be done using a truth table.)

$$(p \wedge q) \to (p \vee q) \equiv \neg(p \wedge q) \vee (p \vee q)$$ by Example 3

$$\equiv (\neg p \vee \neg q) \vee (p \vee q)$$ by the first De Morgan law

$$\equiv (\neg p \vee p) \vee (\neg q \vee q)$$ by the associative and commutative laws for disjunction

$$\equiv \mathbf{T} \vee \mathbf{T}$$ by Example 1 and the commutative law for disjunction

$$\equiv \mathbf{T}$$ by the domination law ◀

A truth table can be used to determine whether a compound proposition is a tautology. This can be done by hand for a compound proposition with a small number of variables, but when the number of variables grows, this becomes impractical. For instance, there are $2^{20} = 1,048,576$ rows in the truth table for a compound proposition with 20 variables. Clearly, you need a computer to help you determine, in this way, whether a compound proposition in 20 variables is a tautology. But when there are 1000 variables, can even a computer determine in a reasonable amount of time whether a compound proposition is a tautology? Checking every one of the 2^{1000} (a number with more than 300 decimal digits) possible combinations of truth values simply cannot be done by a computer in even trillions of years. Furthermore, no other procedures are known that a computer can follow to determine in a reasonable amount of time whether a compound proposition in such a large number of variables is a tautology. We will study questions such as this in Chapter 3, when we study the complexity of algorithms.

Normal or Canonical Forms

The simple propositions of two variables are $p \wedge q$, $\neg p \wedge q$, $p \wedge \neg q$ and $\neg p \wedge \neg q$. We know that $p \wedge q$ is true only when p is true and q is true. Similarly $\neg p \wedge q$ is true only when p is false and q is true, $p \wedge \neg q$ is true only when p is true and q is false, $\neg p \wedge \neg q$ is true only when p is false and q is false.

Example 9   Suppose we have the truth table in Table 9, what is the statement that has the desired truth table?

For each case that is true, we select the proposition that is true only in that case and connect these propositions with $\vee$. then we have a statement that has the desired truth table. The three cases that are true correspond to the propositions: $p \wedge q$, $p \wedge \neg q$ and $\neg p \wedge \neg q$. Hence the proposition that has the desired truth table is

$$(p \wedge q) \vee (p \wedge \neg q) \vee (\neg p \wedge \neg q).$$

TABLE 9		
p	q	?
T	T	T
T	F	T
F	T	F
F	F	T

For the propositions with three variables we have an analogous situation. For each case in the following table (Table 10), the proposition is true only if the values of the variables are given in that case and false elsewhere.

Notice that in each case a variable is negated in the corresponding proposition when it is listed as false for that case. If we want to find a proposition with a given truth table, for the lines where the truth value is true, we select the expressions using the lines on the table above corresponding to those cases and connect them with $\vee$. For example, to construct a proposition with the true table (Table 11) we form the proposition

$$(p \wedge q \wedge r) \vee (p \wedge \neg q \wedge \neg r) \vee (\neg p \wedge q \wedge r).$$ ◀

This form of expression for a proposition is called *Disjunctive Normal Form* (DNF). The conjunctive expressions $p \wedge q \wedge r, p \wedge \neg q \wedge \neg r, \neg p \wedge q \wedge r$ are called *minterms*.

Definition 3   A disjunction of conjunctions where every variable or its negation is represented once in each conjunction is called a *minterm*. An expression which is the disjunction of minterms is called *Disjunctive Normal Form* (DNF) and if m_1, m_2, m_3, ..., m_n are minterms then $m_1 \vee m_2 \vee m_3 \vee ... \vee m_n$ is in disjunctive normal form.

Similarly, we know that $p \vee q \vee r$ is false only when p,q and r are all false. In the following table (Table 12), all disjunctions with three variables are listed.

TABLE 10 Minterms	p	q	r
$p \wedge q \wedge r$	T	T	T
$p \wedge q \wedge \neg r$	T	T	F
$p \wedge \neg q \wedge r$	T	F	T
$p \wedge \neg q \wedge \neg r$	T	F	F
$\neg p \wedge q \wedge r$	F	T	T
$\neg p \wedge q \wedge \neg r$	F	T	F
$\neg p \wedge \neg q \wedge r$	F	F	T
$\neg p \wedge \neg q \wedge \neg r$	F	F	F

TABLE 11	p	q	r	?
	T	T	T	T
	T	T	F	F
	T	F	T	F
	T	F	F	T
	F	T	T	T
	F	T	F	F
	F	F	T	F
	F	F	F	F

TABLE 12 Maxterms	p	q	r
$\neg p \vee \neg q \vee \neg r$	T	T	T
$\neg p \vee \neg q \vee r$	T	T	F
$\neg p \vee q \vee \neg r$	T	F	T
$\neg p \vee q \vee r$	T	F	F
$p \vee \neg q \vee \neg r$	F	T	T
$p \vee \neg q \vee r$	F	T	F
$p \vee q \vee \neg r$	F	F	T
$p \vee q \vee r$	F	F	F

Each expression is false on the line where it is located and true elsewhere. Notice that in each case a variable is negated in the corresponding proposition when it is listed as true for that case. If we want to find a proposition with a given truth table, we select the expressions corresponding to the cases that are false and connect them with $\wedge$. For example, to construct a proposition with the true table in Table 11.

There are 5 lines which are false in Table 11, we form the proposition

$$(\neg p \vee \neg q \vee r) \wedge (\neg p \vee q \vee \neg r) \wedge (p \vee \neg q \vee r) \wedge (p \vee q \vee \neg r) \wedge (p \vee q \vee r).$$

This form of expression for a proposition is called *Conjunctive Normal Form* (CNF). The disjunctive expressions $\neg p \vee \neg q \vee r, \neg p \vee q \vee \neg r, p \vee \neg q \vee r, p \vee q \vee \neg r, p \vee q \vee r$ are called *maxterms*.

Definition 4   A conjunction of disjunctions where every variable or its negation is represented once in each disjunction is called a *maxterm*. An expression which is the conjunction of max-terms is called *Conjunctive Normal Form* (CNF) and if $M_1, M_2, M_3, ..., M_n$ are maxterms then $M_1 \wedge M_2 \wedge M_3 \wedge ... \wedge M_n$ is in conjunctive normal form.

Exercises

1. Use truth tables to verify these equivalences.
   a) $p \wedge T \equiv p$ b) $p \vee F \equiv p$ c) $p \wedge F \equiv F$ d) $p \vee T \equiv T$ e) $p \vee p \equiv p$ f) $p \wedge p \equiv p$

2. Use truth tables to verify the commutative laws
   a) $p \vee q \equiv q \vee p$ b) $p \wedge q \equiv q \wedge p$

3. Use a truth table to verify the distributive law
   $p \wedge (q \vee r) \equiv (p \wedge q) \vee (p \wedge r)$.

4. Use De Morgan's laws to find the negation of each of the following statements.
   a) Jan is rich and happy.   b) Carlos will bicycle or run tomorrow.
   c) Mei walks or takes the bus to class.   d) Ibrahim is smart and hard working.

5. Show that each of these conditional statements is a tautology by using truth tables.
   a) $(p \wedge q) \to p$ b) $p \to (p \vee q)$ c) $\neg p \to (p \to q)$ d) $(p \wedge q) \to (p \to q)$
   e) $\neg(p \to q) \to p$ f) $\neg(p \to q) \to \neg q$

6. Show that each conditional statement in Exercise 5 is a tautology without using truth tables.

7. Use truth tables to verify the absorption laws.

   a) $p \vee (p \wedge q) \equiv p$ b) $p \wedge (p \vee q) \equiv p$

8. Determine whether $(\neg q \wedge (p \rightarrow q)) \rightarrow \neg p$ is a tautology.

   Each of Exercises 9–14 asks you to show that two compound propositions are logically equivalent. To do this, either show that both sides are true, or that both sides are false, for exactly the same combinations of truth values of the propositional variables in these expressions (whichever is easier).

9. Show that $\neg(p \leftrightarrow q)$ and $p \leftrightarrow \neg q$ are logically equivalent.

10. Show that $\neg p \leftrightarrow q$ and $p \leftrightarrow \neg q$ are logically equivalent.

11. Show that $\neg(p \leftrightarrow q)$ and $\neg p \leftrightarrow q$ are logically equivalent.

12. Show that $(p \rightarrow r) \wedge (q \rightarrow r)$ and $(p \vee q) \rightarrow r$ are logically equivalent.

13. Show that $(p \rightarrow r) \vee (q \rightarrow r)$ and $(p \wedge q) \rightarrow r$ are logically equivalent.

14. Show that $p \leftrightarrow q$ and $(p \rightarrow q) \wedge (q \rightarrow p)$ are logically equivalent.

15. Show that $(p \rightarrow q) \wedge (q \rightarrow r) \rightarrow (p \rightarrow r)$ is a tautology.

16. Show that $(p \rightarrow q) \rightarrow r$ and $p \rightarrow (q \rightarrow r)$ are not logically equivalent.

17. Show that $(p \rightarrow q) \rightarrow (r \rightarrow s)$ and $(p \rightarrow r) \rightarrow (q \rightarrow s)$ are not logically equivalent.

   The **dual** of a compound proposition that contains only the logical operators $\vee$, $\wedge$, and $\neg$ is the compound proposition obtained by replacing each $\vee$ by $\wedge$, each $\wedge$ by $\vee$, each $\mathbf{T}$ by $\mathbf{F}$, and each $\mathbf{F}$ by $\mathbf{T}$. The dual of s is denoted by s^*.

18. Find the dual of each of these compound propositions.

    a) $p \wedge \neg q \wedge \neg r$ b) $(p \wedge q \wedge r) \vee s$ c) $(p \vee \mathbf{F}) \wedge (q \vee \mathbf{T})$

19. Show that $(s^*)^* = s$ when s is a compound proposition.

**20. Why are the duals of two equivalent compound propositions also equivalent, where these compound propositions contain only the operators $\wedge$, $\vee$, and $\neg$?

21. Find a compound proposition involving the propositional variables p, q, and r that is true when exactly two of p, q, and r are true and is false otherwise. [*Hint:* Form a disjunction of conjunctions. Include a conjunction for each combination of values for which the compound propositional is true. Each conjunction should include each of the three propositional variables or their negations.]

   A collection of logical operators is called **functionally complete** if every compound proposition is logically equivalent to a compound proposition involving only these logical operators.

22. Show that $\neg$, $\wedge$, and $\vee$ form a functionally complete collection of logical operators.

*23. Show that $\neg$ and $\vee$ form a functionally complete collection of logical operators.

   The following exercises involve the logical operators *NAND* and *NOR*. The proposition p *NAND* q is true when either p or q, or both, are false; and it is false when both p and q are true. The proposition p *NOR* q is true when both p and q are false, and it is false otherwise. The propositions p *NAND* q and p *NOR* q are denoted by $p \mid q$ and $p \downarrow q$, respectively. (The operators $\mid$ and $\downarrow$ are called the **Sheffer stroke** and the **Peirce arrow** after H. M. Sheffer and C. S. Peirce, respectively.)

24. Show that $p \mid q$ is logically equivalent to $\neg(p \wedge q)$.

25. Show that $p \downarrow q$ is logically equivalent to $\neg(p \vee q)$.

*26. Find a compound proposition logically equivalent to $p \rightarrow q$ using only the logical operator $\downarrow$.

27. Show that $p \mid q$ and $q \mid p$ are equivalent.

*28. How many different truth tables of compound propositions are there that involve the propositional variables p and q?

29. The following sentence is taken from the specification of a telephone system: "If the directory database is opened, then the monitor is put in a closed state, if the system is not in its initial state." This specification is hard to under stand because it involves two conditional statements. Find an equivalent, easier-to-understand specification that involves disjunctions and negations but not conditional statements.

30. How many of the disjunctions $p \vee \neg q \vee s$, $\neg p \vee \neg r \vee s$, $\neg p \vee \neg r \vee \neg s$, $\neg p \vee q \vee \neg s$, $q \vee r \vee \neg s$, $q \vee \neg r \vee \neg s$, $\neg p \vee \neg q \vee \neg s$, $p \vee r \vee s$, and $p \vee r \vee \neg s$ can be made simultaneously true by an assignment of truth values to p, q, r, and s?

A compound proposition is **satisfiable** if there is an assignment of truth values to the variables in the compound proposition that makes the compound proposition true.

31. Explain how an algorithm for determining whether a compound proposition is satisfiable can be used to determine whether a compound proposition is a tautology. [*Hint:* Look at $\neg p$, where p is the compound proposition that is being examined.]

1.3   Predicates and Quantifiers

Introduction

Propositional logic, studied in Sections 1.1 and 1.2, cannot adequately express the meaning of statements in mathematics and in natural language. For example, suppose that we know that

"Every computer connected to the university network is functioning properly."

No rules of propositional logic allow us to conclude the truth of the statement

"MATH3 is functioning properly,"

where MATH3 is one of the computers connected to the university network. Likewise, we cannot use the rules of propositional logic to conclude from the statement

"CS2 is under attack by an intruder,"

where CS2 is a computer on the university network, to conclude the truth of

"There is a computer on the university network that is under attack by an intruder."

In this section we will introduce a more powerful type of logic called **predicate logic**. We will see how predicate logic can be used to express the meaning of a wide range of statements in mathematics and computer science in ways that permit us to reason and explore relationships between objects. To understand predicate logic, we first need to introduce the concept of a predicate. Afterward, we will introduce the notion of quantifiers, which enable us reason with statements that assert that a certain property holds for all objects of a certain type and with statements that assert the existence of an object with a particular property.

Predicates

Statements involving variables, such as

$$\text{``}x > 3\text{,''} \quad \text{``}x = y + 3\text{,''} \quad \text{``}x + y = z\text{,''}$$

$$\text{``computer } x \text{ is under attack by an intruder,''}$$

and

$$\text{``computer } x \text{ is functioning properly,''}$$

are often found in mathematical assertions, in computer programs, and in system specifications. These statements are neither true nor false when the values of the variables are not specified. In this section, we will discuss the ways that propositions can be produced from such statements.

The statement "x is greater than 3" has two parts. The first part, the variable x, is the subject of the statement. The second part—the **predicate**, "is greater than 3"—refers to a property that the subject of the statement can have. We can denote the statement "x is greater than 3" by $P(x)$, where P denotes the predicate "is greater than 3" and x is the variable. The statement $P(x)$ is also said to be the value of the **propositional function** P at x. Once a value has been assigned to the variable x, the statement $P(x)$ becomes a proposition and has a truth value. Consider Examples 1 and 2.

Example 1   Let $P(x)$ denote the statement "$x > 3$." What are the truth values of $P(4)$ and $P(2)$?

Solution: We obtain the statement $P(4)$ by setting $x = 4$ in the statement "$x > 3$." Hence, $P(4)$, which is the statement "$4 > 3$," is true. However, $P(2)$, which is the statement "$2 > 3$," is false. ◄

Example 2   Let $A(x)$ denote the statement "Computer x is under attack by an intruder." Suppose that of the computers on campus, only CS2 and MATH1 are currently under attack by intruders. What are truth values of $A(CS1)$, $A(CS2)$, and $A(MATH1)$?

Solution: We obtain the statement $A(CS1)$ by setting $x = CS1$ in the statement "Computer x is under attack by an intruder." Because CS1 is not on the list of computers currently under attack, we conclude that $A(CS1)$ is false. Similarly, because CS2 and MATH1 are on the list of computers under attack, we know that $A(CS2)$ and $A(MATH1)$ are true. ◄

We can also have statements that involve more than one variable. For instance, consider the statement "$x = y + 3$." We can denote this statement by $Q(x, y)$, where x and y are variables and Q is the predicate. When values are assigned to the variables x and y, the statement $Q(x, y)$ has a truth value.

Example 3   Let $Q(x, y)$ denote the statement "$x = y + 3$." What are the truth values of the propositions $Q(1, 2)$ and $Q(3, 0)$?

Solution: To obtain $Q(1, 2)$, set $x = 1$ and $y = 2$ in the statement $Q(x, y)$. Hence, $Q(1, 2)$ is the statement "$1 = 2 + 3$," which is false. The statement $Q(3, 0)$ is the proposition "$3 = 0 + 3$," which is true. ◄

Example 4   Let $A(c, n)$ denote the statement "Computer c is connected to network n," where c is a variable representing a computer and n is a variable representing a network. Suppose that the computer MATH1 is connected to network CAMPUS2, but not to network CAMPUS1. What are the values of $A(MATH1, CAMPUS1)$ and $A(MATH1, CAMPUS2)$?

Solution: Because MATH1 is not connected to the CAMPUS1 network, we see that $A(MATH1, CAMPUS1)$ is false. However, because MATH1 is connected to the CAMPUS2 network, we see that $A(MATH1, CAMPUS2)$ is true. ◄

Similarly, we can let $R(x, y, z)$ denote the statement "$x + y = z$." When values are assigned to the variables x, y, and z, this statement has a truth value.

Example 5   What are the truth values of the propositions $R(1, 2, 3)$ and $R(0, 0, 1)$?

Solution: The proposition $R(1, 2, 3)$ is obtained by setting $x = 1$, $y = 2$, and $z = 3$ in the statement $R(x, y, z)$. We see that $R(1, 2, 3)$ is the statement "$1 + 2 = 3$," which is true. Also note that $R(0, 0, 1)$, which is the statement "$0 + 0 = 1$," is false. ◄

In general, a statement involving the n variables $x_1, x_2, \ldots, x_n$ can be denoted by

$$P(x_1, x_2, \ldots, x_n).$$

A statement of the form $P(x_1, x_2, \ldots, x_n)$ is the value of the **propositional function** P at the n-tuple $(x_1, x_2, \ldots, x_n)$, and P is also called a n-**place predicate** or a n-**ary predicate.**

Propositional functions occur in computer programs, as Example 6 demonstrates.

Example 6   Consider the statement

if $x > 0$ **then** $x := x + 1$.

When this statement is encountered in a program, the value of the variable x at that point in the execution of the program is inserted into $P(x)$, which is "$x > 0$." If $P(x)$ is true for this value of x, the assignment statement $x := x + 1$ is executed, so the value of x is increased by 1. If $P(x)$ is false for this value of x, the assignment statement is not executed, so the value of x is not changed.   ◄

Predicates are also used in the verification that computer programs always produce the desired output when given valid input. The statements that describe valid input are known as **precondi- tions** and the conditions that the ouput should satisfy when the program has run are known as **postconditions.** As Example 7 illustrates, we use predicates to describe both preconditions and postconditions.

Example 7   Consider the following program, designed to interchange the values of two vari- ables x and y.

```
temp := x
x := y
y := temp
```

Find predicates that we can use as the precondition and the postcondition to verify the correctness of this program. Then explain how to use them to verify that for all valid input the program does what is intended.

Solution: For the precondition, we need to express that x and y have particular values before we run the program. So, for this precondition we can use the predicate $P(x, y)$, where $P(x, y)$ is the statement "$x = a$ and $y = b$," where a and b are the values of x and y before we run the program. Because we want to verify that the program swaps the values of x and y for all input values, for the postcondition we can use $Q(x, y)$, where $Q(x, y)$ is the statement "$x = b$ and $y = a$."

To verify that the program always does what it is supposed to do, suppose that the precondition $P(x, y)$ holds. That is, we suppose that the statement "$x = a$ and $y = b$" is true. This means that $x = a$ and $y = b$. The first step of the program, *temp* $:= x$, assigns the value of x to the variable *temp*, so after this step we know that $x = a$, *temp* $= a$, and $y = b$. After the second step of the program, $x := y$, we know that $x = b$, *temp* $= a$, and $y = b$. Finally, after the third step, we know that $x = b$, *temp* $= a$, and $y = a$. Consequently, after this program is run, the postcondition $Q(x, y)$ holds, that is, the statement "$x = b$ and $y = a$" is true.   ◄

Quantifiers

When the variables in a propositional function are assigned values, the resulting statement be- comes a proposition with a certain truth value. However, there is another important way, called **quantification,** to create a proposition from a propositional function. Quantification expresses the extent to which a predicate is true over a range of elements. In English, the words *all, some, many, none,* and *few* are used in quantifications. We will focus on two types of quantification here: universal quantification, which tells us that a predicate is true for every element under con- sideration, and existential quantification, which tells us that there is one or more element under consideration for which the predicate is true. The area of logic that deals with predicates and quantifiers is called the **predicate calculus.**

The Universal Quantifier   Many mathematical statements assert that a property is true for all values of a variable in a particular domain, called the **domain of discourse** (or the **universe of discourse**), often just referred to as the **domain.** Such a statement is expressed using universal quantification. The universal quantification of $P(x)$ for a particular domain is the proposition that asserts that $P(x)$ is true for all values of x in this domain. Note that the domain specifies the possible values of the variable x. The meaning of the universal quantification of $P(x)$ changes when we change the domain. The domain must always be specified when a universal quantifier is used; without it, the universal quantification of a statement in not defined.

Definition 1   The *universal quantification* of $P(x)$ is the statement

"$P(x)$ for all values of x in the domain."

The notation $\forall x P(x)$ denotes the universal quantification of $P(x)$. Here $\forall$ is called the **universal quantifier.** We read $\forall x P(x)$ as "for all $xP(x)$" or "for every $xP(x)$." An element for which $P(x)$ is false is called a **counterexample** of $\forall x P(x)$.

The meaning of the universal quantifier is summarized in the first row of Table 1. We illustrate the use of the universal quantifier in Examples 8–13.

Example 8   Let $P(x)$ be the statement "$x+1 > x$." What is the truth value of the quantification $\forall x P(x)$, where the domain consists of all real numbers?

Solution: Because $P(x)$ is true for all real numbers x, the quantification

$$\forall x P(x)$$

is true.   ◄

Remark: Generally, an implicit assumption is made that all domains of discourse for quantifiers are nonempty. Note that if the domain is empty, then $\forall x P(x)$ is true for any propositional function $P(x)$ because there are no elements x in the domain for which $P(x)$ is false.

Besides "for all" and "for every," universal quantification can be expressed in many other ways, including "all of," "for each," "given any," "for arbitrary," "for each," and "for any."

Remark: It is best to avoid using "for any x" because it is often ambiguous as to whether "any" means "every" or "some." In some cases, "any" is unambiguous, such as when it is used in negatives, for example, "there is not any reason to avoid studying."

TABLE 1   Quantifiers.

Statement	When True?	When False?
$\forall x\, P(x)$	$P(x)$ is true for every x.	There is an x for which $P(x)$ is false.
$\exists x\, P(x)$	There is an x for which $P(x)$ is true.	$P(x)$ is false for every x.

A statement $\forall x P(x)$ is false, where $P(x)$ is a propositional function, if and only if $P(x)$ is not always true when x is in the domain. One way to show that $P(x)$ is not always true when x is in the domain is to find a counterexample to the statement $\forall x P(x)$. Note that a single counterexample is all we need to establish that $\forall x P(x)$ is false. Example 9 illustrates how counterexamples are used.

Example 9   Let $Q(x)$ be the statement "$x < 2$." What is the truth value of the quantification $\forall x Q(x)$, where the domain consists of all real numbers?

Solution: $Q(x)$ is not true for every real number x, because, for instance, $Q(3)$ is false. That is, $x = 3$ is a counterexample for the statement $\forall x Q(x)$. Thus

$$\forall x Q(x)$$

is false.   ◄

Example 10   Suppose that $P(x)$ is "$x^2 > 0$." To show that the statement $\forall x P(x)$ is false where the universe of discourse consists of all integers, we give a counterexample. We see that $x = 0$ is a counterexample because $x^2 = 0$ when $x = 0$, so that x^2 is not greater than 0 when $x = 0$.   ◄

Looking for counterexamples to universally quantified statements is an important activity in the study of mathematics, as we will see in subsequent sections of this book.

When all the elements in the domain can be listed—say, $x_1, x_2, \ldots, x_n$—it follows that the universal quantification $\forall x P(x)$ is the same as the conjunction

$$P(x_1) \wedge P(x_2) \wedge \cdots \wedge P(x_n),$$

because this conjunction is true if and only if $P(x_1), P(x_2), \ldots, P(x_n)$ are all true.

Example 11   What is the truth value of $\forall x P(x)$, where $P(x)$ is the statement "$x^2 < 10$" and the domain consists of the positive integers not exceeding 4?

Solution: The statement $\forall x P(x)$ is the same as the conjunction

$$P(1) \wedge P(2) \wedge P(3) \wedge P(4),$$

because the domain consists of the integers 1, 2, 3, and 4. Because $P(4)$, which is the statement "$4^2 < 10$," is false, it follows that $\forall x P(x)$ is false.   ◄

Example 12   What does the statement $\forall x N(x)$ mean if $N(x)$ is "Computer x is connected to the network" and the domain consists of all computers on campus?

Solution: The statement $\forall x N(x)$ means that for every computer x on campus, that computer x is connected to the network. This statement can be expressed in English as "Every computer on campus is connected to the network."   ◄

As we have pointed out, specifying the domain is mandatory when quantifiers are used. The truth value of a quantified statement often depends on which elements are in this domain, as Example 13 shows.

Example 13   What is the truth value of $\forall x (x^2 \geqslant x)$ if the domain consists of all real numbers? What is the truth value of this statement if the domain consists of all integers?

Solution: The universal quantification $\forall x (x^2 \geqslant x)$, where the domain consists of all real numbers, is false. For example, $(\frac{1}{2})^2 \not\geqslant \frac{1}{2}$. Note that $x^2 \geqslant x$ if and only if $x^2 - x = x(x-1) \geqslant 0$. Consequently, $x^2 \geqslant x$ if and only if $x \leqslant 0$ or $x \geqslant 1$. It follows that $\forall x (x^2 \geqslant x)$ is false if the domain consists of all real numbers (because the inequality is false for all real numbers x with $0 < x < 1$). However, if the domain consists of the integers, $\forall x (x^2 \geqslant x)$ is true, because there are no integers x with $0 < x < 1$.   ◄

The Existential Quantifier   Many mathematical statements assert that there is an element with a certain property. Such statements are expressed using existential quantification. With existential quantification, we form a proposition that is true if and only if $P(x)$ is true for at least one value of x in the domain.

Definition 2   The *existential quantification* of $P(x)$ is the proposition

"There exists an element x in the domain such that $P(x)$."

We use the notation $\exists x P(x)$ for the existential quantification of $P(x)$. Here $\exists$ is called the *existential quantifier.*

A domain must always be specified when a statement $\exists x P(x)$ is used. Furthermore, the meaning of $\exists x P(x)$ changes when the domain changes. Without specifying the domain, the statement $\exists x P(x)$ has no meaning.

Besides the words "there exists," we can also express existential quantification in many other ways, such as by using the words "for some," "for at least one," or "there is." The existential quantification $\exists x P(x)$ is read as

"There is an x such that $P(x)$,"

"There is at least one x such that $P(x)$,"

or

'For some $x P(x)$."

The meaning of the existential quantifier is summarized in the second row of Table 1. We illustrate the use of the existential quantifier in Examples 14–16.

Example 14   Let $P(x)$ denote the statement "$x > 3$." What is the truth value of the quantification $\exists x P(x)$, where the domain consists of all real numbers?

Solution: Because "$x > 3$" is sometimes true—for instance, when $x = 4$—the existential quantification of $P(x)$, which is $\exists x P(x)$, is true. ◀

Observe that the statement $\exists x P(x)$ is false if and only if there is no element x in the domain for which $P(x)$ is true. That is, $\exists x P(x)$ is false if and only $P(x)$ is false for every element of the domain. We illustrate this observation in Example 15.

Example 15   Let $Q(x)$ denote the statement "$x = x + 1$." What is the truth value of the quantification $\exists x Q(x)$, where the domain consists of all real numbers?

Solution: Because $Q(x)$ is false for every real number x, the existential quantification of $Q(x)$, which is $\exists x Q(x)$, is false. ◀

Remark: Generally, an implicit assumption is made that all domains of discourse for quantifiers are nonempty. If the domain is empty, then $\exists x Q(x)$ is false whenever $Q(x)$ is a propositional function because when the domain is empty, there can be no element in the domain for which $Q(x)$ is true.

When all elements in the domain can be listed—say, $x_1, x_2, \ldots, x_n$— the existential quantification $\exists x P(x)$ is the same as the disjunction

$$P(x_1) \vee P(x_2) \vee \cdots \vee P(x_n),$$

because this disjunction is true if and only if at least one of $P(x_1), P(x_2), \ldots, P(x_n)$ is true.

Example 16   What is the truth value of $\exists x P(x)$, where $P(x)$ is the statement "$x^2 > 10$" and the universe of discourse consists of the positive integers not exceeding 4?

Solution: Because the domain is $\{1, 2, 3, 4\}$, the proposition $\exists x P(x)$ is the same as the disjunction

$$P(1) \vee P(2) \vee P(3) \vee P(4).$$

Because $P(4)$, which is the statement "$4^2 > 10$," is true, it follows that $\exists x P(x)$ is true. ◀

It is sometimes helpful to think in terms of looping and searching when determining the truth value of a quantification. Suppose that there are n objects in the domain for the variable x. To determine whether $\forall x P(x)$ is true, we can loop through all n values of x to see if $P(x)$ is always true. If we encounter a value x for which $P(x)$ is false, then we have shown that $\forall x P(x)$ is false. Otherwise, $\forall x P(x)$ is true. To see whether $\exists x P(x)$ is true, we loop through the n values of x searching for a value for which $P(x)$ is true. If we find one, then $\exists x P(x)$ is true. If we never find such an x, then we have determined that $\exists x P(x)$ is false. (Note that this searching procedure does not apply if there are infinitely many values in the domain. However, it is still a useful way of thinking about the truth values of quantifications.)

Other Quantifiers

We have now introduced universal and existential quantifiers. These are the most important quantifiers in mathematics and computer science. However, there is no limitation on the number of different quantifiers we can define, such as "there are exactly two," "there are no more than three," "there are at least 100," and so on. Of these other quantifiers, the one that is most often seen is the **uniqueness quantifier,** denoted by $\exists!$ or $\exists_1$. The notation $\exists! x P(x)$ [or $\exists_1 x P(x)$] states "There exists a unique x such that $P(x)$ is true." Other phrases for uniqueness quantification include "there is exactly one" and "there is one and only one." Observe that we can use quantifiers and propositional logic to express uniqueness, so the uniqueness quantifier can be avoided. Generally, it is best to stick with existential and universal quantifiers so that rules of inference for these quantifiers can be used.

Quantifierswith Restricted Domains

An abbreviated notation is often used to restrict the domain of a quantifier. In this notation, a condition a variable must satisfy is included after the quantifier. This is illustrated in Example 17. We will also describe other forms of this notation involving set membership in Section 2.1.

Example 17   What do the statements $\forall x < 0\,(x^2 > 0)$, $\forall y \neq 0\,(y^3 \neq 0)$, and $\exists z > 0\,(z^2 = 2)$ mean, where the domain in each case consists of the real numbers?

Solution: The statement $\forall x < 0\ (x^2 > 0)$ states that for every real number x with $x < 0$, $x^2 > 0$. That is, it states "The square of a negative real number is positive." This statement is the same as $\forall x (x < 0 \rightarrow x^2 > 0)$.

The statement $\forall y \neq 0\,(y^3 \neq 0)$ states that for every real number y with $y \neq 0$, we have $y^3 \neq 0$. That is, it states "The cube of every nonzero real number is nonzero." Note that this statement is equivalent to $\forall y(y \neq 0 \rightarrow y^3 \neq 0)$.

Finally, the statement $\exists z > 0\,(z^2 = 2)$ states that there exists a real number z with $z > 0$ such that $z^2 = 2$. That is, it states "There is a positive square root of 2." This statement is equivalent to $\exists z(z > 0 \wedge z^2 = 2)$.   ◀

Note that the restriction of a universal quantification is the same as the universal quantification of a conditional statement. For instance, $\forall x < 0\,(x^2 > 0)$ is another way of expressing $\forall x(x < 0 \rightarrow x^2 > 0)$. On the other hand, the restriction of an existential quantification is the same as the existential quantification of a conjunction. For instance, $\exists z > 0\,(z^2 = 2)$ is another way of expressing $\exists z(z > 0 \wedge z^2 = 2)$.

Precedence of Quantifiers

The quantifiers $\forall$ and $\exists$ have higher precedence then all logical operators from propositional calculus. For example, $\forall x P(x) \vee Q(x)$ is the disjunction of $\forall x P(x)$ and $Q(x)$. In other words, it means $(\forall x P(x)) \vee Q(x)$ rather than $\forall x(P(x) \vee Q(x))$.

Binding Variables

When a quantifier is used on the variable x, we say that this occurrence of the variable is **bound.** An occurrence of a variable that is not bound by a quantifier or set equal to a particular value is said to be **free.** All the variables that occur in a propositional function must be bound or set equal to a particular value to turn it into a proposition. This can be done using a combination of universal quantifiers, existential quantifiers, and value assignments.

The part of a logical expression to which a quantifier is applied is called the **scope** of this quantifier. Consequently, a variable is free if it is outside the scope of all quantifiers in the formula that specifies this variable.

Example 18   In the statement $\exists x(x + y = 1)$, the variable x is bound by the existential quantification $\exists x$, but the variable y is free because it is not bound by a quantifier and no value is assigned to this variable. This illustrates that in the statement $\exists x(x + y = 1)$, x is bound, but y is free.

In the statement $\exists x(P(x) \wedge Q(x)) \vee \forall x R(x)$, all variables are bound. The scope of the first quantifier, $\exists x$, is the expression $P(x) \wedge Q(x)$ because $\exists x$ is applied only to $P(x) \wedge Q(x)$, and not to the rest of the statement. Similarly, the scope of the second quantifier, $\forall x$, is the expression $R(x)$. That is, the existential quantifier binds the variable x in $P(x) \wedge Q(x)$ and the universal quantifier $\forall x$ binds the variable x in $R(x)$. Observe that we could have written our statement using two different variables x and y, as $\exists x(P(x) \wedge Q(x)) \vee \forall y R(y)$, because the scopes of the two quantifiers do not overlap. The reader should be aware that in common usage, the same letter is often used to represent variables bound by different quantifiers with scopes that do not overlap.   ◀

Logical Equivalences Involving Quantifiers

In Section 1.2 we introduced the notion of logical equivalences of compound propositions. We can extend this notion to expressions involving predicates and quantifiers.

> **Definition 3**   Statements involving predicates and quantifiers are *logically equivalent* if and only if they have the same truth value no matter which predicates are substituted into these statements and which domain of discourse is used for the variables in these propositional functions. We use the notation $S \equiv T$ to indicate that two statements S and T involving predicates and quantifiers are logically equivalent.

Example 19 illustrates how to show that two statements involving predicates and quantifiers are logically equivalent.

Example 19   Show that $\forall x(P(x) \land Q(x))$ and $\forall x P(x) \land \forall x Q(x)$ are logically equivalent (where the same domain is used throughout). This logical equivalence shows that we can distribute a universal quantifier over a conjunction. Furthermore, we can also distribute an existential quantifier over a disjunction. However, we cannot distribute a universal quantifier over a disjunction, nor can we distribute an existential quantifier over a conjunction. (See Exercise 26.)

Solution: To show that these statements are logically equivalent, we must show that they always take the same truth value, no matter what the predicates P and Q are, and no matter which domain of discourse is used. Suppose we have particular predicates P and Q, with a common domain. We can show that $\forall x(P(x) \land Q(x))$ and $\forall x P(x) \land \forall x Q(x)$ are logically equivalent by doing two things. First, we show that if $\forall x(P(x) \land Q(x))$ is true, then $\forall x P(x) \land \forall x Q(x)$ is true. Second, we show that if $\forall x P(x) \land \forall x Q(x)$ is true, then $\forall x(P(x) \land Q(x))$ is true.

So, suppose that $\forall x(P(x) \land Q(x))$ is true. This means that if a is in the domain, then $P(a) \land Q(a)$ is true. Hence, $P(a)$ is true and $Q(a)$ is true. Because $P(a)$ is true and $Q(a)$ is true for every element in the domain, we can conclude that $\forall x P(x)$ and $\forall x Q(x)$ are both true. This means that $\forall x P(x) \land \forall x Q(x)$ is true.

Next, suppose that $\forall x P(x) \land \forall x Q(x)$ is true. It follows that $\forall x P(x)$ is true and $\forall x Q(x)$ is true. Hence, if a is in the domain, then $P(a)$ is true and $Q(a)$ is true [because $P(x)$ and $Q(x)$ are both true for all elements in the domain, there is no conflict using the same value of a here]. It follows that for all a, $P(a) \land Q(a)$ is true. It follows that $\forall x(P(x) \land Q(x))$ is true. We can now conclude that

$$\forall x(P(x) \land Q(x)) \equiv \forall x P(x) \land \forall x Q(x).$$ ◄

Negating Quantified Expressions

We will often want to consider the negation of a quantified expression. For instance, consider the negation of the statement

"Every student in your class has taken a course in calculus."

This statement is a universal quantification, namely,

$$\forall x P(x),$$

where $P(x)$ is the statement "x has taken a course in calculus" and the domain consists of the students in your class. The negation of this statement is "It is not the case that every student in your class has taken a course in calculus." This is equivalent to "There is a student in your class who has not taken a course in calculus." And this is simply the existential quantification of the negation of the original propositional function, namely,

$$\exists x \, \neg P(x).$$

This example illustrates the following logical equivalence:

$$\neg \forall x P(x) \equiv \exists x \, \neg P(x).$$

To show that $\neg \forall x P(x)$ and $\exists x\,(x)$ are logically equivalent no matter what the propositional function $P(x)$ is and what the domain is, first note that $\neg \forall x P(x)$ is true if and only if $\forall x P(x)$ is false. Next, note that $\forall x P(x)$ is false if and only there is an element x in the domain for which $P(x)$ is false. This holds if and only if there is an element x in the domain for which $\neg P(x)$ is true. Finally, note that there is an element x in the domain for which $\neg P(x)$ is true if and only if $\exists x \neg P(x)$ is true. Putting these steps together, we can conclude that $\neg \forall x P(x)$ is true if and only if $\exists x \neg P(x)$ is true. It follows that $\neg \forall x P(x)$ and $\exists x \neg P(x)$ are logically equivalent.

Suppose we wish to negate an existential quantification. For instance, consider the proposition "There is a student in this class who has taken a course in calculus." This is the existential quantification

$$\exists x Q(x),$$

where $Q(x)$ is the statement "x has taken a course in calculus." The negation of this statement is the proposition "It is not the case that there is a student in this class who has taken a course in calculus." This is equivalent to "Every student in this class has not taken calculus," which is just the universal quantification of the negation of the original propositional function, or, phrased in the language of quantifiers,

$$\forall x \neg Q(x).$$

This example illustrates the equivalence

$$\neg \exists x Q(x) \equiv \forall x \neg Q(x).$$

To show that $\neg \exists x Q(x)$ and $\forall x \neg Q(x)$ are logically equivalent no matter what $Q(x)$ is and what the domain is, first note that $\neg \exists x Q(x)$ is true if and only if $\exists x Q(x)$ is false. This is true if and only if no x exists in the domain for which $Q(x)$ is true. Next, note that no x exists in the domain for which $Q(x)$ is true if and only if $Q(x)$ is false for every x in the domain. Finally, note that $Q(x)$ is false for every x in the domain if and only if $\neg Q(x)$ is true for all x in the domain, which holds if and only if $\forall x \neg Q(x)$ is true. Putting these steps together, we see that $\neg \exists x Q(x)$ is true if and only if $\forall x \neg Q(x)$ is true. We conclude that $\neg \exists x Q(x)$ and $\forall x \neg Q(x)$ are logically equivalent.

The rules for negations for quantifiers are called **De Morgan's laws for quantifiers.** These rules are summarized in Table 2.

TABLE 2 De Morgan's Laws for Quantifiers.			
Negation	*Equivalent Statement*	*When Is Negation True?*	*When False?*
$\neg \exists x P(x)$	$\forall x \neg P(x)$	For every x, $P(x)$ is false.	There is an x for which $P(x)$ is true.
$\neg \forall x P(x)$	$\exists x \neg P(x)$	There is an x for which $P(x)$ is false.	$P(x)$ is true for every x.

Remark: When the domain of a predicate $P(x)$ consists of n elements, where n is a positive integer, the rules for negating quantified statements are exactly the same as De Morgan's laws discussed in Section 1.2. This is why these rules are called De Morgan's laws for quantifiers. When the domain has n elements $x_1, x_2, \ldots, x_n$, it follows that $\neg \forall x P(x)$ is the same as $\neg(P(x_1) \wedge P(x_2) \wedge \cdots \wedge P(x_n))$, which is equivalent to $\neg P(x_1) \vee \neg P(x_2) \vee \cdots \vee \neg P(x_n)$ by De Morgan's laws, and this is the same as $\exists x \neg P(x)$. Similarly, $\neg \exists x P(x)$ is the same as $\neg(P(x_1) \vee P(x_2) \vee \cdots \vee P(x_n))$, which by De Morgan's laws is equivalent to $\neg P(x_1) \wedge \neg P(x_2) \wedge \cdots \wedge \neg P(x_n)$, and this is the same as $\forall x \neg P(x)$.

We illustrate the negation of quantified statements in Examples 20 and 21.

Example 20   What are the negations of the statements "There is an honest politician" and "All Americans eat cheeseburgers"?

Solution: Let $H(x)$ denote "x is honest." Then the statement "There is an honest politician" is represented by $\exists x H(x)$, where the domain consists of all politicians. The negation of this statement is $\neg \exists x H(x)$, which is equivalent to $\forall x \neg H(x)$. This negation can be expressed as

"Every politician is dishonest." (*Note:* In English, the statement "All politicians are not honest" is ambiguous. In common usage, this statement often means "Not all politicians are honest." Consequently, we do not use this statement to express this negation.)

Let $C(x)$ denote "x eats cheeseburgers." Then the statement "All Americans eat cheeseburgers" is represented by $\forall x C(x)$, where the domain consists of all Americans. The negation of this statement is $\neg \forall x C(x)$, which is equivalent to $\exists x \neg C(x)$. This negation can be expressed in several different ways, including "Some American does not eat cheeseburgers" and "There is an American who does not eat cheeseburgers."   ◀

Example 21   What are the negations of the statements $\forall x(x^2 > x)$ and $\exists x(x^2 = 2)$?

Solution: The negation of $\forall x(x^2 > x)$ is the statement $\neg \forall x(x^2 > x)$, which is equivalent to $\exists x \neg(x^2 > x)$. This can be rewritten as $\exists x(x^2 \leqslant x)$. The negation of $\exists x(x^2 = 2)$ is the statement $\neg \exists x(x^2 = 2)$, which is equivalent to $\forall x \neg(x^2 = 2)$. This can be rewritten as $\forall x(x^2 \neq 2)$. The truth values of these statements depend on the domain.   ◀

We use De Morgan's laws for quantifiers in Example 22.

Example 22   Show that $\neg \forall x(P(x) \rightarrow Q(x))$ and $\exists x(P(x) \wedge \neg Q(x))$ are logically equivalent.

Solution: By De Morgan's law for universal quantifiers, we know that $\neg \forall x(P(x) \rightarrow Q(x))$ and $\exists x(\neg(P(x) \rightarrow Q(x)))$ are logically equivalent. By the fifth logical equivalence in Table 7 in Section 1.2, we know that $\neg(P(x) \rightarrow Q(x))$ and $P(x) \wedge \neg Q(x)$ are logically equivalent for every x. Because we can substitute one logically equivalent expression for another in a logical equivalence, it follows that $\neg \forall x(P(x) \rightarrow Q(x))$ and $\exists x(P(x) \wedge \neg Q(x))$ are logically equivalent.   ◀

Translating from English into Logical Expressions

Translating sentences in English (or other natural languages) into logical expressions is a crucial task in mathematics, logic programming, artificial intelligence, software engineering, and many other disciplines. We began studying this topic in Section 1.1, where we used propositions to express sentences in logical expressions. In that discussion, we purposely avoided sentences whose translations required predicates and quantifiers. Translating from English to logical expressions becomes even more complex when quantifiers are needed. Furthermore, there can be many ways to translate a particular sentence. (As a consequence, there is no "cookbook" approach that can be followed step by step.) We will use some examples to illustrate how to translate sentences from English into logical expressions. The goal in this translation is to produce simple and useful logical expressions. In this section, we restrict ourselves to sentences that can be translated into logical expressions using a single quantifier; in the next section, we will look at more complicated sentences that require multiple quantifiers.

Example 23   Express the statement "Every student in this class has studied calculus" using predicates and quantifiers.

Solution: First, we rewrite the statement so that we can clearly identify the appropriate quantifiers to use. Doing so, we obtain:

"For every student in this class, that student has studied calculus."

Next, we introduce a variable x so that our statement becomes

"For every student x in this class, x has studied calculus."

Continuing, we introduce $C(x)$, which is the statement "x has studied calculus." Consequently, if the domain for x consists of the students in the class, we can translate our statement as $\forall x C(x)$.

However, there are other correct approaches; different domains of discourse and other predicates can be used. The approach we select depends on the subsequent reasoning we want to carry out. For example, we may be interested in a wider group of people than only those in this class. If we change the domain to consist of all people, we will need to express our statement as

"For every person x, if person x is a student in this class then x has studied calculus."

If $S(x)$ represents the statement that person x is in this class, we see that our statement can be expressed as $\forall x(S(x) \rightarrow C(x))$. [*Caution!* Our statement *cannot* be expressed as $\forall x(S(x) \wedge C(x))$ because this statement says that all people are students in this class and have studied calculus!]

Finally, when we are interested in the background of people in subjects besides calculus, we may prefer to use the two-variable quantifier $Q(x, y)$ for the statement "student x has studied subject y." Then we would replace $C(x)$ by $Q(x, \text{calculus})$ in both approaches to obtain $\forall x Q(x, \text{calculus})$ or $\forall x(S(x) \rightarrow Q(x, \text{calculus}))$.   ◄

In Example 23 we displayed different approaches for expressing the same statement using predicates and quantifiers. However, we should always adopt the simplest approach that is adequate for use in subsequent reasoning.

Example 24   Express the statements "Some student in this class has visited Mexico" and "Every student in this class has visited either Canada or Mexico" using predicates and quantifiers.

Solution: The statement "Some student in this class has visited Mexico" means that

"There is a student in this class with the property that the student has visited Mexico."

We can introduce a variable x, so that our statement becomes

"There is a student x in this class having the property that x has visited Mexico."

We introduce $M(x)$, which is the statement "x has visited Mexico." If the domain for x consists of the students in this class, we can translate this first statement as $\exists x M(x)$.

However, if we are interested in people other than those in this class, we look at the statement a little differently. Our statement can be expressed as

"There is a person x having the properties that x is a student in this class and x has visited Mexico."

In this case, the domain for the variable x consists of all people. We introduce $S(x)$ to represent "x is a student in this class." Our solution becomes $\exists x(S(x) \wedge M(x))$ because the statement is that there is a person x who is a student in this class and who has visited Mexico. [*Caution!* Our statement cannot be expressed as $\exists x(S(x) \rightarrow M(x))$, which is true when there is someone not in the class because, in that case, for such a person x, $S(x) \rightarrow M(x)$ becomes either $\mathbf{F} \rightarrow \mathbf{T}$ or $\mathbf{F} \rightarrow \mathbf{F}$, both of which are true.]

Similarly, the second statement can be expressed as

"For every x in this class, x has the property that x has visited Mexico or x has visited Canada."

(Note that we are assuming the inclusive, rather than the exclusive, *or* here.) We let $C(x)$ be "x has visited Canada." Following our earlier reasoning, we see that if the domain for x consists of the students in this class, this second statement can be expressed as $\forall x(C(x) \vee M(x))$. However, if the domain for x consists of all people, our statement can be expressed as

"For every person x, if x is a student in this class, then x has visited Mexico or x has visited Canada."

In this case, the statement can be expressed as $\forall x(S(x) \rightarrow (C(x) \vee M(x)))$.

Instead of using $M(x)$ and $C(x)$ to represent that x has visited Mexico and x has visited Canada, respectively, we could use a two-place predicate $V(x, y)$ to represent "x has visited country y." In this case, $V(x, \text{Mexico})$ and $V(x, \text{Canada})$ would have the same meaning as $M(x)$ and $C(x)$ and could replace them in our answers. If we are working with many statements that involve people visiting different countries, we might prefer to use this two-variable approach. Otherwise, for simplicity, we would stick with the one-variable predicates $M(x)$ and $C(x)$.   ◄

Using Quantifiers in System Specifications

In Section 1.1 we used propositions to represent system specifications. However, many system specifications involve predicates and quantifications. This is illustrated in Example 25.

Example 25   Use predicates and quantifiers to express the system specifications "Every mail message larger than one megabyte will be compressed" and "If a user is active, at least one network link will be available."

Solution: Let $S(m, y)$ be "Mail message m is larger than y megabytes," where the variable x has the domain of all mail messages and the variable y is a positive real number, and let $C(m)$ denote "Mail message m will be compressed." Then the specification "Every mail message larger than one megabyte will be compressed" can be represented as $\forall m(S(m, 1) \rightarrow C(m))$.

Let $A(u)$ represent "User u is active," where the variable u has the domain of all users, let $S(n, x)$ denote "Network link n is in state x," where n has the domain of all network links and x has the domain of all possible states for a network link. Then the specification "If a user is active, at least one network link will be available" can be represented by $\exists u A(u) \rightarrow \exists n S(n, \text{available})$.

◀

Examples from Lewis Carroll

Lewis Carroll (really C. L. Dodgson writing under a pseudonym), the author of *Alice in Wonderland*, is also the author of several works on symbolic logic. His books contain many examples of reasoning using quantifiers. Examples 26 and 27 come from his book *Symbolic Logic;* other examples from that book are given in the exercises at the end of this section. These examples illustrate how quantifiers are used to express various types of statements.

Example 26   Consider these statements. The first two are called *premises* and the third is called the *conclusion*. The entire set is called an *argument*.

"All lions are fierce."

"Some lions do not drink coffee."

"Some fierce creatures do not drink coffee."

(In Section 1.5 we will discuss the issue of determining whether the conclusion is a valid consequence of the premises. In this example, it is.) Let $P(x)$, $Q(x)$, and $R(x)$ be the statements "x is a lion," "x is fierce," and "x drinks coffee," respectively. Assuming that the domain consists of all creatures, express the statements in the argument using quantifiers and $P(x)$, $Q(x)$, and $R(x)$.

Solution: We can express these statements as:

$$\forall x(P(x) \quad \rightarrow Q(x)).$$
$$\exists x(P(x) \quad \wedge \neg R(x)).$$
$$\exists x(Q(x) \quad \wedge \neg R(x)).$$

Notice that the second statement cannot be written as $\exists x(P(x) \rightarrow \neg R(x))$. The reason is that $P(x) \rightarrow \neg R(x)$ is true whenever x is not a lion, so that $\exists x(P(x) \rightarrow \neg R(x))$ is true as long as there is at least one creature that is not a lion, even if every lion drinks coffee. Similarly, the third statement cannot be written as

$$\exists x(Q(x) \rightarrow \neg R(x)).$$

◀

Example 27   Consider these statements, of which the first three are premises and the fourth is a valid conclusion.

"All hummingbirds are richly colored."

"No large birds live on honey."

"Birds that do not live on honey are dull in color."

"Hummingbirds are small."

Let $P(x)$, $Q(x)$, $R(x)$, and $S(x)$ be the statements "x is a hummingbird," "x is large," "x lives on honey," and "x is richly colored," respectively. Assuming that the domain consists of all birds, express the statements in the argument using quantifiers and $P(x)$, $Q(x)$, $R(x)$, and $S(x)$.

Solution: We can express the statements in the argument as

$$\forall x(P(x) \rightarrow S(x)).$$
$$\neg\exists x(Q(x) \wedge R(x)).$$
$$\forall x(\neg R(x) \rightarrow \neg S(x)).$$
$$\forall x(P(x) \rightarrow \neg Q(x)).$$

(Note we have assumed that "small" is the same as "not large" and that "dull in color" is the same as "not richly colored." To show that the fourth statement is a valid conclusion of the first three, we need to use rules of inference that will be discussed in Section 1.5.)   ◀

Logic Programming

An important type of programming language is designed to reason using the rules of predicate logic. Prolog (from *Programming in Logic*), developed in the 1970s by computer scientists working in the area of artificial intelligence, is an example of such a language. Prolog programs include a set of declarations consisting of two types of statements, **Prolog facts** and **Prolog rules.** Prolog facts define predicates by specifying the elements that satisfy these predicates. Prolog rules are used to define new predicates using those already defined by Prolog facts. Example 28 illustrates these notions.

Example 28   Consider a Prolog program given facts telling it the instructor of each class and in which classes students are enrolled. The program uses these facts to answer queries concerning the professors who teach particular students. Such a program could use the predicates *instructor*(p, c) and *enrolled*(s, c) to represent that professor p is the instructor of course c and that student s is enrolled in course c, respectively. For example, the Prolog facts in such a program might include:

```
instructor(chan,math273)
instructor(patel,ee222)
instructor(grossman,cs301)
enrolled(kevin,math273)
enrolled(juana,ee222)
enrolled(juana,cs301)
enrolled(kiko,math273)
enrolled(kiko,cs301)
```

(Lowercase letters have been used for entries because Prolog considers names beginning with an uppercase letter to be variables.)

A new predicate *teaches*(p, s), representing that professor p teaches student s, can be defined using the Prolog rule

```
teaches(P,S) :-instructor(P,C), enrolled(S,C)
```

which means that *teaches*(p, s) is true if there exists a class c such that professor p is the instructor of class c and student s is enrolled in class c. (Note that a comma is used to represent a conjunction of predicates in Prolog. Similarly, a semicolon is used to represent a disjunction of predicates.)

Prolog answers queries using the facts and rules it is given. For example, using the facts and rules listed, the query

```
?enrolled(kevin,math273)
```

produces the response

```
yes
```

because the fact *enrolled* (kevin, math273) was provided as input. The query

```
?enrolled(X,math273)
```

produces the response

```
kevin
```

`kiko`

To produce this response, Prolog determines all possible values of X for which *enrolled*(X, math273) has been included as a Prolog fact. Similarly, to find all the professors who are instructors in classes being taken by Juana, we use the query

`?teaches(X,juana)`

This query returns

`patel`

`grossman`

◄

Exercises

---

1. Let $P(x)$ denote the statement "$x \leqslant 4$." What are those truth values?
   - a) $P(0)$ b) $P(4)$ c) $P(6)$

2. Let $Q(x, y)$ denote the statement "x is the capital of y." What are these truth values?
   - a) Q(Denver, Colorado)   b) Q(Detroit, Michigan)
   - c) Q(Massachusetts, Boston)   d) Q(New York, New York)

3. Let $P(x)$ be the statement "x spends more than five hours every weekday in class," where the domain for x consists of all students. Express each of these quantifications in English.
   - a) $\exists x P(x)$ b) $\forall x P(x)$ c) $\exists x \neg P(x)$ d) $\forall x \neg P(x)$

4. Translate these statements into English, where $C(x)$ is "x is a comedian" and $F(x)$ is "x is funny" and the domain consists of all people.
   - a) $\forall x(C(x) \rightarrow F(x))$ b) $\forall x(C(x) \land F(x))$ c) $\exists x(C(x) \rightarrow F(x))$ d) $\exists x(C(x) \land F(x))$

5. Let $P(x)$ be the statement "x can speak Russian" and let $Q(x)$ be the statement "x knows the computer language C++." Express each of these sentences in terms of $P(x)$, $Q(x)$, quantifiers, and logical connectives. The domain for quantifiers consists of all students at your school.
   - a) There is a student at your school who can speak Russian and who knows C++.
   - b) There is a student at your school who can speak Russian but who doesn't know C++.
   - c) Every student at your school either can speak Russian or knows C++.
   - d) No student at your school can speak Russian or knows C++.

6. Let $P(x)$ be the statement "$x = x^2$." If the domain consists of the integers, what are the truth values?
   - a) $P(0)$ b) $P(1)$ c) $P(2)$ d) $P(-1)$ e) $\exists x P(x)$ f) $\forall x P(x)$

7. Determine the truth value of each of these statements if the domain consists of all integers.
   - a) $\forall n(n + 1 > n)$ b) $\exists n(2n = 3n)$ c) $\exists n(n = -n)$ d) $\forall n(n^2 \geqslant n)$

8. Determine the truth value of each of these statements if the domain for all variables consists of all integers.
   - a) $\forall n(n^2 \geqslant 0)$ b) $\exists n(n^2 = 2)$ c) $\forall n(n^2 \geqslant n)$ d) $\exists n(n^2 < 0)$

9. Suppose that the domain of the propositional function $P(x)$ consists of the integers 0, 1, 2, 3, and 4. Write out each of these propositions using disjunctions, conjunctions, and negations.
   - a) $\exists x P(x)$ b) $\forall x P(x)$ c) $\exists x \neg P(x)$ d) $\forall x \neg P(x)$ e) $\neg \exists x P(x)$ f) $\neg \forall x P(x)$

10. Suppose that the domain of the propositional function $P(x)$ consists of the integers 1, 2, 3, 4, and 5. Express these statements without using quantifiers, instead using only negations, disjunctions, and conjunctions.
    - a) $\exists x P(x)$ b) $\forall x P(x)$ c) $\neg \exists x P(x)$ d) $\neg \forall x P(x)$
    - e) $\forall x((x \neq 3) \rightarrow P(x)) \lor \exists x \neg P(x)$

11. For each of these statements find a domain for which the statement is true and a domain for which the statement is false.
    - a) Everyone is studying discrete mathematics.   b) Everyone is older than 21 years.
    - c) Every two people have the same mother.   d) No two different people have the same grandmother.

12. Translate in two ways each of these statements into logical expressions using predicates, quantifiers, and logical connectives. First, let the domain consist of the students in your class and second, let it consist of all people.

a) Someone in your class can speak Hindi.   b) Everyone in your class is friendly.

c) There is a person in your class who was not born in California.

d) A student in your class has been in a movie.

e) No student in your class has taken a course in logic programming.

13. Translate each of these statements into logical expressions using predicates, quantifiers, and logical connectives.

a) No one is perfect.   b) Not everyone is perfect.

c) All your friends are perfect.   d) At least one of your friends is perfect.

e) Everyone is your friend and is perfect.   f) Not everybody is your friend or someone is not perfect.

14. Translate each of these statements into logical expressions in three different ways by varying the domain and by using predicates with one and with two variables.

a) A student in your school has lived in Vietnam.

b) There is a student in your school who cannot speak Hindi.

c) A student in your school knows Java, Prolog, and C++.

d) Everyone in your class enjoys Thai food.

e) Someone in your class does not play hockey.

15. Express each of these statements using logical operators, predicates, and quantifiers.

a) Some propositions are tautologies.

b) The negation of a contradiction is a tautology.

c) The disjunction of two contingencies can be a tautology.

d) The conjunction of two tautologies is a tautology.

16. Suppose that the domain of $Q(x, y, z)$ consists of triples x, y, z, where $x = 0, 1,$ or 2, $y = 0$ or 1, and $z = 0$ or 1. Write out these propositions using disjunctions and conjunctions.

a) $\forall y Q(0, y, 0)$ b) $\exists x Q(x, 1, 1)$ c) $\exists z \neg Q(0, 0, z)$ d) $\exists x \neg Q(x, 0, 1)$

17. Express each of these statements using quantifiers. Then form the negation of the statement, so that no negation is to the left of a quantifier. Next, express the negation in simple English. (Do not simply use the words "It is not the case that.")

a) Some old dogs can learn new tricks.   b) No rabbit knows calculus.   c) Every bird can fly.

d) There is no dog that can talk.   e) There is no one in this class who knows French and Russian.

18. Find a counterexample, if possible, to these universally quantified statements, where the domain for all variables consists of all integers.

a) $\forall x (x^2 \geqslant x)$ b) $\forall x (x > 0 \vee x < 0)$ c) $\forall x (x = 1)$

19. Express each of these statements using predicates and quantifiers.

a) A passenger on an airline qualifies as an elite flyer if the passenger flies more than 25,000 miles in a year or takes more than 25 flights during that year.

b) A man qualifies for the marathon if his best previous time is less than 3 hours and a woman qualifies for the marathon if her best previous time is less than 3.5 hours.

c) A student must take at least 60 course hours, or at least 45 course hours and write a master's thesis, and receive a grade no lower than a B in all required courses, to receive a master's degree.

d) There is a student who has taken more than 21 credit hours in a semester and received all A's.

Exercises 20–21 deal with the translation between system specification and logical expressions involving quantifiers.

20. Translate these specifications into English where $F(p)$ is "Printer p is out of service," $B(p)$ is "Printer p is busy," $L(j)$ is "Print job j is lost," and $Q(j)$ is "Print job j is queued."

a) $\exists p(F(p) \wedge B(p)) \rightarrow \exists j L(j)$ b) $\forall p B(p) \rightarrow \exists j Q(j)$ c) $\exists j(Q(j) \wedge L(j)) \rightarrow \exists p F(p)$

d) $(\forall p B(p) \wedge \forall j Q(j)) \rightarrow \exists j L(j)$

21. Express each of these system specifications using predicates, quantifiers, and logical connectives.

a) At least one mail message, among the nonempty set of messages, can be saved if there is a disk with more than 10 kilobytes of free space.

b) Whenever there is an active alert, all queued messages are transmitted.

c) The diagnostic monitor tracks the status of all systems except the main console.

d) Each participant on the conference call whom the host of the call did not put on a special list was billed.

22. Determine whether $\forall x(P(x) \rightarrow Q(x))$ and $\forall x P(x) \rightarrow \forall x Q(x)$ are logically equivalent. Justify your answer.

23. Show that $\exists x(P(x) \vee Q(x))$ and $\exists x P(x) \vee \exists x Q(x)$ are logically equivalent.

Exercises 24–25 establish rules for **null quantification** that we can use when a quantified variable does not appear in part of a statement.

24. Establish these logical equivalences, where x does not occur as a free variable in A. Assume that the domain is nonempty.

a) $(\forall x P(x)) \wedge A \equiv \forall x(P(x) \wedge A)$ b) $(\exists x P(x)) \wedge A \equiv \exists x(P(x) \wedge A)$

25. Establish these logical equivalences, where x does not occur as a free variable in A. Assume that the domain is nonempty.

a) $\forall x(P(x) \rightarrow A) \equiv \exists x P(x) \rightarrow A$ b) $\exists x(P(x) \rightarrow A) \equiv \forall x P(x) \rightarrow A$

26. Show that $\exists x P(x) \wedge \exists x Q(x)$ and $\exists x(P(x) \wedge Q(x))$ are not logically equivalent.

27. What are the truth values of these statements?

a) $\exists! x P(x) \rightarrow \exists x P(x)$ b) $\forall x P(x) \rightarrow \exists! x P(x)$ c) $\exists! x \neg P(x) \rightarrow \neg \forall x P(x)$

28. Given the Prolog facts in Example 28, what would Prolog return given these queries?

a) ?instructor(chan,math273)   b) ?instructor(patel,cs301)

c) ?enrolled(X,cs301)   d) ?enrolled(kiko,Y)   e) ?teaches(grossman,Y)

29. Suppose that Prolog facts are used to define the predicates $mother(M,Y)$ and $father(F,X)$, which represent that M is the mother of Y and F is the father of X, respectively. Give a Prolog rule to define the predicate $sibling(X,Y)$, which represents that X and Y are siblings (that is, have the same mother and the same father).

Exercises 30–31 are based on questions found in the book *Symbolic Logic* by Lewis Carroll.

30. Let $P(x)$, $Q(x)$, and $R(x)$ be the statements "x is a professor," "x is ignorant," and "x is vain," respectively. Express each of these statements using quantifiers; logical connectives; and $P(x)$, $Q(x)$, and $R(x)$, where the domain consists of all people.

a) No professors are ignorant.   b) All ignorant people are vain.

c) No professors are vain.   d) Does (c) follow from (a) and (b)?

31. Let $P(x)$, $Q(x)$, $R(x)$, and $S(x)$ be the statements "x is a baby," "x is logical," "x is able to manage a crocodile," and "x is despised," respectively. Suppose that the domain consists of all people. Express each of these statements using quantifiers; logical connectives; and $P(x)$, $Q(x)$, $R(x)$, and $S(x)$.

a) Babies are illogical.   b) Nobody is despised who can manage a crocodile.

c) Illogical persons are despised.   d) Babies cannot manage crocodiles.

*e) Does (d) follow from (a), (b), and (c)? If not, is there a correct conclusion?

1.4   Nested Quantifiers

Introduction

In Section 1.3 we defined the existential and universal quantifiers and showed how they can be used to represent mathematical statements. We also explained how they can be used to translate English sentences into logical expressions. In this section we will study **nested quantifiers**. Two quantifiers are nested if one is within the scope of the other, such as

$$\forall x \exists y (x + y = 0).$$

Note that everything within the scope of a quantifier can be thought of as a propositional function. For example,

$$\forall x \exists y (x + y = 0)$$

is the same thing as $\forall x Q(x)$, where $Q(x)$ is $\exists y P(x, y)$, where $P(x, y)$ is $x + y = 0$. Nested quantifiers commonly occur in mathematics and computer science. Although nested quantifiers can sometimes be difficult to understand, the rules we have already studied in Section 1.3 can help us use them.

To understand these statements involving many quantifiers, we need to unravel what the quantifiers and predicates that appear mean. This is illustrated in Examples 1 and 2.

Example 1   Assume that the domain for the variables x and y consists of all real numbers. The statement

$$\forall x \forall y (x + y = y + x)$$

says that $x + y = y + x$ for all real numbers x and y. This is the commutative law for addition of real numbers. Likewise, the statement

$$\forall x \exists y (x + y = 0)$$

says that for every real number x there is a real number y such that $x + y = 0$. This states that every real number has an additive inverse. Similarly, the statement

$$\forall x \forall y \forall z (x + (y + z) = (x + y) + z)$$

is the associative law for addition of real numbers.   ◀

Example 2   Translate into English the statement

$$\forall x \forall y ((x > 0) \land (y < 0) \rightarrow (xy < 0)),$$

where the domain for both variables consists of all real numbers.

Solution: This statement says that for every real number x and for every real number y, if $x > 0$ and $y < 0$, then $xy < 0$. That is, this statement says that for real numbers x and y, if x is positive and y is negative, then xy is negative. This can be stated more succinctly as "The product of a positive real number and a negative real number is always a negative real number."   ◀

Thinking of Quantification as loops   In working with quantifications of more than one variable, it is sometimes helpful to think in terms of nested loops. (Of course, if there are infinitely many elements in the domain of some variable, we cannot actually loop through all values. Nevertheless, this way of thinking is helpful in understanding nested quantifiers.) For example, to see whether $\forall x \forall y P(x, y)$ is true, we loop through the values for x, and for each x we loop through the values for y. If we find that $P(x, y)$ is true for all values for x and y, we have determined that $\forall x \forall y P(x, y)$ is true. If we ever hit a value x for which we hit a value y for which $P(x, y)$ is false, we have shown that $\forall x \forall y P(x, y)$ is false.

Similarly, to determine whether $\forall x \exists y P(x, y)$ is true, we loop through the values for x. For each x we loop through the values for y until we find a y for which $P(x, y)$ is true. If for every x we hit such a y, then $\forall x \exists y P(x, y)$ is true; if for some x we never hit such a y, then $\forall x \exists y P(x, y)$ is false.

To see whether $\exists x \forall y P(x, y)$ is true, we loop through the values for x until we find an x for which $P(x, y)$ is always true when we loop through all values for y. Once we find such an x, we know that $\exists x \forall y P(x, y)$ is true. If we never hit such an x, then we know that $\exists x \forall y P(x, y)$ is false.

Finally, to see whether $\exists x \exists y P(x, y)$ is true, we loop through the values for x, where for each x we loop through the values for y until we hit an x for which we hit a y for which $P(x, y)$ is true. The statement $\exists x \exists y P(x, y)$ is false only if we never hit an x for which we hit a y such that $P(x, y)$ is true.

The Order of Quantifiers

Many mathematical statements involve multiple quantifications of propositional functions involving more than one variable. It is important to note that the order of the quantifiers is important, unless all the quantifiers are universal quantifiers or all are existential quantifiers.

These remarks are illustrated by Examples 3–5.

Example 3   Let $P(x, y)$ be the statement "$x + y = y + x$." What are the truth values of the quantifications $\forall x \forall y P(x, y)$ and $\forall y \forall x P(x, y)$ where the domain for all variables consists of all real numbers?

Solution: The quantification

$$\forall x \forall y P(x, y)$$

denotes the proposition

"For all real numbers x, for all real numbers y, $x + y = y + x$."

Because $P(x, y)$ is true for all real numbers x and y, the proposition $\forall x \forall y P(x, y)$ is true. Note that the statement $\forall y \forall x P(x, y)$ says "For all real numbers y, for all real numbers x, $x+y = y+x$." This has the same meaning as the statement as "For all real numbers x, for all real numbers y, $x+y = y+x$." That is, $\forall x \forall y P(x, y)$ and $\forall y \forall x P(x, y)$ have the same meaning, and both are true. This illustrates the principle that the order of nested universal quantifiers in a statement without other quantifiers can be changed without changing the meaning of the quantified statement.   ◄

Example 4   Let $Q(x, y)$ denote "$x + y = 0$." What are the truth values of the quantifications $\exists y \forall x Q(x, y)$ and $\forall x \exists y Q(x, y)$, where the domain for all variables consists of all real numbers?

Solution: The quantification

$$\exists y \forall x Q(x, y)$$

denotes the proposition

"There is a real number y such that for every real number x, $Q(x, y)$."

No matter what value of y is chosen, there is only one value of x for which $x + y = 0$. Because there is no real number y such that $x + y = 0$ for all real numbers x, the statement $\exists y \forall x Q(x, y)$ is false.

The quantification

$$\forall x \exists y Q(x, y)$$

denotes the proposition

"For every real number x there is a real number y such that $Q(x, y)$."

Given a real number x, there is a real number y such that $x + y = 0$; namely, $y = -x$. Hence, the statement $\forall x \exists y Q(x, y)$ is true.   ◄

TABLE 1 Quantifications of Two Variables.

Statement	When True?	When False?
$\forall x \forall y P(x, y)$ $\forall y \forall x P(x, y)$	$P(x, y)$ is true for every pair x, y.	There is a pair x, y for which $P(x, y)$ is false.
$\forall x \exists y P(x, y)$	For every x there is a y for which $P(x, y)$ is true.	There is an x such that $P(x, y)$ is false for every y.
$\exists x \forall y P(x, y)$	There is an x for which $P(x, y)$ is true for every y.	For every x there is a y for which $P(x, y)$ is false.
$\exists x \exists y P(x, y)$ $\exists y \exists x P(x, y)$	There is a pair x, y for which $P(x, y)$ is true.	$P(x, y)$ is false for every pair x, y.

Example 4 illustrates that the order in which quantifiers appear makes a difference. The statements $\exists y \forall x P(x, y)$ and $\forall x \exists y P(x, y)$ are not logically equivalent. The statement $\exists y \forall x P(x, y)$ is true if and only if there is a y that makes $P(x, y)$ true for every x. So, for this statement to be true, there must be a particular value of y for which $P(x, y)$ is true regardless of the choice of x. On the other hand, $\forall x \exists y P(x, y)$ is true if and only if for every value of x there is a value of y for which $P(x, y)$ is true. So, for this statement to be true, no matter which x you choose, there must be a value of y (possibly depending on the x you choose) for which $P(x, y)$ is true. In other words, in the second case, y can depend on x, whereas in the first case, y is a constant independent of x.

From these observations, it follows that if $\exists y \forall x P(x, y)$ is true, then $\forall x \exists y P(x, y)$ must also be true. However, if $\forall x \exists y P(x, y)$ is true, it is not necessary for $\exists y \forall x P(x, y)$ to be true. (See Supplementary Exercise 13 at the end of this chapter.)

Table 1 summarizes the meanings of the different possible quantifications involving two variables.

Quantifications of more than two variables are also common, as Example 5 illustrates.

Example 5   Let $Q(x, y, z)$ be the statement "$x + y = z$." What are the truth values of the statements $\forall x \forall y \exists z Q(x, y, z)$ and $\exists z \forall x \forall y Q(x, y, z)$, where the domain of all variables consists of all real numbers?

Solution: Suppose that x and y are assigned values. Then, there exists a real number z such that $x + y = z$. Consequently, the quantification

$$\forall x \forall y \exists z Q(x, y, z),$$

which is the statement

"For all real numbers x and for all real numbers y there is a real number z such that $x+y = z$," is true. The order of the quantification here is important, because the quantification

$$\exists z \forall x \forall y Q(x, y, z),$$

which is the statement

"There is a real number z such that for all real numbers x and for all real numbers y it is true that $x + y = z$," is false, because there is no value of z that satisfies the equation $x + y = z$ for all values of x and y.   ◄

Translating Mathematical Statements into Statements Involving Nested Quantifiers

Mathematical statements expressed in English can be translated into logical expressions, as Examples 6–8 show.

Example 6   Translate the statement "The sum of two positive integers is always positive" into a logical expression.

Solution: To translate this statement into a logical expression, we first rewrite it so that the implied quantifiers and a domain are shown: "For every two integers, if these integers are both positive, then the sum of these integers is positive." Next, we introduce the variables x and y to obtain "For all positive integers x and y, $x + y$ is positive." Consequently, we can express this statement as

$$\forall x \forall y ((x > 0) \wedge (y > 0) \rightarrow (x + y > 0)),$$

where the domain for both variables consists of all integers. Note that we could also translate this using the positive integers as the domain. Then the statement "The sum of two positive integers is always positive" becomes "For every two positive integers, the sum of these integers is positive." We can express this as

$$\forall x \forall y (x + y > 0),$$

where the domain for both variables consists of all positive integers. ◄

Example 7   Translate the statement "Every real number except zero has a multiplicative inverse." (A **multiplicative inverse** of a real number x is a real number y such that $xy = 1$.)

Solution: We first rewrite this as "For every real number x except zero, x has a multiplicative inverse." We can rewrite this as "For every real number x, if $x \neq 0$, then there exists a real number y such that $xy = 1$." This can be rewritten as

$$\forall x ((x \neq 0) \rightarrow \exists y (xy = 1)).$$ ◄

One example that you may be familiar with is the concept of limit, which is important in calculus.

Example 8 (*Requires Calculus*)   Express the definition of a limit using quantifiers.

Solution: Recall that the definition of the statement

$$\lim_{x \to a} f(x) = L$$

is: For every real number $\epsilon > 0$ there exists a real number $\delta > 0$ such that $|f(x) - L| < \epsilon$ whenever $0 < |x - a| < \delta$. This definition of a limit can be phrased in terms of quantifiers by

$$\forall \epsilon \exists \delta \forall x (0 < |x - a| < \delta \rightarrow |f(x) - L| < \epsilon),$$

where the domain for the variables δ and ϵ consists of all positive real numbers and for x consists of all real numbers.

This definition can also be expressed as

$$\forall \epsilon > 0 \, \exists \delta > 0 \, \forall x (0 < |x - a| < \delta \rightarrow |f(x) - L| < \epsilon)$$

when the domain for the variables ϵ and δ consists of all real numbers, rather than just the positive real numbers. [Here, restricted quantifiers have been used. Recall that $\forall x > 0 \, P(x)$ means that for all x with $x > 0$, $P(x)$ is true.] ◄

Translating from Nested Quantifiers into English

Expressions with nested quantifiers expressing statements in English can be quite complicated. The first step in translating such an expression is to write out what the quantifiers and predicates in the expression mean. The next step is to express this meaning in a simpler sentence. This process is illustrated in Examples 9 and 10.

Example 9   Translate the statement

$$\forall x (C(x) \vee \exists y (C(y) \wedge F(x, y)))$$

into English, where $C(x)$ is "x has a computer," $F(x, y)$ is "x and y are friends," and the domain for both x and y consists of all students in your school.

Solution: The statement says that for every student x in your school, x has a computer or there is a student y such that y has a computer and x and y are friends. In other words, every student in your school has a computer or has a friend who has a computer. ◄

Example 10   Translate the statement

$$\exists x \forall y \forall z ((F(x,y) \wedge F(x,z) \wedge (y \neq z)) \rightarrow \neg F(y,z))$$

into English, where $F(a,b)$ means a and b are friends and the domain for x, y, and z consists of all students in your school.

Solution: We first examine the expression $(F(x,y) \wedge F(x,z) \wedge (y \neq z)) \rightarrow \neg F(y,z)$. This expression says that if students x and y are friends, and students x and z are friends, and furthermore, if y and z are not the same student, then y and z are not friends. It follows that the original statement, which is triply quantified, says that there is a student x such that for all students y and all students z other than y, if x and y are friends and x and z are friends, then y and z are not friends. In other words, there is a student none of whose friends are also friends with each other. ◄

Translating English Sentences into Logical Expressions

In Section 1.3 we showed how quantifiers can be used to translate sentences into logical expressions. However, we avoided sentences whose translation into logical expressions required the use of nested quantifiers. We now address the translation of such sentences.

Example 11   Express the statement "If a person is female and is a parent, then this person is someone's mother" as a logical expression involving predicates, quantifiers with a domain consisting of all people, and logical connectives.

Solution: The statement "If a person is female and is a parent, then this person is someone's mother" can be expressed as "For every person x, if person x is female and person x is a parent, then there exists a person y such that person x is the mother of person y." We introduce the propositional functions $F(x)$ to represent "x is female," $P(x)$ to represent "x is a parent," and $M(x,y)$ to represent "x is the mother of y." The original statement can be represented as

$$\forall x((F(x) \wedge P(x)) \rightarrow \exists y M(x,y)).$$

Using the null quantification rule in part (b) of Exercise 24 in Section 1.3, we can move $\exists y$ to the left so that it appears just after $\forall x$, because y does not appear in $F(x) \wedge P(x)$. We obtain the logically equivalent expression

$$\forall x \exists y((F(x) \wedge P(x)) \rightarrow M(x,y)).$$ ◄

Example 12   Express the statement "Everyone has exactly one best friend" as a logical expression involving predicates, quantifiers with a domain consisting of all people, and logical connectives.

Solution: The statement "Everyone has exactly one best friend" can be expressed as "For every person x, person x has exactly one best friend." Introducing the universal quantifier, we see that this statement is the same as "$\forall x$ (person x has exactly one best friend)," where the domain consists of all people.

To say that x has exactly one best friend means that there is a person y who is the best friend of x, and furthermore, that for every person z, if person z is not person y, then z is not the best friend of x. When we introduce the predicate $B(x,y)$ to be the statement "y is the best friend of x," the statement that x has exactly one best friend can be represented as

$$\exists y(B(x,y) \wedge \forall z((z \neq y) \rightarrow \neg B(x,z))).$$

Consequently, our original statement can be expressed as

$$\forall x \exists y(B(x,y) \wedge \forall z((z \neq y) \rightarrow \neg B(x,z))).$$

[Note that we can write this statement as $\forall x \exists! y B(x, y)$, where $\exists!$ is the "uniqueness quantifier" defined on page 37.] ◀

Example 13 Use quantifiers to express the statement "There is a woman who has taken a flight on every airline in the world."

Solution: Let $P(w, f)$ be "w has taken f" and $Q(f, a)$ be "f is a flight on a." We can express the statement as

$$\exists w \forall a \exists f (P(w, f) \wedge Q(f, a)),$$

where the domains of discourse for w, f, and a consist of all the women in the world, all airplane flights, and all airlines, respectively.

The statement could also be expressed as

$$\exists w \forall a \exists f R(w, f, a),$$

where $R(w, f, a)$ is "w has taken f on a." Although this is more compact, it somewhat obscures the relationships among the variables. Consequently, the first solution is usually preferable. ◀

Negating Nested Quantifiers

Statements involving nested quantifiers can be negated by successively applying the rules for negating statements involving a single quantifier. This is illustrated in Examples 14–16.

Example 14 Express the negation of the statement $\forall x \exists y (xy = 1)$ so that no negation precedes a quantifier.

Solution: By successively applying De Morgan's laws for quantifiers in Table 2 of Section 1.3, we can move the negation in $\neg \forall x \exists y (xy = 1)$ inside all the quantifiers. We find that $\neg \forall x \exists y (xy = 1)$ is equivalent to $\exists x \neg \exists y (xy = 1)$, which is equivalent to $\exists x \forall y \neg (xy = 1)$. Because $\neg (xy = 1)$ can be expressed more simply as $xy \neq 1$, we conclude that our negated statement can be expressed as $\exists x \forall y (xy \neq 1)$. ◀

Example 15 Use quantifiers to express the statement that "There does not exist a woman who has taken a flight on every airline in the world."

Solution: This statement is the negation of the statement "There is a woman who has taken a flight on every airline in the world" from Example 13. By Example 13, our statement can be expressed as $\neg \exists w \forall a \exists f (P(w, f) \wedge Q(f, a))$, where $P(w, f)$ is "w has taken f" and $Q(f, a)$ is "f is a flight on a." By successively applying De Morgan's laws for quantifiers in Table 2 of Section 1.3 to move the negation inside successive quantifiers and by applying De Morgan's law for negating a conjunction in the last step, we find that our statement is equivalent to each of this sequence of statements:

$$\forall w \neg \forall a \exists f (P(w, f) \wedge Q(f, a)) \equiv \forall w \exists a \neg \exists f (P(w, f) \wedge Q(f, a))$$
$$\equiv \forall w \exists a \forall f \neg (P(w, f) \wedge Q(f, a))$$
$$\equiv \forall w \exists a \forall f (\neg P(w, f) \vee \neg Q(f, a)).$$

This last statement states "For every woman there is an airline such that for all flights, this woman has not taken that flight or that flight is not on this airline." ◀

Example 16 (*Requires Calculus*) Use quantifiers and predicates to express the fact that $\lim_{x \to a} f(x)$ does not exist.

Solution: To say that $\lim_{x \to a} f(x)$ does not exist means that for all real numbers L, $\lim_{x \to a} f(x) \neq L$. By using Example 8, the statement $\lim_{x \to a} f(x) \neq L$ can be expressed as

$$\neg \forall \epsilon > 0 \ \exists \delta > 0 \ \forall x (0 < |x - a| < \delta \to |f(x) - L| < \epsilon).$$

Successively applying the rules for negating quantified expressions, we construct this sequence of equivalent statements

$$\neg \forall \epsilon > 0 \; \exists \delta > 0 \; \forall x (0 < |x - a| < \delta \rightarrow |f(x) - L| < \epsilon)$$

$$\equiv \exists \epsilon > 0 \; \neg \exists \delta > 0 \; \forall x (0 < |x - a| < \delta \rightarrow |f(x) - L| < \epsilon)$$

$$\equiv \exists \epsilon > 0 \; \forall \delta > 0 \; \neg \forall x (0 < |x - a| < \delta \rightarrow |f(x) - L| < \epsilon)$$

$$\equiv \exists \epsilon > 0 \; \forall \delta > 0 \; \exists x \; \neg (0 < |x - a| < \delta \rightarrow |f(x) - L| < \epsilon)$$

$$\equiv \exists \epsilon > 0 \; \forall \delta > 0 \; \exists x (0 < |x - a| < \delta \wedge |f(x) - L| \geqslant \epsilon).$$

In the last step we used the equivalence $\neg(p \rightarrow q) \equiv p \wedge \neg q$, which follows from the fifth equivalence in Table 7 of Section 1.2.

Because the statement "$\lim_{x \to a} f(x)$ does not exist" means for all real numbers L, $\lim_{x \to a} f(x) \neq L$, this can be expressed as

$$\forall L \exists \epsilon > 0 \; \forall \delta > 0 \; \exists x (0 < |x - a| < \delta \wedge |f(x) - L| \geqslant \epsilon).$$

This last statement says that for every real number L there is a real number $\epsilon > 0$ such that for every real number $\delta > 0$, there exists a real number x such that $0 < |x-a| < \delta$ and $|f(x)-L| \geqslant \epsilon$.

◀

Exercises

1. Translate these statements into English, where the domain for each variable consists of all real numbers.
   a) $\forall x \exists y (x < y)$ b) $\forall x \forall y (((x \geqslant 0) \wedge (y \geqslant 0)) \rightarrow (xy \geqslant 0))$ c) $\forall x \forall y \exists z (xy = z)$

2. Let $Q(x,y)$ be the statement "x has sent an e-mail message to y," where the domain for both x and y consists of all students in your class. Express each of these quantifications in English.
   a) $\exists x \exists y Q(x,y)$ b) $\exists x \forall y Q(x,y)$ c) $\forall x \exists y Q(x,y)$ d) $\exists y \forall x Q(x,y)$ e) $\forall y \exists x Q(x,y)$
   f) $\forall x \forall y Q(x,y)$

3. Let $W(x,y)$ mean that student x has visited website y, where the domain for x consists of all students in your school and the domain for y consists of all websites. Express each of these statements by a simple English sentence.
   a) W(Sarah Smith, www.att.com)   b) $\exists x W(x, \text{www.imdb.org})$
   c) $\exists y W(\text{Jose Orez}, y)$ d) $\exists y (W(\text{Ashok Puri}, y) \wedge W(\text{Cindy Yoon}, y))$
   e) $\exists y \forall z (y \neq (\text{David Belcher}) \wedge (W(\text{David Belcher}, z) \rightarrow W(y,z)))$
   f) $\exists x \exists y \forall z ((x \neq y) \wedge (W(x,z) \leftrightarrow W(y,z)))$

4. Let $T(x,y)$ mean that student x likes cuisine y, where the domain for x consists of all students at your school and the domain for y consists of all cuisines. Express each of these statements by a simple English sentence.
   a) $\neg T$(Abdallah Hussein, Japanese)   b) $\exists x T(x, \text{Korean}) \wedge \forall x T(x, \text{Mexican})$
   c) $\exists y (T(\text{Monique Arsenault}, y) \vee T(\text{Jay Johnson}, y))$ d) $\forall x \forall z \exists y ((x \neq z) \rightarrow \neg(T(x,y) \wedge T(z,y)))$
   e) $\exists x \exists z \forall y (T(x,y) \leftrightarrow T(z,y))$ f) $\forall x \forall z \exists y (T(x,y) \leftrightarrow T(z,y))$

5. Let $L(x,y)$ be the statement "x loves y," where the domain for both x and y consists of all people in the world. Use quantifiers to express each of these statements.
   a) Everybody loves Jerry.   b) Everybody loves somebody.
   c) There is somebody whom everybody loves.   d) Nobody loves everybody.

e) There is somebody whom Lydia does not love.   f) There is somebody whom no one loves.

g) There is exactly one person whom everybody loves.

h) There are exactly two people whom Lynn loves.

i) Everyone loves himself or herself.

j) There is someone who loves no one besides himself or herself.

6. Let $S(x)$ be the predicate "x is a student," $F(x)$ the predicate "x is a faculty member," and $A(x,y)$ the predicate "x has asked y a question," where the domain consists of all people associated with your school. Use quantifiers to express each of these statements.

a) Lois has asked Professor Michaels a question.

b) Every student has asked Professor Gross a question.

c) Every faculty member has either asked Professor Miller a question or been asked a question by Professor Miller.

d) Some student has not asked any faculty member a question.

e) There is a faculty member who has never been asked a question by a student.

f) Some student has asked every faculty member a question.

g) There is a faculty member who has asked every other faculty member a question.

h) Some student has never been asked a question by a faculty member.

7. Let $M(x,y)$ be "x has sent y an e-mail message" and $T(x,y)$ be "x has telephoned y," where the domain consists of all students in your class. Use quantifiers to express each of these statements. (Assume that all e-mail messages that were sent are received, which is not the way things often work.)

a) Chou has never sent an e-mail message to Koko.

b) Arlene has never sent an e-mail message to or telephoned Sarah.

c) Jose has never received an e-mail message from Deborah.

d) Every student in your class has sent an e-mail message to Ken.

e) No one in your class has telephoned Nina.

f) Everyone in your class has either telephoned Avi or sent him an e-mail message.

g) There is a student in your class who has sent everyone else in your class an e-mail message.

h) There is someone in your class who has either sent an e-mail message or telephoned everyone else in your class.

i) There are two different students in your class who have sent each other e-mail messages.

j) There is a student who has sent himself or herself an e-mail message.

k) There is a student in your class who has not received an e-mail message from anyone else in the class and who has not been called by any other student in the class.

l) Every student in the class has either received an e-mail message or received a telephone call from another student in the class.

m) There are at least two students in your class such that one student has sent the other e-mail and the second student has telephoned the first student.

n) There are two different students in your class who between them have sent an e-mail message to or telephoned everyone else in the class.

8. Use quantifiers and predicates with more than one variable to express these statements.

a) Every computer science student needs a course in discrete mathematics.

b) There is a student in this class who owns a personal computer.

c) Every student in this class has taken at least one computer science course.

d) There is a student in this class who has taken at least one course in computer science.

e) Every student in this class has been in every building on campus.

f) There is a student in this class who has been in every room of at least one building on campus.

g) Every student in this class has been in at least one room of every building on campus.

9. Express each of these system specifications using predicates, quantifiers, and logical connectives, if necessary.

a) Every user has access to exactly one mailbox.

b) There is a process that continues to run during all error conditions only if the kernel is working correctly.

c) All users on the campus network can access all websites whose url has a .edu extension.

*d) There are exactly two systems that monitor every remote server.

10. Express each of these statements using mathematical and logical operators, predicates, and quantifiers, where the domain consists of all integers.

a) The sum of two negative integers is negative.

b) The difference of two positive integers is not necessarily positive.

c) The sum of the squares of two integers is greater than or equal to the square of their sum.

d) The absolute value of the product of two integers is the product of their absolute values.

11. Use predicates, quantifiers, logical connectives, and mathematical operators to express the statement that every positive integer is the sum of the squares of four integers.

12. Express each of these mathematical statements using predicates, quantifiers, logical connectives, and mathematical operators.

a) The product of two negative real numbers is positive.

b) The difference of a real number and itself is zero.

c) Every positive real number has exactly two square roots.

d) A negative real number does not have a square root that is a real number.

13. Translate each of these nested quantifications into an English statement that expresses a mathematical fact. The domain in each case consists of all real numbers.

a) $\exists x \forall y (xy = y)$ b) $\forall x \forall y (((x < 0) \wedge (y < 0)) \rightarrow (xy > 0))$

c) $\exists x \exists y ((x^2 > y) \wedge (x < y))$ d) $\forall x \forall y \exists z (x + y = z)$

14. Determine the truth value of each of these statements if the domain for all variables consists of all integers.

a) $\forall n \exists m (n^2 < m)$ b) $\exists n \forall m (n < m^2)$ c) $\forall n \exists m (n + m = 0)$ d) $\exists n \forall m (nm = m)$

e) $\exists n \exists m (n^2 + m^2 = 5)$ f) $\exists n \exists m (n^2 + m^2 = 6)$ g) $\exists n \exists m (n + m = 4 \wedge n - m = 1)$

h) $\exists n \exists m (n + m = 4 \wedge n - m = 2)$ i) $\forall n \forall m \exists p (p = (m + n)/2)$

15. Suppose the domain of the propositional function $P(x, y)$ consists of pairs x and y, where x is 1, 2, or 3 and y is 1, 2, or 3. Write out these propositions using disjunctions and conjunctions.

a) $\forall x \forall y P(x, y)$ b) $\exists x \exists y P(x, y)$ c) $\exists x \forall y P(x, y)$ d) $\forall y \exists x P(x, y)$

16. Express the negations of each of these statements so that all negation symbols immediately precede predicates.

a) $\forall x \exists y \forall z T(x, y, z)$ b) $\forall x \exists y P(x, y) \vee \forall x \exists y Q(x, y)$

c) $\forall x \exists y (P(x, y) \wedge \exists z R(x, y, z))$ d) $\forall x \exists y (P(x, y) \rightarrow Q(x, y))$

17. Rewrite each of these statements so that negations appear only within predicates (that is, so that no negation is outside a quantifier or an expression involving logical connectives).

a) $\neg \forall x \forall y P(x, y)$ b) $\neg \forall y \exists x P(x, y)$ c) $\neg \forall y \forall x (P(x, y) \vee Q(x, y))$

d) $\neg (\exists x \exists y \neg P(x, y) \wedge \forall x \forall y Q(x, y))$ e) $\neg \forall x (\exists y \forall z P(x, y, z) \wedge \exists z \forall y P(x, y, z))$

18. Find a common domain for the variables $x, y, z,$ and w for which the statement $\forall x \forall y \forall z \exists w ((w \neq x) \wedge (w \neq y) \wedge (w \neq z))$ is true and another common domain for these variables for which it is false.

19. Express each of these statements using quantifiers. Then form the negation of the statement so that no negation is to the left of a quantifier. Next, express the negation in simple English. (Do not simply use the words "It is not the case that.")

a) Every student in this class has taken exactly two mathematics classes at this school.

b) Someone has visited every country in the world except Libya.

c) No one has climbed every mountain in the Himalayas.

d) Every movie actor has either been in a movie with Kevin Bacon or has been in a movie with someone who has been in a movie with Kevin Bacon.

20. Find a counterexample, if possible, to these universally quantified statements, where the domain for all variables consists of all integers.

a) $\forall x \forall y (x^2 = y^2 \to x = y)$ b) $\forall x \exists y (y^2 = x)$ c) $\forall x \forall y (xy \geqslant x)$

21. Use quantifiers to express the associative law for multiplication of real numbers.

22. Use quantifiers and logical connectives to express the fact that every linear polynomial (that is, polynomial of degree 1) with real coefficients and where the coefficient of x is nonzero, has exactly one real root.

23. Determine the truth value of the statement $\forall x \exists y (xy = 1)$ if the domain for the variables consists of

a) the nonzero real numbers.   b) the nonzero integers.   c) the positive real numbers.

24. Show that the two statements $\neg \exists x \forall y P(x, y)$ and $\forall x \exists y \neg P(x, y)$, where both quantifiers over the first variable in $P(x, y)$ have the same domain, and both quantifiers over the second variable in $P(x, y)$ have the same domain, are logically equivalent.

*25. a) Show that $\forall x P(x) \wedge \exists x Q(x)$ is logically equivalent to $\forall x \exists y (P(x) \wedge Q(y))$, where all quantifiers have the same nonempty domain.

b) Show that $\forall x P(x) \vee \exists x Q(x)$ is equivalent to $\forall x \exists y (P(x) \vee Q(y))$, where all quantifiers have the same nonempty domain.

A statement is in **prenex normal form (PNF)** if and only if it is of the form

$$Q_1 x_1 Q_2 x_2 \cdots Q_k x_k P(x_1, x_2, \ldots, x_k),$$

where each $Q_i, i = 1, 2, \ldots, k$, is either the existential quantifier or the universal quantifier, and $P(x_1, \ldots, x_k)$ is a predicate involving no quantifiers. For example, $\exists x \forall y (P(x, y) \wedge Q(y))$ is in prenex normal form, whereas $\exists x P(x) \vee \forall x Q(x)$ is not (because the quantifiers do not all occur first).

Every statement formed from propositional variables, predicates, **T**, and **F** using logical connectives and quantifiers is equivalent to a statement in prenex normal form. Exercise 26 asks for a proof of this fact.

**26. Show how to transform an arbitrary statement to a statement in prenex normal form that is equivalent to the given statement.

1.5 Rules of Inference

Introduction

Later in this chapter we will study proofs. Proofs in mathematics are valid arguments that establish the truth of mathematical statements. By an **argument,** we mean a sequence of statements that end with a conclusion. By **valid,** we mean that the conclusion, or final statement of the argument, must follow from the truth of the preceding statements, or **premises,** of the argument. That is, an argument is valid if and only if it is impossible for all the premises to be true and the conclusion to be false. To deduce new statements from statements we already have, we use rules of inference which are templates for constructing valid arguments. Rules of inference are our basic tools for establishing the truth of statements.

Before we study mathematical proofs, we will look at arguments that involve only compound propositions. We will define what it means for an argument involving compound propositions to be valid. Then we will introduce a collection of rules of inference in propositional logic. These rules of inference are among the most important ingredients in producing valid arguments. After we illustrate how rules of inference are used to produce valid arguments, we will describe some common forms of incorrect reasoning, called **fallacies,** which lead to invalid arguments.

After studying rules of inference in propositional logic, we will introduce rules of inference for quantified statements. We will describe how these rules of inference can be used to produce valid arguments. These rules of inference for statements involving existential and universal quantifiers play an important role in proofs in computer science and mathematics, although they are often used without being explicitly mentioned.

Finally, we will show how rules of inference for propositions and for quantified statements can be combined. These combinations of rule of inference are often used together in complicated arguments.

Valid Arguments in Propositional Logic

Consider the following argument involving propositions (which, by definition, is a sequence of propositions):

"If you have a current password, then you can log onto the network."
"You have a current password."
Therefore,
"You can log onto the network."

We would like to determine whether this is a valid argument. That is, we would like to determine whether the conclusion "You can log onto the network" must be true when the premises "If you have a current password, then you can log onto the network" and "You have a current password" are both true.

Before we discuss the validity of this particular argument, we will look at its form. Use p to represent "You have a current password" and q to represent "You can log onto the network." Then, the argument has the form

$$p \rightarrow q$$
$$p$$
$$\therefore\ q$$

where $\therefore$ is the symbol that denotes "therefore."

We know that when p and q are propositional variables, the statement $((p \rightarrow q) \wedge p) \rightarrow q$ is a tautology. In particular, when both $p \rightarrow q$ and p are true, we know that q must also be true. We say this form of argument is **valid** because whenever all its premises (all statements in the argument other than the final one, the conclusion) are true, the conclusion must also be true. Now suppose that both "If you have a current password, then you can log onto the network" and "You have a current password" are true statements. When we replace p by "You have a current password" and q by "You can log onto the network," it necessarily follows that the conclusion "You can log onto the network" is true. This argument is **valid** because its form is valid. Note that whenever we replace p and q by propositions where $p \rightarrow q$ and p are both true, then q must also be true.

What happens when we replace p and q in this argument form by propositions where not both p and $p \rightarrow q$ are true? For example, suppose that p represents "You have access to the network" and q represents "You can change your grade" and that p is true, but $p \rightarrow q$ is false. The argument we obtain by substituting these values of p and q into the argument form is

"If you have access to the network, then you can change your grade."
"You have access to the network."
$\therefore$ "You can change your grade."

The argument we obtained is a valid argument, but because one of the premises, namely the first premise, is false, we cannot conclude that the conclusion is true. (Most likely, this conclusion is false.)

In our discussion, to analyze an argument, we replaced propositions by propositional variables. This changed an argument to an **argument form.** We saw that the validity of an argument follows from the validity of the form of the argument. We summarize the terminology used to discuss the validity of arguments with our definition of the key notions.

Definition 1   An *argument* in propositional logic is a sequence of propositions. All but the final proposition in the argument are called *premises* and the final proposition is called the *conclusion.* An argument is *valid* if the truth of all its premises implies that the conclusion is true.

An *argument form* in propositional logic is a sequence of compound propositions involving propositional variables. An argument form is *valid* if no matter which particular propositions are substituted for the propositional variables in its premises, the conclusion is true if the premises are all true.

From the definition of a valid argument form we see that the argument form with premises p_1, $p_2, \ldots, p_n$ and conclusion q is valid, when $(p_1 \wedge p_2 \wedge \cdots \wedge p_n) \rightarrow q$ is a tautology.

The key to showing that an argument in propositional logic is valid is to show that its argument form is valid. Consequently, we would like techniques to show that argument forms are valid. We will now develop methods for accomplishing this task.

Rules of Inference for Propositional Logic

We can always use a truth table to show that an argument form is valid. We do this by showing that whenever the premises are true, the conclusion must also be true. However, this can be a tedious approach. For example, when an argument form involves 10 different propositional variables, to use a truth table to show this argument form is valid requires $2^{10} = 1024$ different rows. Fortunately, we do not have to resort to truth tables. Instead, we can first establish the validity of some relatively simple argument forms, called **rules of inference.** These rules of inference can be used as building blocks to construct more complicated valid argument forms. We will now introduce the most important rules of inference in propositional logic.

The tautology $(p \wedge (p \rightarrow q)) \rightarrow q$ is the basis of the rule of inference called **modus ponens,** or the **law of detachment.** (Modus ponens is Latin for *mode that affirms.*) This tautology leads to the following valid argument form, which we have already seen in our initial discussion about arguments (where, as before, the symbol $\therefore$ denotes "therefore."):

$$p$$
$$\underline{p \rightarrow q}$$
$$\therefore \quad q$$

Using this notation, the hypotheses are written in a column, followed by a horizontal bar, followed by a line that begins with the therefore symbol and ends with the conclusion. In particular, modus ponens tells us that if a conditional statement and the hypothesis of this conditional statement are both true, then the conclusion must also be true. Example 1 illustrates the use of modus ponens.

Example 1   Suppose that the conditional statement "If it snows today, then we will go skiing" and its hypothesis, "It is snowing today," are true. Then, by modus ponens, it follows that the conclusion of the conditional statement, "We will go skiing," is true.   ◀

As we mentioned earlier, a valid argument can lead to an incorrect conclusion if one or more of its premises is false. We illustrate this again in Example 2.

Example 2   Determine whether the argument given here is valid and determine whether its conclusion must be true because of the validity of the argument.

"If $\sqrt{2} > \frac{3}{2}$, then $\left(\sqrt{2}\right)^2 > \left(\frac{3}{2}\right)^2$. We know that $\sqrt{2} > \frac{3}{2}$. Consequently,
$\left(\sqrt{2}\right)^2 = 2 > \left(\frac{3}{2}\right)^2 = \frac{9}{4}$."

Solution: Let p be the proposition "$\sqrt{2} > \frac{3}{2}$" and q the proposition "$2 > \left(\frac{3}{2}\right)^2$." The premises of the argument are $p \rightarrow q$ and p, and q is its conclusion. This argument is valid because it is constructed by using modus ponens, a valid argument form. However, one of its premises, $\sqrt{2} > \frac{3}{2}$, is false. Consequently, we cannot conclude that the conclusion is true. Furthermore, note that the conclusion of this argument is false, because $2 < \frac{9}{4}$.   ◄

Table 1 lists the most important rules of inference for propositional logic. Exercises 5 and 8 in Section 1.2 ask for the verifications that these rules of inference are valid argument forms. We now give examples of arguments that use these rules of inference. In each argument, we first use propositional variables to express the propositions in the argument. We then show that the resulting argument form is a rule of inference from Table 1.

TABLE 1 Rules of Inference.		
Rule of Inference	*Tautology*	*Name*
p $p \rightarrow q$ $\therefore q$	$[p \wedge (p \rightarrow q)] \rightarrow q$	Modus ponens
$\neg q$ $p \rightarrow q$ $\therefore \neg p$	$[\neg q \wedge (p \rightarrow q)] \rightarrow \neg p$	Modus tollens
$p \rightarrow q$ $q \rightarrow r$ $\therefore p \rightarrow r$	$[(p \rightarrow q) \wedge (q \rightarrow r)] \rightarrow (p \rightarrow r)$	Hypothetical syllogism
$p \vee q$ $\neg p$ $\therefore q$	$[(p \vee q) \wedge \neg p] \rightarrow q$	Disjunctive syllogism
p $\therefore p \vee q$	$p \rightarrow (p \vee q)$	Addition
$p \wedge q$ $\therefore p$	$(p \wedge q) \rightarrow p$	Simplification
p q $\therefore p \wedge q$	$[(p) \wedge (q)] \rightarrow (p \wedge q)$	Conjunction
$p \vee q$ $\neg p \vee r$ $\therefore q \vee r$	$[(p \vee q) \wedge (\neg p \vee r)] \rightarrow (q \vee r)$	Resolution

Example 3   State which rule of inference is the basis of the following argument: "It is below freezing now. Therefore, it is either below freezing or raining now."

Solution: Let p be the proposition "It is below freezing now" and q the proposition "It is raining now." Then this argument is of the form

$$\frac{p}{\therefore \ p \lor q}$$

This is an argument that uses the addition rule.   ◄

Example 4   State which rule of inference is the basis of the following argument: "It is below freezing and raining now. Therefore, it is below freezing now."

Solution: Let p be the proposition "It is below freezing now," and let q be the proposition "It is raining now." This argument is of the form

$$\frac{p \land q}{\therefore \ p}$$

This argument uses the simplification rule.   ◄

Example 5   State which rule of inference is used in the argument:

If it rains today, then we will not have a barbecue today. If we do not have a barbecue today, then we will have a barbecue tomorrow. Therefore, if it rains today, then we will have a barbecue tomorrow.

Solution: Let p be the proposition "It is raining today," let q be the proposition "We will not have a barbecue today," and let r be the proposition "We will have a barbecue tomorrow." Then this argument is of the form

$$\begin{array}{c} p \to q \\ q \to r \\ \hline \therefore \ p \to r \end{array}$$

Hence, this argument is a hypothetical syllogism.   ◄

Using Rules of Inference to Build Arguments

When there are many premises, several rules of inference are often needed to show that an argument is valid. This is illustrated by Examples 6 and 7, where the steps of arguments are displayed on separate lines, with the reason for each step explicitly stated. These examples also show how arguments in English can be analyzed using rules of inference.

Example 6   Show that the hypotheses "It is not sunny this afternoon and it is colder than yesterday," "We will go swimming only if it is sunny," "If we do not go swimming, then we will take a canoe trip," and "If we take a canoe trip, then we will be home by sunset" lead to the conclusion "We will be home by sunset."

Solution: Let p be the proposition "It is sunny this afternoon," q the proposition "It is colder than yesterday," r the proposition "We will go swimming," s the proposition "We will take a canoe trip," and t the proposition "We will be home by sunset." Then the hypotheses become $\lnot p \land q$, $r \to p$, $\lnot r \to s$, and $s \to t$. The conclusion is simply t. We need to give a valid argument with hypotheses $\lnot p \land q$, $r \to p$, $\lnot r \to s$, and $s \to t$ and conclusion t.

We construct an argument to show that our hypotheses lead to the desired conclusion as follows.

Step	Reason
1. $\lnot p \land q$	Hypothesis
2. $\lnot p$	Simplification using (1)

3. $r \rightarrow p$ Hypothesis
4. $\neg r$ Modus tollens using (2) and (3)
5. $\neg r \rightarrow s$ Hypothesis
6. s Modus ponens using (4) and (5)
7. $s \rightarrow t$ Hypothesis
8. t Modus ponens using (6) and (7)

Note that we could have used a truth table to show that whenever each of the four hypotheses is true, the conclusion is also true. However, because we are working with five propositional variables, $p, q, r, s,$ and t, such a truth table would have 32 rows. ◄

Example 7   Show that the hypotheses "If you send me an e-mail message, then I will finish writing the program," "If you do not send me an e-mail message, then I will go to sleep early," and "If I go to sleep early, then I will wake up feeling refreshed" lead to the conclusion "If I do not finish writing the program, then I will wake up feeling refreshed."

Solution: Let p be the proposition "You send me an e-mail message," q the proposition "I will finish writing the program," r the proposition "I will go to sleep early," and s the proposition "I will wake up feeling refreshed." Then the hypotheses are $p \rightarrow q$, $\neg p \rightarrow r$, and $r \rightarrow s$. The desired conclusion is $\neg q \rightarrow s$. We need to give a valid argument with hypotheses $p \rightarrow q$, $\neg p \rightarrow r$, and $r \rightarrow s$ and conclusion $\neg q \rightarrow s$.

This argument form shows that the hypotheses p lead to the desired conclusion.

Step	Reason
1. $p \rightarrow q$	Hypothesis
2. $\neg q \rightarrow \neg p$	Contrapositive of (1)
3. $\neg p \rightarrow r$	Hypothesis
4. $\neg q \rightarrow r$	Hypothetical syllogism using (2) and (3)
5. $r \rightarrow s$	Hypothesis
6. $\neg q \rightarrow s$	Hypothetical syllogism using (4) and (5) ◄

Resolution

Computer programs have been developed to automate the task of reasoning and proving theorems. Many of these programs make use of a rule of inference known as **resolution.** This rule of inference is based on the tautology

$$((p \vee q) \wedge (\neg p \vee r)) \rightarrow (q \vee r).$$

The final disjunction in the resolution rule, $q \vee r$, is called the **resolvent.** When we let $q = r$ in this tautology, we obtain $(p \vee q) \wedge (\neg p \vee q) \rightarrow q$. Furthermore, when we let $r = \mathbf{F}$, we obtain $(p \vee q) \wedge (\neg p) \rightarrow q$ (because $q \vee \mathbf{F} \equiv q$), which is the tautology on which the rule of disjunctive syllogism is based.

Example 8   Use resolution to show that the hypotheses "Jasmine is skiing or it is not snowing" and "It is snowing or Bart is playing hockey" imply that "Jasmine is skiing or Bart is playing hockey."

Solution: Let p be the proposition "It is snowing," q the proposition "Jasmine is skiing," and r the proposition "Bart is playing hockey." We can represent the hypotheses as $\neg p \vee q$ and $p \vee r$, respectively. Using resolution, the proposition $q \vee r$, "Jasmine is skiing or Bart is playing hockey," follows. ◄

Resolution plays an important role in programming languages based on the rules of logic, such as Prolog (where resolution rules for quantified statements are applied). Furthermore, it can be used to build automatic theorem proving systems. To construct proofs in propositional logic using resolution as the only rule of inference, the hypotheses and the conclusion must be expressed as **clauses,** where a clause is a disjunction of variables or negations of these variables. We can replace a statement in propositional logic that is not a clause by one or more equivalent statements that are clauses. For example, suppose we have a statement of the form $p \vee (q \wedge r)$. Because $p \vee (q \wedge r) \equiv (p \vee q) \wedge (p \vee r)$, we can replace the single statement $p \vee (q \wedge r)$ by two statements $p \vee q$ and $p \vee r$, each of which is a clause. We can replace a statement of the form $\neg(p \vee q)$ by the two statements $\neg p$ and $\neg q$ because De Morgan's law tells us that $\neg(p \vee q) \equiv \neg p \wedge \neg q$. We can also replace a conditional statement $p \rightarrow q$ with the equivalent disjunction $\neg p \vee q$.

Example 9   Show that the hypotheses $(p \wedge q) \vee r$ and $r \rightarrow s$ imply the conclusion $p \vee s$.

Solution: We can rewrite the hypothesis $(p \wedge q) \vee r$ as two clauses, $p \vee r$ and $q \vee r$. We can also replace $r \rightarrow s$ by the equivalent clause $\neg r \vee s$. Using the two clauses $p \vee r$ and $\neg r \vee s$, we can use resolution to conclude $p \vee s$.   ◄

Fallacies

Several common fallacies arise in incorrect arguments. These fallacies resemble rules of inference but are based on contingencies rather than tautologies. These are discussed here to show the distinction between correct and incorrect reasoning.

   The proposition $[(p \rightarrow q) \wedge q] \rightarrow p$ is not a tautology, because it is false when p is false and q is true. However, there are many incorrect arguments that treat this as a tautology. In other words, they treat the argument with premises $p \rightarrow q$ and q and conclusion p as a valid argument form, which it is not. This type of incorrect reasoning is called the **fallacy of affirming the conclusion.**

Example 10   Is the following argument valid?

   If you do every problem in this book, then you will learn discrete mathematics. You learned discrete mathematics.

   Therefore, you did every problem in this book.

Solution: Let p be the proposition "You did every problem in this book." Let q be the proposition "You learned discrete mathematics." Then this argument is of the form: if $p \rightarrow q$ and q, then p. This is an example of an incorrect argument using the fallacy of affirming the conclusion. Indeed, it is possible for you to learn discrete mathematics in some way other than by doing every problem in this book. (You may learn discrete mathematics by reading, listening to lectures, doing some, but not all, the problems in this book, and so on.)   ◄

   The proposition $[(p \rightarrow q) \wedge \neg p] \rightarrow \neg q$ is not a tautology, because it is false when p is false and q is true. Many incorrect arguments use this incorrectly as a rule of inference. This type of incorrect reasoning is called the **fallacy of denying the hypothesis.**

Example 11   Let p and q be as in Example 10. If the conditional statement $p \rightarrow q$ is true, and $\neg p$ is true, is it correct to conclude that $\neg q$ is true? In other words, is it correct to assume that you did not learn discrete mathematics if you did not do every problem in the book, assuming that if you do every problem in this book, then you will learn discrete mathematics?

Solution: It is possible that you learned discrete mathematics even if you did not do every problem in this book. This incorrect argument is of the form $p \rightarrow q$ and $\neg p$ imply $\neg q$, which is an example of the fallacy of denying the hypothesis.   ◄

Rules of Inference for Quantified Statements

We have discussed rules of inference for propositions. We will now describe some important rules of inference for statements involving quantifiers. These rules of inference are used extensively in mathematical arguments, often without being explicitly mentioned.

   Universal instantiation is the rule of inference used to conclude that $P(c)$ is true, where c is a particular member of the domain, given the premise $\forall x P(x)$. Universal instantiation is used when we conclude from the statement "All women are wise" that "Lisa is wise," where Lisa is a member of the domain of all women.

Universal generalization is the rule of inference that states that $\forall x P(x)$ is true, given the premise that $P(c)$ is true for all elements c in the domain. Universal generalization is used when we show that $\forall x P(x)$ is true by taking an arbitrary element c from the domain and showing that $P(c)$ is true. The element c that we select must be an arbitrary, and not a specific, element of the domain. That is, when we assert from $\forall x P(x)$ the existence of an element c in the domain, we have no control over c and cannot make any other assumptions about c other than it comes from the domain. Universal generalization is used implicitly in many proofs in mathematics and is seldom mentioned explicitly. However, the error of adding unwarranted assumptions about the arbitrary element c when universal generalization is used is all too common in incorrect reasoning.

Existential instantiation is the rule that allows us to conclude that there is an element c in the domain for which $P(c)$ is true if we know that $\exists x P(x)$ is true. We cannot select an arbitrary value of c here, but rather it must be a c for which $P(c)$ is true. Usually we have no knowledge of what c is, only that it exists. Because it exists, we may give it a name (c) and continue our argument.

Existential generalization is the rule of inference that is used to conclude that $\exists x P(x)$ is true when a particular element c with $P(c)$ true is known. That is, if we know one element c in the domain for which $P(c)$ is true, then we know that $\exists x P(x)$ is true.

We summarize these rules of inference in Table 2. We will illustrate how one of these rules of inference for quantified statements is used in Example 12.

TABLE 2   Rules of Inference for Quantified Statements.

Rule of Inference	Name
$\dfrac{\forall x\, P(x)}{\therefore\ P(c)}$	Universal instantiation
$\dfrac{P(c) \text{ for an arbitrary } c}{\therefore\ \forall x\, P(x)}$	Universal generalization
$\dfrac{\exists x\, P(x)}{\therefore\ P(c) \text{ for some element } c}$	Existential instantiation
$\dfrac{P(c) \text{ for some element } c}{\therefore\ \exists x\, P(x)}$	Existential generalization

Example 12   Show that the premises "Everyone in this discrete mathematics class has taken a course in computer science" and "Marla is a student in this class" imply the conclusion "Marla has taken a course in computer science."

Solution: Let $D(x)$ denote "x is in this discrete mathematics class," and let $C(x)$ denote "x has taken a course in computer science." Then the premises are $\forall x(D(x) \rightarrow C(x))$ and $D(\text{Marla})$. The conclusion is $C(\text{Marla})$.

The following steps can be used to establish the conclusion from the premises.

Step	Reason
1. $\forall x(D(x) \rightarrow C(x))$	Premise
2. $D(\text{Marla}) \rightarrow C(\text{Marla})$	Universal instantiation from (1)
3. $D(\text{Marla})$	Premise
4. $C(\text{Marla})$	Modus ponens from (2) and (3) ◄

Example 13   Show that the premises "A student in this class has not read the book," and "Everyone in this class passed the first exam" imply the conclusion "Someone who passed the first exam has not read the book."

Solution: Let $C(x)$ be "x is in this class," $B(x)$ be "x has read the book," and $P(x)$ be "x passed the first exam." The premises are $\exists x(C(x) \land \neg B(x))$ and $\forall x(C(x) \to P(x))$. The conclusion is $\exists x(P(x) \land \neg B(x))$. These steps can be used to establish the conclusion from the premises.

Step	Reason
1. $\exists x(C(x) \land \neg B(x))$	Premise
2. $C(a) \land \neg B(a)$	Existential instantiation from (1)
3. $C(a)$	Simplification from (2)
4. $\forall x(C(x) \to P(x))$	Premise
5. $C(a) \to P(a)$	Universal instantiation from (4)
6. $P(a)$	Modus ponens from (3) and (5)
7. $\neg B(a)$	Simplification from (2)
8. $P(a) \land \neg B(a)$	Conjunction from (6) and (7)
9. $\exists x(P(x) \land \neg B(x))$	Existential generalization from (8)

◄

Combining Rules of Inference for Propositions and Quantified Statements

We have developed rules of inference both for propositions and for quantified statements. Note that in our arguments in Examples 12 and 13 we used both universal instantiation, a rule of inference for quantified statements, and modus ponens, a rule of inference for propositional logic. We will often need to use this combination of rules of inference. Because universal instantiation and modus ponens are used so often together, this combination of rules is sometimes called **universal modus ponens**. This rule tells us that if $\forall x(P(x) \to Q(x))$ is true, and if $P(a)$ is true for a particular element a in the domain of the universal quantifier, then $Q(a)$ must also be true. To see this, note that by universal instantiation, $P(a) \to Q(a)$ is true. Then, by modus ponens, $Q(a)$ must also be true. We can describe universal modus ponens as follows:

$$\forall x(P(x) \to Q(x))$$
$$P(a), \text{where } a \text{ is a particular element in the domain}$$
$$\therefore \quad Q(a)$$

Universal modus ponens is commonly used in mathematical arguments. This is illustrated in Example 14.

Example 14   Assume that "For all positive integers n, if n is greater than 4, then n^2 is less than 2^n" is true. Use universal modus ponens to show that $100^2 < 2^{100}$.

Solution: Let $P(n)$ denote "$n > 4$" and $Q(n)$ denote "$n^2 < 2^n$." The statement "For all positive integers n, if n is greater than 4, then n^2 is less than 2^n" can be represented by $\forall n(P(n) \to Q(n))$, where the domain consists of all positive integers. We are assuming that $\forall n(P(n) \to Q(n))$ is true. Note that $P(100)$ is true because $100 > 4$. It follows by universal modus ponens that $Q(n)$ is true, namely that $100^2 < 2^{100}$.   ◄

Another useful combination of a rule of inference from propositional logic and a rule of inference for quantified statements is **universal modus tollens**. Universal modus tollens combines universal instantiation and modus tollens and can be expressed in the following way:

$$\forall x(P(x) \to Q(x))$$
$$\neg Q(a), \text{where } a \text{ is a particular element in the domain}$$
$$\therefore \quad \neg P(a)$$

We leave the verification of universal modus tollens to the reader (see Exercise 13).

Exercises

1. Find the argument form for the following argument and determine whether it is valid. Can we conclude that the conclusion is true if the premises are true?

   If Socrates is human, then Socrates is mortal.

   Socrates is human.

   ─────────────────────────────────────

   ∴ Socrates is mortal.

2. What rule of inference is used in each of these arguments?

   a) Alice is a mathematics major. Therefore, Alice is either a mathematics major or a computer science major.

   b) Jerry is a mathematics major and a computer science major. Therefore, Jerry is a mathematics major.

   c) If it is rainy, then the pool will be closed. It is rainy. Therefore, the pool is closed.

   d) If it snows today, the university will close. The university is not closed today. Therefore, it did not snow today.

   e) If I go swimming, then I will stay in the sun too long. If I stay in the sun too long, then I will sunburn. Therefore, if I go swimming, then I will sunburn.

3. Use rules of inference to show that the hypotheses "Randy works hard," "If Randy works hard, then he is a dull boy," and "If Randy is a dull boy, then he will not get the job" imply the conclusion "Randy will not get the job."

4. What rules of inference are used in this famous argument? "All men are mortal. Socrates is a man. Therefore, Socrates is mortal."

5. For each of these sets of premises, what relevant conclusion or conclusions can be drawn? Explain the rules of inference used to obtain each conclusion from the premises.

   a) "If I take the day off, it either rains or snows." "I took Tuesday off or I took Thursday off." "It was sunny on Tuesday." "It did not snow on Thursday."

   b) "If I eat spicy foods, then I have strange dreams." "I have strange dreams if there is thunder while I sleep." "I did not have strange dreams."

   c) "I am either clever or lucky." "I am not lucky." "If I am lucky, then I will win the lottery."

   d) "Every computer science major has a personal computer." "Ralph does not have a personal computer." "Ann has a personal computer."

   e) "What is good for corporations is good for the United States." "What is good for the United States is good for you." "What is good for corporations is for you to buy lots of stuff."

   f) "All rodents gnaw their food." "Mice are rodents." "Rabbits do not gnaw their food." "Bats are not rodents."

6. Show that the argument form with premises $p_1, p_2, \ldots, p_n$ and conclusion $q \rightarrow r$ is valid if the argument form with premises $p_1, p_2, \ldots, p_n, q$, and conclusion r is valid.

7. For each of these arguments, explain which rules of inference are used for each step.

   a) "Doug, a student in this class, knows how to write programs in JAVA. Everyone who knows how to write programs in JAVA can get a high-paying job. Therefore, someone in this class can get a high-paying job."

   b) "Somebody in this class enjoys whale watching. Every person who enjoys whale watching cares about ocean pollution. Therefore, there is a person in this class who cares about ocean pollution."

   c) "Each of the 93 students in this class owns a personal computer. Everyone who owns a personal computer can use a word processing program. Therefore, Zeke, a student in this class, can use a word processing program."

   d) "Everyone in New Jersey lives within 50 miles of the ocean. Someone in New Jersey has never seen the ocean. Therefore, someone who lives within 50 miles of the ocean has never seen the ocean."

8. For each of these arguments determine whether the argument is correct or incorrect and explain why.

   a) All students in this class understand logic. Xavier is a student in this class. Therefore, Xavier understands logic.

   b) Every computer science major takes discrete mathematics. Natasha is taking discrete mathematics. Therefore, Natasha is a computer science major.

   c) All parrots like fruit. My pet bird is not a parrot. Therefore, my pet bird does not like fruit.

   d) Everyone who eats granola every day is healthy. Linda is not healthy. Therefore, Linda does not eat granola every day.

9. What is wrong with this argument? Let $H(x)$ be "x is happy." Given the premise $\exists x H(x)$, we conclude that $H(\text{Lola})$. Therefore, Lola is happy.

10. Determine whether each of these arguments is valid. If an argument is correct, what rule of inference is being used? If it is not, what logical error occurs?

   a) If n is a real number such that $n > 1$, then $n^2 > 1$. Suppose that $n^2 > 1$. Then $n > 1$.

   b) If n is a real number with $n > 3$, then $n^2 > 9$. Suppose that $n^2 \leqslant 9$. Then $n \leqslant 3$.

   c) If n is a real number with $n > 2$, then $n^2 > 4$. Suppose that $n \leqslant 2$. Then $n^2 \leqslant 4$.

11. Which rules of inference are used to establish the conclusion of Lewis Carroll's argument described in Example 26 of Section 1.3?

12. Identify the error or errors in this argument that supposedly shows that if $\exists x P(x) \land \exists x Q(x)$ is true then $\exists x (P(x) \land Q(x))$ is true.

   1. $\exists x P(x) \lor \exists x Q(x)$ Premise
   2. $\exists x P(x)$ Simplification from (1)
   3. $P(c)$ Existential instantiation from (2)
   4. $\exists x Q(x)$ Simplification from (1)
   5. $Q(c)$ Existential instantiation from (4)
   6. $P(c) \land Q(c)$ Conjunction from (3) and (5)
   7. $\exists x (P(x) \land Q(x))$ Existential generalization

13. Justify the rule of universal modus tollens by showing that the premises $\forall x (P(x) \rightarrow Q(x))$ and $\neg Q(a)$ for a particular element a in the domain, imply $\neg P(a)$.

14. Use rules of inference to show that if $\forall x (P(x) \rightarrow (Q(x) \land S(x)))$ and $\forall x (P(x) \land R(x))$ are true, then $\forall x (R(x) \land S(x))$ is true.

15. Use rules of inference to show that if $\forall x (P(x) \lor Q(x))$, $\forall x (\neg Q(x) \lor S(x))$, $\forall x (R(x) \rightarrow \neg S(x))$, and $\exists x \neg P(x)$ are true, then $\exists x \neg R(x)$ is true.

16. Use resolution to show that the hypotheses "It is not raining or Yvette has her umbrella," "Yvette does not have her umbrella or she does not get wet," and "It is raining or Yvette does not get wet" imply that "Yvette does not get wet."

17. Use resolution to show that the compound proposition $(p \lor q) \land (\neg p \lor q) \land (p \lor \neg q) \land (\neg p \lor \neg q)$ is not satisfiable.

*18. Determine whether this argument, taken from Kalish and Montague [KaMo64], is valid.

> If Superman were able and willing to prevent evil, he would do so. If Superman were unable to prevent evil, he would be impotent; if he were unwilling to prevent evil, he would be malevolent. Superman does not prevent evil. If Superman exists, he is neither impotent nor malevolent. Therefore, Superman does not exist.

1.6   Introduction to Proofs

Introduction

In this section we introduce the notion of a proof and describe methods for constructing proofs. A proof is a valid argument that establishes the truth of a mathematical statement. A proof can use the hypotheses of the theorem, if any, axioms assumed to be true, and previously proven theorems. Using these ingredients and rules of inference, the final step of the proof establishes the truth of the statement being proved.

In our discussion we move from formal proofs of theorems toward more informal proofs. The arguments we introduced in Section 1.5 to show that statements involving propositions and quantified statements are true were formal proofs, where all steps were supplied, and the rules for each step in the argument were given. However, formal proofs of useful theorems can be extremely long and hard to follow. In practice, the proofs of theorems designed for human consumption are almost always **informal proofs,** where more than one rule of inference may be used in each step, where steps may be skipped, where the axioms being assumed and the rules of inference used are not explicitly stated. Informal proofs can often explain to humans why theorems are true, while computers are perfectly happy producing formal proofs using automated reasoning systems.

The methods of proof discussed in this chapter are important not only because they are used to prove mathematical theorems, but also for their many applications to computer science. These applications include verifying that computer programs are correct, establishing that operating systems are secure, making inferences in artificial intelligence, showing that system specifications are consistent, and so on. Consequently, understanding the techniques used in proofs is essential both in mathematics and in computer science.

Some Terminology

Formally, a **theorem** is a statement that can be shown to be true. In mathematical writing, the term theorem is usually reserved for a statement that is considered at least somewhat important. Less important theorems sometimes are called **propositions.** (Theorems can also be referred to as **facts** or **results.**) A theorem may be the universal quantification of a conditional statement with one or more premises and a conclusion. However, it may be some other type of logical statement, as the examples later in this chapter will show. We demonstrate that a theorem is true with a **proof.** A proof is a valid argument that establishes the truth of a theorem. The statements used in a proof can include **axioms** (or **postulates**), which are statements we assume to be true, the premises, if any, of the theorem, and previously proven theorems. Axioms may be stated using primitive terms that do not require definition, but all other terms used in theorems and their proofs must be defined. Rules of inference, together with definitions of terms, are used to draw conclusions from other assertions, tying together the steps of a proof. In practice, the final step of a proof is usually just the conclusion of the theorem. However, for clarity, we will often recap the statement of the theorem as the final step of a proof.

A less important theorem that is helpful in the proof of other results is called a **lemma** (plural *lemmas* or *lemmata*). Complicated proofs are usually easier to understand when they are proved using a series of lemmas, where each lemma is proved individually. A **corollary** is a theorem that can be established directly from a theorem that has been proved. A **conjecture** is a statement that is being proposed to be a true statement, usually on the basis of some partial evidence, a heuristic argument, or the intuition of an expert. When a proof of a conjecture is found, the conjecture becomes a theorem. Many times conjectures are shown to be false, so they are not theorems.

Understanding How Theorems Are Stated

Before we introduce methods for proving theorems, we need to understand how many mathematical theorems are stated. Many theorems assert that a property holds for all elements in a domain, such as the integers or the real numbers. Although the precise statement of such theorems needs to include a universal quantifier, the standard convention in mathematics is to omit it. For example, the statement

"If $x > y$, where x and y are positive real numbers, then $x^2 > y^2$."

really means

"For all positive real numbers x and y, if $x > y$, then $x^2 > y^2$."

Furthermore, when theorems of this type are proved, the law of universal instantiation is often used without explicit mention. The first step of the proof usually involves selecting a general element of the domain. Subsequent steps show that this element has the property in question. Finally, universal generalization implies that the theorem holds for all members of the domain.

Methods of Proving Theorems

We now turn our attention to proofs of mathematical theorems. Proving theorems can be difficult. We need all the ammunition that is available to help us prove different results. We now introduce a battery of different proof methods. These methods should become part of your repertoire for proving theorems.

To prove a theorem of the form $\forall x(P(x) \rightarrow Q(x))$, our goal is to show that $P(c) \rightarrow Q(c)$ is true, where c is an arbitrary element of the domain, and then apply universal generalization. In this proof, we need to show that a conditional statement is true. Because of this, we now focus on methods that show that conditional statements are true. Recall that $p \rightarrow q$ is true unless p is true but q is false. Note that when the statement $p \rightarrow q$ is proved, it need only be shown that q is true if p is true. The following discussion will give the most common techniques for proving conditional statements. Later we will discuss methods for proving other types of statements. In this section, and in Section 1.7, we will develop an arsenal of many different proof techniques that can be used to prove a wide variety of theorems.

When you read proofs, you will often find the words "obviously" or "clearly." These words indicate that steps have been omitted that the author expects the reader to be able to fill in. Unfortunately, this assumption is often not warranted and readers are not at all sure how to fill in the gaps. We will assiduously try to avoid using these words and try not to omit too many steps. However, if we included all steps in proofs, our proofs would often be excruciatingly long.

Direct Proofs

A **direct proof** of a conditional statement $p \rightarrow q$ is constructed when the first step is the assumption that p is true; subsequent steps are constructed using rules of inference, with the final step showing that q must also be true. A direct proof shows that a conditional statement $p \rightarrow q$ is true by showing that if p is true, then q must also be true, so that the combination p true and q false never occurs. In a direct proof, we assume that p is true and use axioms, definitions, and previously proven theorems, together with rules of inference, to show that q must also be true. You will find that direct proofs of many results are quite straightforward, with a fairly obvious sequence of steps leading from the hypothesis to the conclusion. However, direct proofs sometimes require particular insights and can be quite tricky. The first direct proofs we present here are quite straightforward; later in the text you will see some that are less obvious.

We will provide examples of several different direct proofs. Before we give the first example, we need a definition.

Definition 1   The integer n is *even* if there exists an integer k such that $n = 2k$, and n is *odd* if there exists an integer k such that $n = 2k + 1$. (Note that an integer is either even or odd, and no integer is both even and odd.)

Example 1   Give a direct proof of the theorem "If n is an odd integer, then n^2 is odd."

Solution: Note that this theorem states $\forall n P((n) \rightarrow Q(n))$, where $P(n)$ is "n is an odd integer" and $Q(n)$ is "n^2 is odd." As we have said, we will follow the usual convention in mathematical proofs by showing that $P(n)$ implies $Q(n)$, and not explicitly using universal instantiation. To begin a direct proof of this theorem, we assume that the hypothesis of this conditional statement is true, namely, we assume that n is odd. By the definition of an odd integer, it follows that

$n = 2k + 1$, where k is some integer. We want to show that n^2 is also odd. We can square both sides of the equation $n = 2k+1$ to obtain a new equation that expresses n^2. When we do this, we find that $n^2 = (2k+1)^2 = 4k^2 + 4k + 1 = 2(2k^2 + 2k) + 1$. By the definition of an odd integer, we can conclude that n^2 is an odd integer (it is one more than twice an integer). Consequently, we have proved that if n is an odd integer, then n^2 is an odd integer.   ◀

Example 2   Give a direct proof that if m and n are both perfect squares, then nm is also a perfect square. (An integer a is a **perfect square** if there is an integer b such that $a = b^2$.)

Solution: To produce a direct proof of this theorem, we assume that the hypothesis of this conditional statement is true, namely, we assume that m and n are both perfect squares. By the definition of a perfect square, it follows that there are integers s and t such that $m = s^2$ and $n = t^2$. The goal of the proof is to show that mn must also be a perfect square when m and n are; looking ahead we see how we can show this by multiplying the two equations $m = s^2$ and $n = t^2$ together. This shows that $mn = s^2 t^2$, which implies that $mn = (st)^2$ (using commutativity and associativity of multiplication). By the definition of perfect square, it follows that mn is also a perfect square, because it is the square of st, which is an integer. We have proved that if m and n are both perfect squares, then mn is also a perfect square.   ◀

Proof by Contraposition

Direct proofs lead from the hypothesis of a theorem to the conclusion. They begin with the premises, continue with a sequence of deductions, and end with the conclusion. However, we will see that attempts at direct proofs often reach dead ends. We need other methods of proving theorems of the form $\forall x(P(x) \rightarrow Q(x))$. Proofs of theorems of this type that are not direct proofs, that is, that do not start with the hypothesis and end with the conclusion, are called **indirect proofs.**

An extremely useful type of indirect proof is known as **proof by contraposition.** Proofs by contraposition make use of the fact that the conditional statement $p \rightarrow q$ is equivalent to its contrapositive, $\neg q \rightarrow \neg p$. This means that the conditional statement $p \rightarrow q$ can be proved by showing that its contrapositive, $\neg q \rightarrow \neg p$, is true. In a proof by contraposition of $p \rightarrow q$, we take $\neg q$ as a hypothesis, and using axioms, definitions, and previously proven theorems, together with rules of inference, we show that $\neg p$ must follow. We will illustrate proof by contraposition with two examples. These examples show that proof by contraposition can succeed when we cannot easily find a direct proof.

Example 3   Prove that if n is an integer and $3n + 2$ is odd, then n is odd.

Solution: We first attempt a direct proof. To construct a direct proof, we first assume that $3n+2$ is an odd integer. This means that $3n + 2 = 2k + 1$ for some integer k. Can we use this fact to show that n is odd? We see that $3n + 1 = 2k$, but there does not seem to be any direct way to conclude that n is odd. Because our attempt at a direct proof failed, we next try a proof by contraposition.

The first step in a proof by contraposition is to assume that the conclusion of the conditional statement "If $3n + 2$ is odd, then n is odd" is false; namely, assume that n is even. Then, by the definition of an even integer, $n = 2k$ for some integer k. Substituting $2k$ for n, we find that $3n + 2 = 3(2k) + 2 = 6k + 2 = 2(3k + 1)$. This tells us that $3n + 2$ is even (because it is a multiple of 2), and therefore not odd. This is the negation of the hypothesis of the theorem. Because the negation of the conclusion of the conditional statement implies that the hypothesis is false, the original conditional statement is true. Our proof by contraposition succeeded; we have proved the theorem "If $3n + 2$ is odd, then n is odd."   ◀

Example 4   Prove that if $n = ab$, where a and b are positive integers, then $a \leqslant \sqrt{n}$ or $b \leqslant \sqrt{n}$.

Solution: Because there is no obvious way of showing that $a \leqslant \sqrt{n}$ or $b \leqslant \sqrt{n}$ directly from the equation $n = ab$, where a and b are positive integers, we attempt a proof by contraposition.

The first step in a proof by contraposition is to assume that the conclusion of the conditional statement "If $n = ab$, where a and b are positive integers, then $a \leqslant \sqrt{n}$ or $b \leqslant \sqrt{n}$" is false. That is, we assume that the statement $(a \leqslant \sqrt{n}) \vee (b \leqslant \sqrt{n})$ is false. Using the meaning of disjunction together with De Morgan's law, we see that this implies that both $a \leqslant \sqrt{n}$ and $b \leqslant \sqrt{n}$ are false. This implies that $a > \sqrt{n}$ and $b > \sqrt{n}$. We can multiply these inequalities together (using the fact that if $0 < t$ and $0 < v$, then $su < tv$) to obtain $ab > \sqrt{n} \cdot \sqrt{n} = n$. This shows that $ab \neq n$, which contradicts the statement $n = ab$.

Because the negation of the conclusion of the conditional statement implies that the hypothesis is false, the original conditional statement is true. Our proof by contraposition succeeded; we have proved that if $n = ab$, where a and b are positive integers, then $a \leqslant \sqrt{n}$ or $b \leqslant \sqrt{n}$. ◀

Vacuous and Trivial Proofs We can quickly prove that a conditional statement $p \rightarrow q$ is true when we know that p is false, because $p \rightarrow q$ must be true when p is false. Consequently, if we can show that p is false, then we have a proof, called a **vacuous proof,** of the conditional statement $p \rightarrow q$. Vacuous proofs are often used to establish special cases of theorems that state that a conditional statement is true for all positive integers [i.e., a theorem of the kind $\forall n P(n)$, where $P(n)$ is a propositional function].

Example 5   Show that the proposition $P(0)$ is true, where $P(n)$ is "If $n > 1$, then $n^2 > n$" and the domain consists of all integers.

Solution: Note that $P(0)$ is "If $0 > 1$, then $0^2 > 0$." We can show $P(0)$ using a vacuous proof, because the hypothesis $0 > 1$ is false. This tells us that $P(0)$ is automatically true. ◀

Remark: The fact that the conclusion of this conditional statement, $0^2 > 0$, is false is irrelevant to the truth value of the conditional statement, because a conditional statement with a false hypothesis is guaranteed to be true.

We can also quickly prove a conditional statement $p \rightarrow q$ if we know that the conclusion q is true. By showing that q is true, it follows that $p \rightarrow q$ must also be true. A proof of $p \rightarrow q$ that uses the fact that q is true is called a **trivial proof.** Trivial proofs are often important when special cases of theorems are proved (see the discussion of proof by cases in Section 1.7) and in mathematical induction.

Example 6   Let $P(n)$ be "If a and b are positive integers with $a \geqslant b$, then $a^n \geqslant b^n$," where the domain consists of all integers. Show that $P(0)$ is true.

Solution: The proposition $P(0)$ is "If $a \geqslant b$, then $a^0 \geqslant b^0$." Because $a^0 = b^0 = 1$, the conclusion of the conditional statement "If $a \geqslant b$, then $a^0 \geqslant b^0$" is true. Hence, this conditional statement, which is $P(0)$, is true. This is an example of a trivial proof. Note that the hypothesis, which is the statement "$a \geqslant b$," was not needed in this proof. ◀

A Little Proof Strategy We have described two important approaches for proving theorems of the form $\forall x(P(x) \rightarrow Q(x))$: direct proof and proof by contraposition. We have also given examples that show how each is used. However, when you are presented with a theorem of the form $\forall x(P(x) \rightarrow Q(x))$, which method should you use to attempt to prove it? We will provide a few rules of thumb here; in Section 1.7 we will discuss proof strategy at greater length. When you want to prove a statement of the form $\forall x(P(x) \rightarrow Q(x))$, first evaluate whether a direct proof looks promising. Begin by expanding the definitions in the hypotheses. Start to reason using these hypotheses, together with axioms and available theorems. If a direct proof does not seem to go anywhere, try the same thing with a proof by contraposition. Recall that in a proof by contraposition you assume that the conclusion of the conditional statement is false and use a direct proof to show this implies that the hypothesis must be false. We illustrate this strategy in Examples 7 and 8. Before we present our next example, we need a definition.

Definition 2   The real number r is *rational* if there exist integers p and q with $q \neq 0$ such that $r = p/q$. A real number that is not rational is called *irrational*.

Example 7   Prove that the sum of two rational numbers is rational. (Note that if we include the implicit quantifiers here, the theorem we want to prove is "For every real number r and every real number s, if r and s are rational numbers, then $r + s$ is rational.")

Solution: We first attempt a direct proof. To begin, suppose that r and s are rational numbers. From the definition of a rational number, it follows that there are integers p and q, with $q \neq 0$, such that $r = p/q$, and integers t and u, with $u \neq 0$, such that $s = t/u$. Can we use this information to show that $r + s$ is rational? The obvious next step is to add $r = p/q$ and $s = t/u$, to obtain

$$r + s = \frac{p}{q} + \frac{t}{u} = \frac{pu + qt}{qu}.$$

Because $q \neq 0$ and $u \neq 0$, it follows that $qu \neq 0$. Consequently, we have expressed $r + s$ as the ratio of two integers, $pu + qt$ and qu, where $qu \neq 0$. This means that $r + s$ is rational. We have proved that the sum of two rational numbers is rational; our attempt to find a direct proof succeeded.   ◄

Example 8   Prove that if n is an integer and n^2 is odd, then n is odd.

Solution: We first attempt a direct proof. Suppose that n is an integer and n^2 is odd. Then, there exists an integer k such that $n^2 = 2k + 1$. Can we use this information to show that n is odd? There seems to be no obvious approach to show that n is odd because solving for n produces the equation $n = \pm\sqrt{2k + 1}$, which is not terribly useful.

Because this attempt to use a direct proof did not bear fruit, we next attempt a proof by contraposition. We take as our hypothesis the statement that n is not odd. Because every integer is odd or even, this means that n is even. This implies that there exists an integer k such that $n = 2k$. To prove the theorem, we need to show that this hypothesis implies the conclusion that n^2 is not odd, that is, that n^2 is even. Can we use the equation $n = 2k$ to achieve this? By squaring both sides of this equation, we obtain $n^2 = 4k^2 = 2(2k^2)$, which implies that n^2 is also even because $n^2 = 2t$, where $t = 2k^2$. We have proved that if n is an integer and n^2 is odd, then n is odd. Our attempt to find a proof by contraposition succeeded.   ◄

Proofs by Contradiction

Suppose we want to prove that a statement p is true. Furthermore, suppose that we can find a contradiction q such that $\neg p \rightarrow q$ is true. Because q is false, but $\neg p \rightarrow q$ is true, we can conclude that $\neg p$ is false, which means that p is true. How can we find a contradiction q that might help us prove that p is true in this way?

Because the statement $r \wedge \neg r$ is a contradiction whenever r is a proposition, we can prove that p is true if we can show that $\neg p \rightarrow (r \wedge \neg r)$ is true for some proposition r. Proofs of this type are called **proofs by contradiction.** Because a proof by contradiction does not prove a result directly, it is another type of indirect proof. We provide three examples of proof by contradiction. The first is an example of an application of the pigeonhole principle, a combinatorial technique that we will cover in depth in Section 3.2.

Example 9   Show that at least four of any 22 days must fall on the same day of the week.

Solution: Let p be the proposition "At least four of 22 chosen days fall on the same day of the week." Suppose that $\neg p$ is true. This means that at most three of the 22 days fall on the same day of the week. Because there are seven days of the week, this implies that at most 21 days could have been chosen because for each of the days of the week, at most three of the chosen days could fall on that day. This contradicts the hypothesis that we have 22 days under consideration. That is, if r is the statement that 22 days are chosen, then we have shown that $\neg p \rightarrow (r \wedge \neg r)$. Consequently, we know that p is true. We have proved that at least four of 22 chosen days fall on the same day of the week.   ◄

Example 10   Prove that $\sqrt{2}$ is irrational by giving a proof by contradiction.

Solution: Let p be the proposition "$\sqrt{2}$ is irrational." To start a proof by contradiction, we suppose that $\neg p$ is true. Note that $\neg p$ is the statement "It is not the case that $\sqrt{2}$ is irrational," which says that $\sqrt{2}$ is rational. We will show that assuming that $\neg p$ is true leads to a contradiction.

If $\sqrt{2}$ is rational, there exist integers a and b with $\sqrt{2} = a/b$, where a and b have no common factors (so that the fraction a/b is in lowest terms.) (Here, we are using the fact that every rational number can be written in lowest terms.) Because $\sqrt{2} = a/b$, when both sides of this equation are squared, it follows that

$$2 = a^2/b^2.$$

Hence,

$$2b^2 = a^2.$$

By the definition of an even integer it follows that a^2 is even. We next use the fact that if a^2 is even, a must also be even. Furthermore, because a is even, by the definition of an even integer, $a = 2c$ for some integer c. Thus,

$$2b^2 = 4c^2.$$

Dividing both sides of this equation by 2 gives

$$b^2 = 2c^2.$$

By the definition of even, this means that b^2 is even. Again using the fact that if the square of an integer is even, then the integer itself must be even, we conclude that b must be even as well.

We have now shown that the assumption of $\neg p$ leads to the equation $\sqrt{2} = a/b$, where a and b have no common factors, but both a and b are even, that is, 2 divides both a and b. Note that the statement that $\sqrt{2} = a/b$, where a and b have no common factors, means, in particular, that 2 does not divide both a and b. Because our assumption of $\neg p$ leads to the contradiction that 2 divides both a and b and 2 does not divide both a and b, $\neg p$ must be false. That is, the statement p, "$\sqrt{2}$ is irrational," is true. We have proved that $\sqrt{2}$ is irrational.   ◀

Proof by contradiction can be used to prove conditional statements. In such proofs, we first assume the negation of the conclusion. We then use the premises of the theorem and the negation of the conclusion to arrive at a contradiction. (The reason that such proofs are valid rests on the logical equivalence of $p \rightarrow q$ and $(p \wedge \neg q) \rightarrow \mathbf{F}$. To see that these statements are equivalent, simply note that each is false in exactly one case, namely when p is true and q is false.)

Note that we can rewrite a proof by contraposition of a conditional statement as a proof by contradiction. In a proof of $p \rightarrow q$ by contraposition, we assume that $\neg q$ is true. We then show that $\neg p$ must also be true. To rewrite a proof by contraposition of $p \rightarrow q$ as a proof by contradiction, we suppose that both p and $\neg q$ are true. Then, we use the steps from the proof of $\neg q \rightarrow \neg p$ to show that $\neg p$ is true. This leads to the contradiction $p \wedge \neg p$, completing the proof. Example 11 illustrates how a proof by contraposition of a conditional statement can be rewritten as a proof by contradiction.

Example 11   Give a proof by contradiction of the theorem "If $3n + 2$ is odd, then n is odd."

Solution: Let p be "$3n + 2$ is odd" and q be "n is odd." To construct a proof by contradiction, assume that both p and $\neg q$ are true. That is, assume that $3n + 2$ is odd and that n is not odd. Because n is not odd, we know that it is even. Following the steps in the solution of Example 3 (a proof by contraposition), we can show that if n is even, then $3n + 2$ is even. First, because n is even, there is an integer k such that $n = 2k$. This implies that $3n + 2 = 3(2k) + 2 = 6k + 2 = 2(3k + 1)$. Because $3n + 2$ is $2t$, where $t = 3k + 1$, $3n + 2$ is even. Note that the statement "$3n + 2$ is even" $\neg p$, because an integer is even if and only if it is not odd. Because both p and $\neg p$ are true, we have a contradiction. This completes the proof by contradiction, proving that if $3n + 2$ is odd, then n is odd.   ◀

Note that we can also prove by contradiction that $p \rightarrow q$ is true by assuming that p and $\neg q$ are true, and showing that q must be also be true. This implies that $\neg q$ and q are both true, a contradiction. This observation tells us that we can turn a direct proof into a proof by contradiction.

Proofs of Equivalence   To prove a theorem that is a biconditional statement, that is, a statement of the form $p \leftrightarrow q$, we show that $p \rightarrow q$ and $q \rightarrow p$ are both true. The validity of this approach is based on the tautology

$$(p \leftrightarrow q) \leftrightarrow [(p \rightarrow q) \wedge (q \rightarrow p)].$$

Example 12   Prove the theorem "If n is a positive integer, then n is odd if and only if n^2 is odd."

Solution: This theorem has the form "p if and only if q," where p is "n is odd" and q is "n^2 is odd." (As usual, we do not explicitly deal with the universal quantification.) To prove this theorem, we need to show that $p \rightarrow q$ and $q \rightarrow p$ are true.

We have already shown (in Example 1) that $p \rightarrow q$ is true and (in Example 8) that $q \rightarrow p$ is true.

Because we have shown that both $p \rightarrow q$ and $q \rightarrow p$ are true, we have shown that the theorem is true.   ◄

Sometimes a theorem states that several propositions are equivalent. Such a theorem states that propositions $p_1, p_2, p_3, \ldots, p_n$ are equivalent. This can be written as

$$p_1 \leftrightarrow p_2 \leftrightarrow \cdots \leftrightarrow p_n,$$

which states that all n propositions have the same truth values, and consequently, that for all i and j with $1 \leqslant i \leqslant n$ and $1 \leqslant j \leqslant n$, p_i and p_j are equivalent. One way to prove these mutually equivalent is to use the tautology

$$[p_1 \leftrightarrow p_2 \leftrightarrow \cdots \leftrightarrow p_n] \leftrightarrow [(p_1 \rightarrow p_2) \wedge (p_2 \rightarrow p_3) \wedge \cdots \wedge (p_n \rightarrow p_1)].$$

This shows that if the conditional statements $p_1 \rightarrow p_2$, $p_2 \rightarrow p_3, \ldots, p_n \rightarrow p_1$ can be shown to be true, then the propositions $p_1, p_2, \ldots, p_n$ are all equivalent.

This is much more efficient than proving that $p_i \rightarrow p_j$ for all $i \neq j$ with $1 \leqslant i \leqslant n$ and $1 \leqslant j \leqslant n$.

When we prove that a group of statements are equivalent, we can establish any chain of conditional statements we choose as long as it is possible to work through the chain to go from any one of these statements to any other statement. For example, we can show that p_1, p_2, and p_3 are equivalent by showing that $p_1 \rightarrow p_3$, $p_3 \rightarrow p_2$, and $p_2 \rightarrow p_1$.

Example 13   Show that these statements about the integer n are equivalent:

p_1: n is even.
p_2: $n - 1$ is odd.
p_3: n^2 is even.

Solution: We will show that these three statements are equivalent by showing that the conditional statements $p_1 \rightarrow p_2$, $p_2 \rightarrow p_3$, and $p_3 \rightarrow p_1$ are true.

We use a direct proof to show that $p_1 \rightarrow p_2$. Suppose that n is even. Then $n = 2k$ for some integer k. Consequently, $n - 1 = 2k - 1 = 2(k - 1) + 1$. This means that $n - 1$ is odd because it is of the form $2m + 1$, where m is the integer $k - 1$.

We also use a direct proof to show that $p_2 \rightarrow p_3$. Now suppose $n - 1$ is odd. Then $n - 1 = 2k + 1$ for some integer k. Hence, $n = 2k + 2$ so that $n^2 = (2k + 2)^2 = 4k^2 + 8k + 4 = 2(2k^2 + 4k + 2)$. This means that n^2 is twice the integer $2k^2 + 4k + 2$, and hence is even.

To prove $p_3 \rightarrow p_1$, we use a proof by contraposition. That is, we prove that if n is not even, then n^2 is not even. This is the same as proving that if n is odd, then n^2 is odd, which we have already done in Example 1. This completes the proof.   ◄

Counterexamples   In Section 1.3 we stated that to show that a statement of the form $\forall x P(x)$ is false, we need only find a **counterexample**, that is, an example x for which $P(x)$ is false. When presented with a statement of the form $\forall x P(x)$, which we believe to be false or which has resisted all proof attempts, we look for a counterexample. We illustrate the use of counterexamples in Example 14.

Example 14   Show that the statement "Every positive integer is the sum of the squares of two integers" is false.

Solution: To show that this statement is false, we look for a counterexample, which is a particular integer that is not the sum of the squares of two integers. It does not take long to find a counterexample, because 3 cannot be written as the sum of the squares of two integers. To show this is the case, note that the only perfect squares not exceeding 3 are $0^2 = 0$ and $1^2 = 1$. Furthermore, there is no way to get 3 as the sum of two terms each of which is 0 or 1. Consequently, we have shown that "Every positive integer is the sum of the squares of two integers" is false.   ◄

Mistakes in Proofs

There are many common errors made in constructing mathematical proofs. We will briefly describe some of these here. Among the most common errors are mistakes in arithmetic and basic algebra. Even professional mathematicians make such errors, especially when working with complicated formulae. Whenever you use such computations you should check them as carefully as possible. (You should also review any troublesome aspects of basic algebra.)

Each step of a mathematical proof needs to be correct and the conclusion needs to follow logically from the steps that precede it. Many mistakes result from the introduction of steps that do not logically follow from those that precede it. This is illustrated in Examples 15–17.

Example 15   What is wrong with this famous supposed "proof" that $1 = 2$?

"***Proof***:" We use these steps, where a and b are two equal positive integers.

Step	Reason
1. $a = b$	Given
2. $a^2 = ab$	Multiply both sides of (1) by a
3. $a^2 - b^2 = ab - b^2$	Subtract b^2 from both sides of (2)
4. $(a - b)(a + b) = b(a - b)$	Factor both sides of (3)
5. $a + b = b$	Divide both sides of (4) by $a - b$
6. $2b = b$	Replace a by b in (5) because $a = b$
	and simplify
7. $2 = 1$	Divide both sides of (6) by b

Solution: Every step is valid except for one, step 5 where we divided both sides by $a - b$. The error is that $a - b$ equals zero; division of both sides of an equation by the same quantity is valid as long as this quantity is not zero.   ◄

Example 16   What is wrong with this "proof"?

"Theorem:" If n^2 is positive, then n is positive.

"***Proof***:" Suppose that n^2 is positive. Because the conditional statement "If n is positive, then n^2 is positive" is true, we can conclude that n is positive.

Solution: Let $P(n)$ be "n is positive" and $Q(n)$ be "n^2 is positive." Then our hypothesis is $Q(n)$. The statement "If n is positive, then n^2 is positive" is the statement $\forall n(P(n) \rightarrow Q(n))$. From the hypothesis $Q(n)$ and the statement $\forall n(P(n) \rightarrow Q(n))$ we cannot conclude $P(n)$, because we are not using a valid rule of inference. Instead, this is an example of the fallacy of affirming the conclusion. A counterexample is supplied by $n = -1$ for which $n^2 = 1$ is positive, but n is negative.   ◄

Example 17   What is wrong with this "proof"?

"Theorem:" If n is not positive, then n^2 is not positive. (This is the contrapositive of the "theorem" in Example 16.)

"***Proof***:" Suppose that n is not positive. Because the conditional statement "If n is positive, then n^2 is positive" is true, we can conclude that n^2 is not positive.

Solution: Let $P(n)$ and $Q(n)$ be as in the solution of Example 16. Then our hypothesis is $\neg P(n)$ and the statement "If n is positive, then n^2 is positive" is the statement $\forall n(P(n) \rightarrow Q(n))$. From the hypothesis $\neg P(n)$ and the statement $\forall n(P(n) \rightarrow Q(n))$ we cannot conclude $\neg Q(n)$, because we are not using a valid rule of inference. Instead, this is an example of the fallacy of denying the hypothesis. A counterexample is supplied by $n = -1$, as in Example 16.   ◄

Finally, we briefly discuss a particularly nasty type of error. Many incorrect arguments are based on a fallacy called **begging the question.** This fallacy occurs when one or more steps of a proof are based on the truth of the statement being proved. In other words, this fallacy arises when a statement is proved using itself, or a statement equivalent to it. That is why this fallacy is also called **circular reasoning.**

Example 18   Is the following argument correct? It supposedly shows that n is an even integer whenever n^2 is an even integer.

Suppose that n^2 is even. Then $n^2 = 2k$ for some integer k. Let $n = 2l$ for some integer l. This shows that n is even.

Solution: This argument is incorrect. The statement "let $n = 2l$ for some integer l" occurs in the proof. No argument has been given to show that n can be written as $2l$ for some integer l. This is circular reasoning because this statement is equivalent to the statement being proved, namely, "n is even." Of course, the result itself is correct; only the method of proof is wrong.   ◄

Making mistakes in proofs is part of the learning process. When you make a mistake that someone else finds, you should carefully analyze where you went wrong and make sure that you do not make the same mistake again. Even professional mathematicians make mistakes in proofs. More than a few incorrect proofs of important results have fooled people for many years before subtle errors in them were found.

Just a Beginning

We have now developed a basic arsenal of proof methods. In the next section we will introduce other important proof methods. We will also introduce several important proof techniques, including mathematical induction, which can be used to prove results that hold for all positive integers. In Chapter 3 we will introduce the notion of combinatorial proofs.

In this section we introduced several methods for proving theorems of the form $\forall x(P(x) \rightarrow Q(x))$, including direct proofs and proofs by contraposition. There are many theorems of this type whose proofs are easy to construct by directly working through the hypotheses and definitions of the terms of the theorem. However, it is often difficult to prove a theorem without resorting to a clever use of a proof by contraposition or a proof by contradiction, or some other proof technique. In Section 1.7 we will address proof strategy. We will describe various approaches that can be used to find proofs when straightforward approaches do not work. Constructing proofs is an art that can be learned only through experience, including writing proofs, having your proofs critiqued, and reading and analyzing other proofs.

Exercises

1. Use a direct proof to show that the sum of two odd integers is even.

2. Show that the square of an even number is an even number using a direct proof.

3. Prove that if $m + n$ and $n + p$ are even integers, where m, n, and p are integers, then $m + p$ is even. What kind of proof did you use?

4. Use a direct proof to show that every odd integer is the difference of two squares.

5. Use a proof by contradiction to prove that the sum of an irrational number and a rational number is irrational.

6. Prove or disprove that the product of two irrational numbers is irrational.

7. Prove that if x is irrational, then $1/x$ is irrational.

8. Use a proof by contraposition to show that if $x + y \geqslant 2$, where x and y are real numbers, then $x \geqslant 1$ or $y \geqslant 1$.

9. Show that if n is an integer and $n^3 + 5$ is odd, then n is even using

   a) a proof by contraposition.   b) a proof by contradiction.

10. Prove the proposition $P(0)$, where $P(n)$ is the proposition "If n is a positive integer greater than 1, then $n^2 > n$." What kind of proof did you use?

11. Let $P(n)$ be the proposition "If a and b are positive real numbers, then $(a + b)^n \geqslant a^n + b^n$." Prove that $P(1)$ is true. What kind of proof did you use?

12. Show that at least 10 of any 64 days chosen must fall on the same day of the week.

13. Use a proof by contradiction to show that there is no rational number r for which $r^3 + r + 1 = 0$. [Hint: Assume that $r = a/b$ is a root, where a and b are integers and a/b is in lowest terms. Obtain an equation involving integers by multiplying by b^3. Then look at whether a and b are each odd or even.]

14. Prove that if n is a positive integer, then n is odd if and only if $5n + 6$ is odd.

15. Prove or disprove that if m and n are integers such that $mn = 1$, then either $m = 1$ and $n = 1$, or else $m = -1$ and $n = -1$.

16. Show that these statements about the integer x are equivalent: (i) $3x + 2$ is even, (ii) $x + 5$ is odd, (iii) x^2 is even.

17. Show that these statements about the real number x are equivalent: (i) x is irrational, (ii) $3x + 2$ is irrational, (iii) $x/2$ is irrational.

18. Are these steps for finding the solutions of $\sqrt{x + 3} = 3 - x$ correct? (1) $\sqrt{x + 3} = 3 - x$ is given; (2) $x + 3 = x^2 - 6x + 9$, obtained by squaring both sides of (1); (3) $0 = x^2 - 7x + 6$, obtained by subtracting $x + 3$ from both sides of (2); (4) $0 = (x - 1)(x - 6)$, obtained by factoring the right-hand side of (3); (5) $x = 1$ or $x = 6$, which follows from (4) because $ab = 0$ implies that $a = 0$ or $b = 0$.

19. Show that the propositions p_1, p_2, p_3, p_4, and p_5 can be shown to be equivalent by proving that the conditional statements $p_1 \rightarrow p_4$, $p_3 \rightarrow p_1$, $p_4 \rightarrow p_2$, $p_2 \rightarrow p_5$, and $p_5 \rightarrow p_3$ are true.

20. Prove that at least one of the real numbers $a_1, a_2, \ldots, a_n$ is greater than or equal to the average of these numbers. What kind of proof did you use?

21. Prove that if n is an integer, these four statements are equivalent: (i) n is even, (ii) $n + 1$ is odd, (iii) $3n + 1$ is odd, (iv) $3n$ is even.

1.7   Proof Methods and Strategy

Introduction

In Section 1.6 we introduced a variety of different methods of proof and illustrated how each method is used. In this section we continue this effort. We will introduce several other important proof methods, including proofs where we consider different cases separately and proofs where we prove the existence of objects with desired properties.

In Section 1.6 we only briefly discussed the strategy behind constructing proofs. This strategy includes selecting a proof method and then successfully constructing an argument step by step, based on this method. In this section, after we have developed a wider arsenal of proof methods, we will study some additional aspects of the art and science of proofs. We will provide advice on how to find a proof of a theorem. We will describe some tricks of the trade, including how proofs can be found by working backward and by adapting existing proofs.

When mathematicians work, they formulate conjectures and attempt to prove or disprove them. We will briefly describe this process here by proving results about tiling checkerboards with dominoes and other types of pieces. Looking at tilings of this kind, we will be able to quickly formulate conjectures and prove theorems without first developing a theory.

We will conclude the section by discussing the role of open questions. In particular, we will discuss some interesting problems either that have been solved after remaining open for hundreds of years or that still remain open.

Exhaustive Proof and Proof by Cases

Sometimes we cannot prove a theorem using a single argument that holds for all possible cases. We now introduce a method that can be used to prove a theorem, by considering different cases separately. This method is based on a rule of inference that we will now introduce. To prove a conditional statement of the form

$$(p_1 \lor p_2 \lor \cdots \lor p_n) \to q$$

the tautology

$$[(p_1 \lor p_2 \lor \cdots \lor p_n) \to q] \leftrightarrow [(p_1 \to q) \land (p_2 \to q) \land \cdots \land (p_n \to q)]$$

can be used as a rule of inference. This shows that the original conditional statement with a hypothesis made up of a disjunction of the propositions $p_1, p_2, \ldots, p_n$ can be proved by proving each of the n conditional statements $p_i \to q$, $i = 1, 2, \ldots, n$, individually. Such an argument is called a **proof by cases.** Sometimes to prove that a conditional statement $p \to q$ is true, it is convenient to use a disjunction $p_1 \lor p_2 \lor \cdots \lor p_n$ instead of p as the hypothesis of the conditional statement, where p and $p_1 \lor p_2 \lor \cdots \lor p_n$ are equivalent.

Exhaustive Proof   Some theorems can be proved by examining a relatively small number of examples. Such proofs are called **exhaustive proofs,** because these proofs proceed by exhausting all possibilities. An exhaustive proof is a special type of proof by cases where each case involves checking a single example. We now provide some illustrations of exhaustive proofs.

Example 1   Prove that $(n + 1)^2 \geqslant 3^n$ if n is a positive integer with $n \leqslant 4$.

Solution: We use a proof by exhaustion. We only need verify the inequality $(n + 1)^2 \geqslant 3^n$ when $n = 1, 2, 3$, and 4. For $n = 1$, we have $(n + 1)^2 = 2^2 = 4$ and $3^n = 3^1 = 3$; for $n = 2$, we have $(n + 1)^2 = 3^2 = 9$ and $3^n = 3^2 = 9$; for $n = 3$, we have $(n + 1)^3 = 4^3 = 64$ and $3^n = 3^3 = 27$; and for $n = 4$, we have $(n + 1)^3 = 5^3 = 125$ and $3^n = 3^4 = 81$. In each of these four cases, we see that $(n + 1)^2 \geqslant 3^n$. We have used the method of exhaustion to prove that $(n + 1)^2 \geqslant 3^n$ if n is a positive integer with $n \leqslant 4$.   ◀

Example 2   Prove that the only consecutive positive integers not exceeding 100 that are perfect powers are 8 and 9. (An integer is a **perfect power** if it equals n^a, where a is an integer greater than 1.)

Solution: We can prove this fact by showing that the only pair $n, n + 1$ of consecutive positive integers that are both perfect powers with $n < 100$ arises when $n = 8$. We can prove this fact by examining positive integers n not exceeding 100, first checking whether n is a perfect power, and if it is, checking whether $n + 1$ is also a perfect power. A quicker way to do this is simply to look at all perfect powers not exceeding 100 and checking whether the next largest integer is also a perfect power. The squares of positive integers not exceeding 100 are $1, 4, 9, 16, 25, 36, 49, 64, 81$, and 100. The cubes of positive integers not exceeding 100 are $1, 8, 27$, and 64. The fourth powers of positive integers not exceeding 100 are 1, 16, and 81. The fifth powers of positive integers not exceeding 100 are 1 and 32. The sixth powers of positive integers not exceeding 100 are 1 and 64. There are no powers of positive integers higher than the sixth power not exceeding 100, other than 1. Looking at this list of perfect powers not exceeding 100, we see that $n = 8$ is the only perfect power n for which $n + 1$ is also a perfect power. That is, $2^3 = 8$ and $3^2 = 9$ are the only two consecutive perfect powers not exceeding 100.   ◄

People can carry out exhaustive proofs when it is necessary to check only a relatively small number of instances of a statement. Computers do not complain when they are asked to check a much larger number of instances of a statement, but they still have limitations. Note that not even a computer can check all instances when it is impossible to list all instances to check.

Proof By Cases   A proof by cases must cover all possible cases that arise in a theorem. We illustrate proof by cases with a couple of examples. In each example, you should check that all possible cases are covered.

Example 3   Prove that if n is an integer, then $n^2 \geqslant n$.

Solution: We can prove that $n^2 \geqslant n$ for every integer by considering three cases, when $n = 0$, when $n \geqslant 1$, and when $n \leqslant -1$. We split the proof into three cases because it is straightforward to prove the result by considering zero, positive integers, and negative integers separately.

Case (i). When $n = 0$, because $0^2 = 0$, we see that $0^2 \geqslant 0$. It follows that $n^2 \geqslant n$ is true in this case.

Case (ii). When $n \geqslant 1$, when we multiply both sides of the inequality $n \geqslant 1$ by the positive integer n, we obtain $n \cdot n \geqslant n \cdot 1$. This implies that $n^2 \geqslant n$ for $n \geqslant 1$.

Case (iii). In this case $n \leqslant -1$. However, $n^2 \geqslant 0$. It follows that $n^2 \geqslant n$.

Because the inequality $n^2 \geqslant n$ holds in all three cases, we can conclude that if n is an integer, then $n^2 \geqslant n$.   ◄

Example 4   Use a proof by cases to show that $|xy| = |x||y|$, where x and y are real numbers. (Recall that $|a|$, the absolute value of a, equals a when $a \geqslant 0$ and equals $-a$ when $a \leqslant 0$.)

Solution: In our proof of this theorem, we remove absolute values using the fact that $|a| = a$ when $a \geqslant 0$ and $|a| = -a$ when $a < 0$. Because both $|x|$ and $|y|$ occur in our formula, we will need four cases: *(i)* x and y both nonnegative, *(ii)* x nonnegative and y is negative, *(iii)* x negative and y nonnegative, and *(iv)* x negative and y negative.

(Note that we can remove the absolute value signs by making the appropriate choice of signs within each case.)

Case (i). We see that $p_1 \rightarrow q$ because $xy \geqslant 0$ when $x \geqslant 0$ and $y \geqslant 0$, so that $|xy| = xy = |x||y|$.

Case (ii). To see that $p_2 \rightarrow q$, note that if $x \geqslant 0$ and $y < 0$, then $xy \leqslant 0$, so that $|xy| = -xy = x(-y) = |x||y|$. (Here, because $y < 0$, we have $|y| = -y$.)

Case (iii). To see that $p_3 \rightarrow q$, we follow the same reasoning as the previous case with the roles of x and y reversed.

Case (iv). To see that $p_4 \rightarrow q$, note that when $x < 0$ and $y < 0$, it follows that $xy > 0$. Hence, $|xy| = xy = (-x)(-y) = |x||y|$.

Because we have completed all four cases and these cases exhaust all possibilities, we can conclude that $|xy| = |x||y|$, whenever x and y are real numbers.   ◄

Leveraging Proof by Cases   The examples we have presented illustrating proof by cases provide some insight into when to use this method of proof. In particular, when it is not possible to consider all cases of a proof at the same time, a proof by cases should be considered. When should you use such a proof? Generally, look for a proof by cases when there is no obvious way to begin a proof, but when extra information in each case helps move the proof forward. Example 5 illustrates how the method of proof by cases can be used effectively.

Example 5   Formulate a conjecture about the decimal digits that occur as the final digit of the square of an integer and prove your result.

Solution: The smallest perfect squares are $1, 4, 9, 16, 25, 36, 49, 64, 81, 100, 121, 144, 169, 196, 225$, and so on. We notice that the digits that occur as the final digit of a square are $0, 1, 4, 5, 6$, and

9, with $2, 3, 7$, and 8 never appearing as the final digit of a square. We conjecture this theorem: The final decimal digit of a perfect square is $0, 1, 4, 5, 6$ or 9. How can we prove this theorem?

We first note that we can express an integer n as $10a + b$, where a and b are positive integers and b is $0, 1, 2, 3, 4, 5, 6, 7, 8,$ or 9. Here a is the integer obtained by subtracting the final decimal digit of n from n and dividing by 10. Next, note that $(10a + b)^2 = 100a^2 + 20ab + b^2 = 10(10a^2 + 2b) + b^2$, so that the final decimal digit of n^2 is the same as the final decimal digit of b^2. Furthermore, note that the final decimal digit of b^2 is the same as the final decimal digit of $(10 - b)^2 = 100 - 20b + b^2$. Consequently, we can reduce our proof to the consideration of six cases.

Case (i). The final digit of n is 1 or 9. Then the final decimal digit of n^2 is the final decimal digit of $1^2 = 1$ or $9^2 = 81$, namely, 1.

Case (ii). The final digit of n is 2 or 8. Then the final decimal digit of n^2 is the final decimal digit of $2^2 = 4$ or $8^2 = 64$, namely, 4.

Case (iii). The final digit of n is 3 or 7. Then the final decimal digit of n^2 is the final decimal digit of $3^2 = 9$ or $7^2 = 49$, namely, 9.

Case (iv). The final digit of n is 4 or 6. Then the final decimal digit of n^2 is the final decimal digit of $4^2 = 16$ or $6^2 = 36$, namely, 6.

Case (v). The final decimal digit of n is 5. Then the final decimal digit of n^2 is the final decimal digit of $5^2 = 25$, namely 5.

Case (vi). The final decimal digit of n is 0. Then the final decimal digit of n^2 is the final decimal digit of $0^2 = 0$, namely 0.

Because we have considered all six cases, we can conclude that the final decimal digit of n^2, where n is an integer is either $0, 1, 2, 4, 5, 6,$ or 9.   ◄

Sometimes we can eliminate all but a few examples in a proof by cases, as Example 6 illustrates.

Example 6   Show that there are no solutions in integers x and y of $x^2 + 3y^2 = 8$.

Solution: We can quickly reduce a proof to checking just a few simple cases because $x^2 > 8$ when $|x| \geqslant 3$ and $3y^2 > 8$ when $|y| \geqslant 2$. This leaves the cases when x takes on one of the values $-2, -1, 0, 1,$ or 2 and y takes on one of the values $-1, 0,$ or 1. We can finish using an exhaustive proof. To dispense with the remaining cases, we note that possible values for x^2 are $0, 1,$ and 4, and possible values for $3y^2$ are 0 and 3, and the largest sum of possible values for x^2 and $3y^2$ is 7. Consequently, it is impossible for $x^2 + 3y^2 = 8$ to hold when x and y are integers.   ◄

Without Loss of Generality   In the proof in Example 4, we dismissed case *(iii)*, where $x < 0$ and $y \geqslant 0$, because it is the same as case *(ii)*, where $x \geqslant 0$ and $y < 0$, with the roles of x and y reversed. To shorten the proof, we could have proved cases *(ii)* and *(iii)* together by assuming, **without loss of generality,** that $x \geqslant 0$ and $y < 0$. Implicit in this statement is that we can complete the case with $x < 0$ and $y \geqslant 0$ using the same argument as we used for the case with $x \geqslant 0$ and $y < 0$, but with the obvious changes. In general, when the phrase "without loss of generality" is used in a proof (often abbreviated as WLOG), we assert that by proving one case of a theorem, no additional argument is required to prove other specified cases. That is, other cases follow by making straightforward changes to the argument, or by filling in some straightforward initial step. Of course, incorrect use of this principle can lead to unfortunate errors. Sometimes assumptions are made that lead to a loss in generality. Such assumptions can be made that do not take into account that one case may be substantially different from others. This can lead to an incomplete, and possibly unsalvageable, proof. In fact, many incorrect proofs of famous theorems turned out to rely on arguments that used the idea of "without loss of generality" to establish cases that could not be quickly proved from simpler cases.

We now illustrate a proof where without loss of generality is used effectively.

Example 7   Show that $(x + y)^r < x^r + y^r$ whenever x and y are positive real numbers and r is a real number with $0 < r < 1$.

Solution: Without loss of generality we can assume that $x + y = 1$. [To see this, suppose we have proved the theorem with the assumption that $x + y = 1$. Suppose that $x + y = t$. Then $(x/t) + (y/t) = 1$, which implies that $((x/t) + (y/t))^r < (x/t)^r + (y/t)^r$. Multiplying both sides of this last equation by t^r shows that $(x + y)^r < x^r + y^r$.]

Assuming that $x + y = 1$, because x and y are positive, we have $0 < x < 1$ and $0 < y < 1$. Because $0 < r < 1$, it follows that $0 < 1 - r < 1$, so $x^{1-r} < 1$ and $y^{1-r} < 1$. This means that $x < x^r$ and $y < y^r$. Consequently, $x^r + y^r > x + y = 1$. This means that $(x+y)^r = 1^r < x^r + y^r$. This proves the theorem for $x + y = 1$.

Because we could assume $x + y = 1$ without loss of generality, we know that $(x + y)^r < x^r + y^r$ whenever x and y are positive real numbers and r is a real number with $0 < r < 1$.   ◀

Common Errors with Exhaustive Proof and Proof by Cases   A common error of reasoning is to draw incorrect conclusions from examples. No matter how many separate examples are considered, a theorem is not proved by considering examples unless every possible case is covered. The problem of proving a theorem is analogous to showing that a computer program always produces the output desired. No matter how many input values are tested, unless all input values are tested, we cannot conclude that the program always produces the correct output.

Example 8   Is it true that every positive integer is the sum of 18 fourth powers of integers?

Solution: To determine whether n can be written as the sum of 18 fourth powers of integers, we might begin by examining whether n is the sum of 18 fourth powers of integers for the smallest positive integers. Because the fourth powers of integers are $0, 1, 16, 81, \ldots$, if we can select 18 terms from these numbers that add up to n, then n is the sum of 18 fourth powers. We can show that all positive integers up to 78 can be written as the sum of 18 fourth powers. (The details are left to the reader.) However, if we decided this was enough checking, we would come to the wrong conclusion. It is not true that every positive integer is the sum of 18 fourth powers because 79 is not the sum of 18 fourth powers (as the reader can verify).   ◀

Another common error involves making unwarranted assumptions that lead to incorrect proofs by cases where not all cases are considered. This is illustrated in Example 9.

Example 9   What is wrong with this "proof"?

"*Theorem*:" If x is a real number, then x^2 is a positive real number.

"***Proof***:" Let p_1 be "x is positive," let p_2 be "x is negative," and let q be "x^2 is positive." To show that $p_1 \to q$ is true, note that when x is positive, x^2 is positive because it is the product of two positive numbers, x and x. To show that $p_2 \to q$, note that when x is negative, x^2 is positive because it is the product of two negative numbers, x and x. This completes the proof.

Solution: The problem with the proof we have given is that we missed the case $x = 0$. When $x = 0$, $x^2 = 0$ is not positive, so the supposed theorem is false. If p is "x is a real number," then we can prove results where p is the hypothesis with three cases, p_1, p_2, and p_3, where p_1 is "x is positive," p_2 is "x is negative," and p_3 is "$x = 0$" because of the equivalence $p \leftrightarrow p_1 \lor p_2 \lor p_3$.   ◀

Existence Proofs

Many theorems are assertions that objects of a particular type exist. A theorem of this type is a proposition of the form $\exists x P(x)$, where P is a predicate. A proof of a proposition of the form $\exists x P(x)$ is called an **existence proof.** There are several ways to prove a theorem of this type. Sometimes an existence proof of $\exists x P(x)$ can be given by finding an element a such that $P(a)$ is true. Such an existence proof is called **constructive.** It is also possible to give an existence proof that is **nonconstructive;** that is, we do not find an element a such that $P(a)$ is true, but rather prove that $\exists x P(x)$ is true in some other way. One common method of giving a nonconstructive existence proof is to use proof by contradiction and show that the negation of the existential quantification implies a contradiction. The concept of a constructive existence proof is illustrated by Example 10 and the concept of a nonconstructive existence proof is illustrated by Example 11.

Example 10   **A Constructive Existence Proof**   Show that there is a positive integer that can be written as the sum of cubes of positive integers in two different ways.

Solution: After considerable computation (such as a computer search) we find that

$$1729 = 10^3 + 9^3 = 12^3 + 1^3.$$

Because we have displayed a positive integer that can be written as the sum of cubes in two different ways, we are done.   ◄

Example 11   **A Nonconstructive Existence Proof**   Show that there exist irrational numbers x and y such that x^y is rational.

Solution: By Example 10 in Section 1.6 we know that $\sqrt{2}$ is irrational. Consider the number $\sqrt{2}^{\sqrt{2}}$. If it is rational, we have two irrational numbers x and y with x^y rational, namely, $x = \sqrt{2}$ and $y = \sqrt{2}$. On the other hand if $\sqrt{2}^{\sqrt{2}}$ is irrational, then we can let $x = \sqrt{2}^{\sqrt{2}}$ and $y = \sqrt{2}$ so that $x^y = (\sqrt{2}^{\sqrt{2}})^{\sqrt{2}} = \sqrt{2}^{(\sqrt{2} \cdot \sqrt{2})} = \sqrt{2}^2 = 2$.

This proof is an example of a nonconstructive existence proof because we have not found irrational numbers x and y such that x^y is rational. Rather, we have shown that either the pair $x = \sqrt{2}, y = \sqrt{2}$ or the pair $x = \sqrt{2}^{\sqrt{2}}, y = \sqrt{2}$ have the desired property, but we do not know which of these two pairs works!   ◄

Nonconstructive existence proofs often are quite subtle, as Example 12 illustrates.

Example 12   **Chomp** is a game played by two players. In this game, cookies are laid out on a rectangular grid. The cookie in the top left position is poisoned, as shown in Figure 1(a). The two players take turns making moves; at each move, a player is required to eat a remaining cookie, together with all cookies to the right and/or below it (see Figure 1(b), for example). The loser is the player who has no choice but to eat the poisoned cookie. We ask whether one of the two players has a winning strategy. That is, can one of the players always make moves that are guaranteed to lead to a win?

Solution: We will give a nonconstructive existence proof of a winning strategy for the first player. That is, we will show that the first player always has a winning strategy without explicitly describing the moves this player must follow.

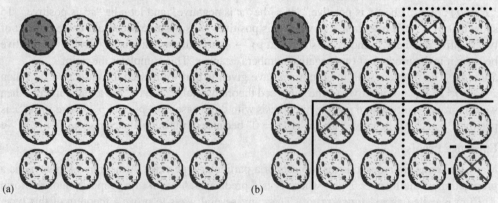

(a)   (b)

Figure 1   (a) Chomp, the Top Left Cookie is Poison   (b) Three Possible Moves.

First, note that the game ends and cannot finish in a draw because with each move at least one cookie is eaten, so after no more than $m \times n$ moves the game ends, where the initial grid is $m \times n$. Now, suppose that the first player begins the game by eating just the cookie in the bottom right corner. There are two possibilities, this is the first move of a winning strategy for the first player, or the second player can make a move that is the first move of a winning strategy for the second player. In this second case, instead of eating just the cookie in the bottom right corner, the first player could have made the same move that the second player made as the first move of a winning strategy (and then continued to follow that winning strategy). This would guarantee a win for the first player.

Note that we showed that a winning strategy exists, but we did not specify an actual winning strategy. Consequently, the proof is a nonconstructive existence proof. In fact, no one has been able to describe a winning strategy for that Chomp that applies for all rectangular grids by describing the moves that the first player should follow. However, winning strategies can be described for certain special cases, such as when the grid is square and when the grid only has two rows of cookies. ◀

Uniqueness Proofs

Some theorems assert the existence of a unique element with a particular property. In other words, these theorems assert that there is exactly one element with this property. To prove a statement of this type we need to show that an element with this property exists and that no other element has this property. The two parts of a **uniqueness proof** are:

Existence: We show that an element x with the desired property exists.

Uniqueness: We show that if $y \neq x$, then y does not have the desired property.

Equivalently, we can show that if x and y both have the desired property, then $x = y$.

Remark: Showing that there is a unique element x such that $P(x)$ is the same as proving the statement $\exists x(P(x) \wedge \forall y(y \neq x \rightarrow \neg P(y)))$.

We illustrate the elements of a uniqueness proof in Example 13.

Example 13 Show that if a and b are real numbers and $a \neq 0$, then there is a unique real number r such that $ar + b = 0$.

Solution: First, note that the real number $r = -b/a$ is a solution of $ar + b = 0$ because $a(-b/a) + b = -b + b = 0$. Consequently, a real number r exists for which $ar + b = 0$. This is the existence part of the proof.

Second, suppose that s is a real number such that $as + b = 0$. Then $ar + b = as + b$, where $r = -b/a$. Subtracting b from both sides, we find that $ar = as$. Dividing both sides of this last equation by a, which is nonzero, we see that $r = s$. This means that if $s \neq r$, then $as + b \neq 0$. This establishes the uniqueness part of the proof. ◀

Proof Strategies

Finding proofs can be a challenging business. When you are confronted with a statement to prove, you should first replace terms by their definitions and then carefully analyze what the hypotheses and the conclusion mean. After doing so, you can attempt to prove the result using one of the available methods of proof. Generally, if the statement is a conditional statement, you should first try a direct proof; if this fails, you can try an indirect proof. If neither of these approaches works, you might try a proof by contradiction.

Forward and Backward Reasoning Whichever method you choose, you need a starting point for your proof. To begin a direct proof of a conditional statement, you start with the premises. Using these premises, together with axioms and known theorems, you can construct a proof using a sequence of steps that leads to the conclusion. This type of reasoning, called *forward reasoning,* is the most common type of reasoning used to prove relatively simple results. Similarly, with indirect reasoning you can start with the negation of the conclusion and, using a sequence of steps, obtain the negation of the premises.

Unfortunately, forward reasoning is often difficult to use to prove more complicated results, because the reasoning needed to reach the desired conclusion may be far from obvious. In such cases it may be helpful to use *backward reasoning*. To reason backward to prove a statement q, we find a statement p that we can prove with the property that $p \rightarrow q$. (Note that it is not helpful to find a statement r that you can prove such that $q \rightarrow r$, because it is the fallacy of begging the question to conclude from $q \rightarrow r$ and r that q is true.) Backward reasoning is illustrated in Examples 14 and 15.

Example 14   Given two positive real numbers x and y, their **arithmetic mean** is $(x + y)/2$ and their **geometric mean** is $\sqrt{xy}$. When we compare the arithmetic and geometric means of pairs of distinct positive real numbers, we find that the arithmetic mean is always greater than the geometric mean. [For example, when $x = 4$ and $y = 6$, we have $5 = (4+6)/2 > \sqrt{4 \cdot 6} = \sqrt{24}$.] Can we prove that this inequality is always true?

Solution: To prove that $(x+y)/2 > \sqrt{xy}$ when x and y are distinct positive real numbers, we can work backward. We construct a sequence of equivalent inequalities. The equivalent inequalities are

$$(x + y)/2 > \sqrt{xy},$$

$$(x + y)^2/4 > xy,$$

$$(x + y)^2 > 4xy,$$

$$x^2 + 2xy + y^2 > 4xy,$$

$$x^2 - 2xy + y^2 > 0,$$

$$(x - y)^2 > 0.$$

Because $(x - y)^2 > 0$ when $x \neq y$, it follows that the final inequality is true. Because all these inequalities are equivalent, it follows that $(x + y)/2 > \sqrt{xy}$ when $x \neq y$. Once we have carried out this backward reasoning, we can easily reverse the steps to construct a proof using forward reasoning. We now give this proof.

Suppose that x and y are distinct real numbers. Then $(x - y)^2 > 0$ because the square of a nonzero real number is positive. Because $(x - y)^2 = x^2 - 2xy + y^2$, this implies that $x^2 - 2xy + y^2 > 0$. Adding $4xy$ to both sides, we obtain $x^2 + 2xy + y^2 > 4xy$. Because $x^2 + 2xy + y^2 = (x + y)^2$, this means that $(x + y)^2 \geqslant 4xy$. Dividing both sides of this equation by 4, we see that $(x + y)^2/4 > xy$. Finally, taking square roots of both sides (which preserves the inequality because both sides are positive) yields $(x + y)/2 > \sqrt{xy}$. We conclude that if x and y are distinct positive real numbers, then their arithmetic mean $(x+y)/2$ is greater than their geometric mean $\sqrt{xy}$.   ◀

Example 15   Suppose that two people play a game taking turns removing one, two, or three stones at a time from a pile that begins with 15 stones. The person who removes the last stone wins the game. Show that the first player can win the game no matter what the second player does.

Solution: To prove that the first player can always win the game, we work backward. At the last step, the first player can win if this player is left with a pile containing one, two, or three stones. The second player will be forced to leave one, two, or three stones if this player has to remove stones from a pile containing four stones. Consequently, one way for the first person to win is to leave four stones for the second player on the next-to-last move. The first person can leave four stones when there are five, six, or seven stones left at the beginning of this player's move, which happens when the second player has to remove stones from a pile with eight stones. Consequently, to force the second player to leave five, six , or seven stones, the first player should leave eight stones for the second player at the second-to-last move for the first player. This means that there are nine, ten, or eleven stones when the first player makes this move. Similarly, the first player should leave twelve stones when this player makes the first move. We can reverse this argument to show that the first player can always make moves so that this player wins the game no matter what the second player does. These moves successively leave twelve, eight, and four stones for the second player.   ◀

Adapting Existing Proofs   An excellent way to look for possible approaches that can be used to prove a statement is to take advantage of existing proofs. Often an existing proof can be adapted to prove a new result. Even when this is not the case, some of the ideas used in existing proofs may be helpful. Because existing proofs provide clues for new proofs, you should read and understand the proofs you encounter in your studies. This process is illustrated in Example 16.

Example 16   In Example 10 of Section 1.6 we proved that $\sqrt{2}$ is irrational. We now conjecture that $\sqrt{3}$ is irrational. Can we adapt the proof in Example 10 in Section 1.6 to show that $\sqrt{3}$ is irrational?

Solution: To adapt the proof in Example 10 in Section 1.6, we begin by mimicking the steps in that proof, but with $\sqrt{2}$ replaced with $\sqrt{3}$. First, we suppose that $\sqrt{3} = d/c$ where the fraction c/d is in lowest terms. Squaring both sides tells us that $3 = c^2/d^2$, so that $3d^2 = c^2$. Can we use this equation to show that 3 must be a factor of both c and d, similar to how we used the equation $2b^2 = a^2$ in Example 10 in Section 1.6 to show that 2 must be a factor of both a and b? (Recall that an integer s is a factor of the integer t if t/s is an integer. An integer n is even if and only if 2 is a factor of n.) In turns out that we can, but we need some ammunition from number theory. We sketch out the remainder of the proof. Because 3 is a factor of c^2, it must also be a factor of c. Furthermore, because 3 is a factor of c, 9 is a factor of c^2, which means that 9 is a factor of $3d^2$. This implies that 3 is a factor of d^2, which means that 3 is a factor of that d. This makes 3 a factor of both c and d, which is a contradiction. After we have filled in the justification for these steps, we will have shown that $\sqrt{3}$ is irrational by adapting the proof that $\sqrt{2}$ is irrational. Note that this proof can be extended to show that $\sqrt{n}$ is irrational whenever n is a positive integer that is not a perfect square.   ◄

A good tip is to look for existing proofs that you might adapt when you are confronted with proving a new theorem, particularly when the new theorem seems similar to one you have already proved.

Looking for Counterexamples

In Section 1.5 we introduced the use of counterexamples to show that certain statements are false. When confronted with a conjecture, you might first try to prove this conjecture, and if your attempts are unsuccessful, you might try to find a counterexample. If you cannot find a counterexample, you might again try to prove the statement. In any case, looking for counterexamples is an extremely important pursuit, which often provides insights into problems. We will illustrate the role of counterexamples with a few examples.

Example 17   In Example 14 in Section 1.6 we showed that the statement "Every positive integer is the sum of two squares of integers" is false by finding a counterexample. That is, there are positive integers that cannot be written as the sum of the squares of two integers. Although we cannot write every positive integer as the sum of the squares of two integers, maybe we can write every positive integer as the sum of the squares of three integers. That is, is the statement "Every positive integer is the sum of the squares of three integers" true or false?

Solution: Because we know that not every positive integer can be written as the sum of two squares of integers, we might initially be skeptical that every positive integer can be written as the sum of three squares of integers. So, we first look for a counterexample. That is, we can show that the statement "Every positive integer is the sum of three squares of integers" is false if we can find a particular integer that is not the sum of the squares of three integers. To look for a counterexample, we try to write successive positive integers as a sum of three squares. We find that $1 = 0^2 + 0^2 + 1^2$, $2 = 0^2 + 1^2 + 1^2$, $3 = 1^2 + 1^2 + 1^2$, $4 = 0^2 + 0^2 + 2^2$, $5 = 0^2 + 1^2 + 2^2$, $6 = 1^2 + 1^2 + 2^2$, but we cannot find a way to write 7 as the sum of three squares. To show that there are not three squares that add up to 7, we note that the only possible squares we can use are those not exceeding 7, namely, 0, 1, and 4. Because no three terms where each term is 0, 1, or 4 add up to 7, it follows that 7 is a counterexample. We conclude that the statement "Every positive integer is the sum of the squares of three integers" is false.

We have shown that not every positive integer is the sum of the squares of three integers. The next question to ask is whether every positive integer is the sum of the squares of four positive integers. Some experimentation provides evidence that the answer is yes. For example, $7 = 1^2 + 1^2 + 1^2 + 2^2$, $25 = 4^2 + 2^2 + 2^2 + 1^2$, and $87 = 9^2 + 2^2 + 1^2 + 1^2$. It turns out the conjecture "Every positive integer is the sum of the squares of four integers" is true. For a proof, see [Ro05].
◄

Proof Strategy in Action

Mathematics is generally taught as if mathematical facts were carved in stone. Mathematics texts (including the bulk of this book) formally present theorems and their proofs. Such presentations do not convey the discovery process in mathematics. This process begins with exploring concepts and examples, asking questions, formulating conjectures, and attempting to settle these conjectures either by proof or by counterexample. These are the day-to-day activities of mathematicians. Believe it or not, the material taught in textbooks was originally developed in this way.

People formulate conjectures on the basis of many types of possible evidence. The examination of special cases can lead to a conjecture, as can the identification of possible patterns. Altering the hypotheses and conclusions of known theorems also can lead to plausible conjectures. At other times, conjectures are made based on intuition or a belief that a result holds. No matter how a conjecture was made, once it has been formulated, the goal is to prove or disprove it. When mathematicians believe that a conjecture may be true, they try to find a proof. If they cannot find a proof, they may look for a counterexample. When they cannot find a counterexample, they may switch gears and once again try to prove the conjecture. Although many conjectures are quickly settled, a few conjectures resist attack for hundreds of years and lead to the development of new parts of mathematics. We will mention a few famous conjectures later in this section.

Tilings

We can illustrate aspects of proof strategy through a brief study of tilings of checkerboards. Looking at tilings of checkerboards is a fruitful way to quickly discover and prove many different results, with these proofs using a variety of proof methods. There are almost an endless number of conjectures that can be made and studied in this area too. To begin, we need to define some terms. A **checkerboard** is a rectangle divided into squares of the same size by horizontal and vertical lines. The game of checkers is played on a board with 8 rows and 8 columns; this board is called the **standard checkerboard** and is shown in Figure 2. In this section we use the term **board** to refer to a checkerboard of any rectangular size as well as parts of checkerboards obtained by removing one or more squares. A **domino** is a rectangular piece that is one square by two squares, as shown in Figure 3. We say that a board is **tiled** by dominoes when all its squares are covered with no overlapping dominoes and no dominoes overhanging the board. We now develop some results about tiling boards using dominoes.

Example 18   Can we tile the standard checkerboard using dominoes?

Solution: We can find many ways to tile the standard checkerboard using dominoes. For example, we can tile it by placing 32 dominoes horizontally, as shown in Figure 4. The existence of one such tiling completes a constructive existence proof. Of course, there are a large number of other ways to do this tiling. We can place 32 dominoes vertically on the board or we can place some tiles vertically and some horizontally. But for a constructive existence proof we needed to find just one such tiling.
◄

Example 19   Can we tile a board obtained by removing one of the four corner squares of a standard checkerboard?

Solution: To answer this question, note that a standard checkerboard has 64 squares, so removing a square produces a board with 63 squares. Now suppose that we could tile a board obtained from the standard checkerboard by removing a corner square. The board has an even number of squares because each domino covers two squares and no two dominoes overlap and no dominoes overhang the board. Consequently, we can prove by contradiction that a standard checkerboard with one square removed cannot be tiled using dominoes because such a board has an odd number of squares.   ◀

We now consider a trickier situation.

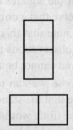

Figure 2   The Standard Checkerboard.   Figure 3   Two Dominoes.

Example 20   Can we tile the board obtained by deleting the upper left and lower right corner squares of a standard checkerboard, shown in Figure 5?

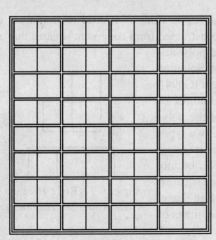

Figure 4   Tiling the Standard Checkerboard.   Figure 5   The Standard Checkerboard with the Upper
                                                                                    Left and Lower Right Squares Removed.

Solution: A board obtained by deleting two squares of a standard checkerboard contains 64 − 2 = 62 squares. Because 62 is even, we cannot quickly rule out the existence of a tiling of the standard checkerboard with its upper left and lower right squares removed, unlike Example 19, where we ruled out the existence of a tiling of the standard checkerboard with one corner square removed. Trying to construct a tiling of this board by successively placing dominoes might be a first approach, as the reader should attempt. However, no matter how much we try, we cannot find such a tiling. Because our efforts do not produce a tiling, we are led to conjecture that no tiling exists.

We might try to prove that no tiling exists by showing that we reach a dead end however we successively place dominoes on the board. To construct such a proof, we would have to consider all possible cases that arise as we run through all possible choices of successively placing dominoes. For example, we have two choices for covering the square in the second column of the first row, next to the removed top left corner. We could cover it with a horizontally placed tile or a vertically placed tile. Each of these two choices leads to further choices, and so on. It does not take long to see that this is not a fruitful plan of attack for a person, although a computer could be used to complete such a proof by exhaustion. (Exercise 11 asks you to supply such a proof to show that a 4×4 checkerboard with opposite corners removed cannot be tiled.)

We need another approach. Perhaps there is an easier way to prove there is no tiling of a standard checkerboard with two opposite corners. As with many proofs, a key observation can help. We color the squares of this checkerboard using alternating white and black squares, as in Figure 2. Observe that a domino in a tiling of such a board covers one white square and one black square. Next, note that this board has unequal numbers of white square and black squares. We can use these observations to prove by contradiction that a standard checkerboard with opposite corners removed cannot be tiled using dominoes. We now present such a proof.

Proof: Suppose we can use dominoes to tile a standard checkerboard with opposite corners removed. Note that the standard checkerboard with opposite corners removed contains $64 - 2 = 62$ squares. The tiling would use $62/2 = 31$ dominoes. Note that each domino in this tiling covers one white and one black square. Consequently, the tiling covers 31 white squares and 31 black squares. However, when we remove two opposite corner squares, either 32 of the remaining squares are white and 30 are black or else 30 are white and 32 are black. This contradicts the assumption that we can use dominoes to cover a standard checkerboard with opposite corners removed, completing the proof.   ◄

We can use other types of pieces besides dominoes in tilings. Instead of dominoes we can study tilings that use identically shaped pieces constructed from congruent squares that are connected along their edges. Such pieces are called **polyomi-noes**, a term coined in 1953 by the mathematician Solomon Golomb, the author of an entertaining book about them [Go94]. We will consider two polyominoes with the same number of squares the same if we can rotate and/or flip one of the poly-ominoes to get the other one. For example, there are two types of triominoes (see Figure 6), which are polyominoes made up of three squares connected by their sides. One type of triomino, the **straight triomino**, has three horizontally connected squares; the other type, **right triominoes**, resembles the letter L in shape, flipped and/or rotated, if necessary. We will study the tilings of a checkerboard by straight triominoes here.

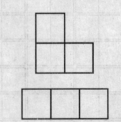

Figure 6   A Right Triomino and a Straight Triomino.

Example 21   Can you use straight triominoes to tile a standard checkerboard?

Solution: The standard checkerboard contains 64 squares and each triomino covers three squares. Consequently, if triominoes tile a board, the number of squares of the board must be a multiple of 3. Because 64 is not a multiple of 3, triominoes cannot be used to cover an 8×8 checkerboard.

◄

In Example 22, we consider the problem of using straight triominoes to tile a standard checkerboard with one corner missing.

Example 22   Can we use straight triominoes to tile a standard checkerboard with one of its four corners removed? An 8×8 checkerboard with one corner removed contains $64 - 1 = 63$ squares. Any tiling by straight triominoes of one of these four boards uses $63/3 = 21$ triominoes. However, when we experiment, we cannot find a tiling of one of these boards using straight triominoes. A proof by exhaustion does not appear promising. Can we adapt our proof from Example 20 to prove that no such tiling exists?

Solution: We will color the squares of the checkerboard in an attempt to adapt the proof by contradiction we gave in Example 20 of the impossibility of using dominoes to tile a standard checkerboard with opposite corners removed. Because we are using straight triominoes rather than dominoes, we color the squares using three colors rather than two colors, as shown in Figure 7. Note that there are 21 green squares, 21 black squares, and 22 white squares in this coloring. Next, we make the crucial observation that when a straight triomino covers three squares of the checkerboard, it covers one green square, one black square, and one white square. Next, note that each of the three colors appears in a corner square. Thus without loss of generality, we may assume that we have rotated the coloring so that the missing square is colored green. Therefore, we assume that the remaining board contains 20 green squares, 21 black squares, and 22 white squares.

Figure 7   Coloring the Squares of the Standard Checkerboard with Opposite Squares Removed
with Three Colors.

If we could tile this board using straight triominoes, then we would use $63/3 = 21$ straight triominoes. These triominoes would cover 21 green squares, 21 black squares, and 21 white squares. This contradicts the fact that this board contains 20 green squares, 21 black squares, and 22 white squares. Therefore we cannot tile this board using straight triominoes.   ◄

The Role of Open Problems

Many advances in mathematics have been made by people trying to solve famous unsolved problems. In the past 20 years, many unsolved problems have finally been resolved, such as the proof of a conjecture in number theory made more than 300 years ago. This conjecture asserts the truth of the statement known as **Fermat's Last Theorem**.

Theorem 1   Fermat's Last Theorem   The equation

$$x^n + y^n = z^n$$

has no solutions in integers x, y, and z with $xyz \neq 0$ whenever n is an integer with $n > 2$.

Remark: The equation $x^2 + y^2 = z^2$ has infinitely many solutions in integers x, y, and z; these solutions are called Pythagorean triples and correspond to the lengths of the sides of right triangles with integer lengths.

This problem has a fascinating history. In the seventeenth century, Fermat jotted in the margin of his copy of the works of Diophantus that he had a "wondrous proof" that there are no integer solutions of $x^n + y^n = z^n$ when n is an integer greater than 2 with $xyz \neq 0$. However, he never published a proof (Fermat published almost nothing), and no proof could be found in the papers he left when he died. Mathematicians looked for a proof for three centuries without success, although many people were convinced that a relatively simple proof could be found. (Proofs of special cases were found, such as the proof of the case when $n = 3$ by Euler and the proof of the $n = 4$ case by Fermat himself.) Over the years, several established mathematicians thought that they had proved this theorem. In the nineteenth century, one of these failed attempts led to the development of the part of number theory called algebraic number theory. A correct proof, requiring hundreds of pages of advanced mathematics, was not found until the 1990s, when Andrew Wiles used recently developed ideas from a sophisticated area of number theory called the theory of elliptic curves to prove Fermat's last theorem. Wiles's quest to find a proof of Fermat's last theorem using this powerful theory, described in a program in the *Nova* series on public television, took close to ten years! (The interested reader should consult [Ro05] for more information about Fermat's Last Theorem and for additional references concerning this problem and its resolution.)

We now state an open problem that is simple to describe, but that seems quite difficult to resolve.

Example 23   *The $3x + 1$ Conjecture*   Let T be the transformation that sends an even integer x to $x/2$ and an odd integer x to $3x + 1$. A famous conjecture, sometimes known as the **$3x + 1$ conjecture,** states that for all positive integers x, when we repeatedly apply the transformation T, we will eventually reach the integer 1. For example, starting with $x = 13$, we find $T(13) = 3 \cdot 13 + 1 = 40$, $T(40) = 40/2 = 20$, $T(20) = 20/2 = 10$, $T(10) = 10/2 = 5$, $T(5) = 3 \cdot 5 + 1 = 16$, $T(16) = 8$, $T(8) = 4$, $T(4) = 2$, and $T(2) = 1$. The $3x + 1$ conjecture has been verified for all integers x up to $5.6 \cdot 10^{13}$.

The $3x + 1$ conjecture has an interesting history and has attracted the attention of mathematicians since the 1950s. The conjecture has been raised many times and goes by many other names, including the Collatz problem, Hasse's algorithm, Ulam's problem, the Syracuse problem, and Kakutani's problem. Many mathematicians have been diverted from their work to spend time attacking this conjecture. This led to the joke that this problem was part of a conspiracy to slow down American mathematical research. See the article by Jeffrey Lagarias [La85] for a fascinating discussion of this problem and the results that have been found by mathematicians attacking it.   ◀

Additional Proof Methods

In this chapter we introduced the basic methods used in proofs. We also described how to leverage these methods to prove a variety of results. We will use these proof methods in Chapter 2 to prove results about sets, functions, algorithms, and number theory. Among the theorems we will prove is the famous halting theorem which states that there is a problem that cannot be solved using any procedure. However, there are many important proof methods besides those we have covered. We will introduce some of these methods later in this book. We will use the Cantor diagonalization method, which can be used to prove results about the size of infinite sets, in Section 2.4. In Chapter 3 we will introduce the notion of combinatorial proofs, which can be used to prove results by counting arguments. The reader should note that entire books have been devoted to the activities discussed in this section, including many excellent works by George Pólya ([Po61], [Po71], [Po90]).

Finally, note that we have not given a procedure that can be used for proving theorems in mathematics. It is a deep theorem of mathematical logic that there is no such procedure.

Exercises

1. Prove that $n^2 + 1 \geqslant 2^n$ when n is a positive integer with $1 \leqslant n \leqslant 4$.

2. Prove that if x and y are real numbers, then $\max(x, y) + \min(x, y) = x + y$. [*Hint:* Use a proof by cases, with the two cases corresponding to $x \geqslant y$ and $x < y$, respectively.]

3. Prove the **triangle inequality,** which states that if x and y are real numbers, then $|x| + |y| \geqslant |x + y|$ (where $|x|$ represents the absolute value of x, which equals x if $x \geqslant 0$ and equals $-x$ if $x < 0$).

4. Prove that there are 100 consecutive positive integers that are not perfect squares. Is your proof constructive or nonconstructive?

5. Prove that there exists a pair of consecutive integers such that one of these integers is a perfect square and the other is a perfect cube.

6. Prove or disprove that there is a rational number x and an irrational number y such that x^y is irrational.

7. Show that each of these statements can be used to express the fact that there is a unique element x such that $P(x)$ is true. [Note that we can also write this statement as $\exists! x P(x)$.]
   a) $\exists x \forall y (P(y) \leftrightarrow x = y)$ b) $\exists x P(x) \wedge \forall x \forall y (P(x) \wedge P(y) \rightarrow x = y)$
   c) $\exists x (P(x) \wedge \forall y (P(y) \rightarrow x = y))$

8. Suppose that a and b are odd integers with $a \neq b$. Show there is a unique integer c such that $|a - c| = |b - c|$.

9. Show that if n is an odd integer, then there is a unique integer k such that n is the sum of $k - 2$ and $k + 3$.

10. Prove that given a real number x there exist unique numbers n and ϵ such that $x = n - \epsilon$, n is an integer, and $0 \leqslant \epsilon < 1$.

11. The **harmonic mean** of two real numbers x and y equals $2xy/(x + y)$. By computing the harmonic and geometric means of different pairs of positive real numbers, formulate a conjecture about their relative sizes and prove your conjecture.

*12. Write the numbers $1, 2, \ldots, 2n$ on a blackboard, where n is an odd integer. Pick any two of the numbers, j and k, write $|j - k|$ on the board and erase j and k. Continue this process until only one integer is written on the board. Prove that this integer must be odd.

13. Formulate a conjecture about the decimal digits that appear as the final decimal digit of the fourth power of an integer. Prove your conjecture using a proof by cases.

14. Prove that there is no positive integer n such that $n^2 + n^3 = 100$.

15. Prove that there are no solutions in positive integers x and y to the equation $x^4 + y^4 = 625$.

16. Adapt the proof in Example 4 in Section 1.6 to prove that if $n = abc$, where a, b, and c are positive integers, then $a \leqslant \sqrt[3]{n}$, $b \leqslant \sqrt[3]{n}$, or $c \leqslant \sqrt[3]{n}$.

17. Prove that between every two rational numbers there is an irrational number.

*18. Let $S = x_1 y_1 + x_2 y_2 + \cdots + x_n y_n$, where $x_1, x_2, \ldots, x_n$ and $y_1, y_2, \ldots, y_n$ are orderings of two different sequences of positive real numbers, each containing n elements.

   a) Show that S takes its maximum value over all orderings of the two sequences when both sequences are sorted (so that the elements in each sequence are in nondecreasing order).
   b) Show that S takes its minimum value over all orderings of the two sequences when one sequence is sorted into nondecreasing order and the other is sorted into nonincreasing order.

19. Verify the $3x + 1$ conjecture for these integers.
   a) 6   b) 7   c) 17   d) 21

20. Prove or disprove that you can use dominoes to tile the standard checkerboard with two adjacent corners removed (that is, corners that are not opposite).

21. Prove that you can use dominoes to tile a rectangular checkerboard with an even number of squares.

22. Use a proof by exhaustion to show that a tiling using dominoes of a 4×4 checkerboard with opposite corners removed does not exist. [*Hint:* First show that you can assume that the squares in the upper left and lower right corners are removed. Number the squares of the original checkerboard from 1 to 16, starting in the first row, moving right in this row, then starting in the leftmost square in the second row and moving right, and so on. Remove squares 1 and 16. To begin the proof, note that square 2 is covered either by a domino laid horizontally, which covers squares 2 and 3, or vertically, which covers squares 2 and 6. Consider each of these cases separately, and work through all the subcases that arise.]

23. Show that by removing two white squares and two black squares from an 8×8 checkerboard (colored as in the text) you can make it impossible to tile the remaining squares using dominoes.

*__24.__ a) Draw each of the five different tetrominoes, where a tetromino is a polyomino consisting of four squares.

b) For each of the five different tetrominoes, prove or disprove that you can tile a standard checkerboard using these tetrominoes.

Key Terms and Results

TERMS

proposition: a statement that is true or false

propositional variable: a variable that represents a proposition

truth value: true or false

$\neg p$ **(negation of p):** the proposition with truth value opposite to the truth value of p

logical operators: operators used to combine propositions

compound proposition: a proposition constructed by combining propositions using logical operators

truth table: a table displaying the truth values of propositions

$p \vee q$ **(disjunction of p and q):** the proposition "p or q," which is true if and only if at least one of p and q is true

$p \wedge q$ **(conjunction of p and q):** the proposition "p and q" which is true if and only if both p and q are true

$p \oplus q$ **(exclusive or of p and q):** the proposition "p XOR q" which is true when exactly one of p and q is true

$p \rightarrow q$ **(p implies q):** the proposition "if p, then q," which is false if and only if p is true and q is false

converse of $p \rightarrow q$: the conditional statement $q \rightarrow p$

contrapositive of $p \rightarrow q$: the conditional statement $\neg q \rightarrow \neg p$

inverse of $p \rightarrow q$: the conditional statement $\neg p \rightarrow \neg q$

$p \leftrightarrow q$ **(biconditional):** the proposition "p if and only if q," which is true if and only if p and q have the same truth value

bit: either a 0 or a 1

Boolean variable: a variable that has a value of 0 or 1

bit operation: an operation on a bit or bits

bit string: a list of bits

bitwise operations: operations on bit strings that operate on each bit in one string and the corresponding bit in the other string

tautology: a compound proposition that is always true

contradiction: a compound proposition that is always false

contingency: a compound proposition that is sometimes true and sometimes false

consistent compound propositions: compound propositions for which there is an assignment of truth values to the variables that makes all these propositions true

logically equivalent compound propositions: compound propositions that always have the same truth values

predicate: part of a sentence that attributes a property to the subject

propositional function: a statement containing one or more variables that becomes a proposition when each of its variables is assigned a value or is bound by a quantifier

domain (or universe) of discourse: the values a variable in a propositional function may take

∃x P(x) (existential quantification of P(x)): the proposition that is true if and only if there exists an x in the domain such that $P(x)$ is true

∀xP(x) (universal quantification of P(x)): the proposition that is true if and only if $P(x)$ is true for every x in the domain

logically equivalent expressions: expressions that have the same truth value no matter which propositional functions and domains are used

free variable: a variable not bound in a propositional function

bound variable: a variable that is quantified

scope of a quantifier: portion of a statement where the quantifier binds its variable

argument: a sequence of statements

argument form: a sequence of compound propositions involving propositional variables

premise: a statement, in an argument, or argument form, other than the final one

conclusion: the final statement in an argument or argument form

valid argument form: a sequence of compound propositions involving propositional variables where the truth of all the premises implies the truth of the conclusion

valid argument: an argument with a valid argument form

rule of inference: a valid argument form that can be used in the demonstration that arguments are valid

fallacy: an invalid argument form often used incorrectly as a rule of inference (or sometimes, more generally, an incorrect argument)

circular reasoning or begging the question: reasoning where one or more steps are based on the truth of the statement being proved

theorem: a mathematical assertion that can be shown to be true

conjecture: a mathematical assertion proposed to be true, but that has not been proved

proof: a demonstration that a theorem is true

axiom: a statement that is assumed to be true and that can be used as a basis for proving theorems

lemma: a theorem used to prove other theorems

corollary: a proposition that can be proved as a consequence of a theorem that has just been proved

vacuous proof: a proof that $p \rightarrow q$ is true based on the fact that p is false

trivial proof: a proof that $p \rightarrow q$ is true based on the fact that q is true

direct proof: a proof that $p \rightarrow q$ is true that proceeds by showing that q must be true when p is true

proof by contraposition: a proof that $p \rightarrow q$ is true that proceeds by showing that p must be false when q is false

proof by contradiction: a proof that p is true based on the truth of the conditional statement $\neg p \rightarrow q$, where q is a contradiction

exhaustive proof: a proof that establishes a result by checking a list of all cases

proof by cases: a proof broken into separate cases where these cases cover all possibilities

without loss of generality: an assumption in a proof that makes it possible to prove a theorem by reducing the number of cases needed in the proof

counterexample: an element x such that $P(x)$ is false

constructive existence proof: a proof that an element with a specified property exists that explicitly finds such an element

nonconstructive existence proof: a proof that an element with a specified property exists that does not explicitly find such an element

rational number: a number that can be expressed as the ratio of two integers p and q such that $q \neq 0$

uniqueness proof: a proof that there is exactly one element satisfying a specified property

RESULTS

The logical equivalences given in Tables 6, 7, and 8 in Section 1.2.
De Morgan's laws for quantifiers.

Rules of inference for propositional calculus.
Rules of inference for quantified statements.

Review Questions

1. a) Define the negation of a proposition.

   b) What is the negation of "This is a boring course"?

2. a) Define (using truth tables) the disjunction, conjunction, exclusive or, conditional, and biconditional of the propositions p and q.

   b) What are the disjunction, conjunction, exclusive or, conditional, and biconditional of the propositions "I'll go to the movies tonight" and "I'll finish my discrete mathematics homework"?

3. a) Describe at least five different ways to write the conditional statement $p \rightarrow q$ in English.

   b) Define the converse and contrapositive of a conditional statement.

   c) State the converse and the contrapositive of the conditional statement "If it is sunny tomorrow, then I will go for a walk in the woods."

4. a) What does it mean for two propositions to be logically equivalent?

   b) Describe the different ways to show that two compound propositions are logically equivalent.

   c) Show in at least two different ways that the compound propositions $\neg p \vee (r \rightarrow \neg q)$ and $\neg p \vee \neg q \vee \neg r$ are equivalent.

5. *(Depends on the Exercise Set in Section 1.2)*

   a) Given a truth table, explain how to use disjunctive normal form to construct a compound proposition with this truth table.

   b) Explain why part (a) shows that the operators $\wedge$, $\vee$, and $\neg$ are functionally complete.

   c) Is there an operator such that the set containing just this operator is functionally complete?

6. What are the universal and existential quantifications of a predicate $P(x)$? What are their negations?

7. a) What is the difference between the quantification $\exists x \forall y P(x, y)$ and $\forall y \exists x P(x, y)$, where $P(x, y)$ is a predicate?

   b) Give an example of a predicate $P(x, y)$ such that $\exists x \forall y P(x, y)$ and $\forall y \exists x P(x, y)$ have different truth values.

8. Describe what is meant by a valid argument in propositional logic and show that the argument "If the earth is flat, then you can sail off the edge of the earth," "You cannot sail off the edge of the earth," therefore, "The earth is not flat" is a valid argument.

9. Use rules of inference to show that if the premises "All zebras have stripes" and "Mark is a zebra" are true, then the conclusion "Mark has stripes" is true.

10. a) Describe what is meant by a direct proof, a proof by contraposition, and a proof by contradiction of a conditional statement $p \rightarrow q$.

    b) Give a direct proof, a proof by contraposition and a proof by contradiction of the statement: "If n is even, then $n + 4$ is even."

11. a) Describe a way to prove the biconditional $p \leftrightarrow q$.

    b) Prove the statement: "The integer $3n + 2$ is odd if and only if the integer $9n + 5$ is even, where n is an integer."

12. To prove that the statements p_1, p_2, p_3, and p_4 are equivalent, is it sufficient to show that the conditional statements $p_4 \rightarrow p_2$, $p_3 \rightarrow p_1$, and $p_1 \rightarrow p_2$ are valid? If not, provide another set of conditional statements that can be used to show that the four statements are equivalent.

13. a) Suppose that a statement of the form $\forall x P(x)$ is false. How can this be proved?

    b) Show that the statement "For every positive integer n, $n^2 \geqslant 2n$" is false.

14. What is the difference between a constructive and nonconstructive existence proof? Give an example of each.

15. What are the elements of a proof that there is a unique element x such that $P(x)$, where $P(x)$ is a propositional function?

16. Explain how a proof by cases can be used to prove a result about absolute values, such as the fact that $|xy| = |x||y|$ for all real numbers x and y.

Supplementary Exercises

1. Let p be the proposition "I will do every exercise in this book" and q be the proposition "I will get an "A" in this course." Express each of these as a combination of p and q.
    a) I will get an "A" in this course only if I do every exercise in this book.
    b) I will get an "A" in this course and I will do every exercise in this book.
    c) Either I will not get an "A" in this course or I will not do every exercise in this book.
    d) For me to get an "A" in this course it is necessary and sufficient that I do every exercise in this book.

2. Find the truth table of the compound proposition $(p \vee q) \rightarrow (p \wedge \neg r)$.

3. Show that these compound propositions are tautologies.
    a) $(\neg q \wedge (p \rightarrow q)) \rightarrow \neg p$ b) $((p \vee q) \wedge \neg p) \rightarrow q$

4. Give the converse, the contrapositive, and the inverse of these conditional statements.
    a) If it rains today, then I will drive to work.   b) If $|x| = x$, then $x \geqslant 0$.
    c) If n is greater than 3, then n^2 is greater than 9.

5. Given a conditional statement $p \rightarrow q$, find the converse of its inverse, the converse of its converse, and the converse of its contrapositive.

6. Given a conditional statement $p \rightarrow q$, find the inverse of its inverse, the inverse of its converse, and the inverse of its contrapositive.

7. Find a compound proposition involving the propositional variables p, q, r, and s that is true when exactly three of these propositional variables are true and is false otherwise.

8. Show that these statements are inconsistent: "If Sergei takes the job offer then he will get a signing bonus." "If Sergei takes the job offer, then he will receive a higher salary." "If Sergei gets a signing bonus, then he will not receive a higher salary." "Sergei takes the job offer."

9. Show that these statements are inconsistent: "If Miranda does not take a course in discrete mathematics, then she will not graduate." "If Miranda does not graduate, then she is not qualified for the job." "If Miranda reads this book, then she is qualified for the job." "Miranda does not take a course in discrete mathematics but she reads this book."

10. Suppose that you meet three people, A, B, and C, on the island of knights and knaves described in Example 18 in Section 1.1. What are A, B, and C if A says "I am a knave and B is a knight" and B says "Exactly one of the three of us is a knight"?

11. (Adapted from [Sm78]) Suppose that on an island there are three types of people, knights, knaves, and normals. Knights always tell the truth, knaves always lie, and normals sometimes lie and sometimes tell the truth. Detectives questioned three inhabitants of the island—Amy, Brenda, and Claire—as part of the investigation of a crime. The detectives knew that one of the three committed the crime, but not which one. They also knew that the criminal was a knight, and that the other two were not. Additionally, the detectives recorded these statements: Amy: "I am innocent." Brenda: "What Amy says is true." Claire: "Brenda is not a normal." After analyzing their information, the detectives positively identified the guilty party. Who was it?

12. Show that if S is a proposition, where S is the conditional statement "If S is true, then unicorns live," then "Unicorns live" is true. Show that it follows that S cannot be a proposition. (This paradox is known as *Löb's paradox*.)

13. Show that the argument with premises "The tooth fairy is a real person" and "The truth fairy is not a real person" and conclusion "You can find gold at the end of the rainbow" is a valid argument. Does this show that the conclusion is true?

14. Let $P(x)$ be the statement "student x knows calculus" and let $Q(y)$ be the statement "class y contains a student who knows calculus." Express each of these as quantifications of $P(x)$ and $Q(y)$.

    a) Some students know calculus.

    b) Not every student knows calculus.

    c) Every class has a student in it who knows calculus.

    d) Every student in every class knows calculus.

    e) There is at least one class with no students who know calculus.

15. Let $P(m, n)$ be the statement "m divides n," where the domain for both variables consists of all positive integers. (By "m divides n" we mean that $n = km$ for some integer k.) Determine the truth values of each of these statements.

    a) $P(4, 5)$ b) $P(2, 4)$ c) $\forall m \, \forall n \, P(m, n)$ d) $\exists m \, \forall n \, P(m, n)$ e) $\exists n \, \forall m \, P(m, n)$ f) $\forall n \, P(1, n)$

16. Find a domain for the quantifiers in $\exists x \exists y (x \neq y \land \forall z ((z = x) \lor (z = y))$ such that this statement is true.

17. Find a domain for the quantifiers in $\exists x \exists y (x \neq y \land \forall z ((z = x) \lor (z = y)))$ such that this statement is false.

18. Use existential and universal quantifiers to express the statement "No one has more than three grandmothers" using the propositional function $G(x, y)$, which represents "x is the grandmother of y."

19. Use existential and universal quantifiers to express the statement "Everyone has exactly two biological parents" using the propositional function $P(x, y)$, which represents "x is the biological parent of y."

20. The quantifier $\exists_n$ denotes "there exists exactly n," so that $\exists_n x P(x)$ means there exist exactly n values in the domain such that $P(x)$ is true. Determine the true value of these statement where the domain consists of all real numbers.

    a) $\exists_0 x (x^2 = -1)$ b) $\exists_1 x (|x| = 0)$ c) $\exists_2 x (x^2 = 2)$ d) $\exists_3 x (x = |x|)$

21. Express each of these statements using existential and universal quantifiers and propositional logic where $\exists_n$ is defined in Exercise 20.

    a) $\exists_0 x P(x)$ b) $\exists_1 x P(x)$ c) $\exists_2 x P(x)$ d) $\exists_3 x P(x)$

22. Let $P(x, y)$ be a propositional function. Show that $\exists x \, \forall y \, P(x, y) \to \forall y \, \exists x \, P(x, y)$ is a tautology.

23. Let $P(x)$ and $Q(x)$ be propositional functions. Show that $\exists x \, (P(x) \to Q(x))$ and $\forall x \, P(x) \to \exists x \, Q(x)$ always have the same truth value.

24. If $\forall y \, \exists x \, P(x, y)$ is true, does it necessarily follow that $\exists x \, \forall y \, P(x, y)$ is true?

25. If $\forall x \, \exists y \, P(x, y)$ is true, does it necessarily follow that $\exists x \, \forall y \, P(x, y)$ is true?

26. Find the negations of these statements.

    a) If it snows today, then I will go skiing tomorrow.

    b) Every person in this class understands mathematical induction.

    c) Some students in this class do not like discrete mathematics.

    d) In every mathematics class there is some student who falls asleep during lectures.

27. Express this statement using quantifiers: "Every student in this class has taken some course in every department in the school of mathematical sciences."

28. Express this statement using quantifiers: "There is a building on the campus of some college in the United States in which every room is painted white."

29. Express the statement "There is exactly one student in this class who has taken exactly one mathematics class at this school" using the uniqueness quantifier. Then express this statement using quantifiers, without using the uniqueness quantifier.

30. Describe a rule of inference that can be used to prove that there are exactly two elements x and y in a domain such that $P(x)$ and $P(y)$ are true. Express this rule of inference as a statement in English.

31. Use rules of inference to show that if the premises $\forall x(P(x) \rightarrow Q(x))$, $\forall x(Q(x) \rightarrow R(x))$, and $\neg R(a)$, where a is in the domain, are true, then the conclusion $\neg P(a)$ is true.

32. Prove that if x^3 is irrational, then x is irrational.

33. Prove that if x is irrational and $x \geqslant 0$, then $\sqrt{x}$ is irrational.

34. Prove that given a nonnegative integer n, there is a unique nonnegative integer m such that $m^2 \leqslant n < (m+1)^2$.

35. Prove that there exists an integer m such that $m^2 > 10^{1000}$. Is your proof constructive or nonconstructive?

36. Prove that there is a positive integer that can be written as the sum of squares of positive integers in two different ways. (Use a computer or calculator to speed up your work.)

37. Disprove the statement that every positive integer is the sum of the cubes of eight nonnegative integers.

38. Disprove the statement that every positive integer is the sum of at most two squares and a cube of nonnegative integers.

39. Disprove the statement that every positive integer is the sum of 36 fifth powers of nonnegative integers.

40. Assuming the truth of the theorem that states that $\sqrt{n}$ is irrational whenever n is a positive integer that is not a perfect square, prove that $\sqrt{2} + \sqrt{3}$ is irrational.

Computer Projects

Write programs with the specifiedinput and output.

1. Given the truth values of the propositions p and q, find the truth values of the conjunction, disjunction, exclusive or, conditional statement, and biconditional of these propositions.

2. Given two bit strings of length n, find the bitwise *AND*, bitwise *OR*, and bitwise *XOR* of these strings.

3. Given the truth values of the propositions p and q in fuzzy logic, find the truth value of the disjunction and the conjunction of p and q (see Exercise 21 of Section 1.1).

*4. Given positive integers m and n, interactively play the game of Chomp.

*5. Given a portion of a checkerboard, look for tilings of this checkerboard with various types of polyominoes, including dominoes, the two types of triominoes, and larger polyominoes.

Computations and Explorations

Use a computational program or programs you have written to do these exercises.

1. Look for positive integers that are not the sum of the cubes of nine different positive integers.

2. Look for positive integers greater than 79 that are not the sum of the fourth powers of 18 positive integers.

3. Find as many positive integers as you can that can be written as the sum of cubes of positive integers, in two different ways, sharing this property with 1729.

*4. Try to find winning strategies for the game of Chomp for different initial configurations of cookies.

*5. Look for tilings of checkerboards and parts of checkerboards with polynominoes.

Writing Projects

Respond to these with essays using outside sources.

1. Discuss logical paradoxes, including the paradox of Epimenides the Cretan, Jourdain's card paradox, and the barber paradox, and how they are resolved.

2. Describe how fuzzy logic is being applied to practical applications. Consult one or more of the recent books on fuzzy logic written for general audiences.

3. Describe the basic rules of *WFF'N PROOF*, *The Game of Modern Logic*, developed by Layman Allen. Give examples of some of the games included in *WFF'N PROOF*.

4. Read some of the writings of Lewis Carroll on symbolic logic. Describe in detail some of the models he used to represent logical arguments and the rules of inference he used in these arguments.

5. Extend the discussion of Prolog given in Section 1.3, explaining in more depth how Prolog employs resolution.

6. Discuss some of the techniques used in computational logic, including Skolem's rule.

7. "Automated theorem proving" is the task of using computers to mechanically prove theorems. Discuss the goals and applications of automated theorem proving and the progress made in developing automated theorem provers.

8. Describe how DNA computing has been used to solve instances of the satisfiability problem.

9. Discuss what is known about winning strategies in the game of Chomp.

10. Describe various aspects of proof strategy discussed by George Pólya in his writings on reasoning, including [Po62], [Po71], and [Po90].

11. Describe a few problems and results about tilings with polyominoes, as described in [Go94] and [Ma91], for example.

Chapter 2

Basic Structures: Sets, Functions, Sequences, and Sums

Much of discrete mathematics is devoted to the study of discrete structures, used to represent discrete objects. Many important discrete structures are built using sets, which are collections of objects. Among the discrete structures built from sets are combinations, unordered collections of objects used extensively in counting; relations, sets of ordered pairs that represent relationships between objects; graphs, sets of vertices and edges that connect vertices; and finite state machines, used to model computing machines. These are some of the topics we will study in later chapters.

The concept of a function is extremely important in discrete mathematics. A function assigns to each element of a set exactly one element of a set. Functions play important roles throughout discrete mathematics. They are used to represent the computational complexity of algorithms, to study the size of sets, to count objects, and in a myriad of other ways. Useful structures such as sequences and strings are special types of functions.

2.1 Sets

Introduction

In this section, we study the fundamental discrete structure on which all other discrete structures are built, namely, the set. Sets are used to group objects together. Often, the objects in a set have similar properties. For instance, all the students who are currently enrolled in your school make up a set. Likewise, all the students currently taking a course in discrete mathematics at any school make up a set. In addition, those students enrolled in your school who are taking a course in discrete mathematics form a set that can be obtained by taking the elements common to the first two collections. The language of sets is a means to study such collections in an organized fashion. We now provide a definition of a set. This definition is an intuitive definition, which is not part of a formal theory of sets.

Definition 1 A *set* is an unordered collection of objects.

Note that the term *object* has been used without specifying what an object is. This description of a set as a collection of objects, based on the intuitive notion of an object, was first stated by the German mathematician Georg Cantor in 1895. The theory that results from this intuitive definition of a set, and the use of the intuitive notion that any property whatever there is a set consisting of exactly the objects with this property, leads to **paradoxes,** or logical inconsistencies. This was shown by the English philosopher Bertrand Russell in 1902. These logical inconsistencies can be avoided by building set theory beginning with axioms. We will use Cantor's original version of set theory, known as **naive set theory,** without developing an axiomatic version of set theory, because all sets considered in this book can be treated consistently using Cantor's original theory.

Definition 2 The objects in a set are called the *elements,* or *members,* of the set. A set is said to *contain* its elements.

We will now introduce notation used to describe membership in sets. We write $a \in A$ to denote that a is an element of the set A. The notation $a \notin A$ denotes that a is not an element of the set A. Note that lowercase letters are usually used to denote elements of sets.

There are several ways to describe a set. One way is to list all the members of a set, when this is possible. We use a notation where all members of the set are listed between braces. For example, the notation $\{a, b, c, d\}$ represents the set with the four elements $a, b, c,$ and d.

Example 1   The set V of all vowels in the English alphabet can be written as $V = \{a, e, i, o, u\}$. ◄

Example 2   The set O of odd positive integers less than 10 can be expressed by $O = \{1, 3, 5, 7, 9\}$. ◄

Example 3   Although sets are usually used to group together elements with common properties, there is nothing that prevents a set from having seemingly unrelated elements. For instance, $\{a, 2,$ Fred, New Jersey$\}$ is the set containing the four elements a, 2, Fred, and New Jersey. ◄

Sometimes the brace notation is used to describe a set without listing all its members. Some members of the set are listed, and then *ellipses* $(\ldots)$ are used when the general pattern of the elements is obvious.

Example 4   The set of positive integers less than 100 can be denoted by $\{1, 2, 3, \ldots, 99\}$. ◄

Another way to describe a set is to use **set builder** notation. We characterize all those elements in the set by stating the property or properties they must have to be members. For instance, the set O of all odd positive integers less than 10 can be written as

$$O = \{x \mid x \text{ is an odd positive integer less than } 10\},$$

or, specifying the universe as the set of positive integers, as

$$O = \{x \in \mathbf{Z}^+ \mid x \text{ is odd and } x < 10\}.$$

We often use this type of notation to describe sets when it is impossible to list all the elements of the set. For instance, the set $\mathbf{Q}^+$ of all positive rational numbers can be written as

$$\mathbf{Q}^+ = \{x \in \mathbf{R} \mid x = p/q, \text{ for some positive integers } p \text{ and } q\}.$$

These sets, each denoted using a boldface letter, play an important role in discrete mathematics:

$\mathbf{N} = \{0, 1, 2, 3, \ldots\}$, the set of **natural numbers**
$\mathbf{Z} = \{\ldots, -2, -1, 0, 1, 2, \ldots\}$, the set of **integers**
$\mathbf{Z}^+ = \{1, 2, 3, \ldots\}$, the set of **positive integers**
$\mathbf{Q} = \{p/q \mid p \in \mathbf{Z}, q \in \mathbf{Z}, \text{ and } q \neq 0\}$, the set of **rational numbers**
$\mathbf{R}$, the set of **real numbers**

(Note that some people do not consider 0 a natural number, so be careful to check how the term *natural numbers* is used when you read other books.)

Sets can have other sets as members, as Example 5 illustrates.

Example 5   The set $\{\mathbf{N}, \mathbf{Z}, \mathbf{Q}, \mathbf{R}\}$ is a set containing four elements, each of which is a set. The four elements of this set are $\mathbf{N}$, the set of natural numbers; $\mathbf{Z}$, the set of integers; $\mathbf{Q}$, the set of rational numbers; and $\mathbf{R}$, the set of real numbers. ◄

Remark: Note that the concept of a datatype, or type, in computer science is built upon the concept of a set. In particular, a **datatype** or **type** is the name of a set, together with a set of operations that can be performed on objects from that set. For example, *boolean* is the name of the set $\{0, 1\}$ together with operators on one or more elements of this set, such as AND, OR, and NOT.

Because many mathematical statements assert that two differently specified collections of objects are really the same set, we need to understand what it means for two sets to be equal.

Definition 3 Two sets are *equal* if and only if they have the same elements. That is, if A and B are sets, then A and B are equal if and only if $\forall x(x \in A \leftrightarrow x \in B)$. We write $A = B$ if A and B are equal sets.

Example 6 The sets $\{1, 3, 5\}$ and $\{3, 5, 1\}$ are equal, because they have the same elements. Note that the order in which the elements of a set are listed does not matter. Note also that it does not matter if an element of a set is listed more than once, so $\{1, 3, 3, 3, 5, 5, 5, 5\}$ is the same as the set $\{1, 3, 5\}$ because they have the same elements. ◄

Sets can be represented graphically using Venn diagrams, named after the English mathematician John Venn, who introduced their use in 1881. In Venn diagrams the **universal set** U, which contains all the objects under consideration, is represented by a rectangle. (Note that the universal set varies depending on which objects are of interest.) Inside this rectangle, circles or other geometrical figures are used to represent sets. Sometimes points are used to represent the particular elements of the set. Venn diagrams are often used to indicate the relationships between sets. We show how a Venn diagram can be used in Example 7.

Example 7 Draw a Venn diagram that represents V, the set of vowels in the English alphabet. *Solution*: We draw a rectangle to indicate the universal set U, which is the set of the 26 letters of the English alphabet. Inside this rectangle we draw a circle to represent V. Inside this circle we indicate the elements of V with points (see Figure 1). ◄

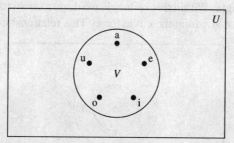

Figure 1 Venn Diagram for the Set of Vowels.

There is a special set that has no elements. This set is called the **empty set,** or **null set,** and is denoted by $\emptyset$. The empty set can also be denoted by $\{\ \}$ (that is, we represent the empty set with a pair of braces that encloses all the elements in this set). Often, a set of elements with certain properties turns out to be the null set. For instance, the set of all positive integers that are greater than their squares is the null set. A set with one element is called a **singleton set.**

A common error is to confuse the empty set $\emptyset$ with the set $\{\emptyset\}$, which is a singleton set. The single element of the set $\{\emptyset\}$ is the empty set itself! A useful analogy for remembering this difference is to think of folders in a computer file system. The empty set can be thought of as an empty folder and the set consisting of just the empty set can be thought of as a folder with exactly one folder inside, namely, the empty folder.

Definition 4 The set A is said to be a *subset* of B if and only if every element of A is also an element of B. We use the notation $A \subseteq B$ to indicate that A is a subset of the set B.

We see that $A \subseteq B$ if and only if the quantification

$$\forall x(x \in A \rightarrow x \in B)$$

is true.

Example 8 The set of all odd positive integers less than 10 is a subset of the set of all positive integers less than 10, the set of rational numbers is a subset of the set of real numbers, the set of all computer science majors at your school is a subset of the set of all students at your school, and the set of all people in China is a subset of the set of all people in China (that is, it is a subset of itself). ◄

Theorem 1 shows that every nonempty set S is guaranteed to have at least two subsets, the empty set and the set S itself, that is, $\emptyset \subseteq S$ and $S \subseteq S$.

Theorem 1   For every set S,

$$(i)\,\emptyset \subseteq S \quad \text{and} \quad (ii)\,S \subseteq S.$$

Proof: We will prove (i) and leave the proof of (ii) as an exercise.

Let S be a set. To show that $\emptyset \subseteq S$, we must show that $\forall x(x \in \emptyset \rightarrow x \in S)$ is true. Because the empty set contains no elements, it follows that $x \in \emptyset$ is always false. It follows that the conditional statement $x \in \emptyset \rightarrow x \in S$ is always true, because its hypothesis is always false and a conditional statement with a false hypothesis is true. That is, $\forall x(x \in \emptyset \rightarrow x \in S)$ is true. This completes the proof of (i). Note that this is an example of a vacuous proof.   ◁

When we wish to emphasize that a set A is a subset of the set B but that $A \neq B$, we write $A \subset B$ and say that A is a **proper subset** of B. For $A \subset B$ to be true, it must be the case that $A \subseteq B$ and there must exist an element x of B that is not an element of A. That is, A is a proper subset of B if

$$\forall x(x \in A \rightarrow x \in B) \wedge \exists x(x \in B \wedge x \notin A)$$

is true. Venn diagrams can be used to illustrate that a set A is a subset of a set B. We draw the universal set U as a rectangle. Within this rectangle we draw a circle for B. Because A is a subset of B, we draw the circle for A within the circle for B. This relationship is shown in Figure 2.

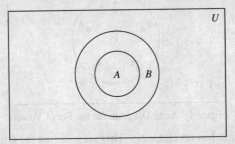

Figure 2   Venn Diagram Showing that A Is a Subset of B.

One way to show that two sets have the same elements is to show that each set is a subset of the other. In other words, we can show that if A and B are sets with $A \subseteq B$ and $B \subseteq A$, then $A = B$. This turns out to be a useful way to show that two sets are equal. That is, $A = B$, where A and B are sets, if and only if $\forall x(x \in A \rightarrow x \in B)$ and $\forall x(x \in B \rightarrow x \in A)$, or equivalently if and only if $\forall x(x \in A \leftrightarrow x \in B)$.

Sets may have other sets as members. For instance, we have the sets

$$A = \{\emptyset, \{a\}, \{b\}, \{a, b\}\} \quad \text{and} \quad B = \{x \mid x \text{ is a subset of the set } \{a, b\}\}.$$

Note that these two sets are equal, that is, $A = B$. Also note that $\{a\} \in A$, but $a \notin A$.

Sets are used extensively in counting problems, and for such applications we need to discuss the size of sets.

Definition 5   Let S be a set. If there are exactly n distinct elements in S where n is a nonnegative integer, we say that S is a *finite set* and that n is the *cardinality* of S. The cardinality of S is denoted by $|S|$.

Example 9   Let A be the set of odd positive integers less than 10. Then $|A| = 5$.   ◀

Example 10   Let S be the set of letters in the English alphabet. Then $|S| = 26$.   ◀

Example 11   Because the null set has no elements, it follows that $|\emptyset| = 0$.   ◀

We will also be interested in sets that are not finite.

Definition 6   A set is said to be *infinite* if it is not finite.

Example 12   The set of positive integers is infinite.   ◀

The cardinality of infinite sets will be discussed in Section 2.4.

The Power Set

Many problems involve testing all combinations of elements of a set to see if they satisfy some property. To consider all such combinations of elements of a set S, we build a new set that has as its members all the subsets of S.

Definition 7   Given a set S, the *power set* of S is the set of all subsets of the set S. The power set of S is denoted by $P(S)$.

Example 13   What is the power set of the set $\{0, 1, 2\}$?

Solution: The power set $P(\{0, 1, 2\})$ is the set of all subsets of $\{0, 1, 2\}$. Hence,

$$P(\{0, 1, 2\}) = \{\emptyset, \{0\}, \{1\}, \{2\}, \{0, 1\}, \{0, 2\}, \{1, 2\}, \{0, 1, 2\}\}.$$

Note that the empty set and the set itself are members of this set of subsets.   ◀

Example 14   What is the power set of the empty set? What is the power set of the set $\{\emptyset\}$?

Solution: The empty set has exactly one subset, namely, itself. Consequently,

$$P(\emptyset) = \{\emptyset\}.$$

The set $\{\emptyset\}$ has exactly two subsets, namely, $\emptyset$ and the set $\{\emptyset\}$ itself. Therefore,

$$P(\{\emptyset\}) = \{\emptyset, \{\emptyset\}\}.$$ ◀

If a set has n elements, then its power set has 2^n elements. We will demonstrate this fact in several ways in subsequent sections of the text.

Cartesian Products

The order of elements in a collection is often important. Because sets are unordered, a different structure is needed to represent ordered collections. This is provided by **ordered n-tuples.**

Definition 8   The *ordered n-tuple* $(a_1, a_2, \ldots, a_n)$ is the ordered collection that has a_1 as its first element, a_2 as its second element, $\ldots$, and a_n as its nth element.

We say that two ordered n-tuples are equal if and only if each corresponding pair of their elements is equal. In other words, $(a_1, a_2, \ldots, a_n) = (b_1, b_2, \ldots, b_n)$ if and only if $a_i = b_i$, for $i = 1, 2, \ldots, n$. In particular, 2-tuples are called **ordered pairs.** The ordered pairs (a, b) and (c, d) are equal if and only if $a = c$ and $b = d$. Note that (a, b) and (b, a) are not equal unless $a = b$.

Many of the discrete structures we will study in later chapters are based on the notion of the *Cartesian product* of sets (named after René Descartes). We first define the Cartesian product of two sets.

Definition 9   Let A and B be sets. The *Cartesian product* of A and B, denoted by $A \times B$, is the set of all ordered pairs (a, b), where $a \in A$ and $b \in B$. Hence,

$$A \times B = \{(a, b) \mid a \in A \wedge b \in B\}.$$

Example 15   Let A represent the set of all students at a university, and let B represent the set of all courses offered at the university. What is the Cartesian product $A \times B$?

Solution: The Cartesian product $A \times B$ consists of all the ordered pairs of the form (a, b), where a is a student at the university and b is a course offered at the university. The set $A \times B$ can be used to represent all possible enrollments of students in courses at the university.   ◀

Example 16   What is the Cartesian product of $A = \{1, 2\}$ and $B = \{a, b, c\}$?

Solution: The Cartesian product $A \times B$ is

$$A \times B = \{(1, a), (1, b), (1, c), (2, a), (2, b), (2, c)\}. \qquad \blacktriangleleft$$

A subset R of the Cartesian product $A \times B$ is called a **relation** from the set A to the set B. The elements of R are ordered pairs, where the first element belongs to A and the second to B. For example, $R = \{(a, 0), (a, 1), (a, 3), (b, 1), (b, 2), (c, 0), (c, 3)\}$ is a relation from the set $\{a, b, c\}$ to the set $\{0, 1, 2, 3\}$. We will study relations at length in Chapter 8.

The Cartesian products $A \times B$ and $B \times A$ are not equal, unless $A = \emptyset$ or $B = \emptyset$ (so that $A \times B = \emptyset$) or $A = B$. This is illustrated in Example 17.

Example 17
Show that the Cartesian product $B \times A$ is not equal to the Cartesian product $A \times B$, where A and B are as in Example 16.

Solution: The Cartesian product $B \times A$ is

$$B \times A = \{(a, 1), (a, 2), (b, 1), (b, 2), (c, 1), (c, 2)\}.$$

This is not equal to $A \times B$, which was found in Example 16. $\qquad \blacktriangleleft$

The Cartesian product of more than two sets can also be defined.

Definition 10 The *Cartesian product* of the sets $A_1, A_2, \ldots, A_n$, denoted by $A_1 \times A_2 \times \cdots \times A_n$, is the set of ordered n-tuples $(a_1, a_2, \ldots, a_n)$, where a_i belongs to A_i for $i = 1, 2, \ldots, n$. In other words,

$$A_1 \times A_2 \times \cdots \times A_n = \{(a_1, a_2, \ldots, a_n) \mid a_i \in A_i \text{ for } i = 1, 2, \ldots, n\}.$$

Example 18   What is the Cartesian product $A \times B \times C$, where $A = \{0, 1\}$, $B = \{1, 2\}$, and $C = \{0, 1, 2\}$?

Solution: The Cartesian product $A \times B \times C$ consists of all ordered triples (a, b, c), where $a \in A$, $b \in B$, and $c \in C$. Hence,

$$A \times B \times C = \{(0, 1, 0), (0, 1, 1), (0, 1, 2), (0, 2, 0), (0, 2, 1), (0, 2, 2), (1, 1, 0), (1, 1, 1),$$
$$(1, 1, 2), (1, 2, 0), (1, 2, 1), (1, 2, 2)\}. \qquad \blacktriangleleft$$

Using Set Notation with Quantifiers

Sometimes we restrict the domain of a quantified statement explicitly by making use of a particular notation. For example, $\forall x \in S(P(x))$ denotes the universal quantification of $P(x)$ over all elements in the set S. In other words, $\forall x \in S(P(x))$ is shorthand for $\forall x(x \in S \rightarrow P(x))$. Similarly, $\exists x \in S(P(x))$ denotes the existential quantification of $P(x)$ over all elements in S. That is, $\exists x \in S(P(x))$ is shorthand for $\exists x(x \in S \wedge P(x))$.

Example 19   What do the statements $\forall x \in \mathbf{R}\ (x^2 \geqslant 0)$ and $\exists x \in \mathbf{Z}\ (x^2 = 1)$ mean?

Solution: The statement $\forall x \in \mathbf{R}(x^2 \geqslant 0)$ states that for every real number x, $x^2 \geqslant 0$. This statement can be expressed as "The square of every real number is nonnegative." This is a true statement.

The statement $\exists x \in \mathbf{Z}(x^2 = 1)$ states that there exists an integer x such that $x^2 = 1$. This statement can be expressed as "There is an integer whose square is 1." This is also a true statement because $x = 1$ is such an integer (as is -1). $\qquad \blacktriangleleft$

Truth Sets of Quantifiers

We will now tie together concepts from set theory and from predicate logic. Given a predicate P, and a domain D, we define the **truth set** of P to be the set of elements x in D for which $P(x)$ is true. The truth set of $P(x)$ is denoted by $\{x \in D \mid P(x)\}$.

Example 20   What are the truth sets of the predicates $P(x)$, $Q(x)$, and $R(x)$, where the domain is the set of integers and $P(x)$ is "$|x| = 1$," $Q(x)$ is "$x^2 = 2$," and $R(x)$ is "$|x| = x$."

Solution: The truth set of P, $\{x \in \mathbf{Z} \mid |x| = 1\}$, is the set of integers for which $|x| = 1$. Because $|x| = 1$ when $x = 1$ or $x = -1$, and for no other integers x, we see that the truth set of P is the set $\{-1, 1\}$.

The truth set of Q, $\{x \in \mathbf{Z} \mid x^2 = 2\}$, is the set of integers for which $x^2 = 2$. This is the empty set because there are no integers x for which $x^2 = 2$.

The truth set of R, $\{x \in \mathbf{Z} \mid |x| = x\}$, is the set of integers for which $|x| = x$. Because $|x| = x$ if and only if $x \geqslant 0$, it follows that the truth set of R is $\mathbf{N}$, the set of nonnegative integers.   ◄

Note that $\forall x P(x)$ is true over the domain U if and only if the truth set of P is the set U. Likewise, $\exists x P(x)$ is true over the domain U if and only if the truth set of P is nonempty.

Exercises

1. List the members of these sets.
    a) $\{x \mid x$ is a real number such that $x^2 = 1\}$ b) $\{x \mid x$ is a positive integer less than 12$\}$
    c) $\{x \mid x$ is the square of an integer and $x < 100\}$ d) $\{x \mid x$ is an integer such that $x^2 = 2\}$

2. Determine whether each of these pairs of sets are equal.
    a) $\{1, 3, 3, 3, 5, 5, 5, 5, 5\}, \{5, 3, 1\}$ b) $\{\{1\}\}, \{1, \{1\}\}$ c) $\emptyset, \{\emptyset\}$

3. For each of the following sets, determine whether 2 is an element of that set.
    a) $\{x \in \mathbf{R} \mid x$ is an integer greater than 1$\}$ b) $\{x \in \mathbf{R} \mid x$ is the square of an integer$\}$
    c) $\{2, \{2\}\}$ d) $\{\{2\}, \{\{2\}\}\}$ e) $\{\{2\}, \{2, \{2\}\}\}$ f) $\{\{\{2\}\}\}$

4. Determine whether each of these statements is true or false.
    a) $0 \in \emptyset$ b) $\emptyset \in \{0\}$ c) $\{0\} \subset \emptyset$ d) $\emptyset \subset \{0\}$ e) $\{0\} \in \{0\}$
    f) $\{0\} \subset \{0\}$ g) $\{\emptyset\} \subseteq \{\emptyset\}$

5. Determine whether each of these statements is true or false.
    a) $x \in \{x\}$ b) $\{x\} \subseteq \{x\}$ c) $\{x\} \in \{x\}$ d) $\{x\} \in \{\{x\}\}$ e) $\emptyset \subseteq \{x\}$
    f) $\emptyset \in \{x\}$

6. Use a Venn diagram to illustrate the set of all months of the year whose names do not contain the letter R in the set of all months of the year.

7. Use a Venn diagram to illustrate the relationships $A \subset B$ and $B \subset C$.

8. Suppose that A, B, and C are sets such that $A \subseteq B$ and $B \subseteq C$. Show that $A \subseteq C$.

9. What is the cardinality of each of these sets?
    a) $\{a\}$ b) $\{\{a\}\}$ c) $\{a, \{a\}\}$ d) $\{a, \{a\}, \{a, \{a\}\}\}$

10. Find the power set of each of these sets, where a and b are distinct elements.
    a) $\{a\}$ b) $\{a, b\}$ c) $\{\emptyset, \{\emptyset\}\}$

11. How many elements does each of these sets have where a and b are distinct elements?
    a) $P(\{a, b, \{a, b\}\})$ b) $P(\{\emptyset, a, \{a\}, \{\{a\}\}\})$ c) $P(P(\emptyset))$

12. Let $A = \{a, b, c, d\}$ and $B = \{y, z\}$. Find
    a) $A \times B$ b) $B \times A$

13. What is the Cartesian product $A \times B \times C$, where A is the set of all airlines and B and C are both the set of all cities in the United States?

14. Let A be a set. Show that $\emptyset \times A = A \times \emptyset = \emptyset$.

15. How many different elements does $A \times B$ have if A has m elements and B has n elements?

16. Explain why $A \times B \times C$ and $(A \times B) \times C$ are not the same.

17. Translate each of these quantifications into English and determine its truth value.

    a) $\forall x \in \mathbf{R}\ (x^2 \neq -1)$ b) $\exists x \in \mathbf{Z}\ (x^2 = 2)$ c) $\forall x \in \mathbf{Z}\ (x^2 > 0)$ d) $\exists x \in \mathbf{R}\ (x^2 = x)$

18. Find the truth set of each of these predicates where the domain is the set of integers.

    a) $P(x)$: "$x^2 < 3$"   b) $Q(x)$: "$x^2 > x$"   c) $R(x)$: "$2x + 1 = 0$"

*19. The defining property of an ordered pair is that two ordered pairs are equal if and only if their first elements are equal and their second elements are equal. Surprisingly, instead of taking the ordered pair as a primitive concept, we can construct ordered pairs using basic notions from set theory. Show that if we define the ordered pair (a, b) to be $\{\{a\}, \{a, b\}\}$, then $(a, b) = (c, d)$ if and only if $a = c$ and $b = d$. [*Hint:* First show that $\{\{a\}, \{a, b\}\} = \{\{c\}, \{c, d\}\}$ if and only if $a = c$ and $b = d$.]

*20. Describe a procedure for listing all the subsets of a finite set.

2.2   Set Operations

Introduction

Two sets can be combined in many different ways. For instance, starting with the set of mathematics majors at your school and the set of computer science majors at your school, we can form the set of students who are mathematics majors or computer science majors, the set of students who are joint majors in mathematics and computer science, the set of all students not majoring in mathematics, and so on.

Definition 1   Let A and B be sets. The *union* of the sets A and B, denoted by $A \cup B$, is the set that contains those elements that are either in A or in B, or in both.

An element x belongs to the union of the sets A and B if and only if x belongs to A or x belongs to B. This tells us that

$$A \cup B = \{x \mid x \in A \vee x \in B\}.$$

The Venn diagram shown in Figure 1 represents the union of two sets A and B. The area that represents $A \cup B$ is the shaded area within either the circle representing A or the circle representing B.

We will give some examples of the union of sets.

Example 1   The union of the sets $\{1, 3, 5\}$ and $\{1, 2, 3\}$ is the set $\{1, 2, 3, 5\}$; that is, $\{1, 3, 5\} \cup \{1, 2, 3\} = \{1, 2, 3, 5\}$.   ◀

Example 2   The union of the set of all computer science majors at your school and the set of all mathematics majors at your school is the set of students at your school who are majoring either in mathematics or in computer science (or in both).   ◀

Definition 2   Let A and B be sets. The *intersection* of the sets A and B, denoted by $A \cap B$, is the set containing those elements in both A and B.

An element x belongs to the intersection of the sets A and B if and only if x belongs to A and x belongs to B. This tells us that

$$A \cap B = \{x \mid x \in A \wedge x \in B\}.$$

The Venn diagram shown in Figure 2 represents the intersection of two sets A and B. The shaded area that is within both the circles representing the sets A and B is the area that represents the intersection of A and B.

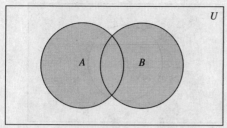

$A \cup B$ is shaded.

Figure 1   Venn Diagram Representing
the Union of A and B.

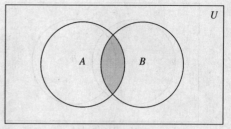

$A \cap B$ is shaded.

Figure 2   Venn Diagram Representing
the Intersection of A and B.

We give some examples of the intersection of sets.

Example 3   The intersection of the sets $\{1, 3, 5\}$ and $\{1, 2, 3\}$ is the set $\{1, 3\}$; that is, $\{1, 3, 5\} \cap \{1, 2, 3\} = \{1, 3\}$. ◀

Example 4   The intersection of the set of all computer science majors at your school and the set of all mathematics majors is the set of all students who are joint majors in mathematics and computer science. ▸ ◀

Definition 3   Two sets are called *disjoint* if their intersection is the empty set.

Example 5   Let $A = \{1, 3, 5, 7, 9\}$ and $B = \{2, 4, 6, 8, 10\}$. Because $A \cap B = \emptyset$, A and B are disjoint. ◀

There are other important ways to combine sets.

Definition 4   Let A and B be sets. The *difference* of A and B, denoted by $A - B$, is the set containing those elements that are in A but not in B. The difference of A and B is also called the *complement of B with respect to A.*

An element x belongs to the difference of A and B if and only if $x \in A$ and $x \notin B$. This tells us that

$$A - B = \{x \mid x \in A \land x \notin B\}.$$

The Venn diagram shown in Figure 3 represents the difference of the sets A and B. The shaded area inside the circle that represents A and outside the circle that represents B is the area that represents $A - B$.

We give some examples of differences of sets.

Example 6   The difference of $\{1, 3, 5\}$ and $\{1, 2, 3\}$ is the set $\{5\}$; that is, $\{1, 3, 5\} - \{1, 2, 3\} = \{5\}$. This is different from the difference of $\{1, 2, 3\}$ and $\{1, 3, 5\}$, which is the set $\{2\}$. ◀

Example 7   The difference of the set of computer science majors at your school and the set of mathematics majors at your school is the set of all computer science majors at your school who are not also mathematics majors. ◀

Once the universal set U has been specified, the **complement** of a set can be defined.

Definition 5   Let U be the universal set. The *complement* of the set A, denoted by $\overline{A}$, is the complement of A with respect to U. In other words, the complement of the set A is $U - A$.

An element belongs to $\overline{A}$ if and only if $x \notin A$. This tells us that

$$\overline{A} = \{x \mid x \notin A\}.$$

In Figure 4 the shaded area outside the circle representing A is the area representing $\overline{A}$.

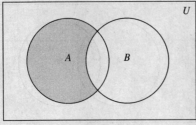

A − B is shaded.

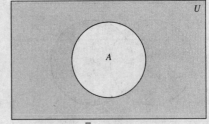

$\overline{A}$ is shaded.

Figure 3   Venn Diagram for the   Figure 4   Venn Diagram for the
Difference of A and B.   Complement of the Set A.

We give some examples of the complement of a set.

Example 8   Let $A = \{a, e, i, o, u\}$ (where the universal set is the set of letters of the English alphabet). Then $\overline{A} = \{b, c, d, f, g, h, j, k, l, m, n, p, q, r, s, t, v, w, x, y, z\}$.   ◄

Example 9   Let A be the set of positive integers greater than 10 (with universal set the set of all positive integers). Then $\overline{A} = \{1, 2, 3, 4, 5, 6, 7, 8, 9, 10\}$.   ◄

Set Identities

Table 1 lists the most important set identities. We will prove several of these identities here, using three different methods. These methods are presented to illustrate that there are often many different approaches to the solution of a problem. The proofs of the remaining identities will be left as exercises. The reader should note the similarity between these set identities and the logical equivalences discussed in Section 1.2. In fact, the set identities given can be proved directly from the corresponding logical equivalences. Furthermore, both are special cases of identities that hold for Boolean algebra.

One way to show that two sets are equal is to show that each is a subset of the other. Recall that to show that one set is a subset of a second set, we can show that if an element belongs to the first set, then it must also belong to the second set. We generally use a direct proof to do this. We illustrate this type of proof by establishing the second of De Morgan's laws.

Example 10   Prove that $\overline{A \cap B} = \overline{A} \cup \overline{B}$.

Solution: To show that $\overline{A \cap B} = \overline{A} \cup \overline{B}$, we will show that $\overline{A \cap B} \subseteq \overline{A} \cup \overline{B}$ and that $\overline{A} \cup \overline{B} \subseteq \overline{A \cap B}$.

First, we will show that $\overline{A \cap B} \subseteq \overline{A} \cup \overline{B}$. So suppose that $x \in \overline{A \cap B}$. By the definition of complement, $x \notin A \cap B$. By the definition of intersection, $\neg((x \in A) \wedge (x \in B))$ is true. Applying De Morgan's law (from logic), we see that $\neg(x \in A)$ or $\neg(x \in B)$. Hence, by the definition of negation, $x \notin A$ or $x \notin B$. By the definition of complement, $x \in \overline{A}$ or $x \in \overline{B}$. It follows by the definition of union that $x \in \overline{A} \cup \overline{B}$. This shows that $\overline{A \cap B} \subseteq \overline{A} \cup \overline{B}$.

Next, we will show that $\overline{A} \cup \overline{B} \subseteq \overline{A \cap B}$. Now suppose that $x \in \overline{A} \cup \overline{B}$. By the definition of union, $x \in \overline{A}$ or $x \in \overline{B}$. Using the definition of complement, we see that $x \notin A$ or $x \notin B$. Consequently, $\neg(x \in A) \vee \neg(x \in B)$ is true. By De Morgan's law (from logic), we conclude that $\neg((x \in A) \wedge (x \in B))$ is true. By the definition of intersection, it follows that $\neg(x \in A \cap B)$ holds. We use the definition of complement to conclude that $x \in \overline{A \cap B}$. This shows that $\overline{A} \cup \overline{B} \subseteq \overline{A \cap B}$. Because we have shown that each set is a subset of the other, the two sets are equal, and the identity is proved.   ◄

We can more succinctly express the reasoning used in Example 10 using set builder notation, as Example 11 illustrates.

TABLE 1 Set Identities.

Identity	Name
$A \cup \emptyset = A$ $A \cap U = A$	Identity laws
$A \cup U = U$ $A \cap \emptyset = \emptyset$	Domination laws
$A \cup A = A$ $A \cap A = A$	Idempotent laws
$\overline{(\overline{A})} = A$	Complementation law
$A \cup B = B \cup A$ $A \cap B = B \cap A$	Commutative laws
$A \cup (B \cup C) = (A \cup B) \cup C$ $A \cap (B \cap C) = (A \cap B) \cap C$	Associative laws
$A \cap (B \cup C) = (A \cap B) \cup (A \cap C)$ $A \cup (B \cap C) = (A \cup B) \cap (A \cup C)$	Distributive laws
$\overline{A \cup B} = \overline{A} \cap \overline{B}$ $\overline{A \cap B} = \overline{A} \cup \overline{B}$	De Morgan's laws
$A \cup (A \cap B) = A$ $A \cap (A \cup B) = A$	Absorption laws
$A \cup \overline{A} = U$ $A \cap \overline{A} = \emptyset$	Complement laws

Example 11   Use set builder notation and logical equivalences to establish the second De Morgan law $\overline{A \cap B} = \overline{A} \cup \overline{B}$.

Solution: We can prove this identity with the following steps.

$$
\begin{aligned}
\overline{A \cap B} &= \{x \mid x \notin A \cap B\} &&\text{by definition of complement}\\
&= \{x \mid \neg(x \in (A \cap B))\} &&\text{by definition of does not belong symbol}\\
&= \{x \mid \neg(x \in A \land x \in B)\} &&\text{by definition of intersection}\\
&= \{x \mid \neg(x \in A) \lor \neg(x \in B)\} &&\text{by the first De Morgan law for logical equivalences}\\
&= \{x \mid x \notin A \lor x \notin B\} &&\text{by definition of does not belong symbol}\\
&= \{x \mid x \in \overline{A} \lor x \in \overline{B}\} &&\text{by definition of complement}\\
&= \{x \mid x \in \overline{A} \cup \overline{B}\} &&\text{by definition of union}\\
&= \overline{A} \cup \overline{B} &&\text{by meaning of set builder notation}
\end{aligned}
$$

Note that besides the definitions of complement, union, set membership, and set builder notation, this proof uses the first De Morgan law for logical equivalences.   ◄

Proving a set identity involving more than two sets by showing each side of the identity is a subset of the other often requires that we keep track of different cases, as illustrated by the proof in Example 12 of one of the distributive laws for sets.

Example 12   Prove the first distributive law from Table 1, which states that $A \cap (B \cup C) = (A \cap B) \cup (A \cap C)$ for all sets A, B, and C.

Solution: We will prove this identity by showing that each side is a subset of the other side.

Suppose that $x \in A \cap (B \cup C)$. Then $x \in A$ and $x \in B \cup C$. By the definition of union, it follows that $x \in A$, and $x \in B$ or $x \in C$ (or both). Consequently, we know that $x \in A$ and $x \in B$ or that $x \in A$ and $x \in C$. By the definition of intersection, it follows that $x \in A \cap B$ or $x \in A \cap C$. Using the definition of union, we conclude that $x \in (A \cap B) \cup (A \cap C)$. We conclude that $A \cap (B \cup C) \subseteq (A \cap B) \cup (A \cap C)$.

Now suppose that $x \in (A \cap B) \cup (A \cap C)$. Then, by the definition of union, $x \in A \cap B$ or $x \in A \cap C$. By the definition of intersection, it follows that $x \in A$ and $x \in B$ or that $x \in A$ and $x \in C$. From this we see that $x \in A$, and $x \in B$ or $x \in C$. Consequently, by the definition of union we see that $x \in A$ and $x \in B \cup C$. Furthermore, by the definition of intersection, it follows that $x \in A \cap (B \cup C)$. We conclude that $(A \cap B) \cup (A \cap C) \subseteq A \cap (B \cup C)$. This completes the proof of the identity.   ◀

Set identities can also be proved using **membership tables.** We consider each combination of sets that an element can belong to and verify that elements in the same combinations of sets belong to both the sets in the identity. To indicate that an element is in a set, a 1 is used; to indicate that an element is not in a set, a 0 is used. (The reader should note the similarity between membership tables and truth tables.)

Example 13   Use a membership table to show that $A \cap (B \cup C) = (A \cap B) \cup (A \cap C)$.

Solution: The membership table for these combinations of sets is shown in Table 2. This table has eight rows. Because the columns for $A \cap (B \cup C)$ and $(A \cap B) \cup (A \cap C)$ are the same, the identity is valid.   ◀

TABLE 2 A Membership Table for the Distributive Property.

A	B	C	$B \cup C$	$A \cap (B \cup C)$	$A \cap B$	$A \cap C$	$(A \cap B) \cup (A \cap C)$
1	1	1	1	1	1	1	1
1	1	0	1	1	1	0	1
1	0	1	1	1	0	1	1
1	0	0	0	0	0	0	0
0	1	1	1	0	0	0	0
0	1	0	1	0	0	0	0
0	0	1	1	0	0	0	0
0	0	0	0	0	0	0	0

Additional set identities can be established using those that we have already proved. Consider Example 14.

Example 14   Let A, B, and C be sets. Show that

$$\overline{A \cup (B \cap C)} = (\overline{C} \cup \overline{B}) \cap \overline{A}.$$

Solution: We have

$$
\begin{aligned}
\overline{A \cup (B \cap C)} &= \overline{A} \cap \overline{(B \cap C)} && \text{by the first De Morgan law} \\
&= \overline{A} \cap (\overline{B} \cup \overline{C}) && \text{by the second De Morgan law} \\
&= (\overline{B} \cup \overline{C}) \cap \overline{A} && \text{by the commutative law for intersections} \\
&= (\overline{C} \cup \overline{B}) \cap \overline{A} && \text{by the commutative law for unions.}
\end{aligned}
$$

◀

Generalized Unions and Intersections

Because unions and intersections of sets satisfy associative laws, the sets $A \cup B \cup C$ and $A \cap B \cap C$ are well defined; that is, the meaning of this notation is unambiguous when A, B, and C are sets. That is, we do not have to use parentheses to indicate which operation comes first because $A \cup (B \cup C) = (A \cup B) \cup C$ and $A \cap (B \cap C) = (A \cap B) \cap C$. Note that $A \cup B \cup C$ contains those elements that are in at least one of the sets A, B, and C, and that $A \cap B \cap C$ contains those elements that are in all of A, B, and C. These combinations of the three sets, A, B, and C, are shown in Figure 5.

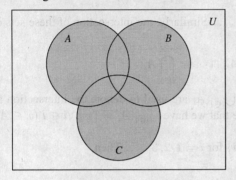
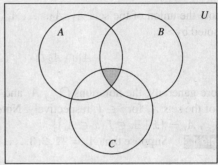

(a) $A \cup B \cup C$ is shaded.   (b) $A \cap B \cap C$ is shaded.

Figure 5   The Union and Intersection of A, B, and C.

Example 15   Let $A = \{0, 2, 4, 6, 8\}$, $B = \{0, 1, 2, 3, 4\}$, and $C = \{0, 3, 6, 9\}$. What are $A \cup B \cup C$ and $A \cap B \cap C$?

Solution: The set $A \cup B \cup C$ contains those elements in at least one of A, B, and C. Hence,

$$A \cup B \cup C = \{0, 1, 2, 3, 4, 6, 8, 9\}.$$

The set $A \cap B \cap C$ contains those elements in all three of A, B, and C. Thus,

$$A \cap B \cap C = \{0\}. \qquad \blacktriangleleft$$

We can also consider unions and intersections of an arbitrary number of sets. We use these definitions.

Definition 6   The *union* of a collection of sets is the set that contains those elements that are members of at least one set in the collection.

We use the notation

$$A_1 \cup A_2 \cup \cdots \cup A_n = \bigcup_{i=1}^{n} A_i$$

to denote the union of the sets $A_1, A_2, \ldots, A_n$.

Definition 7   The *intersection* of a collection of sets is the set that contains those elements that are members of all the sets in the collection.

We use the notation

$$A_1 \cap A_2 \cap \cdots \cap A_n = \bigcap_{i=1}^{n} A_i$$

to denote the intersection of the sets $A_1, A_2, \ldots, A_n$. We illustrate generalized unions and intersections with Example 16.

Example 16   Let $A_i = \{i, i+1, i+2, \ldots\}$. Then,

$$\bigcup_{i=1}^{n} A_i = \bigcup_{i=1}^{n} \{i, i+1, i+2, \ldots\} = \{1, 2, 3, \ldots\},$$

and

$$\bigcap_{i=1}^{n} A_i = \bigcap_{i=1}^{n} \{i, i+1, i+2, \ldots\} = \{n, n+1, n+2, \ldots\}. \quad \blacktriangleleft$$

We can extend the notation we have introduce for unions and intersections to other families of sets. In particular, we can use the notation

$$A_1 \cup A_2 \cup \cdots \cup A_n \cup \cdots = \bigcup_{i=1}^{\infty} A_i$$

to denote the union of the sets $A_1, A_2, \ldots, A_n, \ldots$. Similarly, the intersection of these sets can be denoted by

$$A_1 \cap A_2 \cap \cdots \cap A_n \cap \cdots = \bigcap_{i=1}^{\infty} A_i.$$

More generally, the notations $\bigcap_{i \in I} A_i$ and $\bigcup_{i \in I} A_i$ are used to denote the intersection and union of the sets A_i for $i \in I$, respectively. Note that we have $\bigcap_{i \in I} A_i = \{x \mid \forall i \in I \, (x \in A_i)\}$ and $\bigcup_{i \in I} A_i = \{x \mid \exists i \in I \, (x \in A_i)\}$.

Example 17   Suppose that $A_i = \{1, 2, 3, \ldots, i\}$ for $i = 1, 2, 3, \ldots$. Then,

$$\bigcup_{i=1}^{\infty} A_i = \bigcup_{i=1}^{\infty} \{1, 2, 3, \ldots, i\} = \{1, 2, 3, \ldots\} = \mathbf{Z}^+$$

and

$$\bigcap_{i=1}^{\infty} A_i = \bigcap_{i=1}^{\infty} \{1, 2, 3, \ldots, i\} = \{1\}.$$

To see that the union of these sets is the set of positive integers, note that every positive integer is in at least one of the sets, because the integer n belongs to $A_n = \{1, 2, \ldots, n\}$ and every element of the sets in the union is a positive integer. To see that the intersection of these sets, note that the only element that belongs to all the sets $A_1, A_2, \ldots$ is 1. To see this note that $A_1 = \{1\}$ and $1 \in A_i$ for $i = 1, 2, \ldots$. $\quad \blacktriangleleft$

Computer Representation of Sets

There are various ways to represent sets using a computer. One method is to store the elements of the set in an unordered fashion. However, if this is done, the operations of computing the union, intersection, or difference of two sets would be time-consuming, because each of these operations would require a large amount of searching for elements. We will present a method for storing elements using an arbitrary ordering of the elements of the universal set. This method of representing sets makes computing combinations of sets easy.

Assume that the universal set U is finite (and of reasonable size so that the number of elements of U is not larger than the memory size of the computer being used). First, specify an arbitrary ordering of the elements of U, for instance $a_1, a_2, \ldots, a_n$. Represent a subset A of U with the bit string of length n, where the ith bit in this string is 1 if a_i belongs to A and is 0 if a_i does not belong to A. Example 18 illustrates this technique.

Example 18   Let $U = \{1, 2, 3, 4, 5, 6, 7, 8, 9, 10\}$, and the ordering of elements of U has the elements in increasing order; that is, $a_i = i$. What bit strings represent the subset of all odd integers in U, the subset of all even integers in U, and the subset of integers not exceeding 5 in U?
Solution: The bit string that represents the set of odd integers in U, namely, $\{1, 3, 5, 7, 9\}$, has a one bit in the first, third, fifth, seventh, and ninth positions, and a zero elsewhere. It is

10 1010 1010.

(We have split this bit string of length ten into blocks of length four for easy reading because long bit strings are difficult to read.) Similarly, we represent the subset of all even integers in U, namely, $\{2, 4, 6, 8, 10\}$, by the string

$$01\ 0101\ 0101.$$

The set of all integers in U that do not exceed 5, namely, $\{1, 2, 3, 4, 5\}$, is represented by the string

$$11\ 1110\ 0000. \qquad \blacktriangleleft$$

   Using bit strings to represent sets, it is easy to find complements of sets and unions, intersections, and differences of sets. To find the bit string for the complement of a set from the bit string for that set, we simply change each 1 to a 0 and each 0 to 1, because $x \in A$ if and only if $x \notin \bar{A}$. Note that this operation corresponds to taking the negation of each bit when we associate a bit with a truth value—with 1 representing true and 0 representing false.

Example 19   We have seen that the bit string for the set $\{1, 3, 5, 7, 9\}$ (with universal set $\{1, 2, 3, 4, 5, 6, 7, 8, 9, 10\}$) is

$$10\ 1010\ 1010.$$

What is the bit string for the complement of this set?
Solution: The bit string for the complement of this set is obtained by replacing 0s with 1s and vice versa. This yields the string

$$01\ 0101\ 0101,$$

which corresponds to the set $\{2, 4, 6, 8, 10\}$. $\blacktriangleleft$

   To obtain the bit string for the union and intersection of two sets we perform bitwise Boolean operations on the bit strings representing the two sets. The bit in the ith position of the bit string of the union is 1 if either of the bits in the ith position in the two strings is 1 (or both are 1), and is 0 when both bits are 0. Hence, the bit string for the union is the bitwise *OR* of the bit strings for the two sets. The bit in the ith position of the bit string of the intersection is 1 when the bits in the corresponding position in the two strings are both 1, and is 0 when either of the two bits is 0 (or both are). Hence, the bit string for the intersection is the bitwise *AND* of the bit strings for the two sets.

Example 20   The bit strings for the sets $\{1, 2, 3, 4, 5\}$ and $\{1, 3, 5, 7, 9\}$ are $11\ 1110\ 0000$ and $10\ 1010\ 1010$, respectively. Use bit strings to find the union and intersection of these sets.
Solution: The bit string for the union of these sets is

$$11\ 1110\ 0000 \lor 10\ 1010\ 1010 = 11\ 1110\ 1010,$$

which corresponds to the set $\{1, 2, 3, 4, 5, 7, 9\}$. The bit string for the intersection of these sets is

$$11\ 1110\ 0000 \land 10\ 1010\ 1010 = 10\ 1010\ 0000,$$

which corresponds to the set $\{1, 3, 5\}$. $\blacktriangleleft$

Exercises

1. Let A be the set of students who live within one mile of school and let B be the set of students who walk to classes. Describe the students in each of these sets.
   a) $A \cap B$ b) $A \cup B$ c) $A - B$ d) $B - A$

2. Let $A = \{1, 2, 3, 4, 5\}$ and $B = \{0, 3, 6\}$. Find
   a) $A \cup B$.   b) $A \cap B$.   c) $A - B$.   d) $B - A$.

   In Exercises 3–5 assume that A is a subset of some underlying universal set U.

3. Prove the complementation law in Table 1 by showing that $\overline{\overline{A}} = A$.

4. Prove the domination laws in Table 1 by showing that
   a) $A \cup U = U$.   b) $A \cap \emptyset = \emptyset$.

5. Prove the complement laws in Table 1 by showing that
   a) $A \cup \overline{A} = U$.   b) $A \cap \overline{A} = \emptyset$.

6. Let A and B be sets. Prove the commutative laws from Table 1 by showing that
   a) $A \cup B = B \cup A$.   b) $A \cap B = B \cap A$.

7. Prove the second absorption law from Table 1 by showing that if A and B are sets, then $A \cap (A \cup B) = A$.

8. Prove the first De Morgan law in Table 1 by showing that if A and B are sets, then $\overline{A \cup B} = \overline{A} \cap \overline{B}$
   a) by showing each side is a subset of the other side.   b) using a membership table.

9. Show that if A, B, and C are sets, then $\overline{A \cap B \cap C} = \overline{A} \cup \overline{B} \cup \overline{C}$
   a) by showing each side is a subset of the other side.   b) using a membership table.

10. Show that if A and B are sets, then $A - B = A \cap \overline{B}$.

11. Prove the first associative law from Table 1 by showing that if A, B, and C are sets, then $A \cup (B \cup C) = (A \cup B) \cup C$.

12. Prove the second distributive law from Table 1 by showing that if A, B, and C are sets, then $A \cup (B \cap C) = (A \cup B) \cap (A \cup C)$.

13. Let $A = \{0, 2, 4, 6, 8, 10\}$, $B = \{0, 1, 2, 3, 4, 5, 6\}$, and $C = \{4, 5, 6, 7, 8, 9, 10\}$. Find
   a) $A \cap B \cap C$.   b) $A \cup B \cup C$.   c) $(A \cup B) \cap C$.   d) $(A \cap B) \cup C$.

14. Draw the Venn diagrams for each of these combinations of the sets A, B, and C.
   a) $A \cap (B - C)$ b) $(A \cap B) \cup (A \cap C)$ c) $(A \cap \overline{B}) \cup (A \cap \overline{C})$

15. What can you say about the sets A and B if we know that
   a) $A \cup B = A$? b) $A \cap B = A$? c) $A - B = A$? d) $A \cap B = B \cap A$? e) $A - B = B - A$?

16. Let A and B be subsets of a universal set U. Show that $A \subseteq B$ if and only if $\overline{B} \subseteq \overline{A}$?

   The **symmetric difference** of A and B, denoted by $A \oplus B$, is the set containing those elements in either A or B, but not in both A and B.

17. Find the symmetric difference of the set of computer science majors at a school and the set of mathematics majors at this school.

18. Show that $A \oplus B = (A \cup B) - (A \cap B)$.

19. Show that if A is a subset of a universal set U, then
   a) $A \oplus A = \emptyset$.   b) $A \oplus \emptyset = A$.   c) $A \oplus U = \overline{A}$.   d) $A \oplus \overline{A} = U$.

20. What can you say about the sets A and B if $A \oplus B = A$?

*21. Suppose that A, B, and C are sets such that $A \oplus C = B \oplus C$. Must it be the case that $A = B$?

22. If A, B, C, and D are sets, does it follow that $(A \oplus B) \oplus (C \oplus D) = (A \oplus D) \oplus (B \oplus C)$?

*23. Let $A_i = \{1, 2, 3, \ldots, i\}$ for $i = 1, 2, 3, \ldots$. Find
   a) $\displaystyle\bigcup_{i=1}^{n} A_i$.   b) $\displaystyle\bigcap_{i=1}^{n} A_i$.

24. Let A_i be the set of all nonempty bit strings (that is, bit strings of length at least one) of length not exceeding i. Find
   a) $\displaystyle\bigcup_{i=1}^{n} A_i$.   b) $\displaystyle\bigcap_{i=1}^{n} A_i$.

25. Find $\bigcup_{i=1}^{\infty} A_i$ and $\bigcap_{i=1}^{\infty} A_i$ if for every positive integer i,
    a) $A_i = \{-i, -i+1, \ldots, -1, 0, 1, \ldots, i-1, i\}$.
    b) $A_i = \{-i, i\}$.
    c) $A_i = [-i, i]$, that is, the set of real numbers x with $-i \leqslant x \leqslant i$.
    d) $A_i = [i, \infty]$, that is, the set of real numbers x with $x \geqslant i$.

26. Using the same universal set as in the last problem, find the set specified by each of these bit strings.
    a) 11 1100 1111   b) 01 0111 1000   c) 10 0000 0001

27. What is the bit string corresponding to the difference of two sets?

28. Show how bitwise operations on bit strings can be used to find these combinations of $A = \{a, b, c, d, e\}$, $B = \{b, c, d, g, p, t, v\}$, $C = \{c, e, i, o, u, x, y, z\}$, and $D = \{d, e, h, i, n, o, t, u, x, y\}$.
    a) $A \cup B$ b) $A \cap B$ c) $(A \cup D) \cap (B \cup C)$ d) $A \cup B \cup C \cup D$

29. Find the successors of the following sets.
    a) $\{1, 2, 3\}$ b) $\emptyset$ c) $\{\emptyset\}$ d) $\{\emptyset, \{\emptyset\}\}$

30. Let A and B be the multisets $\{3 \cdot a, 2 \cdot b, 1 \cdot c\}$ and $\{2 \cdot a, 3 \cdot b, 4 \cdot d\}$, respectively. Find
    a) $A \cup B$.   b) $A \cap B$.   c) $A - B$.   d) $B - A$.   e) $A + B$.

Fuzzy sets are used in artificial intelligence. Each element in the universal set U has a **degree of membership**, which is a real number between 0 and 1 (including 0 and 1), in a fuzzy set S. The fuzzy set S is denoted by listing the elements with their degrees of membership (elements with 0 degree of membership are not listed). For instance, we write $\{0.6$ Alice, 0.9 Brian, 0.4 Fred, 0.1 Oscar, 0.5 Rita$\}$ for the set F (of famous people) to indicate that Alice has a 0.6 degree of membership in F, Brian has a 0.9 degree of membership in F, Fred has a 0.4 degree of membership in F, Oscar has a 0.1 degree of membership in F, and Rita has a 0.5 degree of membership in F (so that Brian is the most famous and Oscar is the least famous of these people). Also suppose that R is the set of rich people with $R = \{0.4$ Alice, 0.8 Brian, 0.2 Fred, 0.9 Oscar, 0.7 Rita$\}$.

31. The **complement** of a fuzzy set S is the set $\overline{S}$, with the degree of the membership of an element in $\overline{S}$ equal to 1 minus the degree of membership of this element in S. Find $\overline{F}$ (the fuzzy set of people who are not famous) and $\overline{R}$ (the fuzzy set of people who are not rich).

32. The **intersection** of two fuzzy sets S and T is the fuzzy set $S \cap T$, where the degree of membership of an element in $S \cap T$ is the minimum of the degrees of membership of this element in S and in T. Find the fuzzy set $F \cap R$ of rich and famous people.

2.3 Functions

Introduction

In many instances we assign to each element of a set a particular element of a second set (which may be the same as the first). For example, suppose that each student in a discrete mathematics class is assigned a letter grade from the set $\{A, B, C, D, F\}$. And suppose that the grades are A for Adams, C for Chou, B for Goodfriend, A for Rodriguez, and F for Stevens. This assignment of grades is illustrated in Figure 1.

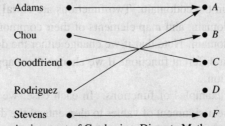

Figure 1   Assignment of Grades in a Discrete Mathematics Class.

This assignment is an example of a function. The concept of a function is extremely important in mathematics and computer science. For example, in discrete mathematics functions are used in the definition of such discrete structures as sequences and strings. Functions are also used to represent how long it takes a computer to solve problems of a given size. Many computer programs and subroutines are designed to calculate values of functions. Recursive functions, which are functions defined in terms of themselves, are used throughout computer science. This section reviews the basic concepts involving functions needed in discrete mathematics.

Definition 1   Let A and B be nonempty sets. A *function f* from A to B is an assignment of exactly one element of B to each element of A. We write $f(a) = b$ if b is the unique element of B assigned by the function f to the element a of A. If f is a function from A to B, we write $f : A \to B$.

Remark: Functions are sometimes also called **mappings** or **transformations**.

Functions are specified in many different ways. Sometimes we explicitly state the assignments, as in Figure 1. Often we give a formula, such as $f(x) = x + 1$, to define a function. Other times we use a computer program to specify a function.

A function $f : A \to B$ can also be defined in terms of a relation from A to B. Recall from Section 2.1 that a relation from A to B is just a subset of $A \times B$. A relation from A to B that contains one, and only one, ordered pair (a, b) for every element $a \in A$, defines a function f from A to B. This function is defined by the assignment $f(a) = b$, where (a, b) is the unique ordered pair in the relation that has a as its first element.

Definition 2   If f is a function from A to B, we say that A is the *domain* of f and B is the *codomain* of f. If $f(a) = b$, we say that b is the *image* of a and a is a *preimage* of b. The *range* of f is the set of all images of elements of A. Also, if f is a function from A to B, we say that f *maps A to B*.

Figure 2 represents a function f from A to B.

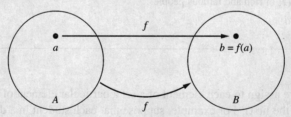

Figure 2   The Function f Maps A to B.

When we define a function we specify its domain, its codomain, and the mapping of elements of the domain to elements in the codomain. Two functions are **equal** when they have the same domain, have the same codomain, and map elements of their common domain to the same elements in their common codomain. Note that if we change either the domain or the codomain of a function, then we obtain a different function. If we change the mapping of elements, then we also obtain a different function.

Examples 1–5 provide examples of functions. In each case, we describe the domain, the codomain, the range, and the assignment of values to elements of the domain.

Example 1   What are the domain, codomain, and range of the function that assigns grades to students described in the first paragraph of the introduction of this section?

Solution: Let G be the function that assigns a grade to a student in our discrete mathematics class. Note that $G(\text{Adams}) = A$, for instance. The domain of G is the set {Adams, Chou, Goodfriend, Rodriguez, Stevens}, and the codomain is the set {A, B, C, D, F}. The range of G is the set {A, B, C, F}, because each grade except D is assigned to some student.   ◄

Example 2   Let R be the relation consisting of ordered pairs (Abdul, 22), (Brenda, 24), (Carla, 21), (Desire, 22), (Eddie, 24), and (Felicia, 22), where each pair consists of a graduate student and the age of this student. What is the function that this relation determines?

Solution: This relation defines the function f, where with $f(\text{Abdul}) = 22$, $f(\text{Brenda}) = 24$, $f(\text{Carla}) = 21$, $f(\text{Desire}) = 22$, $f(\text{Eddie}) = 24$, and $f(\text{Felicia}) = 22$. Here the domain is the set {Abdul, Brenda, Carla, Desire, Eddie, Felicia}. To define the function f, we need to specify a codomain. Here, we can take the codomain to be the set of positive integers to make sure that the codomain contains all possible ages of students. (Note that we could choose a smaller codomain, but that would change the function.) Finally, the range is the set {$21, 22, 24$}.   ◄

Example 3   Let f be the function that assigns the last two bits of a bit string of length 2 or greater to that string. For example, $f(11010) = 10$. Then, the domain of f is the set of all bit strings of length 2 or greater, and both the codomain and range are the set {$00, 01, 10, 11$}.   ◄

Example 4   Let $f: \mathbf{Z} \to \mathbf{Z}$ assign the square of an integer to this integer. Then, $f(x) = x^2$, where the domain of f is the set of all integers, we take the the codomain of f to be the set of all integers, and the range of f is the set of all integers that are perfect squares, namely, {$0, 1, 4, 9, \ldots$}.   ◄

Example 5   The domain and codomain of functions are often specified in programming languages. For instance, the Java statement

   int **floor**(float real){...}

and the Pascal statement

   function *floor*(*x*: **real**): **integer**

both state that the domain of the floor function is the set of real numbers and its codomain is the set of integers.   ◄

   Two real-valued functions with the same domain can be added and multiplied.

Definition 3   Let f_1 and f_2 be functions from A to $\mathbf{R}$. Then $f_1 + f_2$ and $f_1 f_2$ are also functions from A to $\mathbf{R}$ defined by

$$(f_1 + f_2)(x) = f_1(x) + f_2(x),$$
$$(f_1 f_2)(x) = f_1(x) f_2(x).$$

Note that the functions $f_1 + f_2$ and $f_1 f_2$ have been defined by specifying their values at x in terms of the values of f_1 and f_2 at x.

Example 6   Let f_1 and f_2 be functions from $\mathbf{R}$ to $\mathbf{R}$ such that $f_1(x) = x^2$ and $f_2(x) = x - x^2$. What are the functions $f_1 + f_2$ and $f_1 f_2$?

Solution: From the definition of the sum and product of functions, it follows that

$$(f_1 + f_2)(x) = f_1(x) + f_2(x) = x^2 + (x - x^2) = x$$

and

$$(f_1 f_2)(x) = x^2(x - x^2) = x^3 - x^4.$$ ◄

When f is a function from a set A to a set B, the image of a subset of A can also be defined.

Definition 4   Let f be a function from the set A to the set B and let S be a subset of A. The *image* of S under the function f is the subset of B that consists of the images of the elements of S. We denote the image of S by $f(S)$, so

$$f(S) = \{\, t \mid \exists s \in S \,(t = f(s)) \,\}.$$

We also use the shorthand $\{f(s) \mid s \in S\}$ to denote this set.

Remark: The notation $f(S)$ for the image of the set S under the function f is potentially ambiguous. Here, $f(S)$ denotes a set, and not the value of the function f for the set S.

Example 7   Let $A = \{a, b, c, d, e\}$ and $B = \{1, 2, 3, 4\}$ with $f(a) = 2$, $f(b) = 1$, $f(c) = 4$, $f(d) = 1$, and $f(e) = 1$. The image of the subset $S = \{b, c, d\}$ is the set $f(S) = \{1, 4\}$.   ◀

One-to-One and Onto Functions

Some functions never assign the same value to two different domain elements. These functions are said to be **one-to-one.**

Definition 5   A function f is said to be *one-to-one*, or *injective*, if and only if $f(a) = f(b)$ implies that $a = b$ for all a and b in the domain of f. A function is said to be an *injection* if it is one-to-one.

Note that a function f is one-to-one if and only if $f(a) \neq f(b)$ whenever $a \neq b$. This way of expressing that f is one-to-one is obtained by taking the contrapositive of the implication in the definition.

Remark: We can express that f is one-to-one using quantifiers as $\forall a \forall b (f(a) = f(b) \rightarrow a = b)$ or equivalently $\forall a \forall b (a \neq b \rightarrow f(a) \neq f(b))$, where the universe of discourse is the domain of the function.

We illustrate this concept by giving examples of functions that are one-to-one and other functions that are not one-to-one.

Example 8   Determine whether the function f from $\{a, b, c, d\}$ to $\{1, 2, 3, 4, 5\}$ with $f(a) = 4$, $f(b) = 5$, $f(c) = 1$, and $f(d) = 3$ is one-to-one.
Solution: The function f is one-to-one because f takes on different values at the four elements of its domain. This is illustrated in Figure 3.   ◀

Example 9   Determine whether the function $f(x) = x^2$ from the set of integers to the set of integers is one-to-one.
Solution: The function $f(x) = x^2$ is not one-to-one because, for instance, $f(1) = f(-1) = 1$, but $1 \neq -1$.

Note that the function $f(x) = x^2$ with its domain restricted to $\mathbf{Z}^+$ is one-to-one. (Technically, when we restrict the domain of a function, we obtain a new function whose values agree with those of the original function for the elements of the restricted domain. The restricted function is not defined for elements of the original domain outside of the restricted domain.)   ◀

Example 10   Determine whether the function $f(x) = x + 1$ from the set of real numbers to itself is one-to-one.
Solution: The function $f(x) = x + 1$ is a one-to-one function. To demonstrate this, note that $x + 1 \neq y + 1$ when $x \neq y$.   ◀

We now give some conditions that guarantee that a function is one-to-one.

Definition 6   A function f whose domain and codomain are subsets of the set of real numbers is called *increasing* if $f(x) \leqslant f(y)$, and *strictly increasing* if $f(x) < f(y)$, whenever $x < y$ and x and y are in the domain of f. Similarly, f is called *decreasing* if $f(x) \geqslant f(y)$, and *strictly decreasing* if $f(x) > f(y)$, whenever $x < y$ and x and y are in the domain of f. (The word *strictly* in this definition indicates a strict inequality.)

Remark: A function f is increasing if $\forall x \forall y(x < y \to f(x) \leqslant f(y))$, strictly increasing if $\forall x \forall y(x < y \to f(x) < f(y))$, decreasing if $\forall x \forall y(x < y \to f(x) \geqslant f(y))$, and strictly decreasing if $\forall x \forall y(x < y \to f(x) > f(y))$, where the universe of discourse is the domain of f.

From these definitions, we see that a function that is either strictly increasing or strictly decreasing must be one-to-one. However, a function that is increasing, but not strictly increasing, or decreasing, but not strictly decreasing, is not necessarily one-to-one.

For some functions the range and the codomain are equal. That is, every member of the codomain is the image of some element of the domain. Functions with this property are called **onto** functions.

Definition 7   A function f from A to B is called *onto*, or *surjective*, if and only if for every element $b \in B$ there is an element $a \in A$ with $f(a) = b$. A function f is called a *surjection* if it is onto.

Remark: A function f is onto if $\forall y \exists x (f(x) = y)$, where the domain for x is the domain of the function and the domain for y is the codomain of the function.

We now give examples of onto functions and functions that are not onto.

Example 11   Let f be the function from $\{a, b, c, d\}$ to $\{1, 2, 3\}$ defined by $f(a) = 3$, $f(b) = 2$, $f(c) = 1$, and $f(d) = 3$. Is f an onto function?

Solution: Because all three elements of the codomain are images of elements in the domain, we see that f is onto. This is illustrated in Figure 4. Note that if the codomain were $\{1, 2, 3, 4\}$, then f would not be onto.   ◀

Example 12   Is the function $f(x) = x^2$ from the set of integers to the set of integers onto?

Solution: The function f is not onto because there is no integer x with $x^2 = -1$, for instance.   ◀

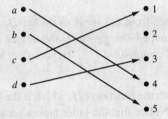

Figure 3   A One-to-One Function.

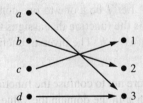

Figure 4   An Onto Function.

Example 13   Is the function $f(x) = x + 1$ from the set of integers to the set of integers onto?

Solution: This function is onto, because for every integer y there is an integer x such that $f(x) = y$. To see this, note that $f(x) = y$ if and only if $x + 1 = y$, which holds if and only if $x = y - 1$.   ◀

Definition 8   The function f is a *one-to-one correspondence*, or a *bijection*, if it is both one-to-one and onto.

Examples 14 and 15 illustrate the concept of a bijection.

Example 14   Let f be the function from $\{a, b, c, d\}$ to $\{1, 2, 3, 4\}$ with $f(a) = 4$, $f(b) = 2$, $f(c) = 1$, and $f(d) = 3$. Is f a bijection?

Solution: The function f is one-to-one and onto. It is one-to-one because no two values in the domain are assigned the same function value. It is onto because all four elements of the codomain are images of elements in the domain. Hence, f is a bijection.   ◀

Figure 5 displays four functions where the first is one-to-one but not onto, the second is onto but not one-to-one, the third is both one-to-one and onto, and the fourth is neither one-to-one nor onto. The fifth correspondence in Figure 5 is not a function, because it sends an element to two different elements.

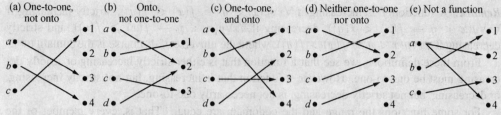

Figure 5   Examples of Different Types of Correspondences.

Suppose that f is a function from a set A to itself. If A is finite, then f is one-to-one if and only if it is onto. This is not necessarily the case if A is infinite (as will be shown in Section 2.4).

Example 15   Let A be a set. The *identity function* on A is the function $\iota_A : A \to A$, where

$$\iota_A(x) = x$$

for all $x \in A$. In other words, the identity function ι_A is the function that assigns each element to itself. The function ι_A is one-to-one and onto, so it is a bijection. (Note that ι is the Greek letter iota.)
◄

Inverse Functions and Compositions of Functions

Now consider a one-to-one correspondence f from the set A to the set B. Because f is an onto function, every element of B is the image of some element in A. Furthermore, because f is also a one-to-one function, every element of B is the image of a *unique* element of A. Consequently, we can define a new function from B to A that reverses the correspondence given by f. This leads to Definition 9.

Definition 9   Let f be a one-to-one correspondence from the set A to the set B. The *inverse function* of f is the function that assigns to an element b belonging to B the unique element a in A such that $f(a) = b$. The inverse function of f is denoted by f^{-1}. Hence, $f^{-1}(b) = a$ when $f(a) = b$.

Remark: Be sure not to confuse the function f^{-1} with the function $1/f$, which is the function that assigns to each x in the domain the value $1/f(x)$. Notice that the latter makes sense only when $f(x)$ is a non-zero real number. They are not the same.
Figure 6 illustrates the concept of an inverse function.

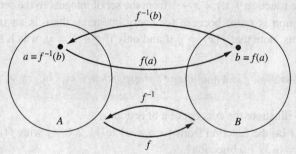

Figure 6   The Function f^{-1} Is the Inverse of Function f.

If a function f is not a one-to-one correspondence, we cannot define an inverse function of f. When f is not a one-to-one correspondence, either it is not one-to-one or it is not onto. If f is not one-to-one, some element b in the codomain is the image of more than one element in the domain. If f is not onto, for some element b in the codomain, no element a in the domain exists for which $f(a) = b$. Consequently, if f is not a one-to-one correspondence, we cannot assign to each element b in the codomain a unique element a in the domain such that $f(a) = b$ (because for some b there is either more than one such a or no such a).

A one-to-one correspondence is called **invertible** because we can define an inverse of this function. A function is **not invertible** if it is not a one-to-one correspondence, because the inverse of such a function does not exist.

Example 16   Let f be the function from $\{a, b, c\}$ to $\{1, 2, 3\}$ such that $f(a) = 2$, $f(b) = 3$, and $f(c) = 1$. Is f invertible, and if it is, what is its inverse?

Solution: The function f is invertible because it is a one-to-one correspondence. The inverse function f^{-1} reverses the correspondence given by f, so $f^{-1}(1) = c$, $f^{-1}(2) = a$, and $f^{-1}(3) = b$.   ◀

Example 17   Let $f : \mathbf{Z} \to \mathbf{Z}$ be such that $f(x) = x + 1$. Is f invertible, and if it is, what is its inverse?

Solution: The function f has an inverse because it is a one-to-one correspondence, as we have shown. To reverse the correspondence, suppose that y is the image of x, so that $y = x + 1$. Then $x = y - 1$. This means that $y - 1$ is the unique element of $\mathbf{Z}$ that is sent to y by f. Consequently, $f^{-1}(y) = y - 1$.   ◀

Example 18   Let f be the function from $\mathbf{R}$ to $\mathbf{R}$ with $f(x) = x^2$. Is f invertible?

Solution: Because $f(-2) = f(2) = 4$, f is not one-to-one. If an inverse function were defined, it would have to assign two elements to 4. Hence, f is not invertible.   ◀

Sometimes we can restrict the domain or the codomain of a function, or both, to obtain an invertible function, as Example 19 illustrates.

Example 19   Show that if we restrict the function $f(x) = x^2$ in Example 18 to a function from the set of all nonnegative real numbers to the set of all nonnegative real numbers, then f is invertible.

Solution: The function $f(x) = x^2$ from the set of nonnegative real numbers to the set of nonnegative real numbers is one-to-one. To see this, note that if $f(x) = f(y)$, then $x^2 = y^2$, so $x^2 - y^2 = (x + y)(x - y) = 0$. This means that $x + y = 0$ or $x - y = 0$, so $x = -y$ or $x = y$. Because both x and y are nonnegative, we must have $x = y$. So, this function is one-to-one. Furthermore, $f(x) = x^2$ is onto when the codomain is the set of all nonnegative real numbers, because each nonnegative real number has a square root. That is, if y is a nonnegative real number, there exists a nonnegative real number x such that $x = \sqrt{y}$, which means that $x^2 = y$. Because the function $f(x) = x^2$ from the set of nonnegative real numbers to the set of nonnegative real numbers is one-to-one and onto, it is invertible. Its inverse is given by the rule $f^{-1}(y) = \sqrt{y}$.   ◀

Definition 10   Let g be a function from the set A to the set B and let f be a function from the set B to the set C. The *composition* of the functions f and g, denoted by $f \circ g$, is defined by

$$(f \circ g)(a) = f(g(a)).$$

In other words, $f \circ g$ is the function that assigns to the element a of A the element assigned by f to $g(a)$. That is, to find $(f \circ g)(a)$ we first apply the function g to a to obtain $g(a)$ and then we apply the function f to the result $g(a)$ to obtain $(f \circ g)(a) = f(g(a))$. Note that the composition $f \circ g$ cannot be defined unless the range of g is a subset of the domain of f. In Figure 7 the composition of functions is shown.

Example 20   Let g be the function from the set $\{a, b, c\}$ to itself such that $g(a) = b$, $g(b) = c$, and $g(c) = a$. Let f be the function from the set $\{a, b, c\}$ to the set $\{1, 2, 3\}$ such that $f(a) = 3$, $f(b) = 2$, and $f(c) = 1$. What is the composition of f and g, and what is the composition of g and f?

Solution: The composition $f \circ g$ is defined by $(f \circ g)(a) = f(g(a)) = f(b) = 2$, $(f \circ g)(b) = f(g(b)) = f(c) = 1$, and $(f \circ g)(c) = f(g(c)) = f(a) = 3$.

Note that $g \circ f$ is not defined, because the range of f is not a subset of the domain of g.   ◄

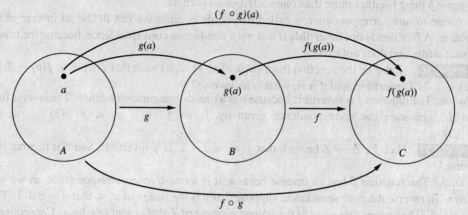

Figure 7   The Composition of the Functions f and g.

Example 21   Let f and g be the functions from the set of integers to the set of integers defined by $f(x) = 2x + 3$ and $g(x) = 3x + 2$. What is the composition of f and g? What is the composition of g and f?

Solution: Both the compositions $f \circ g$ and $g \circ f$ are defined. Moreover,

$$(f \circ g)(x) = f(g(x)) = f(3x + 2) = 2(3x + 2) + 3 = 6x + 7$$

and

$$(g \circ f)(x) = g(f(x)) = g(2x + 3) = 3(2x + 3) + 2 = 6x + 11.$$ ◄

Remark: Note that even though $f \circ g$ and $g \circ f$ are defined for the functions f and g in Example 21, $f \circ g$ and $g \circ f$ are not equal. In other words, the commutative law does not hold for the composition of functions.

When the composition of a function and its inverse is formed, in either order, an identity function is obtained. To see this, suppose that f is a one-to-one correspondence from the set A to the set B. Then the inverse function f^{-1} exists and is a one-to-one correspondence from B to A. The inverse function reverses the correspondence of the original function, so $f^{-1}(b) = a$ when $f(a) = b$, and $f(a) = b$ when $f^{-1}(b) = a$. Hence,

$$(f^{-1} \circ f)(a) = f^{-1}(f(a)) = f^{-1}(b) = a,$$

and

$$(f \circ f^{-1})(b) = f(f^{-1}(b)) = f(a) = b.$$

Consequently $f^{-1} \circ f = \iota_A$ and $f \circ f^{-1} = \iota_B$, where ι_A and ι_B are the identity functions on the sets A and B, respectively. That is, $(f^{-1})^{-1} = f$.

The Graphs of Functions

We can associate a set of pairs in $A \times B$ to each function from A to B. This set of pairs is called the **graph** of the function and is often displayed pictorially to aid in understanding the behavior of the function.

Definition 11   Let f be a function from the set A to the set B. The *graph* of the function f is the set of ordered pairs $\{(a, b) \mid a \in A \text{ and } f(a) = b\}$.

From the definition, the graph of a function f from A to B is the subset of $A \times B$ containing the ordered pairs with the second entry equal to the element of B assigned by f to the first entry.

Example 22   Display the graph of the function $f(n) = 2n + 1$ from the set of integers to the set of integers.

Solution: The graph of f is the set of ordered pairs of the form $(n, 2n + 1)$, where n is an integer. This graph is displayed in Figure 8.   ◄

Example 23   Display the graph of the function $f(x) = x^2$ from the set of integers to the set of integers.

Solution: The graph of f is the set of ordered pairs of the form $(x, f(x)) = (x, x^2)$, where x is an integer. This graph is displayed in Figure 9.   ◄

Some Important Functions

Next, we introduce two important functions in discrete mathematics, namely, the floor and ceiling functions. Let x be a real number. The floor function rounds x down to the closest integer less than or equal to x, and the ceiling function rounds x up to the closest integer greater than or equal to x. These functions are often used when objects are counted. They play an important role in the analysis of the number of steps used by procedures to solve problems of a particular size.

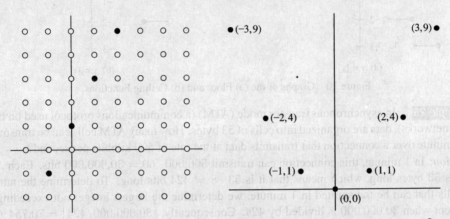

Figure 8   The Graph of $f(n) = 2n + 1$ Figure 9   The Graph of $f(x) = x^2$
             from **Z** to **Z**.   from **Z** to **Z**.

Definition 12   The *floor function* assigns to the real number x the largest integer that is less than or equal to x. The value of the floor function at x is denoted by $\lfloor x \rfloor$. The *ceiling function* assigns to the real number x the smallest integer that is greater than or equal to x. The value of the ceiling function at x is denoted by $\lceil x \rceil$.

Remark: The floor function is often also called the *greatest integer function*. It is often denoted by $[x]$.

Example 24   These are some values of the floor and ceiling functions:

$$\lfloor \tfrac{1}{2} \rfloor = 0, \lceil \tfrac{1}{2} \rceil = 1, \lfloor -\tfrac{1}{2} \rfloor = -1, \lceil -\tfrac{1}{2} \rceil = 0, \lfloor 3.1 \rfloor = 3, \lceil 3.1 \rceil = 4, \lfloor 7 \rfloor = 7, \lceil 7 \rceil = 7.$$ ◄

We display the graphs of the floor and ceiling functions in Figure 10. In Figure 10(a) we display the graph of the floor function $\lfloor x \rfloor$. Note that this function has the same value throughout the interval $[n, n + 1)$, namely n, and then it jumps up to $n + 1$ when $x = n + 1$. In Figure 10(b) we display the graph of the ceiling function $\lceil x \rceil$. Note that this function has the same value throughout the interval $(n, n+1]$, namely $n+1$, and then jumps to $n+2$ when x is a little larger than $n + 1$.

The floor and ceiling functions are useful in a wide variety of applications, including those involving data storage and data transmission. Consider Examples 25 and 26, typical of basic calculations done when database and data communications problems are studied.

Example 25 Data stored on a computer disk or transmitted over a data network are usually represented as a string of bytes. Each byte is made up of 8 bits. How many bytes are required to encode 100 bits of data?

Solution: To determine the number of bytes needed, we determine the smallest integer that is at least as large as the quotient when 100 is divided by 8, the number of bits in a byte. Consequently, $\lceil 100/8 \rceil = \lceil 12.5 \rceil = 13$ bytes are required. ◀

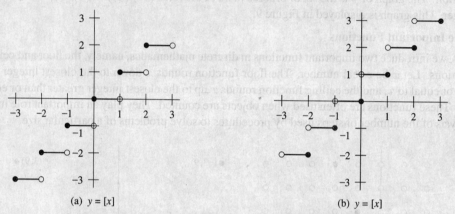

(a) $y = \lfloor x \rfloor$ (b) $y = \lceil x \rceil$

Figure 10   Graphs of the (a) Floor and (b) Ceiling Functions.

Example 26 In asynchronous transfer mode (ATM) (a communications protocol used on backbone networks), data are organized into cells of 53 bytes. How many ATM cells can be transmitted in 1 minute over a connection that transmits data at the rate of 500 kilobits per second?

Solution: In 1 minute, this connection can transmit $500{,}000 \cdot 60 = 30{,}000{,}000$ bits. Each ATM cell is 53 bytes long, which means that it is $53 \cdot 8 = 424$ bits long. To determine the number of cells that can be transmitted in 1 minute, we determine the largest integer not exceeding the quotient when 30,000,000 is divided by 424. Consequently, $\lfloor 30{,}000{,}000/424 \rfloor = 70{,}754$ ATM cells can be transmitted in 1 minute over a 500 kilobit per second connection. ◀

Table 1, with x denoting a real number, displays some simple but important properties of the floor and ceiling functions. Because these functions appear so frequently in discrete mathematics, it is useful to look over these identities. Each property in this table can be established using the definitions of the floor and ceiling functions. Properties (1a), (1b), (1c), and (1d) follow directly from these definitions. For example, (1a) states that $\lfloor x \rfloor = n$ if and only if the integer n is less than or equal to x and $n + 1$ is larger than x. This is precisely what it means for n to be the greatest integer not exceeding x, which is the definition of $\lfloor x \rfloor = n$. Properties (1b), (1c), and (1d) can be established similarly. We will prove property (4a) using a direct proof.

Proof: Suppose that $\lfloor x \rfloor = m$, where m is a positive integer. By property (1a), it follows that $m \leqslant x < m+1$. Adding n to both sides of this inequality shows that $m+n \leqslant x+n < m+n+1$. Using property (1a) again, we see that $\lfloor x + n \rfloor = m + n = \lfloor x \rfloor + n$. This completes the proof. Proofs of the other properties are left as exercises. ◁

The floor and ceiling functions enjoy many other useful properties besides those displayed in Table 1. There are also many statements about these functions that may appear to be correct, but actually are not. We will consider statements about the floor and ceiling functions in Examples 27 and 28.

A useful approach for considering statements about the floor function is to let $x = n + \epsilon$, where $n = \lfloor x \rfloor$ is an integer, and ϵ, the fractional part of x, satisfies the inequality $0 \leqslant \epsilon < 1$. Similarly, when considering statements about the ceiling function, it is useful to write $x = n - \epsilon$, where $n = \lceil x \rceil$ is an integer and $0 \leqslant \epsilon < 1$.

TABLE 1 Useful Properties of the Floor and Ceiling Functions.
(*n* is an integer)

(1a) $\lfloor x \rfloor = n$ if and only if $n \leq x < n+1$

(1b) $\lceil x \rceil = n$ if and only if $n-1 < x \leq n$

(1c) $\lfloor x \rfloor = n$ if and only if $x-1 < n \leq x$

(1d) $\lceil x \rceil = n$ if and only if $x \leq n < x+1$

(2) $x-1 < \lfloor x \rfloor \leq x \leq \lceil x \rceil < x+1$

(3a) $\lfloor -x \rfloor = -\lceil x \rceil$

(3b) $\lceil -x \rceil = -\lfloor x \rfloor$

(4a) $\lfloor x+n \rfloor = \lfloor x \rfloor + n$

(4b) $\lceil x+n \rceil = \lceil x \rceil + n$

Example 27   Prove that if x is a real number, then $\lfloor 2x \rfloor = \lfloor x \rfloor + \lfloor x + \frac{1}{2} \rfloor$.

Solution: To prove this statement we let $x = n + \epsilon$, where n is a positive integer and $0 \leq \epsilon < 1$. There are two cases to consider, depending on whether ϵ is less than or greater than or equal to $\frac{1}{2}$. (The reason we choose these two cases will be made clear in the proof.)

We first consider the case when $0 \leq \epsilon < \frac{1}{2}$. In this case, $2x = 2n + 2\epsilon$ and $\lfloor 2x \rfloor = 2n$ because $0 \leq 2\epsilon < 1$. Similarly, $x + \frac{1}{2} = n + (\frac{1}{2} + \epsilon)$, so $\lfloor x + \frac{1}{2} \rfloor = n$, because $0 < \frac{1}{2} + \epsilon < 1$. Consequently, $\lfloor 2x \rfloor = 2n$ and $\lfloor x \rfloor + \lfloor x + \frac{1}{2} \rfloor = n + n = 2n$.

Next, we consider the case when $\frac{1}{2} \leq \epsilon < 1$. In this case, $2x = 2n + 2\epsilon = (2n+1) + (2\epsilon - 1)$. Because $0 \leq 2\epsilon - 1 < 1$, it follows that $\lfloor 2x \rfloor = 2n + 1$. Because $\lfloor x + \frac{1}{2} \rfloor = \lfloor n + (\frac{1}{2} + \epsilon) \rfloor = \lfloor n+1+(\epsilon-\frac{1}{2}) \rfloor$ and $0 \leq \epsilon - \frac{1}{2} < 1$, it follows that $\lfloor x + \frac{1}{2} \rfloor = n+1$. Consequently, $\lfloor 2x \rfloor = 2n+1$ and $\lfloor x \rfloor + \lfloor x + \frac{1}{2} \rfloor = n + (n+1) = 2n+1$. This concludes the proof.   ◄

Example 28   Prove or disprove that $\lceil x+y \rceil = \lceil x \rceil + \lceil y \rceil$ for all real numbers x and y.

Solution: Although this statement may appear reasonable, it is false. A counterexample is supplied by $x = \frac{1}{2}$ and $y = \frac{1}{2}$. With these values we find that $\lceil x+y \rceil = \lceil \frac{1}{2} + \frac{1}{2} \rceil = \lceil 1 \rceil = 1$, but $\lceil x \rceil + \lceil y \rceil = \lceil \frac{1}{2} \rceil + \lceil \frac{1}{2} \rceil = 1 + 1 = 2$.   ◄

There are certain types of functions that will be used throughout the text. These include polynomial, logarithmic, and exponential functions. In this book the notation $\log x$ will be used to denote the logarithm to the base 2 of x, because 2 is the base that we will usually use for logarithms. We will denote logarithms to the base b, where b is any real number greater than 1, by $\log_b x$, and the natural logarithm by $\ln x$.

Another function we will use throughout this text is the **factorial function** $f : \mathbf{N} \to \mathbf{Z}^+$, denoted by $f(n) = n!$. The value of $f(n) = n!$ is the product of the first n positive integers, so $f(n) = 1 \cdot 2 \cdots (n-1) \cdot n$ [and $f(0) = 0! = 1$].

Example 29   We have $f(1) = 1! = 1$, $f(2) = 2! = 1 \cdot 2 = 2$, $f(6) = 6! = 1 \cdot 2 \cdot 3 \cdot 4 \cdot 5 \cdot 6 = 720$, and $f(20) = 1 \cdot 2 \cdot 3 \cdot 4 \cdot 5 \cdot 6 \cdot 7 \cdot 8 \cdot 9 \cdot 10 \cdot 11 \cdot 12 \cdot 13 \cdot 14 \cdot 15 \cdot 16 \cdot 17 \cdot 18 \cdot 19 \cdot 20 = 2,432,902,008,176,640,000$.
◄

Example 29 illustrates that the factorial function grows extremely rapidly as n grows. The rapid growth of the factorial function is made clearer by Stirling's formula, a result from higher mathematics that tell us that $n! \sim \sqrt{2\pi n}(n/e)^n$. Here, we have used the notation $f(n) \sim g(n)$, which means that the ratio $f(n)/g(n)$ approaches 1 as n grows without bound (that is, $\lim_{n \to \infty} f(n)/g(n) = 1$). The symbol $\sim$ is read "is asymptotic to." Stirling's formula is named after James Stirling, a Scottish mathematician of the eighteenth century.

Exercises

1. Why is f not a function from $\mathbf{R}$ to $\mathbf{R}$ if
   a) $f(x) = 1/x$?   b) $f(x) = \sqrt{x}$?   c) $f(x) = \pm\sqrt{(x^2 + 1)}$?

2. Determine whether f is a function from the set of all bit strings to the set of integers if
   a) $f(S)$ is the position of a 0 bit in S.   b) $f(S)$ is the number of 1 bits in S.
   c) $f(S)$ is the smallest integer i such that the ith bit of S is 1 and $f(S) = 0$ when S is the empty string, the string with no bits.

3. Find the domain and range of these functions. Note that in each case, to find the domain, determine the set of elements assigned values by the function.
   a) the function that assigns to each bit string the number of ones minus the number of zeros
   b) the function that assigns to each bit string twice the number of zeros in that string
   c) the function that assigns the number of bits left over when a bit string is split into bytes (which are blocks of 8 bits)
   d) the function that assigns to each positive integer the largest perfect square not exceeding this integer

4. Find the domain and range of these functions.
   a) the function that assigns to each pair of positive integers the maximum of these two integers
   b) the function that assigns to each positive integer the number of the digits 0, 1, 2, 3, 4, 5, 6, 7, 8, 9 that do not appear as decimal digits of the integer
   c) the function that assigns to a bit string the number of times the block 11 appears
   d) the function that assigns to a bit string the numerical position of the first 1 in the string and that assigns the value 0 to a bit string consisting of all 0s

5. Find these values.
   a) $\lceil \frac{3}{4} \rceil$ b) $\lfloor \frac{7}{8} \rfloor$ c) $\lceil -\frac{3}{4} \rceil$ d) $\lfloor -\frac{7}{8} \rfloor$ e) $\lceil 3 \rceil$ f) $\lfloor -1 \rfloor$ g) $\lfloor \frac{1}{2} + \lceil \frac{3}{2} \rceil \rfloor$ h) $\lfloor \frac{1}{2} \cdot \lfloor \frac{5}{2} \rfloor \rfloor$

6. Determine whether the function $f: \mathbf{Z} \times \mathbf{Z} \to \mathbf{Z}$ is onto if
   a) $f(m, n) = m + n$.   b) $f(m, n) = m^2 + n^2$.   c) $f(m, n) = m$.
   d) $f(m, n) = |n|$.   e) $f(m, n) = m - n$.

7. Give an explicit formula for a function from the set of integers to the set of positive integers that is
   a) one-to-one, but not onto.   b) onto, but not one-to-one.
   c) one-to-one and onto.   d) neither one-to-one nor onto.

8. Determine whether each of these functions is a bijection from $\mathbf{R}$ to $\mathbf{R}$.
   a) $f(x) = 2x + 1$ b) $f(x) = x^2 + 1$ c) $f(x) = x^3$ d) $f(x) = (x^2 + 1)/(x^2 + 2)$

9. Let $f: \mathbf{R} \to \mathbf{R}$ and let $f(x) > 0$. Show that $f(x)$ is strictly decreasing if and only if the function $g(x) = 1/f(x)$ is strictly increasing.

10. Give an example of a decreasing function with the set of real numbers as its domain and codomain that is not one-to-one.

11. Show that the function $f(x) = |x|$ from the set of real numbers to the set of nonnegative real numbers is not invertible, but if the domain is restricted to the set of nonnegative real numbers, the resulting function is invertible.

12. Let $f(x) = \lfloor x^2/3 \rfloor$. Find $f(S)$ if
    a) $S = \{-2, -1, 0, 1, 2, 3\}$.   b) $S = \{0, 1, 2, 3, 4, 5\}$.   c) $S = \{1, 5, 7, 11\}$.   d) $S = \{2, 6, 10, 14\}$.

13. Suppose that g is a function from A to B and f is a function from B to C.
    a) Show that if both f and g are one-to-one functions, then $f \circ g$ is also one-to-one.
    b) Show that if both f and g are onto functions, then $f \circ g$ is also onto.

*14. If f and $f \circ g$ are onto, does it follow that g is onto? Justify your answer.

15. Show that the function $f(x) = ax + b$ from **R** to **R** is invertible, where a and b are constants, with $a \neq 0$, and find the inverse of f.

Let f be a function from the set A to the set B. Let S be a subset of B. We define the **inverse image** of S to be the subset of A whose elements are precisely all pre-images of all elements of S. We denote the inverse image of S by $f^{-1}(S)$, so $f^{-1}(S) = \{a \in A \mid f(a) \in S\}$. (*Beware:* The notation f^{-1} is used in two different ways. Do not confuse the notation introduced here with the notation $f^{-1}(y)$ for the value at y of the inverse of the invertible function f. Notice also that $f^{-1}(S)$, the inverse image of the set S, makes sense for all functions f, not just invertible functions.)

16. Let $g(x) = \lfloor x \rfloor$. Find

    a) $g^{-1}(\{0\})$.   b) $g^{-1}(\{-1, 0, 1\})$.   c) $g^{-1}(\{x \mid 0 < x < 1\})$.

17. Let f be a function from A to B. Let S be a subset of B. Show that $f^{-1}(\overline{S}) = \overline{f^{-1}(S)}$.

18. Show that $\lceil x - \frac{1}{2} \rceil$ is the closest integer to the number x, except when x is midway between two integers, when it is the smaller of these two integers.

19. Show that if x is a real number, then $x - 1 < \lfloor x \rfloor \leqslant x \leqslant \lceil x \rceil < x + 1$.

20. Show that if x is a real number and n is an integer, then

    a) $x < n$ if and only if $\lfloor x \rfloor < n$.   b) $n < x$ if and only if $n < \lceil x \rceil$.

21. Prove that if n is an integer, then $\lfloor n/2 \rfloor = n/2$ if n is even and $(n - 1)/2$ if n is odd.

22. The function INT is found on some calculators, where $\text{INT}(x) = \lfloor x \rfloor$ when x is a nonnegative real number and $\text{INT}(x) = \lceil x \rceil$ when x is a negative real number. Show that this INT function satisfies the identity $\text{INT}(-x) = -\text{INT}(x)$.

23. Let a and b be real numbers with $a < b$. Use the floor and/or ceiling functions to express the number of integers n that satisfy the inequality $a < n < b$.

24. How many bytes are required to encode n bits of data where n equals

    a) 7?   b) 17?   c) 1001?   d) 28,800?

25. Data are transmitted over a particular Ethernet network in blocks of 1500 octets (blocks of 8 bits). How many blocks are required to transmit the following amounts of data over this Ethernet network? (Note that a byte is a synonym for an octet, a kilobyte is 1000 bytes, and a megabyte is 1,000,000 bytes.)

    a) 150 kilobytes of data   b) 384 kilobytes of data   c) 1.544 megabytes of data

    d) 45.3 megabytes of data

26. Draw the graph of the function $f(x) = \lfloor 2x \rfloor$ from **R** to **R**.

27. Draw the graph of the function $f(x) = \lfloor x \rfloor + \lfloor x/2 \rfloor$ from **R** to **R**.

28. Draw graphs of each of these functions.

    a) $f(x) = \lfloor x + \frac{1}{2} \rfloor$ b) $f(x) = \lfloor 2x + 1 \rfloor$ c) $f(x) = \lceil x/3 \rceil$ d) $f(x) = \lceil 1/x \rceil$

    e) $f(x) = \lceil x - 2 \rceil + \lfloor x + 2 \rfloor$ f) $f(x) = \lfloor 2x \rfloor \lceil x/2 \rceil$ g) $f(x) = \lceil \lfloor x - \frac{1}{2} \rfloor + \frac{1}{2} \rceil$

29. Find the inverse function of $f(x) = x^3 + 1$.

30. Let S be a subset of a universal set U. The **characteristic function** f_S of S is the function from U to the set $\{0, 1\}$ such that $f_S(x) = 1$ if x belongs to S and $f_S(x) = 0$ if x does not belong to S. Let A and B be sets. Show that for all x,

    a) $f_{A \cap B}(x) = f_A(x) \cdot f_B(x)$ b) $f_{A \cup B}(x) = f_A(x) + f_B(x) - f_A(x) \cdot f_B(x)$

    c) $f_{\overline{A}}(x) = 1 - f_A(x)$ d) $f_{A \oplus B}(x) = f_A(x) + f_B(x) - 2f_A(x)f_B(x)$

31. Prove or disprove each of these statements about the floor and ceiling functions.

    a) $\lceil \lfloor x \rfloor \rceil = \lfloor x \rfloor$ for all real numbers x.

    b) $\lfloor 2x \rfloor = 2 \lfloor x \rfloor$ whenever x is a real number.

    c) $\lceil x \rceil + \lceil y \rceil - \lceil x + y \rceil = 0$ or 1 whenever x and y are real numbers.

    d) $\lceil xy \rceil = \lceil x \rceil \lceil y \rceil$ for all real numbers x and y.

    e) $\left\lfloor \dfrac{x}{2} \right\rfloor = \left\lfloor \dfrac{x + 1}{2} \right\rfloor$ for all real numbers x.

32. Prove that if x is a positive real number, then

a) $\lfloor \sqrt{\lfloor x \rfloor} \rfloor = \lfloor \sqrt{x} \rfloor$.   b) $\lceil \sqrt{\lceil x \rceil} \rceil = \lceil \sqrt{x} \rceil$.

To study such situations, we use the concept of a partial function. A **partial function** f from a set A to a set B is an assignment to each element a in a subset of A, called the **domain of definition** of f, of a unique element b in B. The sets A and B are called the **domain** and **codomain** of f, respectively. We say that f is **undefined** for elements in A that are not in the domain of definition of f. We write $f : A \rightarrow B$ to denote that f is a partial function from A to B. (This is the same notation as is used for functions. The context in which the notation is used determines whether f is a partial function or a total function.) When the domain of definition of f equals A, we say that f is a **total function.**

33. For each of these partial functions, determine its domain, codomain, domain of definition, and the set of values for which it is undefined. Also, determine whether it is a total function.

a) $f : \mathbf{Z} \rightarrow \mathbf{R}$, $f(n) = 1/n$ b) $f : \mathbf{Z} \rightarrow \mathbf{Z}$, $f(n) = \lceil n/2 \rceil$

c) $f : \mathbf{Z} \times \mathbf{Z} \rightarrow \mathbf{Q}$, $f(m,n) = m/n$ d) $f : \mathbf{Z} \times \mathbf{Z} \rightarrow \mathbf{Z}$, $f(m,n) = mn$

e) $f : \mathbf{Z} \times \mathbf{Z} \rightarrow \mathbf{Z}$, $f(m,n) = m - n$ if $m > n$

34. a) Show that if a set S has cardinality m, where m is a positive integer, then there is a one-to-one correspondence between S and the set $\{1, 2, \ldots, m\}$.

b) Show that if S and T are two sets each with m elements, where m is a positive integer, then there is a one-to-one correspondence between S and T.

*35. Show that the polynomial function $f : \mathbf{Z}^+ \times \mathbf{Z}^+ \rightarrow \mathbf{Z}^+$ with $f(m,n) = (m+n-2)(m+n-1)/2+m$ is one-to-one and onto.

2.4   Sequences and Summations

Introduction

Sequences are ordered lists of elements. Sequences are used in discrete mathematics in many ways. They can be used to represent solutions to certain counting problems, as we will see in Chapter 4. They are also an important data structure in computer science. This section contains a review of the notation used to represent sequences and sums of terms of sequences.

When the elements of an infinite set can be listed, the set is called countable. We will conclude this section with a discussion of both countable and uncountable sets. We will prove that the set of rational numbers is countable, but the set of real numbers is not.

Sequences

A sequence is a discrete structure used to represent an ordered list. For example, 1, 2, 3, 5, 8 is a sequence with five terms and 1, 3, 9, 27, 81 , ..., 30, ... is an infinite sequence.

Definition 1   A *sequence* is a function from a subset of the set of integers (usually either the set $\{0, 1, 2, \ldots\}$ or the set $\{1, 2, 3, \ldots\}$) to a set S. We use the notation a_n to denote the image of the integer n. We call a_n a *term* of the sequence.

We use the notation $\{a_n\}$ to describe the sequence. (Note that a_n represents an individual term of the sequence $\{a_n\}$. Also note that the notation $\{a_n\}$ for a sequence conflicts with the notation for a set. However, the context in which we use this notation will always make it clear when we are dealing with sets and when we are dealing with sequences. Note that although we have used the letter a in the notation for a sequence, other letters or expressions may be used depending on the sequence under consideration. That is, the choice of the letter a is arbitrary.)

We describe sequences by listing the terms of the sequence in order of increasing subscripts.

Example 1   Consider the sequence $\{a_n\}$, where

$$a_n = \frac{1}{n}.$$

The list of the terms of this sequence, beginning with a_1, namely,

$$a_1, a_2, a_3, a_4, \ldots,$$

starts with

$$1, \frac{1}{2}, \frac{1}{3}, \frac{1}{4}, \ldots. \quad \blacktriangleleft$$

Definition 2   A *geometric progression* is a sequence of the form

$$a, ar, ar^2, \ldots, ar^n, \ldots$$

where the *initial term a* and the *common ratio r* are real numbers.

Remark: A geometric progression is a discrete analogue of the exponential function $f(x) = ar^x$.

Example 2   The sequences $\{b_n\}$ with $b_n = (-1)^n$, $\{c_n\}$ with $c_n = 2 \cdot 5^n$, and $\{d_n\}$ with $d_n = 6 \cdot (1/3)^n$ are geometric progressions with initial term and common ratio equal to 1 and -1; 2 and 5; and 6 and 1/3, respectively, if we start at $n = 0$. The list of terms $b_0, b_1, b_2, b_3, b_4, \ldots$ begins with

$$1, -1, 1, -1, 1, \ldots;$$

the list of terms $c_0, c_1, c_2, c_3, c_4, \ldots$ begins with

$$2, 10, 50, 250, 1250, \ldots;$$

and the list of terms $d_0, d_1, d_2, d_3, d_4, \ldots$ begins with

$$6, 2, \frac{2}{3}, \frac{2}{9}, \frac{2}{27}, \ldots. \quad \blacktriangleleft$$

Definition 3   An *arithmetic progression* is a sequence of the form

$$a, a + d, a + 2d, \ldots, a + nd, \ldots$$

where the *initial term a* and the *common difference d* are real numbers.

Remark: An arithmetic progression is a discrete analogue of the linear function $f(x) = dx + a$.

Example 3   The sequences $\{s_n\}$ with $s_n = -1 + 4n$ and $\{t_n\}$ with $t_n = 7 - 3n$ are both arithmetic progressions with initial terms and common differences equal to -1 and 4, and 7 and -3, respectively, if we start at $n = 0$. The list of terms $s_0, s_1, s_2, s_3, \ldots$ begins with

$$-1, 3, 7, 11, \ldots,$$

and the list of terms $t_0, t_1, t_2, t_3, \ldots$ begins with

$$7, 4, 1, -2, \ldots. \quad \blacktriangleleft$$

Sequences of the form $a_1, a_2, \ldots, a_n$ are often used in computer science. These finite sequences are also called **strings**. This string is also denoted by $a_1 a_2 \ldots a_n$. (Recall that bit strings, which are finite sequences of bits, were introduced in Section 1.1.) The **length** of the string S is the number of terms in this string. The **empty string**, denoted by λ, is the string that has no terms. The empty string has length zero.

Example 4   The string *abcd* is a string of length four. $\blacktriangleleft$

Special Integer Sequences

A common problem in discrete mathematics is finding a formula or a general rule for constructing the terms of a sequence. Sometimes only a few terms of a sequence solving a problem are known; the goal is to identify the sequence. Even though the initial terms of a sequence do not determine the entire sequence (after all, there are infinitely many different sequences that start with any finite set of initial terms), knowing the first few terms may help you make an educated conjecture about the identity of your sequence. Once you have made this conjecture, you can try to verify that you have the correct sequence.

When trying to deduce a possible formula or rule for the terms of a sequence from the initial terms, try to find a pattern in these terms. You might also see whether you can determine how a term might have been produced from those preceding it. There are many questions you could ask, but some of the more useful are:

■ Are there runs of the same value? That is, does the same value occur many times in a row?
■ Are terms obtained from previous terms by adding the same amount or an amount that depends on the position in the sequence?
■ Are terms obtained from previous terms by multiplying by a particular amount?
■ Are terms obtained by combining previous terms in a certain way?
■ Are there cycles among the terms?

Example 5   Find formulae for the sequences with the following first five terms: (a) $1, 1/2, 1/4,$ $1/8, 1/16$ (b) $1, 3, 5, 7, 9$ (c) $1, -1, 1, -1, 1.$

Solution: (a) We recognize that the denominators are powers of 2. The sequence with $a_n = 1/2^n$, $n = 0, 1, 2, \ldots$ is a possible match. This proposed sequence is a geometric progression with $a = 1$ and $r = 1/2$.

(b) We note that each term is obtained by adding 2 to the previous term. The sequence with $a_n = 2n + 1, n = 0, 1, 2, \ldots$ is a possible match. This proposed sequence is an arithmetic progression with $a = 1$ and $d = 2$.

(c) The terms alternate between 1 and -1. The sequence with $a_n = (-1)^n, n = 0, 1, 2 \ldots$ is a possible match. This proposed sequence is a geometric progression with $a = 1$ and $r = -1$. ◄

Examples 6 and 7 illustrate how we can analyze sequences to find how the terms are constructed.

Example 6   How can we produce the terms of a sequence if the first 10 terms are 1, 2, 2, 3, 3, 3, 4, 4, 4, 4?

Solution: Note that the integer 1 appears once, the integer 2 appears twice, the integer 3 appears three times, and the integer 4 appears four times. A reasonable rule for generating this sequence is that the integer n appears exactly n times, so the next five terms of the sequence would all be 5, the following six terms would all be 6, and so on. The sequence generated this way is a possible match. ◄

Example 7   How can we produce the terms of a sequence if the first 10 terms are 5, 11, 17, 23, 29, 35, 41, 47, 53, 59?

Solution: Note that each of the first 10 terms of this sequence after the first is obtained by adding 6 to the previous term. (We could see this by noticing that the difference between consecutive terms is 6.) Consequently, the nth term could be produced by starting with 5 and adding 6 a total of $n - 1$ times; that is, a reasonable guess is that the nth term is $5 + 6(n - 1) = 6n - 1$. (This is an arithmetic progression with $a = 5$ and $d = 6$.) ◄

Another useful technique for finding a rule for generating the terms of a sequence is to compare the terms of a sequence of interest with the terms of a well-known integer sequence, such as terms of an arithmetic progression, terms of a geometric progression, perfect squares, perfect cubes, and so on. The first 10 terms of some sequences you may want to keep in mind are displayed in Table 1.

TABLE 1 Some Useful Sequences.

nth Term	First 10 Terms
n^2	$1, 4, 9, 16, 25, 36, 49, 64, 81, 100, \ldots$
n^3	$1, 8, 27, 64, 125, 216, 343, 512, 729, 1000, \ldots$
n^4	$1, 16, 81, 256, 625, 1296, 2401, 4096, 6561, 10000, \ldots$
2^n	$2, 4, 8, 16, 32, 64, 128, 256, 512, 1024, \ldots$
3^n	$3, 9, 27, 81, 243, 729, 2187, 6561, 19683, 59049, \ldots$
$n!$	$1, 2, 6, 24, 120, 720, 5040, 40320, 362880, 3628800, \ldots$

Example 8 Conjecture a simple formula for a_n if the first 10 terms of the sequence $\{a_n\}$ are 1, 7, 25, 79, 241, 727, 2185, 6559, 19681, 59047.

Solution: To attack this problem, we begin by looking at the difference of consecutive terms, but we do not see a pattern. When we form the ratio of consecutive terms to see whether each term is a multiple of the previous term, we find that this ratio, although not a constant, is close to 3. So it is reasonable to suspect that the terms of this sequence are generated by a formula involving 3^n. Comparing these terms with the corresponding terms of the sequence $\{3^n\}$, we notice that the nth term is 2 less than the corresponding power of 3. We see that $a_n = 3^n - 2$ for $1 \leqslant n \leqslant 10$ and conjecture that this formula holds for all n. ◄

We will see throughout this text that integer sequences appear in a wide range of contexts in discrete mathematics. Sequences we have or will encounter include the sequence of prime numbers, the number of ways to order n discrete objects (Chapter 3), the number of moves required to solve the famous Tower of Hanoi puzzle with n disks (Chapter 4), and the number of rabbits on an island after n months (Chapter 4).

Integer sequences appear in an amazingly wide range of subject areas besides discrete mathematics, including biology, engineering, chemistry, and physics, as well as in puzzles. An amazing database of over 100,000 different integer sequences can be found in the *On-Line Encyclopedia of Integer Sequences*. This database was originated by Neil Sloane in the 1960s. The last printed version of this database was published in 1995 ([SIPI95]); the current encyclopedia would occupy more than 150 volumes of the size of the 1995 book. New sequences are added regularly to this database. There is also a program accessible via the Web that you can use to find sequences from the encyclopedia that match initial terms you provide.

Summations

Next, we introduce **summation notation.** We begin by describing the notation used to express the sum of the terms

$$a_m, a_{m+1}, \ldots, a_n$$

from the sequence $\{a_n\}$. We use the notation

$$\sum_{j=m}^{n} a_j, \quad \sum_{j=m}^{n} a_j, \quad \text{or} \quad \sum_{1 \leqslant j \leqslant n} a_j$$

to represent

$$a_m + a_{m+1} + \cdots + a_n.$$

Here, the variable j is called the **index of summation,** and the choice of the letter j as the variable is arbitrary; that is, we could have used any other letter, such as i or k. Or, in notation,

$$\sum_{j=m}^{n} a_j = \sum_{i=m}^{n} a_i = \sum_{k=m}^{n} a_k.$$

Here, the index of summation runs through all integers starting with its **lower limit** m and ending with its **upper limit** n. A large uppercase Greek letter sigma, $\sum$, is used to denote summation.

The usual laws for arithmetic apply to summations. For example, when a and b are real numbers, we have $\sum_{j=1}^{n}(ax_j + by_j) = a\sum_{y=1}^{n} x_j + b\sum_{j=1}^{n} y_j$, where $x_1, x_2, \ldots, x_n$ and $y_1, y_2, \ldots, y_n$ are real numbers. (We do not present a formal proof of this identity here. Such a proof can be constructed using mathematical induction. The proof also uses the commutative and associative laws for addition and the distributive law of multiplication over addition.)

We give some examples of summation notation.

Example 9   Express the sum of the first 100 terms of the sequence $\{a_n\}$, where $a_n = 1/n$ for $n = 1, 2, 3, \ldots$.

Solution: The lower limit for the index of summation is 1, and the upper limit is 100. We write this sum as

$$\sum_{j=1}^{100} \frac{1}{j}.$$ ◀

Example 10   What is the value of $\sum_{j=1}^{5} j^2$?

Solution: We have

$$\sum_{j=1}^{5} j^2 = 1^2 + 2^2 + 3^2 + 4^2 + 5^2$$
$$= 1 + 4 + 9 + 16 + 25$$
$$= 55.$$ ◀

Example 11   What is the value of $\sum_{k=4}^{8}(-1)^k$?

Solution: We have

$$\sum_{k=4}^{8} (-1)^k = (-1)^4 + (-1)^5 + (-1)^6 + (-1)^7 + (-1)^8$$
$$= 1 + (-1) + 1 + (-1) + 1$$
$$= 1.$$ ◀

Sometimes it is useful to shift the index of summation in a sum. This is often done when two sums need to be added but their indices of summation do not match. When shifting an index of summation, it is important to make the appropriate changes in the corresponding summand. This is illustrated by Example 12.

Example 12   Suppose we have the sum

$$\sum_{j=1}^{5} j^2$$

but want the index of summation to run between 0 and 4 rather than from 1 to 5. To do this, we let $k = j - 1$. Then the new summation index runs from 0 to 4, and the term j^2 becomes $(k + 1)^2$. Hence,

$$\sum_{j=1}^{5} j^2 = \sum_{k=0}^{4} (k + 1)^2.$$

It is easily checked that both sums are $1 + 4 + 9 + 16 + 25 = 55$. ◀

Sums of terms of geometric progressions commonly arise (such sums are called **geometric series**). Theorem 1 gives us a formula for the sum of terms of a geometric progression.

Theorem 1   If a and r are real numbers and $r \neq 0$, then

$$\sum_{j=0}^{n} ar^j = \begin{cases} \dfrac{ar^{n+1} - a}{r - 1} & \text{if } r \neq 1 \\[2mm] (n+1)a & \text{if } r = 1. \end{cases}$$

Proof: Let

$$S = \sum_{j=0}^{n} ar^j.$$

To compute S, first multiply both sides of the equality by r and then manipulate the resulting sum as follows:

$$rS = r \sum_{j=0}^{n} ar^j \qquad \text{substituting summation formula for } S$$

$$= \sum_{j=0}^{n} ar^{j+1} \qquad \text{by the distributive property}$$

$$= \sum_{k=1}^{n+1} ar^{k} \qquad \text{shifting the index of summation, with } k = j + 1$$

$$= \left(\sum_{k=0}^{n} ar^{k} \right) + (ar^{n+1} - a) \qquad \text{removing } k = n + 1 \text{ term and adding } k = 0 \text{ term}$$

$$= S + (ar^{n+1} - a) \qquad \text{substituting } S \text{ for summation formula}$$

From these equalities, we see that

$$rS = S + (ar^{n+1} - a).$$

Solving for S shows that if $r \neq 1$, then

$$S = \frac{ar^{n+1} - a}{r - 1}.$$

If $r = 1$, then clearly the sum equals $(n + 1)a$.   ◁

Example 13   Double summations arise in many contexts (as in the analysis of nested loops in computer programs). An example of a double summation is

$$\sum_{i=1}^{4} \sum_{j=1}^{3} ij.$$

To evaluate the double sum, first expand the inner summation and then continue by computing the outer summation:

$$\sum_{i=1}^{4} \sum_{j=1}^{3} ij = \sum_{i=1}^{4} (i + 2i + 3i)$$

$$= \sum_{i=1}^{4} 6i$$

$$= 6 + 12 + 18 + 24 = 60.$$ ◀

We can also use summation notation to add all values of a function, or terms of an indexed set, where the index of summation runs over all values in a set. That is, we write

$$\sum_{s \in S} f(s)$$

to represent the sum of the values $f(s)$, for all members s of S.

Example 14 What is the value of $\sum_{s \in \{0,2,4\}} s$?

Solution: Because $\sum_{s \in \{0,2,4\}} s$ represents the sum of the values of s for all the members of the set $\{0, 2, 4\}$, it follows that

$$\sum_{s \in \{0,2,4\}} s = 0 + 2 + 4 = 6.$$ ◄

Certain sums arise repeatedly throughout discrete mathematics. Having a collection of formulae for such sums can be useful; Table 2 provides a small table of formulae for commonly occurring sums.

We derived the first formula in this table in Theorem 1. The next three formulae give us the sum of the first n positive integers, the sum of their squares, and the sum of their cubes. These three formulae can be derived in many different ways (for example, see Exercise 11 at the end of this section). The last two formulae in the table involve infinite series and will be discussed shortly.

Example 15 illustrates how the formulae in Table 2 can be useful.

TABLE 2 Some Useful Summation Formulae.

Sum	Closed Form
$\sum_{k=0}^{n} ar^k \ (r \neq 0)$	$\dfrac{ar^{n+1} - a}{r - 1}, r \neq 1$
$\sum_{k=1}^{n} k$	$\dfrac{n(n + 1)}{2}$
$\sum_{k=1}^{n} k^2$	$\dfrac{n(n + 1)(2n + 1)}{6}$
$\sum_{k=1}^{n} k^3$	$\dfrac{n^2(n + 1)^2}{4}$
$\sum_{k=0}^{\infty} x^k, |x| < 1$	$\dfrac{1}{1 - x}$
$\sum_{k=1}^{\infty} kx^{k-1}, |x| < 1$	$\dfrac{1}{(1 - x)^2}$

Example 15 Find $\sum_{k=50}^{100} k^2$.

Solution: First note that because $\sum_{k=1}^{100} k^2 = \sum_{k=1}^{49} k^2 + \sum_{k=50}^{100} k^2$, we have

$$\sum_{k=50}^{100} k^2 = \sum_{k=1}^{100} k^2 - \sum_{k=1}^{49} k^2.$$

Using the formula $\sum_{k=1}^{n} k^2 = n(n+1)(2n+1)/6$ from Table 2, we see that

$$\sum_{k=50}^{100} k^2 = \frac{100 \cdot 101 \cdot 201}{6} - \frac{49 \cdot 50 \cdot 99}{6} = 338{,}350 - 40{,}425 = 297{,}925. \quad \blacktriangleleft$$

Some Infinite Series Although most of the summations in this book are finite sums, infinite series are important in some parts of discrete mathematics. Infinite series are usually studied in a course in calculus and even the definition of these series requires the use of calculus, but sometimes they arise in discrete mathematics, because discrete mathematics deals with infinite collections of discrete elements. In particular, in our future studies in discrete mathematics, we will find the closed forms for the infinite series in Examples 16 and 17 to be quite useful.

Example 16 (*Requires calculus*) Let x be a real number with $|x| < 1$. Find $\sum_{n=0}^{\infty} x^n$.

Solution: By Theorem 1 with $a = 1$ and $r = x$ we see that $\sum_{n=0}^{k} x^n = \frac{x^{k+1}-1}{x-1}$. Because $|x| < 1$, x^{k+1} approaches 0 as k approaches infinity. It follows that

$$\sum_{n=0}^{\infty} x^n = \lim_{k \to \infty} \frac{x^{k+1}-1}{x-1} = \frac{-1}{x-1} = \frac{1}{1-x}. \quad \blacktriangleleft$$

We can produce new summation formulae by differentiating or integrating existing formulae.

Example 17 (*Requires calculus*) Differentiating both sides of the equation

$$\sum_{k=0}^{\infty} x^k = \frac{1}{1-x},$$

from Example 16 we find that

$$\sum_{k=1}^{\infty} kx^{k-1} = \frac{1}{(1-x)^2}.$$

(This differentiation is valid for $|x| < 1$ by a theorem about infinite series.) $\blacktriangleleft$

Cardinality

In Section 2.1 we defined the cardinality of a finite set to be the number of elements in the set. That is, the cardinality of a finite set tells us when two finite sets are the same size, or when one is bigger than the other. Can we extend this notion to an infinite set? Recall from Exercise 34 in Section 2.3 that there is a one-to-one correspondence between any two finite sets with the same number of elements. This observation lets us extend the concept of cardinality to all sets, both finite and infinite, with Definition 4.

Definition 4 The sets A and B have the same *cardinality* if and only if there is a one-to-one correspondence from A to B.

We will now split infinite sets into two groups, those with the same cardinality as the set of natural numbers and those with different cardinality.

Definition 5 A set that is either finite or has the same cardinality as the set of positive integers is called *countable*. A set that is not countable is called *uncountable*. When an infinite set S is countable, we denote the cardinality of S by $\aleph_0$ (where $\aleph$ is aleph, the first letter of the Hebrew alphabet). We write $|S| = \aleph_0$ and say that S has cardinality "aleph null."

We now give examples of countable and uncountable sets.

Example 18 Show that the set of odd positive integers is a countable set.

Solution: To show that the set of odd positive integers is countable, we will exhibit a one-to-one correspondence between this set and the set of positive integers. Consider the function

$$f(n) = 2n - 1$$

from $\mathbf{Z}^+$ to the set of odd positive integers. We show that f is a one-to-one correspondence by showing that it is both one-to-one and onto. To see that it is one-to-one, suppose that $f(n) = f(m)$. Then $2n - 1 = 2m - 1$, so $n = m$. To see that it is onto, suppose that t is an odd positive integer. Then t is 1 less than an even integer $2k$, where k is a natural number. Hence $t = 2k - 1 = f(k)$. We display this one-to-one correspondence in Figure 1.   ◄

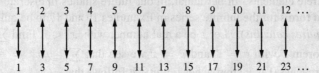

Figure 1   A One-to-One Correspondence Between $\mathbf{Z}^+$ and the Set of Odd Positive Integers.

An infinite set is countable if and only if it is possible to list the elements of the set in a sequence (indexed by the positive integers). The reason for this is that a one-to-one correspondence f from the set of positive integers to a set S can be expressed in terms of a sequence $a_1, a_2, \ldots, a_n, \ldots$, where $a_1 = f(1)$, $a_2 = f(2), \ldots, a_n = f(n), \ldots$. For instance, the set of odd integers can be listed in a sequence $a_1, a_2, \ldots, a_n, \ldots$, where $a_n = 2n - 1$.

We can show that the set of all integers is countable by listing its members.

Example 19   Show that the set of all integers is countable.

Solution: We can list all integers in a sequence by starting with 0 and alternating between positive and negative integers: $0, 1, -1, 2, -2, \ldots$. Alternately, we could find a one-to-one correspondence between the set of positive integers and the set of all integers. We leave it to the reader to show that the function $f(n) = n/2$ when n is even and $f(n) = -(n - 1)/2$ when n is odd is such a function. Consequently, the set of all integers is countable.   ◄

It is not surprising that the set of odd integers and the set of all integers are both countable sets. Many people are amazed to learn that the set of rational numbers is countable, as Example 20 demonstrates.

Example 20   Show that the set of positive rational numbers is countable.

Solution: It may seem surprising that the set of positive rational numbers is countable, but we will show how we can list the positive rational numbers as a sequence $r_1, r_2, \ldots, r_n, \ldots$. First, note that every positive rational number is the quotient p/q of two positive integers. We can arrange the positive rational numbers by listing those with denominator $q = 1$ in the first row, those with denominator $q = 2$ in the second row, and so on, as displayed in Figure 2.

The key to listing the rational numbers in a sequence is to first list the positive rational numbers p/q with $p + q = 2$, followed by those with $p + q = 3$, followed by those with $p + q = 4$, and so on, following the path shown in Figure 2. Whenever we encounter a number p/q that is already listed, we do not list it again. For example, when we come to $2/2 = 1$ we do not list it because we have already listed $1/1 = 1$. The initial terms in the list of positive rational numbers we have constructed are $1, 1/2, 2, 3, 1/3, 1/4, 2/3, 3/2, 4, 5$, and so on. These numbers are shown circled; the uncircled numbers in the list are those we leave out because they are already listed. Because all positive rational numbers are listed once, as the reader can verify, we have shown that the set of positive rational numbers is countable.   ◄

We have seen that the set of rational numbers is a countable set. Do we have a promising candidate for an uncountable set? The first place we might look is the set of real numbers. In Example 21 we use an important proof method, introduced in 1879 by Georg Cantor and known as the **Cantor diagonalization argument,** to prove that the set of real numbers is not countable. This proof method is used extensively in mathematical logic and in the theory of computation.

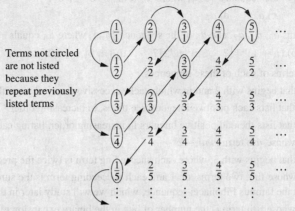

Terms not circled are not listed because they repeat previously listed terms

Figure 2   The Positive Rational Numbers Are Countable.

Example 21   Show that the set of real numbers is an uncountable set.

Solution: To show that the set of real numbers is uncountable, we suppose that the set of real numbers is countable and arrive at a contradiction. Then, the subset of all real numbers that fall between 0 and 1 would also be countable (because any subset of a countable set is also countable). Under this assumption, the real numbers between 0 and 1 can be listed in some order, say, $r_1, r_2, r_3, \ldots$. Let the decimal representation of these real numbers be

$$r_1 = 0.d_{11}d_{12}d_{13}d_{14} \ldots$$
$$r_2 = 0.d_{21}d_{22}d_{23}d_{24} \ldots$$
$$r_3 = 0.d_{31}d_{32}d_{33}d_{34} \ldots$$
$$r_4 = 0.d_{41}d_{42}d_{43}d_{44} \ldots$$
$$\vdots$$

where $d_{ij} \in \{0, 1, 2, 3, 4, 5, 6, 7, 8, 9\}$. (For example, if $r_1 = 0.23794102\ldots$, we have $d_{11} = 2$, $d_{12} = 3$, $d_{13} = 7$, and so on.) Then, form a new real number with decimal expansion $r = 0.d_1d_2d_3d_4 \ldots$, where the decimal digits are determined by the following rule:

$$d_i = \begin{cases} 4 & \text{if } d_{ii} \neq 4 \\ 5 & \text{if } d_{ii} = 4. \end{cases}$$

(As an example, suppose that $r_1 = 0.23794102\ldots$, $r_2 = 0.44590138\ldots$, $r_3 = 0.09118764\ldots$, $r_4 = 0.80553900\ldots$, and so on. Then we have $r = 0.d_1d_2d_3d_4 \ldots = 0.4544\ldots$, where $d_1 = 4$ because $d_{11} \neq 4$, $d_2 = 5$ because $d_{22} = 4$, $d_3 = 4$ because $d_{33} \neq 4$, $d_4 = 4$ because $d_{44} \neq 4$, and so on.)

Every real number has a unique decimal expansion (when the possibility that the expansion has a tail end that consists entirely of the digit 9 is excluded). Then, the real number r is not equal to any of $r_1, r_2, \ldots$ because the decimal expansion of r differs from the decimal expansion of r_i in the ith place to the right of the decimal point, for each i.

Because there is a real number r between 0 and 1 that is not in the list, the assumption that all the real numbers between 0 and 1 could be listed must be false. Therefore, all the real numbers between 0 and 1 cannot be listed, so the set of real numbers between 0 and 1 is uncountable. Any set with an uncountable subset is uncountable (see Exercise 19 at the end of this section). Hence, the set of real numbers is uncountable.   ◄

Exercises

1. Find these terms of the sequence $\{a_n\}$, where $a_n = 2 \cdot (-3)^n + 5^n$.

   a) a_0 b) a_1 c) a_4 d) a_5

2. What are the terms a_0, a_1, a_2, and a_3 of the sequence $\{a_n\}$, where a_n equals

   a) $2^n + 1$?   b) $(n+1)^{n+1}$?   c) $\lfloor n/2 \rfloor$?   d) $\lfloor n/2 \rfloor + \lceil n/2 \rceil$?

3. List the first 10 terms of each of these sequences.

   a) the sequence that begins with 2 and in which each successive term is 3 more than the preceding term

   b) the sequence that lists each positive integer three times, in increasing order

   c) the sequence that lists the odd positive integers in increasing order, listing each odd integer twice

   d) the sequence whose nth term is $n! - 2^n$

   e) the sequence that begins with 3, where each succeeding term is twice the preceding term

   f) the sequence whose first two terms are 1 and each succeeding term is the sum of the two preceding terms (This is the famous Fibonacci sequence, which we will study later in this text.)

   g) the sequence whose nth term is the number of bits in the binary expansion of the number n

   h) the sequence where the nth term is the number of letters in the English word for the index n

4. Find at least three different sequences beginning with the terms 1, 2, 4 whose terms are generated by a simple formula or rule.

5. For each of these lists of integers, provide a simple formula or rule that generates the terms of an integer sequence that begins with the given list. Assuming that your formula or rule is correct, determine the next three terms of the sequence.

   a) $1, 0, 1, 1, 0, 0, 1, 1, 1, 0, 0, 0, 1, \ldots$ b) $1, 2, 2, 3, 4, 4, 5, 6, 6, 7, 8, 8, \ldots$

   c) $1, 0, 2, 0, 4, 0, 8, 0, 16, 0, \ldots$ d) $3, 6, 12, 24, 48, 96, 192, \ldots$

   e) $15, 8, 1, -6, -13, -20, -27, \ldots$ f) $3, 5, 8, 12, 17, 23, 30, 38, 47, \ldots$

   g) $2, 16, 54, 128, 250, 432, 686, \ldots$ h) $2, 3, 7, 25, 121, 721, 5041, 40321, \ldots$

**6. Show that if a_n denotes the nth positive integer that is not a perfect square, then $a_n = n + \{\sqrt{n}\}$, where $\{x\}$ denotes the integer closest to the real number x.

7. What are the values of these sums?

   a) $\sum_{k=1}^{5} (k+1)$ b) $\sum_{j=0}^{4} (-2)^j$ c) $\sum_{i=1}^{10} 3$ d) $\sum_{j=0}^{8} (2^{j+1} - 2^j)$

8. What is the value of each of these sums of terms of a geometric progression?

   a) $\sum_{j=0}^{8} 3 \cdot 2^j$ b) $\sum_{j=1}^{8} 2^j$ c) $\sum_{j=2}^{8} (-3)^j$ d) $\sum_{j=0}^{8} 2 \cdot (-3)^j$

9. Compute each of these double sums.

   a) $\sum_{i=1}^{2} \sum_{j=1}^{3} (i+j)$ b) $\sum_{i=0}^{2} \sum_{j=0}^{3} (2i + 3j)$ c) $\sum_{i=1}^{3} \sum_{j=0}^{2} i$ d) $\sum_{i=0}^{2} \sum_{j=1}^{3} ij$

10. Show that $\sum_{j=1}^{n} (a_j - a_{j-1}) = a_n - a_0$, where $a_0, a_1, \ldots, a_n$ is a sequence of real numbers. This type of sum is called **telescoping**.

11. Sum both sides of the identity $k^2 - (k-1)^2 = 2k - 1$ from $k = 1$ to $k = n$ and use Exercise 10 to find

    a) a formula for $\sum_{k=1}^{n} (2k - 1)$ (the sum of the first n odd natural numbers).

    b) a formula for $\sum_{k=1}^{n} k$.

12. Find $\sum_{k=100}^{200} k$. (Use Table 2.)

*13. Find a formula for $\sum_{k=0}^{m} \lfloor \sqrt{k} \rfloor$, when m is a positive integer.

14. What are the values of the following products?

    a) $\prod_{i=0}^{10} i$ b) $\prod_{i=5}^{8} i$ c) $\prod_{i=1}^{100} (-1)^i$ d) $\prod_{i=1}^{10} 2$

15. Find $\sum_{j=0}^{4} j!$.

16. Determine whether each of these sets is countable or uncountable. For those that are countable, exhibit a one-to-one correspondence between the set of natural numbers and that set.

a) the negative integers   b) the even integers

c) the real numbers between 0 and $\frac{1}{2}$ d) integers that are multiples of 7

17. Determine whether each of these sets is countable or uncountable. For those that are countable, exhibit a one-to-one correspondence between the set of natural numbers and that set.

a) all bit strings not containing the bit 0

b) all positive rational numbers that cannot be written with denominators less than 4

c) the real numbers not containing 0 in their decimal representation

d) the real numbers containing only a finite number of 1s in their decimal representation

18. If A is an uncountable set and B is a countable set, must $A - B$ be uncountable?

19. Show that if A and B are sets, A is uncountable, and $A \subseteq B$, then B is uncountable.

20. Show that if A and B are sets with the same cardinality and C and D are sets with the same cardinality, then $A \times C$ and $B \times D$ have the same cardinality.

**21. Show that the union of a countable number of countable sets is countable.

*22. Show that the set of all finite bit strings is countable.

*23. Show that the set of all computer programs in a particular programming language is countable. [*Hint:* A computer program written in a programming language can be thought of as a string of symbols from a finite alphabet.]

*24. We say that a function is **computable** if there is a computer program that finds the values of this function. Use Exercise23 to show that there are functions that are not computable.

Key Terms and Results

TERMS

set: a collection of distinct objects
axiom: a basic assumption of a theory
paradox: a logical inconsistency
element, member of a set: an object in a set
∅ (empty set, null set): the set with no members
universal set: the set containing all objects under consideration
Venn diagram: a graphical representation of a set or sets
$S = T$ (set equality): S and T have the same elements
$S \subseteq T$ (S is a subset of T): every element of S is also an element of T
$S \subset T$ (S is a proper subset of T): S is a subset of T and $S \neq T$
finite set: a set with n elements, where n is a nonnegative integer
infinite set: a set that is not finite
$|S|$ (the cardinality of S): the number of elements in S
$P(S)$ (the power set of S): the set of all subsets of S
$A \cup B$ (the union of A and B): the set containing those elements that are in at least one of A and B
$A \cap B$ (the intersection of A and B): the set containing those elements that are in both A and B
$A - B$ (the difference of A and B): the set containing those elements that are in A but not in B
$\overline{A}$ (the complement of A): the set of elements in the universal set that are not in A
$A \oplus B$ (the symmetric difference of A and B): the set containing those elements in exactly one of A and B
membership table: a table displaying the membership of elements in sets

function from A to B: an assignment of exactly one element of B to each element of A
domain of f: the set A, where f is a function from A to B
codomain of f: the set B, where f is a function from A to B
b is the image of a under f: $b = f(a)$
a is a pre-image of b under f: $f(a) = b$
range of f: the set of images of f
onto function, surjection: a function from A to B such that every element of B is the image of some element in A
one-to-one function, injection: a function such that the images of elements in its domain are all different
one-to-one correspondence, bijection: a function that is both one-to-one and onto
inverse of f: the function that reverses the correspondence given by f (when f is a bijection)
$f \circ g$ (composition of f and g): the function that assigns $f(g(x))$ to x
$\lfloor x \rfloor$ (floor function): the largest integer not exceeding x
$\lceil x \rceil$ (ceiling function): the smallest integer greater than or equal to x
sequence: a function with domain that is a subset of the set of integers
geometric progression: a sequence of the form $a, ar, ar^2, \ldots$, where a and r are real numbers
arithmetic progression: a sequence of the form $a, a + d, a + 2d, \ldots$, where a and d are real numbers
string: a finite sequence
empty string: a string of length zero
$\sum_{i=1}^{n} a_i$: the sum $a_1 + a_2 + \cdots + a_n$
$\prod_{i=1}^{n} a_i$: the product $a_1 a_2 \cdots a_n$
countable set: a set that either is finite or can be placed in one-to-one correspondence with the set of positive integers
uncountable set: a set that is not countable
Cantor diagonalization argument: a proof technique that can be used to show that the set of real numbers is uncountable

RESULTS

The set identities given in Table 1 in Section 2.2
The summation formulae in Table 2 in Section 2.4
The set of rational numbers is countable.
The set of real numbers is uncountable.

Review Questions

1. Explain what it means for one set to be a subset of another set. How do you prove that one set is a subset of another set?

2. What is the empty set? Show that the empty set is a subset of every set.

3. a) Define $|S|$, the cardinality of the set S.
   b) Give a formula for $|A \cup B|$, where A and B are sets.

4. a) Define the power set of a set S.
   b) When is the empty set in the power set of a set S?
   c) How many elements does the power set of a set S with n elements have?

5. a) Define the union, intersection, difference, and symmetric difference of two sets.
   b) What are the union, intersection, difference, and symmetric difference of the set of positive integers and the set of odd integers?

6. a) Explain what it means for two sets to be equal.
   b) Describe as many of the ways as you can to show that two sets are equal.
   c) Show in at least two different ways that the sets $A - (B \cap C)$ and $(A - B) \cup (A - C)$ are equal.

7. Explain the relationship between logical equivalences and set identities.

8. a) Define the domain, codomain, and the range of a function.

b) Let $f(n)$ be the function from the set of integers to the set of integers such that $f(n) = n^2 + 1$. What are the domain, codomain, and range of this function?

9. a) Define what it means for a function from the set of positive integers to the set of positive integers to be one-to-one.

b) Define what it means for a function from the set of positive integers to the set of positive integers to be onto.

c) Give an example of a function from the set of positive integers to the set of positive integers that is both one-to-one and onto.

d) Give an example of a function from the set of positive integers to the set of positive integers that is one-to-one but not onto.

e) Give an example of a function from the set of positive integers to the set of positive integers that is not one-to-one but is onto.

f) Give an example of a function from the set of positive integers to the set of positive integers that is neither one-to-one nor onto.

10. a) Define the inverse of a function.

b) When does a function have an inverse?

c) Does the function $f(n) = 10 - n$ from the set of integers to the set of integers have an inverse? If so, what is it?

11. a) Define the floor and ceiling functions from the set of real numbers to the set of integers.

b) For which real numbers x is it true that $\lfloor x \rfloor = \lceil x \rceil$?

12. Conjecture a formula for the terms of the sequence that begins $8, 14, 32, 86, 248$ and find the next three terms of your sequence.

13. What is the sum of the terms of the geometric progression $a + ar + \cdots + ar^n$ when $r \neq 1$?

14. Show that the set of odd integers is countable.

15. Give an example of an uncountable set.

Supplementary Exercises

1. Let A be the set of English words that contain the letter x, and let B be the set of English words that contain the letter q. Express each of these sets as a combination of A and B.

a) The set of English words that do not contain the letter x.

b) The set of English words that contain both an x and a q.

c) The set of English words that contain an x but not a q.

d) The set of English words that do not contain either an x or a q.

e) The set of English words that contain an x or a q, but not both.

2. Show that if A is a subset of B, then the power set of A is a subset of the power set of B.

3. Suppose that A and B are sets such that the power set of A is a subset of the power set of B. Does it follow that A is a subset of B?

4. Let $\mathbf{E}$ denote the set of even integers and $\mathbf{O}$ denote the set of odd integers. As usual, let $\mathbf{Z}$ denote the set of all integers. Determine each of these sets.

a) $\mathbf{E} \cup \mathbf{O}$ b) $\mathbf{E} \cap \mathbf{O}$ c) $\mathbf{Z} - \mathbf{E}$ d) $\mathbf{Z} - \mathbf{O}$

5. Show that if A and B are sets, then $A - (A - B) = A \cap B$.

6. Let A and B be sets. Show that $A \subseteq B$ if and only if $A \cap B = A$.

7. Let $A, B,$ and C be sets. Show that $(A - B) - C$ is not necessarily equal to $A - (B - C)$.

8. Suppose that A, B, and C are sets. Prove or disprove that $(A - B) - C = (A - C) - B$.

9. Suppose that A, B, C, and D are sets. Prove or disprove that $(A-B)-(C-D) = (A-C)-(B-D)$.

10. Show that if A and B are finite sets, then $|A \cap B| \leqslant |A \cup B|$. Determine when this relationship is an equality.

11. Let A and B be sets in a finite universal set U. List the following in order of increasing size.
    a) $|A|, |A \cup B|, |A \cap B|, |U|, |\emptyset|$
    b) $|A - B|, |A \oplus B|, |A| + |B|, |A \cup B|, |\emptyset|$

12. Let A and B be subsets of the finite universal set U. Show that $|\overline{A} \cap \overline{B}| = |U| - |A| - |B| + |A \cap B|$.

13. Let f and g be functions from $\{1, 2, 3, 4\}$ to $\{a, b, c, d\}$ and from $\{a, b, c, d\}$ to $\{1, 2, 3, 4\}$, respectively, such that $f(1) = d$, $f(2) = c$, $f(3) = a$, and $f(4) = b$, and $g(a) = 2$, $g(b) = 1$, $g(c) = 3$, and $g(d) = 2$.
    a) Is f one-to-one? Is g one-to-one?
    b) Is f onto? Is g onto?
    c) Does either f or g have an inverse? If so, find this inverse.

14. Let f be a one-to-one function from the set A to the set B. Let S and T be subsets of A. Show that $f(S \cap T) = f(S) \cap f(T)$.

15. Give an example to show that the equality in Exercise 14 may not hold if f is not one-to-one.

    Suppose that f is a function from A to B. We define the function S_f from $P(A)$ to $P(B)$ by the rule $S_f(X) = f(X)$ for each subset X of A. Similarly, we define the function $S_{f^{-1}}$ from $P(B)$ to $P(A)$ by the rule $S_{f^{-1}}(Y) = f^{-1}(Y)$ for each subset Y of B. Here, we are using Definition 4, and the definition of the inverse image of a set found in Section 2.3.

*16. a) Prove that if f is a one-to-one function from A to B, then S_f is a one-to-one function from $P(A)$ to $P(B)$.
    b) Prove that if f is an onto function from A to B, then S_f is an onto function from $P(A)$ to $P(B)$.
    c) Prove that if f is an onto function from A to B, then $S_{f^{-1}}$ is a one-to-one function from $P(B)$ to $P(A)$.
    d) Prove that if f is a one-to-one function from A to B, then $S_{f^{-1}}$ is an onto function from $P(B)$ to $P(A)$.
    e) Use parts (a) through (d) to conclude that if f is a one-to-one correspondence from A to B, then S_f is a one-to-one correspondence from $P(A)$ to $P(B)$ and $S_{f^{-1}}$ is a one-to-one correspondence from $P(B)$ to $P(A)$.

17. Prove that if f and g are functions from A to B and $S_f = S_g$ (using the definition in the preamble to Exercise 16), then $f(x) = g(x)$ for all $x \in A$.

18. Show that if n is an integer, then $n = \lceil n/2 \rceil + \lfloor n/2 \rfloor$.

19. For which real numbers x and y is it true that $\lfloor x + y \rfloor = \lfloor x \rfloor + \lfloor y \rfloor$?

20. For which real numbers x and y is it true that $\lceil x + y \rceil = \lceil x \rceil + \lceil y \rceil$?

21. For which real numbers x and y is it true that $\lceil x + y \rceil = \lceil x \rceil + \lfloor y \rfloor$?

22. Prove that $\lfloor n/2 \rfloor \lceil n/2 \rceil = \lfloor n^2/4 \rfloor$ for all integers n.

23. Prove that if m is an integer, then $\lfloor x \rfloor + \lfloor m - x \rfloor = m - 1$, unless x is an integer, in which case it equals m.

24. Prove that if x is a real number, then $\lfloor \lfloor x/2 \rfloor / 2 \rfloor = \lfloor x/4 \rfloor$.

25. Prove that if n is an odd integer, then $\lceil n^2/4 \rceil = (n^2 + 3)/4$.

26. Prove that if m and n are positive integers and x is a real number, then

$$\left\lfloor \frac{\lfloor x \rfloor + n}{m} \right\rfloor = \left\lfloor \frac{x + n}{m} \right\rfloor.$$

*27. Prove that if m is a positive integer and x is a real number, then

$$\lfloor mx \rfloor = \lfloor x \rfloor \; + \left\lfloor x + \frac{1}{m} \right\rfloor + \left\lfloor x + \frac{2}{m} \right\rfloor + \cdots$$

$$+ \left\lfloor x + \frac{m-1}{m} \right\rfloor .$$

*28. We define the **Ulam numbers** by setting $u_1 = 1$ and $u_2 = 2$. Furthermore, after determining whether the integers less than n are Ulam numbers, we set n equal to the next Ulam number if it can be written uniquely as the sum of two different Ulam numbers. Note that $u_3 = 3$, $u_4 = 4$, $u_5 = 6$, and $u_6 = 8$.

a) Find the first 20 Ulam numbers.

b) Prove that there are infinitely many Ulam numbers.

29. Determine the value of $\prod_{k=1}^{100} \frac{k+1}{k}$. (The notation used here for products is defined in the preamble to Exercise 14 in Section 2.4.)

*30. Determine a rule for generating the terms of the sequence that begins $1, 3, 4, 8, 15, 27, 50, 92, \ldots$, and find the next four terms of the sequence.

*31. Determine a rule for generating the terms of the sequence that begins $2, 3, 3, 5, 10, 13, 39, 43, 172, 177, 885, 891, \ldots$, and find the next four terms of the sequence.

*32. Prove that if A and B are countable sets, then $A \times B$ is also a countable set.

Computer Projects

Write programs with the specified input and output.

1. Given subsets A and B of a set with n elements, use bit strings to find $\overline{A}$, $A \cup B$, $A \cap B$, $A - B$, and $A \oplus B$.

2. Given multisets A and B from the same universal set, find $A \cup B$, $A \cap B$, $A - B$, and $A + B$.

3. Given fuzzy sets A and B, find $\overline{A}$, $A \cup B$, and $A \cap B$.

4. Given a function f from $\{1, 2, \ldots, n\}$ to the set of integers, determine whether f is one-to-one.

5. Given a function f from $\{1, 2, \ldots, n\}$ to itself, determine whether f is onto.

6. Given a bijection f from the set $\{1, 2, \ldots, n\}$ to itself, find f^{-1}.

Computations and Explorations

Use a computational program or programs you have written to do these exercises.

1. Given two finite sets, list all elements in the Cartesian product of these two sets.

2. Given a finite set, list all elements of its power set.

3. Calculate the number of one-to-one functions from a set S to a set T, where S and T are finite sets of various sizes. Can you determine a formula for the number of such functions? (We will find such a formula in Chapter 3.)

4. Calculate the number of onto functions from a set S to a set T, where S and T are finite sets of various sizes. Can you determine a formula for the number of such functions? (We will find such a formula in Chapter 4.)

*5. Develop a collection of different rules for generating the terms of a sequence and a program for randomly selecting one of these rules and the particular sequence generated using these rules. Make this part of an interactive program that prompts for the next term of the sequence and determine whether the response is the intended next term.

Writing Projects

Respond to these with essays using outside sources.

1. Discuss how an axiomatic set theory can be developed to avoid Russell's paradox.

2. Research where the concept of a function first arose, and describe how this concept was first used.

3. Explain the different ways in which the *Encyclopedia of Integer Sequences* has been found useful. Also, describe a few of the more unusual sequences in this encyclopedia and how they arise.

4. Define the recently invented EKG sequence and describe some of its properties and open questions about it.

5. Look up the definition of a transcendental number. Explain how to show that such numbers exist and how such numbers can be constructed. Which famous numbers can be shown to be transcendental and for which famous numbers is it still unknown whether they are transcendental?

6. Discuss infinite cardinal numbers and the continuum hypothesis.

Chapter 3
Counting

Combinatorics, the study of arrangements of objects, is an important part of discrete mathematics. This subject was studied as long ago as the seventeenth century, when combinatorial questions arose in the study of gambling games. Enumeration, the counting of objects with certain properties, is an important part of combinatorics. We must count objects to solve many different types of problems. For instance, counting is used to determine the complexity of algorithms. Counting is also required to determine whether there are enough telephone numbers or Internet protocol addresses to meet demand. Furthermore, counting techniques are used extensively when probabilities of events are computed.

The basic rules of counting, which we will study in Section 3.1, can solve a tremendous variety of problems. For instance, we can use these rules to enumerate the different telephone numbers possible in the United States, the allowable passwords on a computer system, and the different orders in which the runners in a race can finish. Another important combinatorial tool is the pigeonhole principle, which we will study in Section 3.2. This states that when objects are placed in boxes and there are more objects than boxes, then there is a box containing at least two objects. For instance, we can use this principle to show that among a set of 15 or more students, at least 3 were born on the same day of the week.

We can phrase many counting problems in terms of ordered or unordered arrangements of the objects of a set. These arrangements, called permutations and combinations, are used in many counting problems. For instance, suppose the 100 top finishers on a competitive exam taken by 2000 students are invited to a banquet. We can count the possible sets of 100 students that will be invited, as well as the ways in which the top 10 prizes can be awarded.

Another problem in combinatorics involves generating all the arrangements of a specified kind. This is often important in computer simulations. We will devise algorithms to generate arrangements of various types.

3.1 The Basics of Counting

Introduction

Suppose that a password on a computer system consists of six, seven, or eight characters. Each of these characters must be a digit or a letter of the alphabet. Each password must contain at least one digit. How many such passwords are there? The techniques needed to answer this question and a wide variety of other counting problems will be introduced in this section.

Counting problems arise throughout mathematics and computer science. For example, we must count the successful outcomes of experiments and all the possible outcomes of these experiments to determine probabilities of discrete events. We need to count the number of operations used by an algorithm to study its time complexity.

We will introduce the basic techniques of counting in this section. These methods serve as the foundation for almost all counting techniques.

Basic Counting Principles

We will present two basic counting principles, the **product rule** and the **sum rule.** Then we will show how they can be used to solve many different counting problems.

The product rule applies when a procedure is made up of separate tasks.

The Product Rule   Suppose that a procedure can be broken down into a sequence of two tasks. If there are n_1 ways to do the first task and for each of these ways of doing the first task, there are n_2 ways to do the second task, then there are $n_1 n_2$ ways to do the procedure.

Examples 1–10 show how the product rule is used.

Example 1   A new company with just two employees, Sanchez and Patel, rents a floor of a building with 12 offices. How many ways are there to assign different offices to these two employees?

Solution: The procedure of assigning offices to these two employees consists of assigning an office to Sanchez, which can be done in 12 ways, then assigning an office to Patel different from the office assigned to Sanchez, which can be done in 11 ways. By the product rule, there are $12 \cdot 11 = 132$ ways to assign offices to these two employees.   ◄

Example 2   The chairs of an auditorium are to be labeled with a letter and a positive integer not exceeding 100. What is the largest number of chairs that can be labeled differently?

Solution: The procedure of labeling a chair consists of two tasks, namely, assigning one of the 26 letters and then assigning one of the 100 possible integers to the seat. The product rule shows that there are $26 \cdot 100 = 2600$ different ways that a chair can be labeled. Therefore, the largest number of chairs that can be labeled differently is 2600.   ◄

Example 3   There are 32 microcomputers in a computer center. Each microcomputer has 24 ports. How many different ports to a microcomputer in the center are there?

Solution: The procedure of choosing a port consists of two tasks, first picking a microcomputer and then picking a port on this microcomputer. Because there are 32 ways to choose the microcomputer and 24 ways to choose the port no matter which microcomputer has been selected, the product rule shows that there are $32 \cdot 24 = 768$ ports.   ◄

An extended version of the product rule is often useful. Suppose that a procedure is carried out by performing the tasks $T_1, T_2, \cdots, T_m$ in sequence. If each task T_i, $i = 1, 2, \cdots, n$, can be done in n_i ways, regardless of how the previous tasks were done, then there are $n_1 \cdot n_2 \cdots \cdot n_m$ ways to carry out the procedure. This version of the product rule can be proved by mathematical induction from the product rule for two tasks.

Example 4   How many different bit strings of length seven are there?

Solution: Each of the seven bits can be chosen in two ways, because each bit is either 0 or 1. Therefore, the product rule shows there are a total of $2^7 = 128$ different bit strings of length seven.   ◄

Example 5   How many different license plates are available if each plate contains a sequence of three letters followed by three digits (and no sequences of letters are prohibited, even if they are obscene)?

Solution: There are 26 choices for each of the three letters and ten choices for each of the three digits. Hence, by the product rule there are a total of $26 \cdot 26 \cdot 26 \cdot 10 \cdot 10 \cdot 10 = 17,576,000$ possible license plates.   ◄

Example 6   Counting Functions   How many functions are there from a set with m elements to a set with n elements?

Solution: A function corresponds to a choice of one of the n elements in the codomain for each of the m elements in the domain. Hence, by the product rule there are $n \cdot n \cdots \cdot n = n^m$ functions from a set with m elements to one with n elements. For example, there are 5^3 different functions from a set with three elements to a set with five elements.   ◄

Example 7   Counting One-to-One Functions   How many one-to-one functions are there from a set with m elements to one with n elements?

Solution: First note when $m > n$ there are no one-to-one functions from a set with m elements to a set with n elements.

Now let $m \leqslant n$. Suppose the elements in the domain are $a_1, a_2, \cdots, a_m$. There are n ways to choose the value of the function at a_1. Because the function is one-to-one, the value of the function at a_2 can be picked in $n - 1$ ways (because the value used for a_1 cannot be used again). In general, the value of the function at a_k can be chosen in $n - k + 1$ ways. By the product rule, there are $n(n - 1)(n - 2) \cdots (n - m + 1)$ one-to-one functions from a set with m elements to one with n elements.

For example, there are $5 \cdot 4 \cdot 3 = 60$ one-to-one functions from a set with three elements to a set with five elements. ◀

Example 8 **The Telephone Numbering Plan** The format of telephone numbers in North America is specified by a *numbering plan*. A telephone number consists of 10 digits, which are split into a three-digit area code, a three-digit office code, and a four-digit station code. Because of signaling considerations, there are certain restrictions on some of these digits. To specify the allowable format, let X denote a digit that can take any of the values 0 through 9, let N denote a digit that can take any of the values 2 through 9, and let Y denote a digit that must be a 0 or a 1. Two numbering plans, which will be called the old plan and the new plan, will be discussed. (The old plan, in use in the 1960s, has been replaced by the new plan, but the recent rapid growth in demand for new numbers for mobile phones and devices make even this new plan obsolete. In this example, the letters used to represent digits follow the conventions of the *North American Numbering Plan*.) As will be shown, the new plan allows the use of more numbers.

In the old plan, the formats of the area code, office code, and station code are *NYX, NNX,* and *XXXX*, respectively, so that telephone numbers had the form *NYX-NNX-XXXX*. In the new plan, the formats of these codes are *NXX, NXX,* and *XXXX*, respectively, so that telephone numbers have the form *NXX-NXX-XXXX*. How many different North American telephone numbers are possible under the old plan and under the new plan?

Solution: By the product rule, there are $8 \cdot 2 \cdot 10 = 160$ area codes with format *NYX* and $8 \cdot 10 \cdot 10 = 800$ area codes with format *NXX*. Similarly, by the product rule, there are $8 \cdot 8 \cdot 10 = 640$ office codes with format *NNX*. The product rule also shows that there are $10 \cdot 10 \cdot 10 \cdot 10 = 10,000$ station codes with format *XXXX*.

Consequently, applying the product rule again, it follows that under the old plan there are

$$160 \cdot 640 \cdot 10,000 = 1,024,000,000$$

different numbers available in North America. Under the new plan there are

$$800 \cdot 800 \cdot 10,000 = 6,400,000,000$$

different numbers available. ◀

Example 9 What is the value of k after the following code has been executed?

```
k := 0
for i₁ := 1 to n₁
    for i₂ := 1 to n₂
        ·
        ·
        ·
        for iₘ := 1 to nₘ
            k := k + 1
```

Solution: The initial value of k is zero. Each time the nested loop is traversed, 1 is added to k. Let T_i be the task of traversing the ith loop. Then the number of times the loop is traversed is the number of ways to do the tasks $T_1, T_2, \cdots, T_m$. The number of ways to carry out the task T_j, $j = 1, 2, \cdots, m$, is n_j, because the jth loop is traversed once for each integer i_j with $1 \leqslant i_j \leqslant n_j$. By the product rule, it follows that the nested loop is traversed $n_1 n_2 \cdots n_m$ times. Hence, the final value of k is $n_1 n_2 \cdots n_m$. ◀

Example 10   **Counting Subsets of a Finite Set**   Use the product rule to show that the number of different subsets of a finite set S is $2^{|S|}$.

Solution: Let S be a finite set. List the elements of S in arbitrary order. Recall from Section 2.2 that there is a one-to-one correspondence between subsets of S and bit strings of length $|S|$. Namely, a subset of S is associated with the bit string with a 1 in the ith position if the ith element in the list is in the subset, and a 0 in this position otherwise. By the product rule, there are $2^{|S|}$ bit strings of length $|S|$. Hence, $|P(S)| = 2^{|S|}$. ◀

The product rule is often phrased in terms of sets in this way: If $A_1, A_2, \cdots, A_m$ are finite sets, then the number of elements in the Cartesian product of these sets is the product of the number of elements in each set. To relate this to the product rule, note that the task of choosing an element in the Cartesian product $A_1 \times A_2 \times \cdots \times A_m$ is done by choosing an element in A_1, an element in $A_2, \cdots$, and an element in A_m. By the product rule it follows that

$$|A_1 \times A_2 \times \cdots \times A_m| = |A_1| \cdot |A_2| \cdot \cdots \cdot |A_m|.$$

We now introduce the sum rule.

The Sum Rule   If a task can be done either in one of n_1 ways or in one of n_2 ways, where none of the set of n_1 ways is the same as any of the set of n_2 ways, then there are $n_1 + n_2$ ways to do the task.

Example 11 illustrates how the sum rule is used.

Example 11   Suppose that either a member of the mathematics faculty or a student who is a mathematics major is chosen as a representative to a university committee. How many different choices are there for this representative if there are 37 members of the mathematics faculty and 83 mathematics majors and no one is both a faculty member and a student?

Solution: There are 37 ways to choose a member of the mathematics faculty and there are 83 ways to choose a student who is a mathematics major. Choosing a member of the mathematics faculty is never the same as choosing a student who is a mathematics major because no one is both a faculty member and a student. By the sum rule it follows that there are $37 + 83 = 120$ possible ways to pick this representative. ◀

We can extend the sum rule to more than two tasks. Suppose that a task can be done in one of n_1 ways, in one of n_2 ways, $\cdots$, or in one of n_m ways, where none of the set of n_i ways of doing the task is the same as any of the set of n_j ways, for all pairs i and j with $1 \leqslant i < j \leqslant m$. Then the number of ways to do the task is $n_1 + n_2 + \cdots + n_m$. This extended version of the sum rule is often useful in counting problems, as Examples 12 and 13 show. This version of the sum rule can be proved using mathematical induction from the sum rule for two sets. (This is Exercise 30 at the end of the section.)

Example 12   A student can choose a computer project from one of three lists. The three lists contain 23, 15, and 19 possible projects, respectively. No project is on more than one list. How many possible projects are there to choose from?

Solution: The student can choose a project by selecting a project from the first list, the second list, or the third list. Because no project is on more than one list, by the sum rule there are $23 + 15 + 19 = 57$ ways to choose a project. ◀

Example 13   What is the value of k after the following code has been executed?

```
k := 0
for i₁ := 1 to n₁
    k := k + 1
for i₂ := 1 to n₂
    k := k + 1
        ·
        ·
        ·
for iₘ := 1 to nₘ
    k := k + 1
```

Solution: The initial value of k is zero. This block of code is made up of m different loops. Each time a loop is traversed, 1 is added to k. To determine the value of k after this code has been executed, we need to determine how many times we traverse a loop. Note that there are n_i ways to traverse the ith loop. Because we only traverse one loop at a time, the sum rule shows that the final value of k, which is the number of ways to traverse one of the m loops is $n_1 + n_2 + \cdots + n_m$. ◀

The sum rule can be phrased in terms of sets as: If $A_1, A_2, \cdots, A_m$ are disjoint finite sets, then the number of elements in the union of these sets is the sum of the numbers of elements in the sets. To relate this to our statement of the sum rule, note there are $|A_i|$ ways to choose an element from A_i for $i = 1, 2, \cdots, m$. Because the sets are disjoint, when we select an element from one of the sets A_i, we do not also select an element from a different set A_j. Consequently, by the sum rule, because we cannot select an element from two of these sets at the same time, the number of ways to choose an element from one of the sets, which is the number of elements in the union, is

$$|A_1 \cup A_2 \cup \cdots \cup A_m| = |A_1| + |A_2| + \cdots + |A_m|.$$

This equality applies only when the sets in question are disjoint. The situation is much more complicated when these sets have elements in common. That situation will be briefly discussed later in this section and discussed in more depth in Chapter 4.

More Complex Counting Problems

Many counting problems cannot be solved using just the sum rule or just the product rule. However, many complicated counting problems can be solved using both of these rules in combination.

Example 14   In a version of the computer language BASIC, the name of a variable is a string of one or two alphanumeric characters, where uppercase and lowercase letters are not distinguished. (An *alphanumeric* character is either one of the 26 English letters or one of the 10 digits.) Moreover, a variable name must begin with a letter and must be different from the five strings of two characters that are reserved for programming use. How many different variable names are there in this version of BASIC?

Solution: Let V equal the number of different variable names in this version of BASIC. Let V_1 be the number of these that are one character long and V_2 be the number of these that are two characters long. Then by the sum rule, $V = V_1 + V_2$. Note that $V_1 = 26$, because a one-character variable name must be a letter. Furthermore, by the product rule there are $26 \cdot 36$ strings of length two that begin with a letter and end with an alphanumeric character. However, five of these are excluded, so $V_2 = 26 \cdot 36 - 5 = 931$. Hence, there are $V = V_1 + V_2 = 26 + 931 = 957$ different names for variables in this version of BASIC. ◀

Example 15   Each user on a computer system has a password, which is six to eight characters long, where each character is an uppercase letter or a digit. Each password must contain at least one digit. How many possible passwords are there?

Solution: Let P be the total number of possible passwords, and let P_6, P_7, and P_8 denote the number of possible passwords of length 6, 7, and 8, respectively. By the sum rule, $P = P_6 + P_7 + P_8$. We will now find P_6, P_7, and P_8. Finding P_6 directly is difficult. To find P_6 it is easier to find the number of strings of uppercase letters and digits that are six characters long, including those with no digits, and subtract from this the number of strings with no digits. By the product rule, the number of strings of six characters is 36^6, and the number of strings with no digits is 26^6. Hence,

$$P_6 = 36^6 - 26^6 = 2{,}176{,}782{,}336 - 308{,}915{,}776 = 1{,}867{,}866{,}560.$$

Similarly, it can be shown that

$$P_7 = 36^7 - 26^7 = 78{,}364{,}164{,}096 - 8{,}031{,}810{,}176 = 70{,}332{,}353{,}920$$

and

$$P_8 = 36^8 - 26^8 = 2{,}821{,}109{,}907{,}456 - 208{,}827{,}064{,}576 = 2{,}612{,}282{,}842{,}880.$$

Consequently,

$$P = P_6 + P_7 + P_8 = 2{,}684{,}483{,}063{,}360. \qquad \blacktriangleleft$$

Example 16   **Counting Internet Addresses**   In the Internet, which is made up of interconnected physical networks of computers, each computer (or more precisely, each network connection of a computer) is assigned an *Internet address*. In Version 4 of the Internet Protocol (IPv4), now in use, an address is a string of 32 bits. It begins with a *network number* (*netid*). The netid is followed by a *host number* (*hostid*), which identifies a computer as a member of a particular network.

Three forms of addresses are used, with different numbers of bits used for netids and hostids. **Class A addresses,** used for the largest networks, consist of 0, followed by a 7-bit netid and a 24-bit hostid. **Class B addresses,** used for medium-sized networks, consist of 10, followed by a 14-bit netid and a 16-bit hostid. **Class C addresses,** used for the smallest networks, consist of 110, followed by a 21-bit netid and an 8-bit hostid. There are several restrictions on addresses because of special uses: 1111111 is not available as the netid of a Class A network, and the hostids consisting of all 0s and all 1s are not available for use in any network. A computer on the Internet has either a Class A, a Class B, or a Class C address. (Besides Class A, B, and C addresses, there are also Class D addresses, reserved for use in multicasting when multiple computers are addressed at a single time, consisting of 1110 followed by 28 bits, and Class E addresses, reserved for future use, consisting of 11110 followed by 27 bits. Neither Class D nor Class E addresses are assigned as the IP address of a computer on the Internet.) Figure 1 illustrates IPv4 addressing. (Limitations on the number of Class A and Class B netids have made IPv4 addressing inadequate; IPv6, a new version of IP, uses 128-bit addresses to solve this problem.)

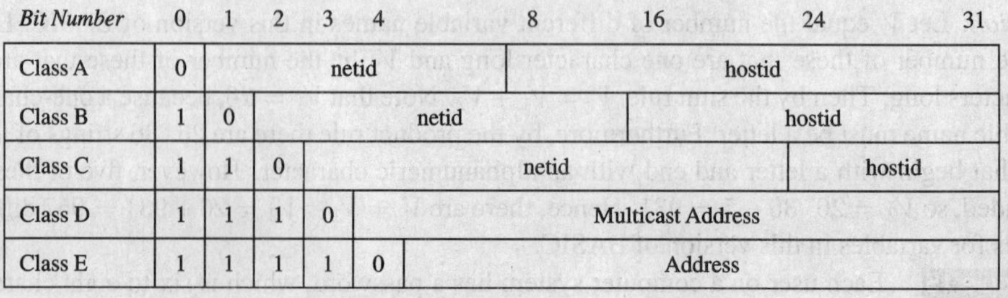

Bit Number	0	1	2	3	4	8	16	24	31
Class A	0		netid				hostid		
Class B	1	0		netid				hostid	
Class C	1	1	0		netid				hostid
Class D	1	1	1	0		Multicast Address			
Class E	1	1	1	1	0	Address			

Figure 1   Internet Addresses (IPv4).

How many different IPv4 addresses are available for computers on the Internet?

Solution: Let x be the number of available addresses for computers on the Internet, and let x_A, x_B, and x_C denote the number of Class A, Class B, and Class C addresses available, respectively. By the sum rule, $x = x_A + x_B + x_C$.

To find x_A, note that there are $2^7 - 1 = 127$ Class A netids, recalling that the netid 1111111 is unavailable. For each netid, there are $2^{24} - 2 = 16{,}777{,}214$ hostids, recalling that the hostids consisting of all 0s and all 1s are unavailable. Consequently, $x_A = 127 \cdot 16{,}777{,}214 = 2{,}130{,}706{,}178$.

To find x_B and x_C, note that there are $2^{14} = 16{,}384$ Class B netids and $2^{21} = 2{,}097{,}152$ Class C netids. For each Class B netid, there are $2^{16} - 2 = 65{,}534$ hostids, and for each Class C netid, there are $2^8 - 2 = 254$ hostids, recalling that in each network the hostids consisting of all 0s and all 1s are unavailable. Consequently, $x_B = 1{,}073{,}709{,}056$ and $x_C = 532{,}676{,}608$.

We conclude that the total number of IPv4 addresses available is $x = x_A + x_B + x_C = 2{,}130{,}706{,}178 + 1{,}073{,}709{,}056 + 532{,}676{,}608 = 3{,}737{,}091{,}842$.   ◀

The Inclusion–Exclusion Principle

Suppose that a task can be done in n_1 or in n_2 ways, but that some of the set of n_1 ways to do the task are the same as some of the n_2 other ways to do the task. In this situation, we cannot use the sum rule to count the number of ways to do the task. Adding the number of ways to do the tasks in these two ways leads to an overcount, because the ways to do the task in the ways that are common are counted twice. To correctly count the number of ways to do the two tasks, we add the number of ways to do it in one way and the number of ways to do it in the other way, and then subtract the number of ways to do the task in a way that is both among the set of n_1 ways and the set of n_2 ways. This technique is called the **principle of inclusion–exclusion**. Sometimes, it is also called the **subtraction principle** for counting. Example 17 illustrates how we can solve counting problems using this principle.

Example 17   How many bit strings of length eight either start with a 1 bit or end with the two bits 00?

Solution: We can construct a bit string of length eight that either starts with a 1 bit or ends with the two bits 00, by constructing a bit string of length eight beginning with a 1 bit or by constructing a bit string of length eight that ends with the two bits 00. We can construct a bit string of length eight that begins with a 1 in $2^7 = 128$ ways. This follows by the product rule, because the first bit can be chosen in only one way and each of the other seven bits can be chosen in two ways. Similarly, we can construct a bit string of length eight ending with the two bits 00, in $2^6 = 64$ ways. This follows by the product rule, because each of the first six bits can be chosen in two ways and the last two bits can be chosen in only one way.

Some of the ways to construct a bit string of length eight starting with a 1 are the same as the ways to construct a bit string of length eight that ends with the two bits 00. There are $2^5 = 32$ ways to construct such a string. This follows by the product rule, because the first bit can be chosen in only one way, each of the second through the sixth bits can be chosen in two ways, and the last two bits can be chosen in one way. Consequently, the number of bit strings of length eight that begin with a 1 or end with a 00, which equals the number of ways to construct a bit string of length eight that begin with a 1 or that ends with 00, equals $128 + 64 - 32 = 160$.   ◀

We can phrase this counting principle in terms of sets. Let A_1 and A_2 be sets. There are $|A_1|$ ways to select an element from A_1 and $|A_2|$ ways to select an element from A_2. The number of ways to select an element from A_1 or from A_2, that is, the number of ways to select an element from their union, is the sum of the number of ways to select an element from A_1 and the number of ways to select an element from A_2, minus the number of ways to select an element that is in both A_1 and A_2. Because there are $|A_1 \cup A_2|$ ways to select an element in either A_1 or in A_2, and $|A_1 \cap A_2|$ ways to select an element common to both sets, we have

$$|A_1 \cup A_2| = |A_1| + |A_2| - |A_1 \cap A_2|.$$

This is the formula given in Section 2.2 for the number of elements in the union of two sets.

We present an example that illustrates how the formulation of the principle of inclusion–exclusion can be used to solve counting problems.

Example 18   A computer company receives 350 applications from computer graduates for a job planning a line of new Web servers. Suppose that 220 of these people majored in computer science, 147 majored in business, and 51 majored both in computer science and in business. How many of these applicants majored neither in computer science nor in business?

Solution: To find the number of these applicants who majored neither in computer science nor in business, we can subtract the number of students who majored either in computer science or in business (or both) from the total number of applicants. Let A_1 be the set of students who majored in computer science and A_2 the set of students who majored in business. Then $A_1 \cup A_2$ is the set of students who majored in computer science or business (or both), and $A_1 \cap A_2$ is the set of students who majored both in computer science and in business. By the principle of inclusion–exclusion, the number of students who majored either in computer science or in business (or both) equals

$$|A_1 \cup A_2| = |A_1| + |A_2| - |A_1 \cap A_2| = 220 + 147 - 51 = 316.$$

We conclude that $350 - 316 = 34$ of the applicants majored neither in computer science nor in business.   ◀

The principle of inclusion–exclusion can be generalized to find the number of ways to do one of n different tasks or, equivalently, to find the number of elements in the union of n sets, whenever n is a positive integer. We will study the inclusion–exclusion principle and some of its many applications in Chapter 4.

Tree Diagrams

Counting problems can be solved using **tree diagrams.** A tree consists of a root, a number of branches leaving the root, and possible additional branches leaving the endpoints of other branches. (We will study trees in detail in Chapter 7.) To use trees in counting, we use a branch to represent each possible choice. We represent the possible outcomes by the leaves, which are the endpoints of branches not having other branches starting at them.

Note that when a tree diagram is used to solve a counting problem, the number of choices required to reach a leaf can vary (see Example 20, for example).

Example 19   How many bit strings of length four do not have two consecutive 1s?

Solution: The tree diagram in Figure 2 displays all bit strings of length four without two consecutive 1s. We see that there are eight bit strings of length four without two consecutive 1s.   ◀

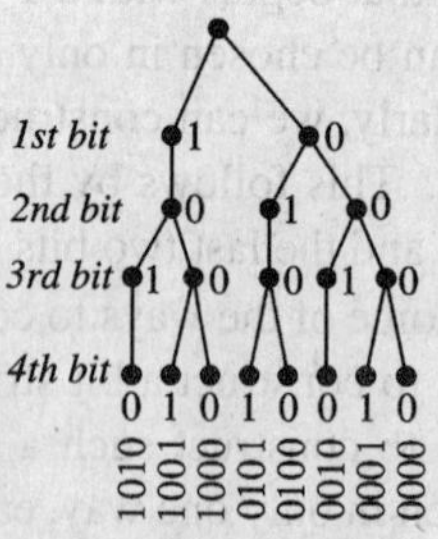

Figure 2   Bit Strings of Length Four without Consecutive 1s.

Example 20   A playoff between two teams consists of at most five games. The first team that wins three games wins the playoff. In how many different ways can the playoff occur?

Solution: The tree diagram in Figure 3 displays all the ways the playoff can proceed, with the winner of each game shown. We see that there are 20 different ways for the playoff to occur.   ◀

Example 21   Suppose that "I Love New Jersey" T-shirts come in five different sizes: S, M, L, XL, and XXL. Further suppose that each size comes in four colors, white, red, green, and black, except for XL, which comes only in red, green, and black, and XXL, which comes only in green and black. How many different shirts does a souvenir shop have to stock to have at least one of each available size and color of the T-shirt?

Solution: The tree diagram in Figure 4 displays all possible size and color pairs. It follows that the souvenir shop owner needs to stock 17 different T-shirts.   ◀

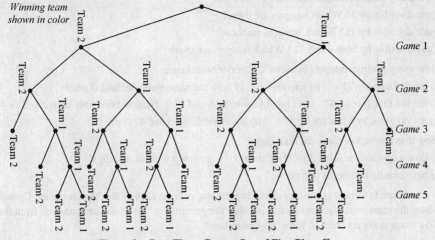

Figure 3   Best Three Games Out of Five Playoffs.

W = white, R = red, G = green, B = black

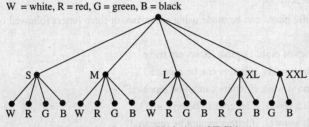

Figure 4   Counting Varieties of T-Shirts.

Exercises

1. There are 18 mathematics majors and 325 computer science majors at a college.
   a) How many ways are there to pick two representatives so that one is a mathematics major and the other is a computer science major?
   b) How many ways are there to pick one representative who is either a mathematics major or a computer science major?

2. A multiple-choice test contains 10 questions. There are four possible answers for each question.
   a) How many ways can a student answer the questions on the test if the student answers every question?
   b) How many ways can a student answer the questions on the test if the student can leave answers blank?

3. Six different airlines fly from New York to Denver and seven fly from Denver to San Francisco. How many different pairs of airlines can you choose on which to book a trip from New York to San Francisco via Denver, when you pick an airline for the flight to Denver and an airline for the continuation flight to San Francisco? How many of these pairs involve more than one airline?

4. How many different three-letter initials can people have?

5. How many different three-letter initials are there that begin with an A?

6. How many bit strings of length ten both begin and end with a 1?

7. How many bit strings with length not exceeding n, where n is a positive integer, consist entirely of 1s?

8. How many strings are there of lowercase letters of length four or less?

9. How many strings of five ASCII characters contain the character @ ("at" sign) at least once? (*Note*: There are 128 different ASCII characters.)

10. How many positive integers between 50 and 100

a)are divisible by 7? Which integers are these?

b)are divisible by 11? Which integers are these?

c)are divisible by both 7 and 11? Which integers are these?

11. How many positive integers between 100 and 999 inclusive

a) are divisible by 7?   b) are odd?   c) have the same three decimal digits?

d) are not divisible by 4?   e) are divisible by 3 or 4?   f) are not divisible by either 3 or 4?

g) are divisible by 3 but not by 4?   h) are divisible by 3 and 4?

12. How many strings of three decimal digits

a) do not contain the same digit three times?   b) begin with an odd digit?

c) have exactly two digits that are 4s?

13. A committee is formed consisting of one representative from each of the 50 states in the United States, where the representative from a state is either the governor or one of the two senators from that state. How many ways are there to form this committee?

14. How many license plates can be made using either two letters followed by four digits or two digits followed by four letters?

15. How many license plates can be made using either two or three letters followed by either two or three digits?

16. How many strings of eight English letters are there

a) that contain no vowels, if letters can be repeated?

b) that contain no vowels, if letters cannot be repeated?

c) that start with a vowel, if letters can be repeated?

d) that start with a vowel, if letters cannot be repeated?

e) that contain at least one vowel, if letters can be repeated?

f) that contain exactly one vowel, if letters can be repeated?

g) that start with X and contain at least one vowel, if letters can be repeated?

h) that start and end with X and contain at least one vowel, if letters can be repeated?

17. How many one-to-one functions are there from a set with five elements to sets with the following number of elements?

a) 4   b) 5   c) 6   d) 7

18. How many functions are there from the set $\{1, 2, \cdots, n\}$, where n is a positive integer, to the set $\{0, 1\}$

a) that are one-to-one?   b) that assign 0 to both 1 and n?

c) that assign 1 to exactly one of the positive integers less than n?

19. How many partial functions (see the preamble to Exercise 33 in Section 2.3) are there from a set with m elements to a set with n elements, where m and n are positive integers?

20. A **palindrome** is a string whose reversal is identical to the string. How many bit strings of length n are palindromes?

21. In how many ways can a photographer at a wedding arrange six people in a row, including the bride and groom, if

a) the bride must be next to the groom?   b) the bride is not next to the groom?

c) the bride is positioned somewhere to the left of the groom?

22. How many bit strings of length 10 either begin with three 0s or end with two 0s?

**23. How many bit strings of length eight contain either three consecutive 0s or four consecutive 1s?

24. How many positive integers not exceeding 100 are divisible either by 4 or by 6?

25. Suppose that a password for a computer system must have at least 8, but no more than 12, characters, where each character in the password is a lowercase English letter, an uppercase English letter, a digit, or one of the six special characters $*$, $>$, $<$, !, $+$, and $=$.

a) How many different passwords are available for this computer system?

b) How many of these passwords contain at least one occurrence of at least one of the six special characters?

c) If it takes one nanosecond for a hacker to check whether each possible password is your password, how long would it take this hacker to try every possible password?

26. Suppose that at some future time every telephone in the world is assigned a number that contains a country code 1 to 3 digits long, that is, of the form X, XX, or XXX, followed by a 10-digit telephone number of the form NXX-NXX-XXXX (as described in Example 8). How many different telephone numbers would be available worldwide under this numbering plan?

27. How many ways are there to arrange the letters a, b, c, and d such that a is not followed immediately by b?

28. Use a tree diagram to determine the number of subsets of $\{3, 7, 9, 11, 24\}$ with the property that the sum of the elements in the subset is less than 28.

29. a) Suppose that a popular style of running shoe is available for both men and women. The woman's shoe comes in sizes 6, 7, 8, and 9, and the man's shoe comes in sizes 8, 9, 10, 11, and 12. The man's shoe comes in white and black, while the woman's shoe comes in white, red, and black. Use a tree diagram to determine the number of different shoes that a store has to stock to have at least one pair of this type of running shoe for all available sizes and colors for both men and women.

b) Answer the question in part (a) using counting rules.

30. Use mathematical induction to prove the sum rule for m tasks from the sum rule for two tasks.

31. How many diagonals does a convex polygon with n sides have? (Recall that a polygon is convex if every line segment connecting two points in the interior or boundary of the polygon lies entirely within this set and that a diagonal of a polygon is a line segment connecting two vertices that are not adjacent.)

3.2 The Pigeonhole Principle

Introduction

Suppose that a flock of 20 pigeons flies into a set of 19 pigeonholes to roost. Because there are 20 pigeons but only 19 pigeonholes, a least one of these 19 pigeonholes must have at least two pigeons in it. To see why this is true, note that if each pigeonhole had at most one pigeon in it, at most 19 pigeons, one per hole, could be accommodated. This illustrates a general principle called the **pigeonhole principle**, which states that if there are more pigeons than pigeonholes, then there must be at least one pigeonhole with at least two pigeons in it (see Figure 1). Of course, this principle applies to other objects besides pigeons and pigeonholes.

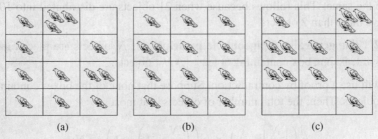

(a)   (b)   (c)

Figure 1   There Are More Pigeons Than Pigeonholes.

Theorem 1   The pigeonhole principle   If k is a positive integer and $k + 1$ or more objects are placed into k boxes, then there is at least one box containing two or more of the objects.

Proof: We will prove the pigeonhole principle using a proof by contraposition. Suppose that none of the k boxes contains more than one object. Then the total number of objects would be at most k. This is a contradiction, because there are at least $k + 1$ objects.   ◁

The pigeonhole principle is also called the **Dirichlet drawer principle**, after the nineteenth-century German mathematician Dirichlet, who often used this principle in his work.

The pigeonhole principle can be used to prove a useful corollary about functions.

Corollary 1   A function f from a set with $k + 1$ or more elements to a set with k elements is not one-to-one.

Proof: Suppose that for each element y in the codomain of f we have a box that contains all elements x of the domain of f such that $f(x) = y$. Because the domain contains $k + 1$ or more elements and the codomain contains only k elements, the pigeonhole principle tells us that one of these boxes contains two or more elements x of the domain. This means that f cannot be one-to-one.   ◁

Examples 1–3 show how the pigeonhole principle is used.

Example 1   Among any group of 367 people, there must be at least two with the same birthday, because there are only 366 possible birthdays.   ◀

Example 2   In any group of 27 English words, there must be at least two that begin with the same letter, because there are 26 letters in the English alphabet.   ◀

Example 3   How many students must be in a class to guarantee that at least two students receive the same score on the final exam, if the exam is graded on a scale from 0 to 100 points?

Solution: There are 101 possible scores on the final. The pigeonhole principle shows that among any 102 students there must be at least 2 students with the same score.   ◀

The pigeonhole principle is a useful tool in many proofs, including proofs of surprising results, such as that given in Example 4.

Example 4   Show that for every integer n there is a multiple of n that has only 0s and 1s in its decimal expansion.

Solution: Let n be a positive integer. Consider the $n + 1$ integers $1, 11, 111, \cdots, 11 \cdots 1$ (where the last integer in this list is the integer with $n + 1$ 1s in its decimal expansion). Note that there are n possible remainders when an integer is divided by n. Because there are $n + 1$ integers in this list, by the pigeonhole principle there must be two with the same remainder when divided by n. The larger of these integers less the smaller one is a multiple of n, which has a decimal expansion consisting entirely of 0s and 1s.   ◀

The Generalized Pigeonhole Principle

The pigeonhole principle states that there must be at least two objects in the same box when there are more objects than boxes. However, even more can be said when the number of objects exceeds a multiple of the number of boxes. For instance, among any set of 21 decimal digits there must be 3 that are the same. This follows because when 21 objects are distributed into 10 boxes, one box must have more than 2 objects.

Corollary 2   The generalized pigeonhole principle   If N objects are placed into k boxes, then there is at least one box containing at least $\lceil N/k \rceil$ objects.

Proof: We will use a proof by contradiction. Suppose that none of the boxes contains more than $\lceil N/k \rceil - 1$ objects. Then, the total number of objects is at most

$$k \left(\left\lceil \frac{N}{k} \right\rceil - 1 \right) < k \left(\left(\frac{N}{k} + 1 \right) - 1 \right) = N,$$

where the inequality $\lceil N/k \rceil < (N/k) + 1$ has been used. This is a contradiction because there are a total of N objects.   ◁

A common type of problem asks for the minimum number of objects such that at least r of these objects must be in one of k boxes when these objects are distributed among the boxes. When we have N objects, the generalized pigeonhole principle tells us there must be at least r objects in one of the boxes as long as $\lceil N/k \rceil \geqslant r$. The smallest integer N with $N/k > r - 1$, namely, $N = k(r - 1) + 1$, is the smallest integer satisfying the inequality $\lceil N/k \rceil \geqslant r$. Could a smaller value of N suffice? The answer is no, because if we have $k(r - 1)$ objects, we could put $r - 1$ of them in each of the k boxes and no box would have at least r objects.

When thinking about problems of this type, it is useful to consider how you can avoid having at least r objects in one of the boxes as you add successive objects. To avoid adding a rth object to any box, you eventually end up with $r - 1$ objects in each box. There is no way to add the next object without putting an rth object in that box.

Examples 5–8 illustrate how the generalized pigeonhole principle is applied.

Example 5   Among 100 people there are at least $\lceil 100/12 \rceil = 9$ who were born in the same month.   ◀

Example 6   What is the minimum number of students required in a discrete mathematics class to be sure that at least six will receive the same grade, if there are five possible grades, A, B, C, D, and F?

Solution: The minimum number of students needed to ensure that at least six students receive the same grade is the smallest integer N such that $\lceil N/5 \rceil = 6$. The smallest such integer is $N = 5 \cdot 5 + 1 = 26$. If you have only 25 students, it is possible for there to be five who have received each grade so that no six students have received the same grade. Thus, 26 is the minimum number of students needed to ensure that at least six students will receive the same grade.   ◀

Example 7   a) How many cards must be selected from a standard deck of 52 cards to guarantee that at least three cards of the same suit are chosen?
b) How many must be selected to guarantee that at least three hearts are selected?
Solution:

a) Suppose there are four boxes, one for each suit, and as cards are selected they are placed in the box reserved for cards of that suit. Using the generalized pigeonhole principle, we see that if N cards are selected, there is at least one box containing at least $\lceil N/4 \rceil$ cards. Consequently, we know that at least three cards of one suit are selected if $\lceil N/4 \rceil \geqslant 3$. The smallest integer N such that $\lceil N/4 \rceil \geqslant 3$ is $N = 2 \cdot 4 + 1 = 9$, so nine cards suffice. Note that if eight cards are selected, it is possible to have two cards of each suit, so more than eight cards are needed. Consequently, nine cards must be selected to guarantee that at least three cards of one suit are chosen. One good way to think about this is to note that after the eighth card is chosen, there is no way to avoid having a third card of some suit.

b) We do not use the generalized pigeonhole principle to answer this question, because we want to make sure that there are three hearts, not just three cards of one suit. Note that in the worst case, we can select all the clubs, diamonds, and spades, 39 cards in all, before we select a single heart. The next three cards will be all hearts, so we may need to select 42 cards to get three hearts.   ◀

Example 8   What is the least number of area codes needed to guarantee that the 25 million phones in a state can be assigned distinct 10-digit telephone numbers? (Assume that telephone numbers are of the form $NXX\text{-}NXX\text{-}XXXX$, where the first three digits form the area code, N represents a digit from 2 to 9 inclusive, and X represents any digit.)
Solution: There are eight million different phone numbers of the form $NXX\text{-}XXXX$ (as shown in Example 8 of Section 5.1). Hence, by the generalized pigeonhole principle, among 25 million telephones, at least $\lceil 25,000,000/8,000,000 \rceil$ of them must have identical phone numbers. Hence,

at least four area codes are required to ensure that all 10-digit numbers are different.   ◄

Example 9, although not an application of the generalized pigeonhole principle, makes use of similar principles.

Example 9   Suppose that a computer science laboratory has 15 workstations and 10 servers. A cable can be used to directly connect a workstation to a server. For each server, only one direct connection to that server can be active at any time. We want to guarantee that at any time any set of 10 or fewer workstations can simultaneously access different servers via direct connections. Although we could do this by connecting every workstation directly to every server (using 150 connections), what is the minimum number of direct connections needed to achieve this goal?

Solution: Suppose that we label the workstations $W_1, W_2, \cdots, W_{15}$ and the servers $S_1, S_2, \cdots, S_{10}$. Furthermore, suppose that we connect W_k to S_k for $k = 1, 2, \cdots, 10$ and each of $W_{11}, W_{12}, W_{13}, W_{14}$, and W_{15} to all 10 servers. We have a total of 60 direct connections. Clearly any set of 10 or fewer workstations can simultaneously access different servers. We see this by noting that if workstation W_j is included with $1 \leqslant j \leqslant 10$, it can access server S_j, and for each workstation W_k with $k \geqslant 11$ included, there must be a corresponding workstation W_j with $1 \leqslant j \leqslant 10$ not included, so W_k can access server S_j. (This follows because there are at least as many available servers S_j as there are workstations W_j with $1 \leqslant j \leqslant 10$ not included.)

Now suppose there are fewer than 60 direct connections between workstations and servers. Then some server would be connected to at most $\lfloor 59/10 \rfloor = 5$ workstations. (If all servers were connected to at least six workstations, there would be at least $6 \cdot 10 = 60$ direct connections.) This means that the remaining nine servers are not enough to allow the other 10 workstations to simultaneously access different servers. Consequently, at least 60 direct connections are needed. It follows that 60 is the answer.   ◄

Some Elegant Applications of the Pigeonhole Principle

In many interesting applications of the pigeonhole principle, the objects to be placed in boxes must be chosen in a clever way. A few such applications will be described here.

Example 10   During a month with 30 days, a baseball team plays at least one game a day, but no more than 45 games. Show that there must be a period of some number of consecutive days during which the team must play exactly 14 games.

Solution: Let a_j be the number of games played on or before the jth day of the month. Then $a_1, a_2, \cdots, a_{30}$ is an increasing sequence of distinct positive integers, with $1 \leqslant a_j \leqslant 45$. Moreover, $a_1 + 14, a_2 + 14, \cdots, a_{30} + 14$ is also an increasing sequence of distinct positive integers, with $15 \leqslant a_j + 14 \leqslant 59$.

The 60 positive integers $a_1, a_2, \cdots, a_{30}, a_1 + 14, a_2 + 14, \cdots, a_{30} + 14$ are all less than or equal to 59. Hence, by the pigeonhole principle two of these integers are equal. Because the integers $a_j, j = 1, 2, \cdots, 30$ are all distinct and the integers $a_j + 14, j = 1, 2, \cdots, 30$ are all distinct, there must be indices i and j with $a_i = a_j + 14$. This means that exactly 14 games were played from day $j + 1$ to day i.   ◄

Example 11   Show that among any $n + 1$ positive integers not exceeding $2n$ there must be an integer that divides one of the other integers.

Solution: Write each of the $n + 1$ integers $a_1, a_2, \cdots, a_{n+1}$ as a power of 2 times an odd integer. In other words, let $a_j = 2^{k_j} q_j$ for $j = 1, 2, \cdots, n + 1$, where k_j is a nonnegative integer and q_j is odd. The integers $q_1, q_2, \cdots, q_{n+1}$ are all odd positive integers less than $2n$. Because there are only n odd positive integers less than $2n$, it follows from the pigeonhole principle that two of the integers $q_1, q_2, \cdots, q_{n+1}$ must be equal. Therefore, there are integers i and j such that $q_i = q_j$. Let q be the common value of q_i and q_j. Then, $a_i = 2^{k_i} q$ and $a_j = 2^{k_j} q$. It follows that if $k_i < k_j$, then a_i divides a_j; while if $k_i > k_j$, then a_j divides a_i.   ◄

A clever application of the pigeonhole principle shows the existence of an increasing or a decreasing subsequence of a certain length in a sequence of distinct integers. Some definitions will be reviewed before this application is presented. Suppose that $a_1, a_2, \cdots, a_N$ is a sequence of real numbers. A **subsequence** of this sequence is a sequence of the form $a_{i_1}, a_{i_2}, \cdots, a_{i_m}$, where $1 \leqslant i_1 < i_2 < \cdots < i_m \leqslant N$. Hence, a subsequence is a sequence obtained from the original sequence by including some of the terms of the original sequence in their original order, and perhaps not including other terms. A sequence is called **strictly increasing** if each term is larger than the one that precedes it, and it is called **strictly decreasing** if each term is smaller than the one that precedes it.

Theorem 3   Every sequence of $n^2 + 1$ distinct real numbers contains a subsequence of length $n + 1$ that is either strictly increasing or strictly decreasing.

We give an example before presenting the proof of Theorem 3.

Example 12   The sequence 8, 11, 9, 1, 4, 6, 12, 10, 5, 7 contains 10 terms. Note that $10 = 3^2 + 1$. There are four increasing subsequences of length four, namely, 1, 4, 6, 12; 1, 4, 6, 7; 1, 4, 6, 10; and 1, 4, 5, 7. There is also a decreasing subsequence of length four, namely, 11, 9, 6, 5.   ◄

The proof of the theorem will now be given.

Proof: Let $a_1, a_2, \cdots, a_{n^2+1}$ be a sequence of $n^2 + 1$ distinct real numbers. Associate an ordered pair with each term of the sequence, namely, associate (i_k, d_k) to the term a_k, where i_k is the length of the longest increasing subsequence starting at a_k, and d_k is the length of the longest decreasing subsequence starting at a_k.

Suppose that there are no increasing or decreasing subsequences of length $n + 1$. Then i_k and d_k are both positive integers less than or equal to n, for $k = 1, 2, \cdots, n^2 + 1$. Hence, by the product rule there are n^2 possible ordered pairs for (i_k, d_k). By the pigeonhole principle, two of these $n^2 + 1$ ordered pairs are equal. In other words, there exist terms a_s and a_t, with $s < t$ such that $i_s = i_t$ and $d_s = d_t$. We will show that this is impossible. Because the terms of the sequence are distinct, either $a_s < a_t$ or $a_s > a_t$. If $a_s < a_t$, then, because $i_s = i_t$, an increasing subsequence of length $i_t + 1$ can be built starting at a_s, by taking a_s followed by an increasing subsequence of length i_t beginning at a_t. This is a contradiction. Similarly, if $a_s > a_t$, it can be shown that d_s must be greater than d_t, which is a contradiction.   ◁

The final example shows how the generalized pigeonhole principle can be applied to an important part of combinatorics called **Ramsey theory,** after the English mathematician F. P. Ramsey. In general, Ramsey theory deals with the distribution of subsets of elements of sets.

Example 13   Assume that in a group of six people, each pair of individuals consists of two friends or two enemies. Show that there are either three mutual friends or three mutual enemies in the group.

Solution: Let A be one of the six people. Of the five other people in the group, there are either three or more who are friends of A, or three or more who are enemies of A. This follows from the generalized pigeonhole principle, because when five objects are divided into two sets, one of the sets has at least $\lceil 5/2 \rceil = 3$ elements. In the former case, suppose that B, C, and D are friends of A. If any two of these three individuals are friends, then these two and A form a group of three mutual friends. Otherwise, B, C and D form a set of three mutual enemies. The proof in the latter case, when there are three or more enemies of A, proceeds in a similar manner.   ◄

The **Ramsey number** $R(m, n)$, where m and n are positive integers greater than or equal to 2, denotes the minimum number of people at a party such that there are either m mutual friends or n mutual enemies, assuming that every pair of people at the party are friends or enemies. Example 13 shows that $R(3, 3) \leqslant 6$. We conclude that $R(3, 3) = 6$ because in a group of five people where every two people are friends or enemies, there may not be three mutual friends or three mutual enemies.

It is possible to prove some useful properties about Ramsey numbers, but for the most part it is difficult to find their exact values. Note that by symmetry it can be shown that $R(m, n) = $

$R(n, m)$. We also have $R(2, n) = n$ for every positive integer $n \geqslant 2$ (see Exercise 14). The exact values of only nine Ramsey numbers $R(m, n)$ with $3 \leqslant m \leqslant n$ are known, including $R(4, 4) = 18$. Only bounds are known for many other Ramsey numbers, including $R(5, 5)$, which is known to satisfy $43 \leqslant R(5, 5) \leqslant 49$. The reader interested in learning more about Ramsey numbers should consult [MiRo91] or [GrRoSp90].

Exercises

1. Show that in any set of six classes, each meeting regularly once a week on a particular day of the week, there must be two that meet on the same day, assuming that no classes are held on weekends.

2. A drawer contains a dozen brown socks and a dozen black socks, all unmatched. A man takes socks out at random in the dark.

   a) How many socks must he take out to be sure that he has at least two socks of the same color?

   b) How many socks must he take out to be sure that he has at least two black socks?

3. Show that among any group of five (not necessarily consecutive) integers, there are two with the same remainder when divided by 4.

4. Let n be a positive integer. Show that in any set of n consecutive integers there is exactly one divisible by n.

5. What is the minimum number of students, each of whom comes from one of the 50 states, who must be enrolled in a university to guarantee that there are at least 100 who come from the same state?

*6. Let (x_i, y_i, z_i), $i = 1, 2, 3, 4, 5, 6, 7, 8, 9$, be a set of nine distinct points with integer coordinates in xyz space. Show that the midpoint of at least one pair of these points has integer coordinates.

7. a) Show that if five integers are selected from the first eight positive integers, there must be a pair of these integers with a sum equal to 9.

   b) Is the conclusion in part (a) true if four integers are selected rather than five?

8. How many numbers must be selected from the set $\{1, 2, 3, 4, 5, 6\}$ to guarantee that at least one pair of these numbers add up to 7?

9. A company stores products in a warehouse. Storage bins in this warehouse are specified by their aisle, location in the aisle, and shelf. There are 50 aisles, 85 horizontal locations in each aisle, and 5 shelves throughout the warehouse. What is the least number of products the company can have so that at least two products must be stored in the same bin?

10. Suppose that every student in a discrete mathematics class of 25 students is a freshman, a sophomore, or a junior.

    a) Show that there are at least nine freshmen, at least nine sophomores, or at least nine juniors in the class.

    b) Show that there are either at least three freshmen, at least 19 sophomores, or at least five juniors in the class.

11. Construct a sequence of 16 positive integers that has no increasing or decreasing subsequence of five terms.

*12. Describe an algorithm in pseudocode for producing the largest increasing or decreasing subsequence of a sequence of distinct integers.

13. Show that in a group of 10 people (where any two people are either friends or enemies), there are either three mutual friends or four mutual enemies, and there are either three mutual enemies or four mutual friends.

14. Show that if n is a positive integer with $n \geqslant 2$, then the Ramsey number $R(2, n)$ equals n.

15. Show that there are at least six people in California (population: 36 million) with the same three initials who were born on the same day of the year (but not necessarily in the same year). Assume that everyone has three initials.

16. There are 38 different time periods during which classes at a university can be scheduled. If there are 677 different classes, how many different rooms will be needed?

17. A computer network consists of six computers. Each computer is directly connected to zero or more of the other computers. Show that there are at least two computers in the network that are directly connected to the same number of other computers. [*Hint:* It is impossible to have a computer linked to none of the others and a computer linked to all the others.]

18. Find the least number of cables required to connect 100 computers to 20 printers to guarantee that 20 computers can directly access 20 different printers. (Here, the assumptions about cables and computers are the same as in Example 9.) Justify your answer.

19. An arm wrestler is the champion for a period of 75 hours. (Here, by an hour, we mean a period starting from an exact hour, such as 1 P.M., until the next hour.) The arm wrestler had at least one match an hour, but no more than 125 total matches. Show that there is a period of consecutive hours during which the arm wrestler had exactly 24 matches.

20. Show that if f is a function from S to T, where S and T are finite sets and $m = \lceil |S|/|T| \rceil$, then there are at least m elements of S mapped to the same value of T. That is, show that there are distinct elements $s_1, s_2, \cdots, s_m$ of S such that $f(s_1) = f(s_2) = \cdots = f(s_m)$.

*21. Let x be an irrational number. Show that for some positive integer j not exceeding n, the absolute value of the difference between jx and the nearest integer to jx is less than $1/n$.

*22. A proof of Theorem 3 based on the generalized pigeonhole principle is outlined in this exercise. The notation used is the same as that used in the proof in the text.

   a) Assume that $i_k \leqslant n$ for $k = 1, 2, \cdots, n^2 + 1$. Use the generalized pigeonhole principle to show that there are $n + 1$ terms $a_{k_1}, a_{k_2}, \cdots, a_{k_{n+1}}$ with $i_{k_1} = i_{k_2} = \cdots = i_{k_{n+1}}$, where $1 \leqslant k_1 < k_2 < \cdots < k_{n+1}$.

   b) Show that $a_{k_j} > a_{k_{j+1}}$ for $j = 1, 2, \cdots, n$. [*Hint:* Assume that $a_{k_j} < a_{k_{j+1}}$, and show that this implies that $i_{k_j} > i_{k_{j+1}}$, which is a contradiction.]

   c) Use parts (a) and (b) to show that if there is no increasing subsequence of length $n + 1$, then there must be a decreasing subsequence of this length.

3.3   Permutations and Combinations

Introduction

Many counting problems can be solved by finding the number of ways to arrange a specified number of distinct elements of a set of a particular size, where the order of these elements matters. Many other counting problems can be solved by finding the number of ways to select a particular number of elements from a set of a particular size, where the order of the elements selected does not matter. For example, in how many ways can we select three students from a group of five students to stand in line for a picture? How many different committees of three students can be formed from a group of four students? In this section we will develop methods to answers questions such as these.

Permutations

We begin by solving the first question posed in the introduction to this section, as well as related questions.

Example 1   In how many ways can we select three students from a group of five students to stand in line for a picture? In how many ways can we arrange all five of these students in a line for a picture?

Solution: First, note that the order in which we select the students matters. There are five ways to select the first student to stand at the start of the line. Once this student has been selected, there are four ways to select the second student in the line. After the first and second students have been selected, there are three ways to select the third student in the line. By the product rule, there are $5 \cdot 4 \cdot 3 = 60$ ways to select three students from a group of five students to stand in line for a picture.

To arrange all five students in a line for a picture, we select the first student in five ways, the second in four ways, the third in three ways, the fourth in two ways, and the fifth in one way. Consequently, there are $5 \cdot 4 \cdot 3 \cdot 2 \cdot 1 = 120$ ways to arrange all five students in a line for a picture. ◀

Example 1 illustrates how ordered arrangements of distinct objects can be counted. This leads to some terminology.

A **permutation** of a set of distinct objects is an ordered arrangement of these objects. We also are interested in ordered arrangements of some of the elements of a set. An ordered arrangement of r elements of a set is called an **r-permutation.**

Example 2   Let $S = \{1, 2, 3\}$. The ordered arrangement 3, 1, 2 is a permutation of S. The ordered arrangement 3, 2 is a 2-permutation of S. ◀

The number of r-permutations of a set with n elements is denoted by $P(n, r)$. We can find $P(n, r)$ using the product rule.

Example 3   Let $S = \{a, b, c\}$. The 2-permutations of S are the ordered arrangements $a, b; a, c; b, a; b, c; c, a;$ and c, b. Consequently, there are six 2-permutations of this set with three elements. To see that there are always six 2-permutations of a set with three elements, note that there are three ways to choose the first element of the arrangement and two ways to choose the second element of the arrangement because it must be different from the first element. By the product rule, it follows that $P(3, 2) = 3 \cdot 2 = 6$. ◀

We now use the product rule to find a formula for $P(n, r)$ whenever n and r are positive integers with $1 \leqslant r \leqslant n$.

Theorem 1   If n is a positive integer and r is an integer with $1 \leqslant r \leqslant n$, then there are

$$P(n, r) = n(n - 1)(n - 2) \cdots (n - r + 1)$$

r-permutations of a set with n distinct elements.

Proof: We will use the product rule to prove that this formula is correct. The first element of the permutation can be chosen in n ways because there are n elements in the set. There are $n - 1$ ways to choose the second element of the permutation, because there are $n - 1$ elements left in the set after using the element picked for the first position. Similarly, there are $n - 2$ ways to choose the third element, and so on, until there are exactly $n - (r - 1) = n - r + 1$ ways to choose the rth element. Consequently, by the product rule, there are

$$n(n - 1)(n - 2) \cdots (n - r + 1)$$

r-permutations of the set. ◁

Note that $P(n, 0) = 1$ whenever n is a nonnegative integer because there is exactly one way to order zero elements. That is, there is exactly one list with no elements in it, namely the empty list.

We now state a useful corollary of Theorem 1.

Corollary 1   If n and r are integers with $0 \leqslant r \leqslant n$, then $P(n, r) = \dfrac{n!}{(n - r)!}$.

Proof: When n and r are integers with $1 \leqslant r \leqslant n$, by Theorem 1 we have

$$P(n, r) = n(n - 1)(n - 2) \cdots (n - r + 1) = \frac{n!}{(n - r)!}$$

Because $\dfrac{n!}{(n - 0)!} = \dfrac{n!}{n!} = 1$ whenever n is a nonnegative integer, we see that the formula

$P(n, r) = \dfrac{n!}{(n-r)!}$ also holds when $r = 0$.   ◁

By Theorem 1 we know that if n is a positive integer, then $P(n, n) = n!$. We will illustrate this result with some examples.

Example 4   How many ways are there to select a first-prize winner, a second-prize winner, and a third-prize winner from 100 different people who have entered a contest?

Solution: Because it matters which person wins which prize, the number of ways to pick the three prize winners is the number of ordered selections of three elements from a set of 100 elements, that is, the number of 3-permutations of a set of 100 elements. Consequently, the answer is

$$P(100, 3) = 100 \cdot 99 \cdot 98 = 970,200.$$ ◀

Example 5   Suppose that there are eight runners in a race. The winner receives a gold medal, the second-place finisher receives a silver medal, and the third-place finisher receives a bronze medal. How many different ways are there to award these medals, if all possible outcomes of the race can occur and there are no ties?

Solution: The number of different ways to award the medals is the number of 3-permutations of a set with eight elements. Hence, there are $P(8, 3) = 8 \cdot 7 \cdot 6 = 336$ possible ways to award the medals.   ◀

Example 6   Suppose that a saleswoman has to visit eight different cities. She must begin her trip in a specified city, but she can visit the other seven cities in any order she wishes. How many possible orders can the saleswoman use when visiting these cities?

Solution: The number of possible paths between the cities is the number of permutations of seven elements, because the first city is determined, but the remaining seven can be ordered arbitrarily. Consequently, there are $7! = 7 \cdot 6 \cdot 5 \cdot 4 \cdot 3 \cdot 2 \cdot 1 = 5040$ ways for the saleswoman to choose her tour. If, for instance, the saleswoman wishes to find the path between the cities with minimum distance, and she computes the total distance for each possible path, she must consider a total of 5040 paths!   ◀

Example 7   How many permutations of the letters $ABCDEFGH$ contain the string ABC?

Solution: Because the letters ABC must occur as a block, we can find the answer by finding the number of permutations of six objects, namely, the block ABC and the individual letters D, E, F, G, and H. Because these six objects can occur in any order, there are $6! = 720$ permutations of the letters $ABCDEFGH$ in which ABC occurs as a block.   ◀

Combinations

We now turn our attention to counting unordered selection of objects. We begin by solving a question posed in the introduction to this section of the chapter.

Example 8   How many different committees of three students can be formed from a group of four students?

Solution: To answer this question, we need only find the number of subsets with three elements from the set containing the four students. We see that there are four such subsets, one for each of the four students, because choosing four students is the same as choosing one of the four students to leave out of the group. This means that there are four ways to choose the three students for the committee, where the order in which these students are chosen does not matter.   ◀

Example 8 illustrates that many counting problems can be solved by finding the number of subsets of a particular size of a set with n elements, where n is a positive integer.

An **r-combination** of elements of a set is an unordered selection of r elements from the set. Thus, an r-combination is simply a subset of the set with r elements.

Example 9   Let S be the set $\{1, 2, 3, 4\}$. Then $\{1, 3, 4\}$ is a 3-combination from S.   ◀

The number of r-combinations of a set with n distinct elements is denoted by $C(n, r)$. Note that $C(n, r)$ is also denoted by $\binom{n}{r}$ and is called a **binomial coefficient**. We will learn where this terminology arises in Section 3.4.

Example 10   We see that $C(4, 2) = 6$, because the 2-combinations of $\{a, b, c, d\}$ are the six subsets $\{a, b\}$, $\{a, c\}$, $\{a, d\}$, $\{b, c\}$, $\{b, d\}$, and $\{c, d\}$.   ◄

We can determine the number of r-combinations of a set with n elements using the formula for the number of r-permutations of a set. To do this, note that the r-permutations of a set can be obtained by first forming r-combinations and then ordering the elements in these combinations. The proof of Theorem 2, which gives the value of $C(n, r)$, is based on this observation.

Theorem 2   The number of r-combinations of a set with n elements, where n is a nonnegative integer and r is an integer with $0 \leqslant r \leqslant n$, equals

$$C(n, r) = \frac{n!}{r! \, (n - r)!}.$$

Proof: The r-permutations of the set can be obtained by forming the $C(n, r)$ r-combinations of the set, and then ordering the elements in each r-combination, which can be done in $P(r, r)$ ways. Consequently,

$$P(n, r) = C(n, r) \cdot P(r, r).$$

This implies that

$$C(n, r) = \frac{P(n, r)}{P(r, r)} = \frac{n!/(n - r)!}{r!/(r - r)!} = \frac{n!}{r! \, (n - r)!}.$$ ◄

The formula in Theorem 2, although explicit, is not helpful when $C(n, r)$ is computed for large values of n and r. The reasons are that it is practical to compute exact values of factorials exactly only for small integer values, and when floating point arithmetic is used, the formula in Theorem 2 may produce a value that is not an integer. When computing $C(n, r)$, first note that when we cancel out $(n - r)!$ from the numerator and denominator of the expression for $C(n, r)$ in Theorem 2, we obtain

$$C(n, r) = \frac{n!}{r! \, (n - r)!} = \frac{n(n - 1) \cdots (n - r + 1)}{r!}.$$

Consequently, to compute $C(n, r)$ you can cancel out all the terms in the larger factorial in the denominator from the numerator and denominator, then multiply all the terms that do not cancel in the numerator and finally divide by the smaller factorial in the denominator. [When doing this calculation by hand, instead of by machine, it is worthwhile to factor out common factors in the numerator $n(n - 1) \cdots (n - r + 1)$ and in the denominator $r!$.] Note that many calculators have a built-in function for $C(n, r)$ that can be used for relatively small values of n and r and many computational programs can be used to find $C(n, r)$. [Such functions may be called $chose(n, k)$ or $binom(n, k)$].

Example 11 illustrates how $C(n, k)$ is computed when k is relatively small compared to n and when k is close to n. It also illustrates a key identity enjoyed by the numbers $C(n, k)$.

Example 11   How many poker hands of five cards can be dealt from a standard deck of 52 cards? Also, how many ways are there to select 47 cards from a standard deck of 52 cards? *Solution*: Because the order in which the five cards are dealt from a deck of 52 cards does not matter, there are

$$C(52, 5) = \frac{52!}{5! 47!}$$

different hands of five cards that can be dealt. To compute the value of $C(52, 5)$, first divide the numerator and denominator by 47! to obtain

$$C(52,5) = \frac{52 \cdot 51 \cdot 50 \cdot 49 \cdot 48}{5 \cdot 4 \cdot 3 \cdot 2 \cdot 1}.$$

This expression can be simplified by first dividing the factor 5 in the denominator into the factor
in the numerator to obtain a factor 10 in the numerator, then dividing the factor 4 in the
denominator into the factor 48 in the numerator to obtain a factor of 12 in the numerator, then
dividing the factor 3 in the denominator into the factor 51 in the numerator to obtain a factor of
17 in the numerator, and finally, dividing the factor 2 in the denominator into the factor 52 in the
numerator to obtain a factor of 26 in the numerator. We find that

$$C(52,5) = 26 \cdot 17 \cdot 10 \cdot 49 \cdot 12 = 2,598,960.$$

Consequently, there are 2,598,960 different poker hands of five cards that can be dealt from a
standard deck of 52 cards.

Note that there are

$$C(52,47) = \frac{52!}{47!5!}$$

different ways to select 47 cards from a standard deck of 52 cards. We do not need to compute
this value because $C(52,47) = C(52,5)$. (Only the order of the factors 5! and 47! is different
in the denominators in the formulae for these quantities.) It follows that there are also 2,598,960
different ways to select 47 cards from a standard deck of 52 cards.   ◄

In Example 11 we observed that $C(52,5) = C(52,47)$. This is a special case of the useful
identity for the number of r-combinations of a set given in Corollary 2.

Corollary 2 Let n and r be nonnegative integers with $r \leqslant n$. Then $C(n,r) = C(n,n-r)$.

Proof: From Theorem 2 it follows that

$$C(n,r) = \frac{n!}{r!\,(n-r)!}$$

and

$$C(n,n-r) = \frac{n!}{(n-r)!\,[n-(n-r)]!} = \frac{n!}{(n-r)!\,r!}.$$

Hence, $C(n,r) = C(n,n-r)$.   ◄

We can also prove Corollary 2 using a proof that shows that both sides of the equation in
Corollary 2 count the same objects using different reasoning. We describe this important type of
proof in Definition 1.

Definition 1 A *combinatorial proof* of an identity is a proof that uses counting arguments to
prove that both sides of the identity count the same objects but in different ways.

Many identities involving binomial coefficients can be proved using combinatorial proofs. We
now provide a combinatorial proof of Corollary 2.

Proof: Suppose that S is a set with n elements. Every subset A of S with r elements corresponds
to a subset of S with $n - r$ elements, namely $\overline{A}$. Consequently, $C(n,r) = C(n,n-r)$.   ◄

Example 12   How many ways are there to select five players from a 10-member tennis team to
make a trip to a match at another school?

Solution: The answer is given by the number of 5-combinations of a set with 10 elements. By
Theorem 2, the number of such combinations is

$$C(10,5) = \frac{10!}{5!\,5!} = 252.$$ ◄

Example 13   A group of 30 people have been trained as astronauts to go on the first mission to Mars. How many ways are there to select a crew of six people to go on this mission (assuming that all crew members have the same job)?

Solution: The number of ways to select a crew of six from the pool of 30 people is the number of 6-combinations of a set with 30 elements, because the order in which these people are chosen does not matter. By Theorem 2, the number of such combinations is

$$C(30,6) = \frac{30!}{6! \, 24!} = \frac{30 \cdot 29 \cdot 28 \cdot 27 \cdot 26 \cdot 25}{6 \cdot 5 \cdot 4 \cdot 3 \cdot 2 \cdot 1} = 593{,}775.$$ ◀

Example 14   How many bit strings of length n contain exactly r 1s?

Solution: The positions of r 1s in a bit string of length n form an r-combination of the set $\{1, 2, 3, \cdots, n\}$. Hence, there are $C(n,r)$ bit strings of length n that contain exactly r 1s. ◀

Example 15   Suppose that there are 9 faculty members in the mathematics department and 11 in the computer science department. How many ways are there to select a committee to develop a discrete mathematics course at a school if the committee is to consist of three faculty members from the mathematics department and four from the computer science department?

Solution: By the product rule, the answer is the product of the number of 3-combinations of a set with nine elements and the number of 4-combinations of a set with 11 elements. By Theorem 2, the number of ways to select the committee is

$$C(9,3) \cdot C(11,4) = \frac{9!}{3!6!} \cdot \frac{11!}{4!7!} = 84 \cdot 330 = 27{,}720.$$ ◀

Exercises

1. List all the permutations of $\{a, b, c\}$.

2. How many permutations of $\{a, b, c, d, e, f, g\}$ end with a?

3. Find the value of each of these quantities.
   a) $P(6,3)$ b) $P(6,5)$ c) $P(8,1)$ d) $P(8,5)$ e) $P(8,8)$ f) $P(10,9)$

4. Find the number of 5-permutations of a set with nine elements.

5. How many possibilities are there for the win, place, and show (first, second, and third) positions in a horse race with 12 horses if all orders of finish are possible?

6. How many bit strings of length 10 contain
   a) exactly four 1s?   b) at most four 1s?   c) at least four 1s?   d) an equal number of 0s and 1s?

7. A group contains n men and n women. How many ways are there to arrange these people in a row if the men and women alternate?

8. In how many ways can a set of five letters be selected from the English alphabet?

9. How many subsets with more than two elements does a set with 100 elements have?

10. A coin is flipped 10 times where each flip comes up either heads or tails. How many possible outcomes
    a) are there in total?   b) contain exactly two heads?
    c) contain at most three tails?   d) contain the same number of heads and tails?

11. How many permutations of the letters $ABCDEFG$ contain
    a) the string BCD?   b) the string $CFGA$?   c) the strings BA and GF?
    d) the strings ABC and DE?   e) the strings ABC and CDE?   f) the strings CBA and BED?

12. How many ways are there for eight men and five women to stand in a line so that no two women stand next to each other? [Hint: First position the men and then consider possible positions for the women.]

13. One hundred tickets, numbered $1, 2, 3, \cdots, 100$, are sold to 100 different people for a drawing. Four different prizes are awarded, including a grand prize (a trip to Tahiti). How many ways are there to award the prizes if
    a) there are no restrictions?
    b) the person holding ticket 47 wins the grand prize?
    c) the person holding ticket 47 wins one of the prizes?
    d) the person holding ticket 47 does not win a prize?
    e) the people holding tickets 19 and 47 both win prizes?
    f) the people holding tickets 19, 47, and 73 all win prizes?
    g) the people holding tickets 19, 47, 73, and 97 all win prizes?
    h) none of the people holding tickets 19, 47, 73, and 97 wins a prize?
    i) the grand prize winner is a person holding ticket 19, 47, 73, or 97?
    j) the people holding tickets 19 and 47 win prizes, but the people holding tickets 73 and 97 do not win prizes?
14. A club has 25 members.
    a) How many ways are there to choose four members of the club to serve on an executive committee?
    b) How many ways are there to choose a president, vice president, secretary, and treasurer of the club, where no person can hold more than one office?
*15. How many 4-permutations of the positive integers not exceeding 100 contain three consecutive integers $k, k + 1, k + 2$, in the correct order
    a) where these consecutive integers can perhaps be separated by other integers in the permutation?
    b) where they are in consecutive positions in the permutation?
16. The English alphabet contains 21 consonants and five vowels. How many strings of six lowercase letters of the English alphabet contain
    a) exactly one vowel?   b) exactly two vowels?   c) at least one vowel?   d) at least two vowels?
17. Suppose that a department contains 10 men and 15 women. How many ways are there to form a committee with six members if it must have the same number of men and women?
18. How many bit strings contain exactly eight 0s and 10 1s if every 0 must be immediately followed by a 1?
19. How many bit strings of length 10 contain at least three 1s and at least three 0s?
20. How many license plates consisting of three letters followed by three digits contain no letter or digit twice?
21. How many ways are there for a horse race with three horses to finish if ties are possible? (*Note:* Two or three horses may tie.)
*22. There are six runners in the 100-yard dash. How many ways are there for three medals to be awarded if ties are possible? (The runner or runners who finish with the fastest time receive gold medals, the runner or runners who finish with exactly one runner ahead receive silver medals, and the runner or runners who finish with exactly two runners ahead receive bronze medals.)

3.4 Binomial Coefficients

As we remarked in Section 3.3, the number of r-combinations from a set with n elements is often denoted by $\binom{n}{r}$. This number is also called a **binomial coefficient** because these numbers occur as coefficients in the expansion of powers of binomial expressions such as $(a + b)^n$. We will discuss the **Binomial Theorem,** which gives a power of a binomial expression as a sum of terms involving binomial coefficients. We will prove this theorem using a combinatorial proof. We will also show how combinatorial proofs can be used to establish some of the many different identities that express relationships among binomial coefficients.

The Binomial Theorem

The Binomial Theorem gives the coefficients of the expansion of powers of binomial expressions. A **binomial** expression is simply the sum of two terms, such as $x + y$. (The terms can be products of constants and variables, but that does not concern us here.) Example 1 illustrates why this theorem holds.

Example 1   The expansion of $(x + y)^3$ can be found using combinatorial reasoning instead of multiplying the three terms out. When $(x+y)^3 = (x+y)(x+y)(x+y)$ is expanded, all products of a term in the first sum, a term in the second sum, and a term in the third sum are added. Terms of the form x^3, x^2y, xy^2, and y^3 arise. To obtain a term of the form x^3, an x must be chosen in each of the sums, and this can be done in only one way. Thus, the x^3 term in the product has a coefficient of 1. To obtain a term of the form x^2y, an x must be chosen in two of the three sums (and consequently a y in the other sum). Hence, the number of such terms is the number of 2-combinations of three objects, namely, $\binom{3}{2}$. Similarly, the number of terms of the form xy^2 is the number of ways to pick one of the three sums to obtain an x (and consequently take a y from each of the other two sums). This can be done in $\binom{3}{1}$ ways. Finally, the only way to obtain a y^3 term is to choose the y for each of the three sums in the product, and this can be done in exactly one way. Consequently, it follows that

$$(x + y)^3 = (x + y)(x + y)(x + y) = (xx + xy + yx + yy)(x + y)$$
$$= xxx + xxy + xyx + xyy + yxx + yxy + yyx + yyy$$
$$= x^3 + 3x^2y + 3xy^2 + y^3.$$
◀

The Binomial Theorem will now be stated.

Theorem 1   The Binomial Theorem   Let x and y be variables, and let n be a nonnegative integer. Then

$$(x + y)^n = \sum_{j=0}^{n} \binom{n}{j} x^{n-j} y^j$$

$$= \binom{n}{0} x^n + \binom{n}{1} x^{n-1} y + \binom{n}{2} x^{n-2} y^2 + \cdots + \binom{n}{n-1} xy^{n-1} + \binom{n}{n} y^n.$$

Proof: A combinatorial proof of the theorem will be given. The terms in the product when it is expanded are of the form $x^{n-j} y^j$ for $j = 0, 1, 2, \cdots, n$. To count the number of terms of the form $x^{n-j} y^j$, note that to obtain such a term it is necessary to choose $n - j$ xs from the n sums (so that the other j terms in the product are ys). Therefore, the coefficient of $x^{n-j} y^j$ is $\binom{n}{n-j}$, which is equal to $\binom{n}{j}$. This proves the theorem.   ◁

The use of the Binomial Theorem is illustrated by Examples 2–4.

Example 2   What is the expansion of $(x + y)^4$?

Solution: From the Binomial Theorem it follows that

$$(x + y)^4 = \sum_{j=0}^{4} \binom{4}{j} x^{4-j} y^j$$

$$= \binom{4}{0} x^4 + \binom{4}{1} x^3 y + \binom{4}{2} x^2 y^2 + \binom{4}{3} xy^3 + \binom{4}{4} y^4$$

$$= x^4 + 4x^3 y + 6x^2 y^2 + 4xy^3 + y^4.$$
◀

Example 3   What is the coefficient of $x^{12} y^{13}$ in the expansion of $(x + y)^{25}$?

Solution: From the Binomial Theorem it follows that this coefficient is

$$\binom{25}{13} = \frac{25!}{13!\,12!} = 5{,}200{,}300.$$

◄

Example 4   What is the coefficient of $x^{12}y^{13}$ in the expansion of $(2x - 3y)^{25}$?
Solution: First, note that this expression equals $(2x + (-3y))^{25}$. By the Binomial Theorem, we have

$$(2x + (-3y))^{25} = \sum_{j=0}^{25} \binom{25}{j}(2x)^{25-j}(-3y)^{j}.$$

Consequently, the coefficient of $x^{12}y^{13}$ in the expansion is obtained when $j = 13$, namely,

$$\binom{25}{13}2^{12}(-3)^{13} = -\frac{25!}{13!\,12!}2^{12}3^{13}.$$

◄

We can prove some useful identities using the Binomial Theorem, as Corollaries 1, 2, and 3 demonstrate.

Corollary 1   Let n be a nonnegative integer. Then

$$\sum_{k=0}^{n} \binom{n}{k} = 2^{n}.$$

Proof: Using the Binomial Theorem with $x = 1$ and $y = 1$, we see that

$$2^{n} = (1+1)^{n} = \sum_{k=0}^{n} \binom{n}{k}1^{k}1^{n-k} = \sum_{k=0}^{n} \binom{n}{k}.$$

This is the desired result.

◁

There is also a nice combinatorial proof of Corollary 1, which we now present.
Proof: A set with n elements has a total of 2^{n} different subsets. Each subset has zero elements, one element, two elements, $\cdots$, or n elements in it. There are $\binom{n}{0}$ subsets with zero elements, $\binom{n}{1}$ subsets with one element, $\binom{n}{2}$ subsets with two elements, $\cdots$, and $\binom{n}{n}$ subsets with n elements. Therefore,

$$\sum_{k=0}^{n} \binom{n}{k}$$

counts the total number of subsets of a set with n elements. This shows that

$$\sum_{k=0}^{n} \binom{n}{k} = 2^{n}.$$

◁

Corollary 2   Let n be a positive integer. Then

$$\sum_{k=0}^{n} (-1)^{k}\binom{n}{k} = 0.$$

Proof: When we use the Binomial Theorem with $x = -1$ and $y = 1$, we see that

$$0 = 0^{n} = ((-1)+1)^{n} = \sum_{k=0}^{n} \binom{n}{k}(-1)^{k}1^{n-k} = \sum_{k=0}^{n} \binom{n}{k}(-1)^{k}.$$

This proves the corollary.   ◁

Remark: Corollary 2 implies that

$$\binom{n}{0} + \binom{n}{2} + \binom{n}{4} + \cdots = \binom{n}{1} + \binom{n}{3} + \binom{n}{5} + \cdots .$$

Corollary 3   Let n be a nonnegative integer. Then

$$\sum_{k=0}^{n} 2^k \binom{n}{k} = 3^n.$$

Proof: We recognize that the left-hand side of this formula is the expansion of $(1+2)^n$ provided by the Binomial Theorem. Therefore, by the Binomial Theorem, we see that

$$(1+2)^n = \sum_{k=0}^{n} \binom{n}{k} 1^{n-k} 2^k = \sum_{k=0}^{n} \binom{n}{k} 2^k.$$

Hence

$$\sum_{k=0}^{n} 2^k \binom{n}{k} = 3^n.$$ ◁

Pascal's Identity and Triangle

The binomial coefficients satisfy many different identities. We introduce one of the most important of these now.

Theorem 2   Pascal's Identity   Let n and k be positive integers with $n \geqslant k$. Then

$$\binom{n+1}{k} = \binom{n}{k-1} + \binom{n}{k}.$$

Proof: Suppose that T is a set containing $n + 1$ elements. Let a be an element in T, and let $S = T - \{a\}$. Note that there are $\binom{n+1}{k}$ subsets of T containing k elements. However, a subset of T with k elements either contains a together with $k - 1$ elements of S, or contains k elements of S and does not contain a. Because there are $\binom{n}{k-1}$ subsets of $k - 1$ elements of S, there are $\binom{n}{k-1}$ subsets of k elements of T that contain a. And there are $\binom{n}{k}$ subsets of k elements of T that do not contain a, because there are $\binom{n}{k}$ subsets of k elements of S. Consequently,

$$\binom{n+1}{k} = \binom{n}{k-1} + \binom{n}{k}.$$ ◁

Remark: A combinatorial proof of Pascal's Identity has been given. It is also possible to prove this identity by algebraic manipulation from the formula for $\binom{n}{r}$ (see Exercise 10 at the end of this section).

Remark: Pascal's Identity, together with the initial conditions $\binom{n}{0} = \binom{n}{n} = 1$ for all integers n, can be used to recursively define binomial coefficients. This recursive definition is useful in the computation of binomial coefficients because only addition, and not multiplication, of integers is needed to use this recursive definition.

Pascal's Identity is the basis for a geometric arrangement of the binomial coefficients in a triangle, as shown in Figure 1.

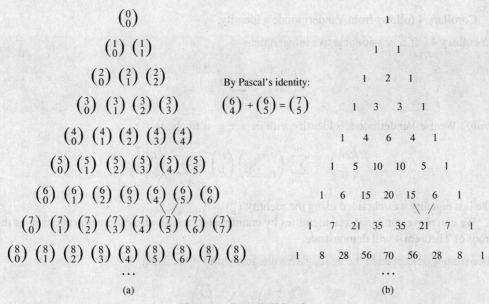

Figure 1 Pascal's Triangle.

The nth row in the triangle consists of the binomial coefficients

$$\binom{n}{k}, \ k = 0, 1, \cdots, n.$$

This triangle is known as **Pascal's triangle.** Pascal's Identity shows that when two adjacent binomial coefficients in this triangle are added, the binomial coefficient in the next row between these two coefficients is produced.

Some Other Identities of the Binomial Coefficients

We conclude this section with combinatorial proofs of two of the many identities enjoyed by the binomial coefficients.

Theorem 3   Vandermonde's Identity   Let m, n, and r be nonnegative integers with r not exceeding either m or n. Then

$$\binom{m+n}{r} = \sum_{k=0}^{r} \binom{m}{r-k}\binom{n}{k}.$$

Remark: This identity was discovered by mathematician Alexandre-Théophile Vandermonde in the eighteenth century.

Proof: Suppose that there are m items in one set and n items in a second set. Then the total number of ways to pick r elements from the union of these sets is $\binom{m+n}{r}$. Another way to pick r elements from the union is to pick k elements from the first set and then $r - k$ elements from the second set, where k is an integer with $0 \leqslant k \leqslant r$. This can be done in $\binom{m}{k}\binom{n}{r-k}$ ways, using the product rule. Hence, the total number of ways to pick r elements from the union also equals

$$\binom{m+n}{r} = \sum_{k=0}^{r} \binom{m}{r-k}\binom{n}{k}.$$

This proves Vandermonde's Identity.   ◁

Corollary 4 follows from Vandermonde's Identity.

Corollary 4   If n is a nonnegative integer, then

$$\binom{2n}{n} = \sum_{k=0}^{n} \binom{n}{k}^2.$$

Proof: We use Vandermonde's Identity with $m = r = n$ to obtain

$$\binom{2n}{n} = \sum_{k=0}^{n} \binom{n}{n-k}\binom{n}{k} = \sum_{k=0}^{n} \binom{n}{k}^2.$$

The last equality was obtained using the identity $\binom{n}{k} = \binom{n}{n-k}$.   ◁

We can prove combinatorial identities by counting bit strings with different properties, as the proof of Theorem 4 will demonstrate.

Theorem 4   Let n and r be nonnegative integers with $r \leqslant n$. Then

$$\binom{n+1}{r+1} = \sum_{j=r}^{n} \binom{j}{r}.$$

Proof: We use a combinatorial proof. By Example 14 in Section 3.3, the left-hand side, $\binom{n+1}{r+1}$, counts the bit strings of length $n+1$ containing $r+1$ ones.

We show that the right-hand side counts the same objects by considering the cases corresponding to the possible locations of the final 1 in a string with $r+1$ ones. This final one must occur at position $r+1, r+2, \cdots$, or $n+1$. Furthermore, if the last one is the kth bit there must be r ones among the first $k-1$ positions. Consequently, by Example 14 in Section 3.3, there are $\binom{k-1}{r}$ such bit strings. Summing over k with $r+1 \leqslant k \leqslant n+1$, we find that there are

$$\sum_{k=r+1}^{n+1} \binom{k-1}{r} = \sum_{j=r}^{n} \binom{j}{r}$$

bit strings of length n containing exactly $r+1$ ones. (Note that the last step follows from the change of variables $j = k-1$.) Because the left-hand side and the right-hand side count the same objects, they are equal. This completes the proof.   ◁

Exercises

1. Find the expansion of $(x+y)^4$
   a) using combinatorial reasoning, as in Example 1.   b) using the Binomial Theorem.

2. Find the expansion of $(x+y)^6$.

3. How many terms are there in the expansion of $(x+y)^{100}$ after like terms are collected?

4. What is the coefficient of x^9 in $(2-x)^{19}$?

5. What is the coefficient of $x^{101}y^{99}$ in the expansion of $(2x - 3y)^{200}$?

*6. Give a formula for the coefficient of x^k in the expansion of $(x^2 - 1/x)^{100}$, where k is an integer.

7. What is the row of Pascal's triangle containing the binomial coefficients $\binom{9}{k}, 0 \leqslant k \leqslant 9$?

8. Show that $\binom{n}{k} \leqslant 2^n$ for all positive integers n and all integers k with $0 \leqslant k \leqslant n$.

9. Show that if n and k are integers with $1 \leqslant k \leqslant n$, then $\binom{n}{k} \leqslant n^k/2^{k-1}$.

10. Prove Pascal's Identity, using the formula for $\binom{n}{r}$.

11. Prove that if n and k are integers with $1 \leqslant k \leqslant n$, then $k\binom{n}{k} = n\binom{n-1}{k-1}$

    a) using a combinatorial proof. [*Hint:* Show that the two sides of the identity count the number of ways to select a subset with k elements from a set with n elements and then an element of this subset.]

    b) using an algebraic proof based on the formula for $\binom{n}{r}$ given in Theorem 2 in Section 3.3.

12. Show that if n and k are positive integers, then

$$\binom{n+1}{k} = (n+1)\binom{n}{k-1} \Big/ k.$$

Use this identity to construct an inductive definition of the binomial coefficients.

13. Let n be a positive integer. Show that $\binom{2n}{n+1} + \binom{2n}{n} = \binom{2n+2}{n+1}/2$.

*14. Prove that

$$\sum_{k=0}^{r} \binom{n+k}{k} = \binom{n+r+1}{r}$$

whenever n and r are positive integers,

    a) using a combinatorial argument.   b) using Pascal's identity.

*15. Give a combinatorial proof that $\sum_{k=1}^{n} k\binom{n}{k} = n2^{n-1}$. [*Hint:* Count in two ways the number of ways to select a committee and to then select a leader of the committee.]

16. Show that a nonempty set has the same number of subsets with an odd number of elements as it does subsets with an even number of elements.

17. In this exercise we will count the number of paths in the xy plane between the origin $(0, 0)$ and point (m, n) such that each path is made up of a series of steps, where each step is a move one unit to the right or a move one unit upward. (No moves to the left or downward are allowed.) Two such paths from $(0, 0)$ to $(5, 3)$ are illustrated here.

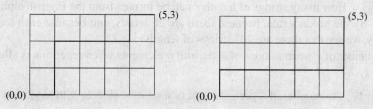

    a) Show that each path of the type described can be represented by a bit string consisting of m 0s and n 1s, where a 0 represents a move one unit to the right and a 1 represents a move one unit upward.

    b) Conclude from part (a) that there are $\binom{m+n}{n}$ paths of the desired type.

18. Use Exercise 17 to prove Theorem 4. [*Hint:* Count the number of paths with n steps of the type described in Exercise 17. Every such path must end at one of the points $(n-k, k)$ for $k = 0, 1, 2, \cdots, n$.]

19. Prove the identity in Exercise 14 using Exercise 17. [*Hint:* First, note that the number of paths from $(0, 0)$ to $(n + 1, r)$ equals $\binom{n+1+r}{r}$. Second, count the number of paths by summing the number of these paths that start by going k units upward for $k = 0, 1, 2, \cdots, r$.]

*20. Determine a formula involving binomial coefficients for the nth term of a sequence if its initial terms are those listed. [*Hint:* Looking at Pascal's triangle will be helpful. Although infinitely many sequences start with a specified set of terms, each of the following lists is the start of a sequence of the type desired.]

    a) 1, 3, 6, 10, 15, 21, 28, 36, 45, 55, 66, $\cdots$ b) 1, 4, 10, 20, 35, 56, 84, 120, 165, 220, $\cdots$

    c) 1, 2, 6, 20, 70, 252, 924, 3432, 12870, 48620, $\cdots$ d) 1, 1, 2, 3, 6, 10, 20, 35, 70, 126, $\cdots$

    e) 1, 1, 1, 3, 1, 5, 15, 35, 1, 9, $\cdots$ f) 1, 3, 15, 84, 495, 3003, 18564, 116280, 735471, 4686825, $\cdots$

3.5   Generalized Permutations and Combinations

Introduction

In many counting problems, elements may be used repeatedly. For instance, a letter or digit may be used more than once on a license plate. When a dozen donuts are selected, each variety can be chosen repeatedly. This contrasts with the counting problems discussed earlier in the chapter where we considered only permutations and combinations in which each item could be used at most once. In this section we will show how to solve counting problems where elements may be used more than once.

Also, some counting problems involve indistinguishable elements. For instance, to count the number of ways the letters of the word *SUCCESS* can be rearranged, the placement of identical letters must be considered. This contrasts with the counting problems discussed earlier where all elements were considered distinguishable. In this section we will describe how to solve counting problems in which some elements are indistinguishable.

Moreover, in this section we will explain how to solve another important class of counting problems, problems involving counting the ways to place distinguishable elements in boxes. An example of this type of problem is the number of different ways poker hands can be dealt to four players.

Taken together, the methods described earlier in this chapter and the methods introduced in this section form a useful toolbox for solving a wide range of counting problems. When the additional methods discussed in Chapter 7 are added to this arsenal, you will be able to solve a large percentage of the counting problems that arise in a wide range of areas of study.

Permutations with Repetition

Counting permutations when repetition of elements is allowed can easily be done using the product rule, as Example 1 shows.

Example 1   How many strings of length r can be formed from the English alphabet?

Solution: By the product rule, because there are 26 letters, and because each letter can be used repeatedly, we see that there are 26^r strings of length r.   ◄

The number of r-permutations of a set with n elements when repetition is allowed is given in Theorem 1.

Theorem 1   The number of r-permutations of a set of n objects with repetition allowed is n^r.

Proof: There are n ways to select an element of the set for each of the r positions in the r-permutation when repetition is allowed, because for each choice all n objects are available. Hence, by the product rule there are n^r r-permutations when repetition is allowed.   ◁

Combinations with Repetition

Consider these examples of combinations with repetition of elements allowed.

Example 2   How many ways are there to select four pieces of fruit from a bowl containing apples, oranges, and pears if the order in which the pieces are selected does not matter, only the type of fruit and not the individual piece matters, and there are at least four pieces of each type of fruit in the bowl?

Solution: To solve this problem we list all the ways possible to select the fruit. There are 15 ways:

4 apples	4 oranges	4 pears
3 apples, 1 orange	3 apples, 1 pear	3 oranges, 1 apple
3 oranges, 1 pear	3 pears, 1 apple	3 pears, 1 orange
2 apples, 2 oranges	2 apples, 2 pears	2 oranges, 2 pears
2 apples, 1 orange, 1 pear	2 oranges, 1 apple, 1 pear	2 pears, 1 apple, 1 orange

The solution is the number of 4-combinations with repetition allowed from a three-element set, {*apple*, *orange*, *pear*}.   ◄

To solve more complex counting problems of this type, we need a general method for counting the r-combinations of an n-element set. In Example 3 we will illustrate such a method.

Example 3   How many ways are there to select five bills from a cash box containing $1 bills, $2 bills, $5 bills, $10 bills, $20 bills, $50 bills, and $100 bills? Assume that the order in which the bills are chosen does not matter, that the bills of each denomination are indistinguishable, and that there are at least five bills of each type.

Solution: Because the order in which the bills are selected does not matter and seven different types of bills can be selected as many as five times, this problem involves counting 5-combinations with repetition allowed from a set with seven elements. Listing all possibilities would be tedious, because there are a large number of solutions. Instead, we will illustrate the use of a technique for counting combinations with repetition allowed.

Suppose that a cash box has seven compartments, one to hold each type of bill, as illustrated in Figure 1. These compartments are separated by six dividers, as shown in the picture. The choice of five bills corresponds to placing five markers in the compartments holding different types of bills. Figure 2 illustrates this correspondence for three different ways to select five bills, where the six dividers are represented by bars and the five bills by stars.

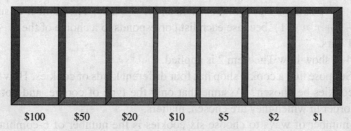

$100 $50 $20 $10 $5 $2 $1

Figure 1   Cash Box with Seven Types of Bills.

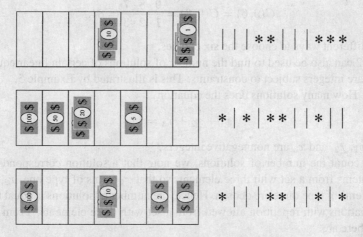

Figure 2   Examples of Ways to Select Five Bills.

The number of ways to select five bills corresponds to the number of ways to arrange six bars and five stars. Consequently, the number of ways to select the five bills is the number of ways to select the positions of the five stars, from 11 possible positions. This corresponds to the number of unordered selections of 5 objects from a set of 11 objects, which can be done in $C(11, 5)$ ways. Consequently, there are

$$C(11,5) = \frac{11!}{5!\,6!} = 462$$

ways to choose five bills from the cash box with seven types of bills.   ◀

Theorem 2 generalizes this discussion.

Theorem 2   There are $C(n+r-1,r) = C(n+r-1,n-1)$ r-combinations from a set with n elements when repetition of elements is allowed.

Proof: Each r-combination of a set with n elements when repetition is allowed can be represented by a list of $n-1$ bars and r stars. The $n-1$ bars are used to mark off n different cells, with the ith cell containing a star for each time the ith element of the set occurs in the combination. For instance, a 6-combination of a set with four elements is represented with three bars and six stars. Here

$$** \mid * \mid \mid ***$$

represents the combination containing exactly two of the first element, one of the second element, none of the third element, and three of the fourth element of the set.

As we have seen, each different list containing $n-1$ bars and r stars corresponds to an r-combination of the set with n elements, when repetition is allowed. The number of such lists is $C(n-1+r,r)$, because each list corresponds to a choice of the r positions to place the r stars from the $n-1+r$ positions that contain r stars and $n-1$ bars. The number of such lists is also equal to $C(n-1+r,n-1)$, because each list corresponds to a choice of the $n-1$ positions to place the $n-1$ bars.   ◁

Examples 4–6 show how Theorem 2 is applied.

Example 4   Suppose that a cookie shop has four different kinds of cookies. How many different ways can six cookies be chosen? Assume that only the type of cookie, and not the individual cookies or the order in which they are chosen, matters.

Solution: The number of ways to choose six cookies is the number of 6-combinations of a set with four elements. From Theorem 2 this equals $C(4+6-1,6) = C(9,6)$. Because

$$C(9,6) = C(9,3) = \frac{9 \cdot 8 \cdot 7}{1 \cdot 2 \cdot 3} = 84,$$

there are 84 different ways to choose the six cookies.   ◀

Theorem 2 can also be used to find the number of solutions of certain linear equations where the variables are integers subject to constraints. This is illustrated by Example 5.

Example 5   How many solutions does the equation

$$x_1 + x_2 + x_3 = 11$$

have, where x_1, x_2, and x_3 are nonnegative integers?

Solution: To count the number of solutions, we note that a solution corresponds to a way of selecting 11 items from a set with three elements so that x_1 items of type one, x_2 items of type two, and x_3 items of type three are chosen. Hence, the number of solutions is equal to the number of 11-combinations with repetition allowed from a set with three elements. From Theorem 2 it follows that there are

$$C(3+11-1,11) = C(13,11) = C(13,2) = \frac{13 \cdot 12}{1 \cdot 2} = 78$$

solutions.

The number of solutions of this equation can also be found when the variables are subject to constraints. For instance, we can find the number of solutions where the variables are integers with $x_1 \geqslant 1$, $x_2 \geqslant 2$, and $x_3 \geqslant 3$. A solution to the equation subject to these constraints corresponds to a selection of 11 items with x_1 items of type one, x_2 items of type two, and x_3 items of type three, where, in addition, there is at least one item of type one, two items of type two, and three items of type three. So, choose one item of type one, two of type two, and three of type three. Then select five additional items. By Theorem 2 this can be done in

$$C(3 + 5 - 1, 5) = C(7, 5) = C(7, 2) = \frac{7 \cdot 6}{1 \cdot 2} = 21$$

ways. Thus, there are 21 solutions of the equation subject to the given constraints.   ◀

Example 6 shows how counting the number of combinations with repetition allowed arises in determining the value of a variable that is incremented each time a certain type of nested loop is traversed.

Example 6   What is the value of k after the following pseudocode has been executed?

```
k := 0
for i₁ := 1 to n
    for i₂ := 1 to i₁
        .
        .
        .
        for iₘ := 1 to iₘ₋₁
            k := k + 1
```

Solution: Note that the initial value of k is 0 and that 1 is added to k each time the nested loop is traversed with a sequence of integers $i_1, i_2, \cdots, i_m$ such that

$$1 \leqslant i_m \leqslant i_{m-1} \leqslant \cdots \leqslant i_1 \leqslant n.$$

The number of such sequences of integers is the number of ways to choose m integers from $\{1, 2, \cdots, n\}$, with repetition allowed. (To see this, note that once such a sequence has been selected, if we order the integers in the sequence in nondecreasing order, this uniquely defines an assignment of $i_m, i_{m-1}, \cdots, i_1$. Conversely, every such assignment corresponds to a unique unordered set.) Hence, from Theorem 2, it follows that $k = C(n + m - 1, m)$ after this code has been executed.   ◀

The formulae for the numbers of ordered and unordered selections of r elements, chosen with and without repetition allowed from a set with n elements, are shown in Table 1.

Permutations with Indistinguishable Objects

Some elements may be indistinguishable in counting problems. When this is the case, care must be taken to avoid counting things more than once. Consider Example 7.

TABLE 1 Combinations and Permutations with and without Repetition.		
Type	*Repetition Allowed?*	*Formula*
r-permutations	No	$\dfrac{n!}{(n-r)!}$
r-combinations	No	$\dfrac{n!}{r!\,(n-r)!}$
r-permutations	Yes	n^r
r-combinations	Yes	$\dfrac{(n+r-1)!}{r!\,(n-1)!}$

Example 7   How many different strings can be made by reordering the letters of the word *SUCCESS?*

Solution: Because some of the letters of *SUCCESS* are the same, the answer is *not* given by the number of permutations of seven letters. This word contains three Ss, two Cs, one U, and one E. To determine the number of different strings that can be made by reordering the letters, first note that the three Ss can be placed among the seven positions in $C(7, 3)$ different ways, leaving four positions free. Then the two Cs can be placed in $C(4, 2)$ ways, leaving two free positions. The U can be placed in $C(2, 1)$ ways, leaving just one position free. Hence E can be placed in $C(1, 1)$ way. Consequently, from the product rule, the number of different strings that can be made is

$$C(7, 3)C(4, 2)C(2, 1)C(1, 1) = \frac{7!}{3!\,4!} \cdot \frac{4!}{2!\,2!} \cdot \frac{2!}{1!\,1!} \cdot \frac{1!}{1!\,0!}$$

$$= \frac{7!}{3!\,2!\,1!\,1!}$$

$$= 420. \qquad \blacktriangleleft$$

We can prove Theorem 3 using the same sort of reasoning as in Example 7.

Theorem 3   The number of different permutations of n objects, where there are n_1 indistinguishable objects of type 1, n_2 indistinguishable objects of type 2, $\cdots$, and n_k indistinguishable objects of type k, is

$$\frac{n!}{n_1!\,n_2! \cdots n_k!}.$$

Proof: To determine the number of permutations, first note that the n_1 objects of type one can be placed among the n positions in $C(n, n_1)$ ways, leaving $n - n_1$ positions free. Then the objects of type two can be placed in $C(n - n_1, n_2)$ ways, leaving $n - n_1 - n_2$ positions free. Continue placing the objects of type three, $\cdots$, type $k - 1$, until at the last stage, n_k objects of type k can be placed in $C(n - n_1 - n_2 - \cdots - n_{k-1}, n_k)$ ways. Hence, by the product rule, the total number of different permutations is

$$C(n, n_1)C(n - n_1, n_2) \cdots C(n - n_1 - \cdots - n_{k-1}, n_k)$$

$$= \frac{n!}{n_1!\,(n - n_1)!} \frac{(n - n_1)!}{n_2!\,(n - n_1 - n_2)!} \cdots \frac{(n - n_1 - \cdots - n_{k-1})!}{n_k!\,0!}$$

$$= \frac{n!}{n_1!\,n_2! \cdots n_k!}. \qquad \triangleleft$$

Distributing Objects into Boxes

Many counting problems can be solved by enumerating the ways objects can be placed into boxes (where the order these objects are placed into the boxes does not matter). The objects can be either *distinguishable*, that is, different from each other, or *indistinguishable*, that is, considered identical. Distinguishable objects are sometimes said to be *labeled*, whereas indistinguishable objects are said to be *unlabeled*. Similarly, boxes can be *distinguishable*, that is, different, or *indinguishable*, that is, identical. Distinguishable boxes are often said to be *labeled*, while indistinguishable boxes are said to be *unlabeled*. When you solve a counting problem using the model of distributing objects into boxes, you need to determine whether the objects are distinguishable and whether the boxes are distinguishable. Although the context of the counting problem makes these two decisions clear, counting problems are sometimes ambiguous and it may be unclear which model applies. In such a case it is best to state whatever assumptions you are making and explain why the particular model you choose conforms to your assumptions.

We will see that there are closed formulae for counting the ways to distribute objects, distinguishable or indistinguishable, into distinguishable boxes. We are not so lucky when we count the ways to distribute objects, distinguishable or indistinguishable, into indistinguishable boxes; there are no closed formulae to use in these cases.

Distinguishable Objects and Distinguishable Boxes   We first consider the case when distinguishable objects are placed into distinguishable boxes. Consider Example 8 in which the objects are cards and the boxes are hands of players.

Example 8   How many ways are there to distribute hands of 5 cards to each of four players from the standard deck of 52 cards?

Solution: We will use the product rule to solve this problem. To begin, note that the first player can be dealt 5 cards in $C(52,5)$ ways. The second player can be dealt 5 cards in $C(47,5)$ ways, because only 47 cards are left. The third player can be dealt 5 cards in $C(42,5)$ ways. Finally, the fourth player can be dealt 5 cards in $C(37,5)$ ways. Hence, the total number of ways to deal four players 5 cards each is

$$C(52,5)C(47,5)C(42,5)C(37,5) = \frac{52!}{47!\,5!} \cdot \frac{47!}{42!\,5!} \cdot \frac{42!}{37!\,5!} \cdot \frac{37!}{32!\,5!}$$

$$= \frac{52!}{5!\,5!\,5!\,5!\,32!}. \qquad \blacktriangleleft$$

Remark: The solution to Example 8 equals the number of permutations of 52 objects, with 5 indistinguishable objects of each of four different types, and 32 objects of a fifth type. This equality can be seen by defining a one-to-one correspondence between permutations of this type and distributions of cards to the players. To define this correspondence, first order the cards from 1 to 52. Then cards dealt to the first player correspond to the cards in the positions assigned to objects of the first type in the permutation. Similarly, cards dealt to the second, third, and fourth players, respectively, correspond to cards in the positions assigned to objects of the second, third, and fourth type, respectively. The cards not dealt to any player correspond to cards in the positions assigned to objects of the fifth type. The reader should verify that this is a one-to-one correspondence.

Example 8 is a typical problem that involves distributing distinguishable objects into distinguishable boxes. The distinguishable objects are the 52 cards, and the five distinguishable boxes are the hands of the four players and the rest of the deck. Counting problems that involve distributing distinguishable objects into boxes can be solved using Theorem 4.

Theorem 4   The number of ways to distribute n distinguishable objects into k distinguishable boxes so that n_i objects are placed into box i, $i = 1, 2, \cdots, k$, equals

$$\frac{n!}{n_1!\,n_2! \cdots n_k!}.$$

Theorem 4 can be proved using the product rule. We leave the details as Exercise 24. It can also be proved by setting up a one-to-one correspondence between the permutations counted by Theorem 3 and the ways to distribute objects counted by Theorem 4.

Indistinguishable Objects and Distinguishable Boxes   Counting the number of ways of placing n indistinguishable objects into k distinguishable boxes turns out to be the same as counting the number of n-combinations for a set with k elements when reptitions are allowed. The reason behind this is that there is a one-to-one correspondence between n-combinations from a set with k elements when repetition is allowed and the ways to place n indistinguishable balls into k distinguishable boxes. To set up this correspondence, we put a ball in the ith bin each time the ith element of the set is included in the n-combination.

Example 9   How many ways are there to place 10 indistinguishable balls into eight distinguishable bins?

Solution: The number of ways to place 10 indistinguishable balls into eight bins equals the number of 10-combinations from a set with eight elements when repetition is allowed. Consequently, there are

$$C(8 + 10 - 1, 10) = C(17, 10) = \frac{17!}{10!7!} = 19{,}448.$$ ◄

This means that there are $C(n + r - 1, n - 1)$ ways to place r indistinguishable objects into n distinguishable boxes.

Distinguishable Objects and Indistinguishable Boxes   Counting the ways to place n distinguishable objects into k indistinguishable boxes is more difficult than counting the ways to place objects, distinguishable or indistinguishable objects, into distinguishable boxes. We illustrate this with an example.

Example 10   How many ways are there to put four different employees into three indistinguishable offices, when each office can contain any number of employees?

Solution: We will solve this problem by enumerating all the ways these employees can be placed into the offices. We represent the four employees by A, B, C, and D. First, we note that we can distribute employees so that all four are put into one office, three are put into one office and a fourth is put into a second office, two employees are put into one office and two put into a second office, and finally, two are put into one office, and one each put into the other two offices. Each way to distribute these employees to these offices can be represented by a way to partition the elements A, B, C, and D into disjoint subsets.

We can put all four employees into one office in exactly one way, represented by $\{\{A, B, C, D\}\}$. We can put three employees into one office and the fourth employee into a different office in exactly four ways, represented by $\{\{A, B, C\}, \{D\}\}$, $\{\{A, B, D\}, \{C\}\}$, $\{\{A, C, D\}, \{B\}\}$, and $\{\{B, C, D\}, \{A\}\}$. We can put two employees into one office and two into a second office in exactly three ways, represented by $\{\{A, B\}, \{C, D\}\}$, $\{\{A, C\}, \{B, D\}\}$, and $\{\{A, D\}, \{B, C\}\}$. Finally, we can put two employees into one office, and one each into each of the remaining two offices in six ways, represented by $\{\{A, B\}, \{C\}, \{D\}\}$, $\{\{A, C\}, \{B\}, \{D\}\}$, $\{\{A, D\}, \{B\}, \{C\}\}$, $\{\{B, C\}, \{A\}, \{D\}\}$, $\{\{B, D\}, \{A\}, \{C\}\}$, and $\{\{C, D\}, \{A\}, \{B\}\}$.

Counting all the possibilities, we find that there are 14 ways to put four different employees into three indistinguishable offices. Another way to look at this problem is to look at the number of offices into which we put employees. Note that there six ways to put four different employees into three indistinguishable offices so that no office is empty, seven ways to put four different employees into two indistinguishable offices so that no office is empty, and one way to put four employees into one office so that it is not empty. ◄

There is no simple closed formula for the number of ways to distribute n distinguishable objects into j indistinguishable boxes. However, there is a rather complicated formula, which we will now describe; readers can omit the discussion of this formula if desired. Let $S(n, j)$ denote the number of ways to distribute n distinguishable objects into j indistinguishable boxes so that no box is empty. The numbers $S(n, j)$ are called **Stirling numbers of the second kind.** For instance, Example 10 shows that $S(4, 3) = 6$, $S(4, 2) = 7$, and $S(4, 1) = 1$. We see that the number of ways to distribute n distinguishable objects into k indistinguishable boxes (where the number of boxes that are nonempty equals k, $k - 1, \cdots, 2$, or 1) equals $\sum_{j=1}^{k} S(n, j)$. For instance, following the reasoning in Example 10, the number of ways to distribute four distinguishable objects into three indistinguishable boxes equals $S(4, 1) + S(4, 2) + S(4, 3) = 1 + 7 + 6 = 14$. Using the inclusion–exclusion principle (see Section 4.6) it can be shown that

$$S(n, j) = \frac{1}{j!} \sum_{i=0}^{j-1} (-1)^i \binom{j}{i} (j - i)^n.$$

Consequently, the number of ways to distribute n distinguishable objects into k indistinguishable boxes equals

$$\sum_{j=1}^{k} S(n,j) = \sum_{j=1}^{k} \frac{1}{j!} \sum_{i=0}^{j-1} (-1)^i \binom{j}{i} (j-i)^n.$$

(For more information about Stirling numbers of the second kind, see combinatorics textbooks such as [B607], [Br99], and [RoTe05], and Chapter 6 in [MiRo91].)

Indistinguishable Objects and Indistinguishable Boxes   Some counting problems can be solved by determining the number of ways to distribute indistinguishable objects into indistinguishable boxes. We illustrate this principle with an example.

Example 11   How many ways are there to pack six copies of the same book into four identical boxes, where a box can contain as many as six books?

Solution: We will enumerate all ways to pack the books. For each way to pack the books, we will list the number of books in the box with the largest number of books, followed by the numbers of books in each box containing at least one book, in order of decreasing number of books in a box. The ways we can pack the books are

6,
5, 1
4, 2
4, 1, 1
3, 3
3, 2, 1
3, 1, 1, 1
2, 2, 2
2, 2, 1, 1.

For example, $4, 1, 1$ indicates that one box contains four books, a second box contains a single book, and a third box contains a single book (and the fourth box is empty). Because we have enumerated all ways to pack six books into at most four boxes, we see that there are nine ways to pack them in this way.   ◀

Observe that distributing n indistinguishable objects into k indistinguishable boxes is the same as writing n as the sum of at most k positive integers in nonincreasing order. If $a_1 + a_2 + \cdots + a_j = n$, where $a_1, a_2, \cdots, a_j$ are positive integers with $a_1 \geqslant a_2 \geqslant \cdots \geqslant a_j$, we say that $a_1, a_2, \cdots, a_j$ is a **partition** of the positive integer n into j positive integers. We see that if $p_k(n)$ is the number of partitions of n into at most k positive intetgers, then there are $p_k(n)$ ways to distribute n indistinguishable objects into k indistinguishable boxes. No simple closed formula exists for this number.

Exercises

1. In how many different ways can five elements be selected in order from a set with three elements when repetition is allowed?

2. How many strings of six letters are there?

3. How many ways are there to assign three jobs to five employees if each employee can be given more than one job?

4. How many ways are there to select three unordered elements from a set with five elements when repetition is allowed?

5. A bagel shop has onion bagels, poppy seed bagels, egg bagels, salty bagels, pumpernickel bagels, sesame seed bagels, raisin bagels, and plain bagels. How many ways are there to choose

   a) six bagels?   b) a dozen bagels?   c) two dozen bagels?

d) a dozen bagels with at least one of each kind?

e) a dozen bagels with at least three egg bagels and no more than two salty bagels?

6. How many ways are there to choose eight coins from a piggy bank containing 100 identical pennies and 80 identical nickels?

7. A book publisher has 3000 copies of a discrete mathematics book. How many ways are there to store these books in their three warehouses if the copies of the book are indistinguishable?

8. How many solutions are there to the equation

$$x_1 + x_2 + x_3 + x_4 + x_5 = 21,$$

where x_i, $i = 1, 2, 3, 4, 5$, is a nonnegative integer such that

a) $x_1 \geqslant 1$?   b) $x_i \geqslant 2$ for $i = 1, 2, 3, 4, 5$?

c) $0 \leqslant x_1 \leqslant 10$?   d) $0 \leqslant x_1 \leqslant 3$, $1 \leqslant x_2 < 4$, and $x_3 \geqslant 15$?

9. How many strings of 10 ternary digits (0, 1, or 2) are there that contain exactly two 0s, three 1s, and five 2s?

10. Suppose that a large family has 14 children, including two sets of identical triplets, three sets of identical twins, and two individual children. How many ways are there to seat these children in a row of chairs if the identical triplets or twins cannot be distinguished from one another?

11. How many ways are there to distribute six indistinguishable balls into nine distinguishable bins?

12. How many ways are there to distribute 12 distinguishable objects into six distinguishable boxes so that two objects are placed in each box?

13. How many positive integers less than 1,000,000 have the sum of their digits equal to 19?

14. There are 10 questions on a discrete mathematics final exam. How many ways are there to assign scores to the problems if the sum of the scores is 100 and each question is worth at least 5 points?

15. How many different bit strings can be transmitted if the string must begin with a 1 bit, must include three additional 1 bits (so that a total of four 1 bits is sent), must include a total of 12 0 bits, and must have at least two 0 bits following each 1 bit?

16. How many different strings can be made from the letters in *ABRACADABRA*, using all the letters?

17. How many different strings can be made from the letters in *ORONO*, using some or all of the letters?

18. How many strings with seven or more characters can be formed from the letters in *EVERGREEN*?

19. A student has three mangos, two papayas, and two kiwi fruits. If the student eats one piece of fruit each day, and only the type of fruit matters, in how many different ways can these fruits be consumed?

20. How many ways are there to travel in *xyz* space from the origin $(0, 0, 0)$ to the point $(4, 3, 5)$ by taking steps one unit in the positive x direction, one unit in the positive y direction, or one unit in the positive z direction? (Moving in the negative x, y, or z direction is prohibited, so that no backtracking is allowed.)

21. How many ways are there to deal hands of seven cards to each of five players from a standard deck of 52 cards?

22. How many ways are there to deal hands of five cards to each of six players from a deck containing 48 different cards?

23. How many ways can n books be placed on k distinguishable shelves

a) if the books are indistinguishable copies of the same title?

b) if no two books are the same, and the positions of the books on the shelves matter?

*24. Use the product rule to prove Theorem 4, by first placing objects in the first box, then placing objects in the second box, and so on.

*25. In this exercise we will prove Theorem 2 by setting up a one-to-one correspondence between the set of r-combinations with repetition allowed of $S = \{1, 2, 3, \cdots, n\}$ and the set of r-combinations of the set $T = \{1, 2, 3, \cdots, n + r - 1\}$.

a) Arrange the elements in an r-combination, with repetition allowed, of S into an increasing sequence $x_1 \leqslant x_2 \leqslant \cdots \leqslant x_r$. Show that the sequence formed by adding $k-1$ to the kth term is strictly increasing. Conclude that this sequence is made up of r distinct elements from T.

b) Show that the procedure described in (a) defines a one-to-one correspondence between the set of r-combinations, with repetition allowed, of S and the r-combinations of T. [*Hint:* Show the correspondence can be reversed by associating to the r-combination $\{x_1, x_2, \cdots, x_r\}$ of T, with $1 \leqslant x_1 < x_2 < \cdots < x_r \leqslant n+r-1$, the r-combination with repetition allowed from S, formed by subtracting $k-1$ from the kth element.]

c) Conclude that there are $C(n+r-1, r)$ r-combinations with repetition allowed from a set with n elements.

26. How many ways are there to distribute six distinguishable objects into four indistinguishable boxes so that each of the boxes contains at least one object?

27. How many ways are there to put six temporary employees into four identical offices so that there is at least one temporary employee in each of these four offices?

28. How many ways are there to distribute six indistinguishable objects into four indistinguishable boxes so that each of the boxes contains at least one object?

29. How many ways are there to pack nine identical DVDs into three indistinguishable boxes so that each box contains at least two DVDs?

30. How many ways are there to distribute five balls into three boxes if each box must have at least one ball in it if

a) both the balls and boxes are labeled?   b) the balls are labeled, but the boxes are unlabeled?

c) the balls are unlabeled, but the boxes are labeled?   d) both the balls and boxes are unlabeled?

*31. Suppose that a weapons inspector must inspect each of five different sites twice, visiting one site per day. The inspector is free to select the order in which to visit these sites, but cannot visit site X, the most suspicious site, on two consecutive days. In how many different orders can the inspector visit these sites?

*32. Prove the **Multinomial Theorem:** If n is a positive integer, then

$$(x_1 + x_2 + \cdots + x_m)^n = \sum_{n_1 + n_2 + \cdots + n_m = n} C(n; n_1, n_2, \cdots, n_m) x_1^{n_1} x_2^{n_2} \cdots x_m^{n_m},$$

where

$$C(n; n_1, n_2, \cdots, n_m) = \frac{n!}{n_1! \, n_2! \cdots n_m!}$$

is a **multinomial coefficient.**

33. Find the coefficient of $x^3 y^2 z^5$ in $(x+y+z)^{10}$.

3.6   Generating Permutations and Combinations

Introduction

Methods for counting various types of permutations and combinations were described in the previous sections of this chapter, but sometimes permutations or combinations need to be generated, not just counted. Consider the following three problems. First, suppose that a salesman must visit six different cities. In which order should these cities be visited to minimize total travel time? One way to determine the best order is to determine the travel time for each of the $6! = 720$ different orders in which the cities can be visited and choose the one with the smallest travel time. Second, suppose we are given a set of six positive integers and wish to find a subset of them that has 100 as their sum, if such a subset exists. One way to find these numbers is to generate all $2^6 = 64$ subsets and check the sum of their elements. Third, suppose a laboratory has 95 employees. A group of

12 of these employees with a particular set of 25 skills is needed for a project. (Each employee can have one or more of these skills.) One way to find such a set of employees is to generate all sets of 12 of these employees and check whether they have the desired skills. These examples show that it is often necessary to generate permutations and combinations to solve problems.

Generating Permutations

Any set with n elements can be placed in one-to-one correspondence with the set $\{1, 2, 3, \cdots, n\}$. We can list the permutations of any set of n elements by generating the permutations of the n smallest positive integers and then replacing these integers with the corresponding elements. Many different algorithms have been developed to generate the $n!$ permutations of this set. We will describe one of these that is based on the **lexicographic** (or **dictionary**) **ordering** of the set of permutations of $\{1, 2, 3, \cdots, n\}$. In this ordering, the permutation $a_1 a_2 \cdots a_n$ precedes the permutation of $b_1 b_2 \cdots b_n$, if for some k, with $1 \leqslant k \leqslant n$, $a_1 = b_1$, $a_2 = b_2, \cdots$, $a_{k-1} = b_{k-1}$, and $a_k < b_k$. In other words, a permutation of the set of the n smallest positive integers precedes (in lexicographic order) a second permutation if the number in this permutation in the first position where the two permutations disagree is smaller than the number in that position in the second permutation.

Example 1   The permutation 23415 of the set $\{1, 2, 3, 4, 5\}$ precedes the permutation 23514, because these permutations agree in the first two positions, but the number in the third position in the first permutation, 4, is smaller than the number in the third position in the second permutation, 5. Similarly, the permutation 41532 precedes 52143.   ◄

An algorithm for generating the permutations of $\{1, 2, \cdots, n\}$ can be based on a procedure that constructs the next permutation in lexicographic order following a given permutation $a_1 a_2 \cdots a_n$. We will show how this can be done. First, suppose that $a_{n-1} < a_n$. Interchange a_{n-1} and a_n to obtain a larger permutation. No other permutation is both larger than the original permutation and smaller than the permutation obtained by interchanging a_{n-1} and a_n. For instance, the next larger permutation after 234156 is 234165. On the other hand, if $a_{n-1} > a_n$, then a larger permutation cannot be obtained by interchanging these last two terms in the permutation. Look at the last three integers in the permutation. If $a_{n-2} < a_{n-1}$, then the last three integers in the permutation can be rearranged to obtain the next largest permutation. Put the smaller of the two integers a_{n-1} and a_n that is greater than a_{n-2} in position $n - 2$. Then, place the remaining integer and a_{n-2} into the last two positions in increasing order. For instance, the next larger permutation after 234165 is 234516.

On the other hand, if $a_{n-2} > a_{n-1}$ (and $a_{n-1} > a_n$), then a larger permutation cannot be obtained by permuting the last three terms in the permutation. Based on these observations, a general method can be described for producing the next larger permutation in increasing order following a given permutation $a_1 a_2 \cdots a_n$. First, find the integers a_j and a_{j+1} with $a_j < a_{j+1}$ and

$$a_{j+1} > a_{j+2} > \cdots > a_n,$$

that is, the last pair of adjacent integers in the permutation where the first integer in the pair is smaller than the second. Then, the next larger permutation in lexicographic order is obtained by putting in the jth position the least integer among $a_{j+1}, a_{j+2}, \cdots$, and a_n that is greater than a_j and listing in increasing order the rest of the integers $a_j, a_{j+1}, \cdots, a_n$ in positions $j + 1$ to n. It is easy to see that there is no other permutation larger than the permutation $a_1 a_2 \cdots a_n$ but smaller than the new permutation produced. (The verification of this fact is left as an exercise for the reader.)

Example 2   What is the next permutation in lexicographic order after 362541?
Solution: The last pair of integers a_j and a_{j+1} where $a_j < a_{j+1}$ is $a_3 = 2$ and $a_4 = 5$. The least integer to the right of 2 that is greater than 2 in the permutation is $a_5 = 4$. Hence, 4 is placed in the third position. Then the integers 2, 5, and 1 are placed in order in the last three

positions, giving 125 as the last three positions of the permutation. Hence, the next permutation is
364125.   ◀

   To produce the $n!$ permutations of the integers $1, 2, 3, \cdots, n$, begin with the smallest permutation in lexicographic order, namely, $123 \cdots n$, and successively apply the procedure described
for producing the next larger permutation of $n! - 1$ times. This yields all the permutations of the
n smallest integers in lexicographic order.

Example 3   Generate the permutations of the integers 1, 2, 3 in lexicographic order.
Solution: Begin with 123. The next permutation is obtained by interchanging 3 and 2 to obtain
132. Next, because $3 > 2$ and $1 < 3$, permute the three integers in 132. Put the smaller of 3
and 2 in the first position, and then put 1 and 3 in increasing order in positions 2 and 3 to obtain
213. This is followed by 231, obtained by interchanging 1 and 3, because $1 < 3$. The next larger
permutation has 3 in the first position, followed by 1 and 2 in increasing order, namely, 312.
Finally, interchange 1 and 2 to obtain the last permutation, 321.   ◀

   Algorithm 1 displays the procedure for finding the next permutation in lexicographic order
after a permutation that is not $n\, n-1 n-2 \cdots 21$, which is the largest permutation.

Algorithm 1   Generating the Next Permutation in Lexicographic Order.

procedure *next permutation*$(a_1 a_2 \cdots a_n$: permutation of
        $\{1, 2, \cdots, n\}$ not equal to $n\, n-1 \cdots 2\,1)$
$j := n - 1$
while $a_j > a_{j+1}$
    $j := j - 1$
$\{j$ is the largest subscript with $a_j < a_{j+1}\}$
$k := n$
while $a_j > a_k$
    $k := k - 1$
$\{a_k$ is the smallest integer greater than a_j to the right of $a_j\}$
interchange a_j and a_k
$r := n$
$s := j + 1$
while $r > s$
begin
    interchange a_r and a_s
    $r := r - 1$
    $s := s + 1$
end
$\{$this puts the tail end of the permutation after the jth position in increasing order$\}$

Generating Combinations

How can we generate all the combinations of the elements of a finite set? Because a combination
is just a subset, we can use the correspondence between subsets of $\{a_1, a_2, \cdots, a_n\}$ and bit strings
of length n.

   Recall that the bit string corresponding to a subset has a 1 in position k if a_k is in the subset,
and has a 0 in this position if a_k is not in the subset. If all the bit strings of length n can be listed,
then by the correspondence between subsets and bit strings, a list of all the subsets is obtained.

   Recall that a bit string of length n is also the binary expansion of an integer between 0 and
$2^n - 1$. The 2^n bit strings can be listed in order of their increasing size as integers in their binary
expansions. To produce all binary expansions of length n, start with the bit string $000 \cdots 00$, with

n zeros. Then, successively find the next expansion until the bit string $111 \cdots 11$ is obtained. At each stage the next binary expansion is found by locating the first position from the right that is not a 1, then changing all the 1s to the right of this position to 0s and making this first 0 (from the right) a 1.

Example 4   Find the next bit string after 10 0010 0111.

Solution: The first bit from the right that is not a 1 is the fourth bit from the right. Change this bit to a 1 and change all the following bits to 0s. This produces the next larger bit string, 10 0010 1000.   ◀

The procedure for producing the next larger bit string after $b_{n-1}b_{n-2}\cdots b_1 b_0$ is given as Algorithm 2.

Algorithm 2   Generating the Next Larger Bit String.

procedure *next bit string* $(b_{n-1}\, b_{n-2}\cdots b_1 b_0$: bit string not equal to$11\cdots 11)$
$i := 0$
while $b_i = 1$
begin
    $b_i := 0$
    $i := i + 1$
end
$b_i := 1$

Next, an algorithm for generating the r-combinations of the set $\{1, 2, 3, \cdots, n\}$ will be given. An r-combination can be represented by a sequence containing the elements in the subset in increasing order. The r-combinations can be listed using lexicographic order on these sequences. The next combinations after $a_1 a_2 \cdots a_r$ can be obtained in the following way: First, locate the last element a_i in the sequence such that $a_i \neq n - r + i$. Then, replace a_i with $a_i + 1$ and a_j with $a_i + j - i + 1$, for $j = i + 1, i + 2, \cdots, r$. It is left for the reader to show that this produces the next larger combination in lexicographic order. This procedure is illustrated with Example 5.

Example 5   Find the next larger 4-combination of the set $\{1, 2, 3, 4, 5, 6\}$ after $\{1, 2, 5, 6\}$.

Solution: The last term among the terms a_i with $a_1 = 1$, $a_2 = 2$, $a_3 = 5$, and $a_4 = 6$ such that $a_i \neq 6 - 4 + i$ is $a_2 = 2$. To obtain the next larger 4-combination, increment a_2 by 1 to obtain $a_2 = 3$. Then set $a_3 = 3 + 1 = 4$ and $a_4 = 3 + 2 = 5$. Hence the next larger 4-combination is $\{1, 3, 4, 5\}$.   ◀

Algorithm 3 displays pseudocode for this procedure.

Algorithm 3   Generating the Next r-Combination in Lexicographic Order.

procedure *next r-combination*$(\{a_1, a_2, \cdots, a_r\}$: proper subset of
        $\{1, 2, \cdots, n\}$ not equal to $\{n - r + 1, \cdots, n\}$ with
        $a_1 < a_2 < \cdots < a_r)$
$i := r$
while $a_i = n - r + i$
    $i := i - 1$
$a_i := a_i + 1$
for $j := i + 1$ **to** r
    $a_j := a_i + j - i$

Exercises

1. Place these permutations of $\{1, 2, 3, 4, 5\}$ in lexicographic order: 43521, 15432, 45321, 23451, 23514, 14532, 21345, 45213, 31452, 31542.

2. Find the next larger permutation in lexicographic order after each of these permutations.
   a) 1432   b) 54123   c) 12453   d) 45231   e) 6714235   f) 31528764

3. Use Algorithm 1 to generate the 24 permutations of the first four positive integers in lexicographic order.

4. Use Algorithm 3 to list all the 3-combinations of $\{1, 2, 3, 4, 5\}$.

5. Show that Algorithm 3 produces the next larger r-combination in lexicographic order after a given r-combination.

6. List all 3-permutations of $\{1, 2, 3, 4, 5\}$.

   The remaining exercises in this section develop another algorithm for generating the permutations of $\{1, 2, 3, \cdots, n\}$. This algorithm is based on Cantor expansions of integers. Every nonnegative integer less than $n!$ has a unique Cantor expansion

   $$a_1 1! + a_2 2! + \cdots + a_{n-1}(n - 1)!$$

   where a_i is a nonnegative integer not exceeding i, for $i = 1, 2, \cdots, n - 1$. The integers $a_1, a_2, \cdots, a_{n-1}$ are called the **Cantor digits** of this integer.

   Given a permutation of $\{1, 2, \cdots, n\}$, let $a_{k-1}, k = 2, 3, \cdots, n$, be the number of integers less than k that follow k in the permutation. For instance, in the permutation 43215, a_1 is the number of integers less than 2 that follow 2, so $a_1 = 1$. Similarly, for this example $a_2 = 2, a_3 = 3$, and $a_4 = 0$. Consider the function from the set of permutations $\{1, 2, 3, \cdots, n\}$ to the set of nonnegative integers less than $n!$ that sends a permutation to the integer that has $a_1, a_2, \cdots, a_{n-1}$, defined in this way, as its Cantor digits.

*7. Show that the correspondence described here is a bijection between the set of permutations of $\{1, 2, 3, \cdots, n\}$ and the nonnegative integers less than $n!$.

Key Terms and Results

TERMS

combinatorics: the study of arrangements of objects
enumeration: the counting of arrangements of objects
tree diagram: a diagram made up of a root, branches leaving the root, and other branches leaving some of the endpoints of branches
permutation: an ordered arrangement of the elements of a set
r-permutation: an ordered arrangement of r elements of a set
$P(n, r)$: the number of r-permutations of a set with n elements
r-combination: an unordered selection of r elements of a set
$C(n, r)$: the number of r-combinations of a set with n elements
$\binom{n}{r}$ (binomial coefficient): also the number of r-combinations of a set with n elements
combinatorial proof of an identity: a proof that uses counting arguments to prove that both sides of an identity count the same objects but in different ways
Pascal's triangle: a representation of the binomial coefficients where the ith row of the triangle contains $\binom{i}{j}$ for $j = 0, 1, 2, \cdots, i$

RESULTS

the product rule: a basic counting technique, which states that the number of ways to do a procedure that consists of two subtasks is the product of the number of ways to do the first task and the number of ways to do the second task after the first task has been done

the sum rule: a basic counting technique, which states that the number of ways to do a task in one of two ways is the sum of the number of ways to do these tasks if they cannot be done simultaneously

the pigeonhole principle: When more than k objects are placed in k boxes, there must be a box containing more than one object.

the generalized pigeonhole principle: When N objects are placed in k boxes, there must be a box containing at least $\lceil N/k \rceil$ objects.

$$P(n,r) = \frac{n!}{(n-r)!}$$

$$C(n,r) = \binom{n}{r} = \frac{n!}{r!(n-r)!}$$

Pascal's Identity: $\binom{n+1}{k} = \binom{n}{k-1} + \binom{n}{k}$

the Binomial Theorem: $(x+y)^n = \sum_{k=0}^{n} \binom{n}{k} x^{n-k} y^k$

There are n^r r-permutations of a set with n elements when repetition is allowed.

There are $C(n+r-1,r)$ r-combinations of a set with n elements when repetition is allowed.

There are $n!/(n_1! n_2! \cdots n_k!)$ permutations of n objects where there are n_i indistinguishable objects of type i for $i = 1, 2, 3, \cdots, k$.

The algorithm for generating the permutations of the set $\{1, 2, \cdots, n\}$.

Review Questions

1. Explain how the sum and product rules can be used to find the number of bit strings with a length not exceeding 10.

2. Explain how to find the number of bit strings of length not exceeding 10 that have at least one 0 bit.

3. a) How can the product rule be used to find the number of functions from a set with m elements to a set with n elements?

   b) How many functions are there from a set with five elements to a set with 10 elements?

   c) How can the product rule be used to find the number of one-to-one functions from a set with m elements to a set with n elements?

   d) How many one-to-one functions are there from a set with five elements to a set with 10 elements?

   e) How many onto functions are there from a set with five elements to a set with 10 elements?

4. How can you find the number of possible outcomes of a playoff between two teams where the first team that wins four games wins the playoff?

5. How can you find the number of bit strings of length ten that either begin with 101 or end with 010?

6. a) State the pigeonhole principle.

   b) Explain how the pigeonhole principle can be used to show that among any 11 integers, at least two must have the same last digit.

7. a) State the generalized pigeonhole principle.

   b) Explain how the generalized pigeonhole principle can be used to show that among any 91 integers, there are at least ten that end with the same digit.

8. a) What is the difference between an r-combination and an r-permutation of a set with n elements?

   b) Derive an equation that relates the number of r-combinations and the number of r-permutations of a set with n elements.

c) How many ways are there to select six students from a class of 25 to serve on a committee?

d) How many ways are there to select six students from a class of 25 to hold six different executive positions on a committee?

9. a) What is Pascal's triangle?

b) How can a row of Pascal's triangle be produced from the one above it?

10. What is meant by a combinatorial proof of an identity? How is such a proof different from an algebraic one?

11. Explain how to prove Pascal's Identity using a combinatorial argument.

12. a) State the Binomial Theorem.

b) Explain how to prove the Binomial Theorem using a combinatorial argument.

c) Find the coefficient of $x^{100}y^{101}$ in the expansion of $(2x + 5y)^{201}$.

13. a) Explain how to find a formula for the number of ways to select r objects from n objects when repetition is allowed and order does not matter.

b) How many ways are there to select a dozen objects from among objects of five different types if objects of the same type are indistinguishable?

c) How many ways are there to select a dozen objects from these five different types if there must be at least three objects of the first type?

d) How many ways are there to select a dozen objects from these five different types if there cannot be more than four objects of the first type?

e) How many ways are there to select a dozen objects from these five different types if there must be at least two objects of the first type but no more than three objects of the second type?

14. a) Let n and r be positive integers. Explain why the number of solutions of the equation $x_1 + x_2 + \cdots + x_n = r$, where x_i is a nonnegative integer for $i = 1, 2, 3, \cdots, n$, equals the number of r-combinations of a set with n elements.

b) How many solutions in nonnegative integers are there to the equation $x_1 + x_2 + x_3 + x_4 = 17$?

c) How many solutions in positive integers are there to the equation in part (b)?

15. a) Derive a formula for the number of permutations of n objects of k different types, where there are n_1 indistinguishable objects of type one, n_2 indistinguishable objects of type two, $\cdots$, and n_k indistinguishable objects of type k.

b) How many ways are there to order the letters of the word *INDISCREETNESS*?

16. Describe an algorithm for generating all the permutations of the set of the n smallest positive integers.

17. a) How many ways are there to deal hands of five cards to six players from a standard 52-card deck?

b) How many ways are there to distribute n distinguishable objects into k distinguishable boxes so that n_i objects are placed in box i?

18. Describe an algorithm for generating all the combinations of the set of the n smallest positive integers.

Supplementary Exercises

1. How many ways are there to choose 6 items from 10 distinct items when

a) the items in the choices are ordered and repetition is not allowed?

b) the items in the choices are ordered and repetition is allowed?

c) the items in the choices are unordered and repetition is not allowed?

d) the items in the choices are unordered and repetition is allowed?

2. How many ways are there to choose 10 items from 6 distinct items when

a) the items in the choices are ordered and repetition is not allowed?

b) the items in the choices are ordered and repetition is allowed?

c) the items in the choices are unordered and repetition is not allowed?

d) the items in the choices are unordered and repetition is allowed?

3. A test contains 100 true/false questions. How many different ways can a student answer the questions on the test, if answers may be left blank?

4. How many bit strings of length 10 either start with 000 or end with 1111?

5. How many bit strings of length 10 over the alphabet $\{a, b, c\}$ have either exactly three as or exactly four bs?

6. The internal telephone numbers in the phone system on a campus consist of five digits, with the first digit not equal to zero. How many different numbers can be assigned in this system?

7. An ice cream parlor has 28 different flavors, 8 different kinds of sauce, and 12 toppings.

   a) In how many different ways can a dish of three scoops of ice cream be made where each flavor can be used more than once and the order of the scoops does not matter?

   b) How many different kinds of small sundaes are there if a small sundae contains one scoop of ice cream, a sauce, and a topping?

   c) How many different kinds of large sundaes are there if a large sundae contains three scoops of ice cream, where each flavor can be used more than once and the order of the scoops does not matter; two kinds of sauce, where each sauce can be used only once and the order of the sauces does not matter; and three toppings, where each topping can be used only once and the order of the toppings does not matter?

8. How many positive integers less than 1000

   a) have exactly three decimal digits?   b) have an odd number of decimal digits?

   c) have at least one decimal digit equal to 9?   d) have no odd decimal digits?

   e) have two consecutive decimal digits equal to 5?

   f) are palindromes (that is, read the same forward and backward)?

9. When the numbers from 1 to 1000 are written out in decimal notation, how many of each of these digits are used?

   a) 0   b) 1   c) 2   d) 9

10. There are 12 signs of the zodiac. How many people are needed to guarantee that at least six of these people have the same sign?

11. A fortune cookie company makes 213 different fortunes. A student eats at a restaurant that uses fortunes from this company. What is the largest possible number of times that the student can eat at the restaurant without getting the same fortune four times?

12. How many people are needed to guarantee that at least two were born on the same day of the week and in the same month (perhaps in different years)?

13. Show that given any set of 10 positive integers not exceeding 50 there exist at least two different five-element subsets of this set that have the same sum.

14. A package of baseball cards contains 20 cards. How many packages must be purchased to ensure that two cards in these packages are identical if there are a total of 550 different cards?

15. a) How many cards must be chosen from a deck to guarantee that at least two aces are chosen?

   b) How many cards must be chosen from a deck to guarantee that at least two aces and two kinds are chosen?

   c) How many cards must be chosen from a deck to guarantee that there are at least two cards of the same kind?

   d) How many cards must be chosen from a deck to guarantee that there are at least two cards of two different kinds?

*16. Show that in any set of $n + 1$ positive integers not exceeding $2n$ there must be two that are relatively prime.

*17. Show that in a sequence of m integers there exists one or more consecutive terms with a sum divisible by m.

18. Show that if five points are picked in the interior of a square with a side length of 2, then at least two of these points are no farther than $\sqrt{2}$ apart.

19. Show that the decimal expansion of a rational number must repeat itself from some point onward.

20. Once a computer worm infects a personal computer via an infected e-mail message, it sends a copy of itself to 100 e-mail addresses it finds in the electronic message mailbox on this personal computer. What is the maximum number of different computers this one computer can infect in the time it takes for the infected message to be forwarded five times?

21. How many ways are there to choose a dozen donuts from 20 varieties

    a) if there are no two donuts of the same variety?

    b) if all donuts are of the same variety?

    c) if there are no restrictions?

    d) if there are at least two varieties?

    e) if there must be at least six blueberry-filled donuts?

    f) if there can be no more than six blueberry-filled donuts?

22. Find n if
    a) $P(n, 2) = 110$.   b) $P(n, n) = 5040$.   c) $P(n, 4) = 12P(n, 2)$.

23. Find n if
    a) $C(n, 2) = 45$.   b) $C(n, 3) = P(n, 2)$.   c) $C(n, 5) = C(n, 2)$.

24. Show that if n and r are nonnegative integers and $n \geqslant r$, then

$$P(n + 1, r) = P(n, r)(n + 1)/(n + 1 - r).$$

*25. Suppose that S is a set with n elements. How many ordered pairs (A, B) are there such that A and B are subsets of S with $A \subseteq B$? [*Hint:* Show that each element of S belongs to A, $B - A$, or $S - B$.]

26. Give a combinatorial proof of Corollary 2 of Section 3.4 by setting up a correspondence between the subsets of a set with an even number of elements and the subsets of this set with an odd number of elements. [*Hint:* Take an element a in the set. Set up the correspondence by putting a in the subset if it is not already in it and taking it out if it is in the subset.]

27. Let n and r be nonnegative integers with $r < n$. Show that

$$C(n, r - 1) = C(n + 2, r + 1) - 2C(n + 1, r + 1) + C(n, r + 1).$$

28. Prove using mathematical induction that $\sum_{j=2}^{n} C(j, 2) = C(n + 1, 3)$ whenever n is an integer greater than 1.

29. Show that if n is an integer then

$$\sum_{k=0}^{n} 3^k \binom{n}{k} = 4^n.$$

30. In this exercise we will derive a formula for the sum of the squares of the n smallest positive integers. We will count the number of triples (i, j, k) such that i, j, and k are integers such that $0 \leqslant i < k$, $0 \leqslant j < k$, and $1 \leqslant k \leqslant n$ in two ways.

    a) Show that there are k^2 such triples with a fixed k. Conclude that there are $\sum_{k=1}^{n} k^2$ such triples.

    b) Show that the number of such triples with $0 \leqslant i < j < k$ and the number of such triples with $0 \leqslant j < i < k$ both equal $C(n + 1, 3)$.

    c) Show that the number of such triples with $0 \leqslant i = j < k$ equals $C(n + 1, 2)$.

    d) Combining part (a) with parts (b) and (c), conclude that

$$\sum_{k=1}^{n} k^2 = 2C(n + 1, 3) + C(n + 1, 2) = n(n + 1)(2n + 1)/6.$$

*31. How many bit strings of length n, where $n \geqslant 4$, contain exactly two occurrences of 01?

32. Let S be a set. We say that a collection of subsets $A_1, A_2, \cdots , A_n$ each containing d elements, where $d \geqslant 2$, is 2-*colorable* if it is possible to assign to each element of S one of two different colors such that in every subset A_i there are elements that have been assigned each color. Let $m(d)$ be the largest integer such that every collection of fewer than $m(d)$ sets each containing d elements is 2-colorable.

   a) Show that the collection of all subsets with d elements of a set S with $2d - 1$ elements is not 2-colorable.

   b) Show that $m(2) = 3$.

**c) Show that $m(3) = 7$. [*Hint:* Show that the collection $\{1, 3, 5\}$, $\{1, 2, 6\}$, $\{1, 4, 7\}$, $\{2, 3, 4\}$, $\{2, 5, 7\}$, $\{3, 6, 7\}$, $\{4, 5, 6\}$ is not 2-colorable. Then show that all collections of six sets with three elements each are 2-colorable.]

33. A professor writes 20 multiple-choice questions, each with the possible answer a, b, c, or d, for a discrete mathematics test. If the number of questions with a, b, c, and d as their answer is 8, 3, 4, and 5, respectively, how many different answer keys are possible, if the questions can be placed in any order?

34. How many different arrangements are there of eight people seated at a round table, where two arrangements are considered the same if one can be obtained from the other by a rotation?

35. How many ways are there to assign 24 students to five faculty advisors?

36. How many ways are there to choose a dozen apples from a bushel containing 20 indistinguishable Delicious apples, 20 indistinguishable Macintosh apples, and 20 indistinguishable Granny Smith apples, if at least three of each kind must be chosen?

37. How many solutions are there to the equation $x_1 + x_2 + x_3 = 17$, where x_1, x_2, and x_3 are nonnegative integers with

   a) $x_1 > 1$, $x_2 > 2$, and $x_3 > 3$?   b) $x_1 < 6$ and $x_3 > 5$?   c) $x_1 < 4$, $x_2 < 3$, and $x_3 > 5$?

38. a) How many different strings can be made from the word *PEPPERCORN* when all the letters are used?

   b) How many of these strings start and end with the letter P?

   c) In how many of these strings are the three letter Ps consecutive?

39. How many subsets of a set with ten elements

   a) have fewer than five elements?   b) have more than seven elements?

   c) have an odd number of elements?

40. A witness to a hit-and-run accident tells the police that the license plate of the car in the accident, which contains three letters followed by three digits, starts with the letters AS and contains both the digits 1 and 2. How many different license plates can fit this description?

41. How many ways are there to put n identical objects into m distinct containers so that no container is empty?

42. How many ways are there to seat six boys and eight girls in a row of chairs so that no two boys are seated next to each other?

43. How many ways are there to distribute six objects to five boxes if

   a) both the objects and boxes are labeled?   b) the objects are labeled, but the boxes are unlabeled?

   c) the objects are unlabeled, but the boxes are labeled?

   d) both the objects and the boxes are unlabeled?

44. How many ways are there to distribute five objects into six boxes if

   a) both the objects and boxes are labeled?   b) the objects are labeled, but the boxes are unlabeled?

   c) the objects are unlabeled, but the boxes are labeled?

   d) both the objects and the boxes are unlabeled?

45. Devise an algorithm for generating all the r-permutations of a finite set when repetition is allowed.

46. Devise an algorithm for generating all the r-combinations of a finite set when repetition is allowed.

*__47.__ Show that if m and n are integers with $m \geqslant 3$ and $n \geqslant 3$, then $R(m, n) \leqslant R(m, n-1) + R(m-1, n)$.

*__48.__ Show that $R(3, 4) \geqslant 7$ by showing that in a group of six people, where any two people are friends or enemies, there are not necessarily three mutual friends or four mutual enemies.

Computer Projects

Write programs with these input and output.

1. Given a positive integer n and a nonnegative integer not exceeding n, find the number of r-permutations and r-combinations of a set with n elements.

2. Given positive integers n and r, find the number of r-permutations when repetition is allowed and r-combinations when repetition is allowed of a set with n elements.

3. Given a sequence of positive integers, find the longest increasing and the longest decreasing subsequence of the sequence.

*__4.__ Given an equation $x_1 + x_2 + \cdots + x_n = C$, where C is a constant, and $x_1, x_2, \cdots, x_n$ are nonnegative integers, list all the solutions.

5. Given a positive integer n, list all the permutations of the set $\{1, 2, 3, \cdots, n\}$ in lexicographic order.

6. Given a positive integer n and a nonnegative integer r not exceeding n, list all the r-combinations of the set $\{1, 2, 3, \cdots, n\}$ in lexicographic order.

7. Given a positive integer n and a nonnegative integer r not exceeding n, list all the r-permutations of the set $\{1, 2, 3, \cdots, n\}$ in lexicographic order.

8. Given a positive integer n, list all the combinations of the set $\{1, 2, 3, \cdots, n\}$.

9. Given positive integers n and r, list all the r-permutations, with repetition allowed, of the set $\{1, 2, 3, \cdots, n\}$.

10. Given positive integers n and r, list all the r-combinations, with repetition allowed, of the set $\{1, 2, 3, \cdots, n\}$.

Computations and Explorations

Use a computational program or programs you have written to do these exercises.

1. Find the number of possible outcomes in a two-team playoff when the winner is the first team to win 5 out of 9, 6 out of 11, 7 out of 13, and 8 out of 15.

2. Which binomial coefficients are odd? Can you formulate a conjecture based on numerical evidence?

3. Verify that $C(2n, n)$ is divisible by the square of a prime, when $n \neq 1, 2$, or 4, for as many positive integers n as you can. [The theorem that tells that $C(2n, n)$ is divisible by the square of a prime with $n \neq 1, 2$, or 4 was proved in 1996 by Andrew Granville and Olivier Ramaré. Their proof settled a conjecture made in 1980 by by Paul Erdős and Ron Graham.]

4. Find as many odd integers n less than 200 as you can for which $C(n, \lfloor n/2 \rfloor)$ is not divisible by the square of a prime. Formulate a conjecture based on your evidence.

*__5.__ For each integer less than 100 determine whether $C(2n, n)$ is divisible by 3. Can you formulate a conjecture that tells us for which integers n the binomial coefficient $C(2n, n)$ is divisible by 3 based on the digits in the base three expansion of n?

6. Generate all the permutations of a set with eight elements.

7. Generate all the 6-permutations of a set with nine elements.

8. Generate all combinations of a set with eight elements.

9. Generate all 5-combinations with repetition allowed of a set with seven elements.

Writing Projects

Respond to these with essays using outside sources.

1. Describe some of the earliest uses of the pigeonhole principle by Dirichlet and other mathematicians.

2. Discuss ways in which the current telephone numbering plan can be extended to accommodate the rapid demand for more telephone numbers. (See if you can find some of the proposals coming from the telecommunications industry.) For each new numbering plan you discuss, show how to find the number of different telephone numbers it supports.

3. Many combinatorial identities are described in this book. Find some sources of such identities and describe important combinatorial identities besides those already introduced in this book. Give some representative proofs, including combinatorial ones, of some of these identities.

4. Describe the different models used to model the distribution of particles in statistical mechanics, including Maxwell–Boltzmann, Bose–Einstein, and Fermi–Dirac statistics. In each case, describe the counting techniques used in the model.

5. Define the Stirling numbers of the first kind and describe some of their properties and the identities they satisfy.

6. Define the Stirling numbers of the second kind and describe some of their properties and the identities they satisfy.

7. Describe the latest discoveries of values and bounds for Ramsey numbers.

8. Describe additional ways to generate all the permutations of a set with n elements besides those found in Section 3.6. Compare these algorithms and the algorithms described in the text and exercises of Section 3.6 in terms of their computational complexity.

9. Describe at least one way to generate all the partitions of a positive integer n.

Chapter 4
Advanced Counting Techniques

Many counting problems cannot be solved easily using the methods discussed in Chapter 3. One such problem is: How many bit strings of length n do not contain two consecutive zeros? To solve this problem, let a_n be the number of such strings of length n. An argument can be given that shows $a_{n+1} = a_n + a_{n-1}$. This equation, called a recurrence relation, and the initial conditions $a_1 = 2$ and $a_2 = 3$ determine the sequence $\{a_n\}$. Moreover, an explicit formula can be found for a_n from the equation relating the terms of the sequence. As we will see, a similar technique can be used to solve many different types of counting problems.

We will also see that many counting problems can be solved using formal power series, called generating functions, where the coefficients of powers of x represent terms of the sequence we are interested in. Besides solving counting problems, we will also be able to use generating functions to solve recurrence relations and to prove combinatorial identities.

Many other kinds of counting problems cannot be solved using the techniques discussed in Chapter 3, such as: How many ways are there to assign seven jobs to three employees so that each employee is assigned at least one job? How many primes are there less than 1000? Both of these problems can be solved by counting the number of elements in the union of sets. We will develop a technique, called the principle of inclusion–exclusion, that counts the number of elements in a union of sets, and we will show how this principle can be used to solve counting problems.

The techniques studied in this chapter, together with the basic techniques of Chapter 3, can be used to solve many counting problems.

4.1 Recurrence Relations

Introduction

The number of bacteria in a colony doubles every hour. If a colony begins with five bacteria, how many will be present in n hours? To solve this problem, let a_n be the number of bacteria at the end of n hours. Because the number of bacteria doubles every hour, the relationship $a_n = 2a_{n-1}$ holds whenever n is a positive integer. This relationship, together with the initial condition $a_0 = 5$, uniquely determines a_n for all nonnegative integers n. We can find a formula for a_n from this information.

Some of the counting problems that cannot be solved using the techniques discussed in Chapter 3 can be solved by finding relationships, called recurrence relations, between the terms of a sequence, as was done in the problem involving bacteria. We will study a variety of counting problems that can be modeled using recurrence relations. We will develop methods in this section and in Section 4.2 for finding explicit formulae for the terms of sequences that satisfy certain types of recurrence relations.

Recurrence Relations

Recall that a recursive definition of a sequence specifies one or more initial terms and a rule for determining subsequent terms from those that precede them. A rule of the latter sort (whether or not it is part of a recursive definition) is called a **recurrence relation.** Such relations can be used in studying and solving counting problems.

Definition 1   A *recurrence relation* for the sequence $\{a_n\}$ is an equation that expresses a_n in terms of one or more of the previous terms of the sequence, namely, $a_0, a_1, \ldots, a_{n-1}$, for all integers n with $n \geqslant n_0$, where n_0 is a nonnegative integer. A sequence is called a *solution* of a recurrence relation if its terms satisfy the recurrence relation.

There is an important connection between recursion and recurrence relations that we will exploit later in this chapter. A recursive algorithm provides the solution of a problem of size n in terms of the solutions of one or more instances of the same problem of smaller size. Consequently, when we analyze the complexity of a recursive algorithm, we obtain a recurrence relation that expresses the number of operations required to solve a problem of size n in terms of the number of operations required to solve the problem for one or more instances of smaller size.

Example 1   Let $\{a_n\}$ be a sequence that satisfies the recurrence relation $a_n = a_{n-1} - a_{n-2}$ for $n = 2, 3, 4, \ldots$, and suppose that $a_0 = 3$ and $a_1 = 5$. What are a_2 and a_3?

Solution: We see from the recurrence relation that $a_2 = a_1 - a_0 = 5 - 3 = 2$ and $a_3 = a_2 - a_1 = 2 - 5 = -3$. We can find a_4, a_5, and each successive term in a similar way.   ◀

Example 2   Determine whether the sequence $\{a_n\}$, where $a_n = 3n$ for every nonnegative integer n, is a solution of the recurrence relation $a_n = 2a_{n-1} - a_{n-2}$ for $n = 2, 3, 4, \ldots$. Answer the same question where $a_n = 2^n$ and where $a_n = 5$.

Solution: Suppose that $a_n = 3n$ for every nonnegative integer n. Then, for $n \geqslant 2$, we see that $2a_{n-1} - a_{n-2} = 2[3(n-1)] - 3(n-2) = 3n = a_n$. Therefore, $\{a_n\}$, where $a_n = 3n$, is a solution of the recurrence relation.

Suppose that $a_n = 2^n$ for every nonnegative integer n. Note that $a_0 = 1$, $a_1 = 2$, and $a_2 = 4$. Because $2a_1 - a_0 = 2 \cdot 2 - 1 = 3 \neq a_2$, we see that $\{a_n\}$, where $a_n = 2^n$, is not a solution of the recurrence relation.

Suppose that $a_n = 5$ for every nonnegative integer n. Then for $n \geqslant 2$, we see that $a_n = 2a_{n-1} - a_{n-2} = 2 \cdot 5 - 5 = 5 = a_n$. Therefore, $\{a_n\}$, where $a_n = 5$, is a solution of the recurrence relation.   ◀

The **initial conditions** for a sequence specify the terms that precede the first term where the recurrence relation takes effect. For instance, in Example 1, $a_0 = 3$ and $a_1 = 5$ are the initial conditions. The recurrence relation and initial conditions uniquely determine a sequence. This is the case because a recurrence relation, together with initial conditions, provide a recursive definition of the sequence. Any term of the sequence can be found from the initial conditions using the recurrence relation a sufficient number of times. However, there are better ways for computing the terms of certain classes of sequences defined by recurrence relations and initial conditions. We will discuss these methods in this section and in Section 4.2.

Modeling with Recurrence Relations

We can use recurrence relations to model a wide variety of problems, such as finding compound interest, counting rabbits on an island, determining the number of moves in the Tower of Hanoi puzzle, and counting bit strings with certain properties.

Example 3   **Compound Interest**   Suppose that a person deposits \$10,000 in a savings account at a bank yielding 11% per year with interest compounded annually. How much will be in the account after 30 years?

Solution: To solve this problem, let P_n denote the amount in the account after n years. Because the amount in the account after n years equals the amount in the account after $n - 1$ years plus interest for the nth year, we see that the sequence $\{P_n\}$ satisfies the recurrence relation

$$P_n = P_{n-1} + 0.11 P_{n-1} = (1.11) P_{n-1}.$$

The initial condition is $P_0 = 10,000$.

We can use an iterative approach to find a formula for P_n. Note that

$$P_1 = (1.11)P_0$$
$$P_2 = (1.11)P_1 = (1.11)^2 P_0$$
$$P_3 = (1.11)P_2 = (1.11)^3 P_0$$
$$\vdots$$
$$P_n = (1.11)P_{n-1} = (1.11)^n P_0.$$

When we insert the initial condition $P_0 = 10{,}000$, the formula $P_n = (1.11)^n 10{,}000$ is obtained.

We can use mathematical induction to establish its validity. That the formula is valid for $n = 0$ is a consequence of the initial condition. Now assume that $P_n = (1.11)^n 10{,}000$. Then, from the recurrence relation and the induction hypothesis,

$$P_{n+1} = (1.11)P_n = (1.11)(1.11)^n 10{,}000 = (1.11)^{n+1} 10{,}000.$$

This shows that the explicit formula for P_n is valid.

Inserting $n = 30$ into the formula $P_n = (1.11)^n 10{,}000$ shows that after 30 years the account contains

$$P_{30} = (1.11)^{30} 10{,}000 = \$228{,}922.97. \qquad \blacktriangleleft$$

Example 4 shows how the population of rabbits on an island can be modeled using a recurrence relation.

Example 4   **Rabbits and the Fibonacci Numbers**   Consider this problem, which was originally posed by Leonardo Pisano, also known as Fibonacci, in the thirteenth century in his book *Liber abaci*. A young pair of rabbits (one of each sex) is placed on an island. A pair of rabbits does not breed until they are 2 months old. After they are 2 months old, each pair of rabbits produces another pair each month, as shown in Figure 1. Find a recurrence relation for the number of pairs of rabbits on the island after n months, assuming that no rabbits ever die.

Solution: Denote by f_n the number of pairs of rabbits after n months. We will show that f_n, $n = 1, 2, 3, \ldots$, are the terms of the Fibonacci sequence.

The rabbit population can be modeled using a recurrence relation. At the end of the first month, the number of pairs of rabbits on the island is $f_1 = 1$. Because this pair does not breed during the second month, $f_2 = 1$ also. To find the number of pairs after n months, add the number on the island the previous month, f_{n-1}, and the number of newborn pairs, which equals f_{n-2}, because each newborn pair comes from a pair at least 2 months old.

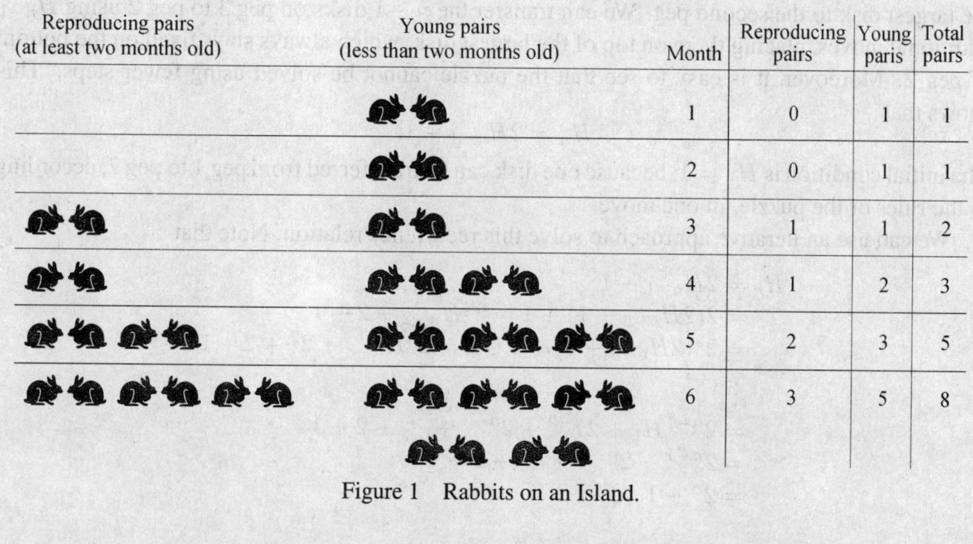

Reproducing pairs (at least two months old)	Young pairs (less than two months old)	Month	Reproducing pairs	Young pairs	Total pairs
		1	0	1	1
		2	0	1	1
		3	1	1	2
		4	1	2	3
		5	2	3	5
		6	3	5	8

Figure 1   Rabbits on an Island.

Consequently, the sequence $\{f_n\}$ satisfies the recurrence relation

$$f_n = f_{n-1} + f_{n-2}$$

for $n \geqslant 3$ together with the initial conditions $f_1 = 1$ and $f_2 = 1$. Because this recurrence relation and the initial conditions uniquely determine this sequence, the number of pairs of rabbits on the island after n months is given by the nth Fibonacci number. ◄

Example 5 involves a famous puzzle.

Example 5   The Tower of Hanoi   A popular puzzle of the late nineteenth century invented by the French mathematician Édouard Lucas, called the Tower of Hanoi, consists of three pegs mounted on a board together with disks of different sizes. Initially these disks are placed on the first peg in order of size, with the largest on the bottom (as shown in Figure 2). The rules of the puzzle allow disks to be moved one at a time from one peg to another as long as a disk is never placed on top of a smaller disk. The goal of the puzzle is to have all the disks on the second peg in order of size, with the largest on the bottom.

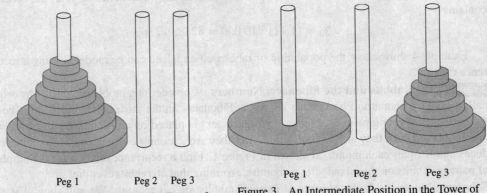

Peg 1   Peg 2   Peg 3   Peg 1   Peg 2   Peg 3

Figure 2   The Initial Position in the Tower of   Figure 3   An Intermediate Position in the Tower of
Hanoi.   Hanoi.

Let H_n denote the number of moves needed to solve the Tower of Hanoi problem with n disks. Set up a recurrence relation for the sequence $\{H_n\}$.

Solution: Begin with n disks on peg 1. We can transfer the top $n - 1$ disks, following the rules of the puzzle, to peg 3 using H_{n-1} moves (see Figure 3 for an illustration of the pegs and disks at this point). We keep the largest disk fixed during these moves. Then, we use one move to transfer the largest disk to the second peg. We can transfer the $n - 1$ disks on peg 3 to peg 2 using H_{n-1} additional moves, placing them on top of the largest disk, which always stays fixed on the bottom of peg 2. Moreover, it is easy to see that the puzzle cannot be solved using fewer steps. This shows that

$$H_n = 2H_{n-1} + 1.$$

The initial condition is $H_1 = 1$, because one disk can be transferred from peg 1 to peg 2, according to the rules of the puzzle, in one move.

We can use an iterative approach to solve this recurrence relation. Note that

$$
\begin{aligned}
H_n &= 2H_{n-1} + 1 \\
&= 2(2H_{n-2} + 1) + 1 = 2^2 H_{n-2} + 2 + 1 \\
&= 2^2(2H_{n-3} + 1) + 2 + 1 = 2^3 H_{n-3} + 2^2 + 2 + 1 \\
&\ \ \vdots \\
&= 2^{n-1}H_1 + 2^{n-2} + 2^{n-3} + \cdots + 2 + 1 \\
&= 2^{n-1} + 2^{n-2} + \cdots + 2 + 1 \\
&= 2^n - 1.
\end{aligned}
$$

We have used the recurrence relation repeatedly to express H_n in terms of previous terms of the sequence. In the next to last equality, the initial condition $H_1 = 1$ has been used. The last equality is based on the formula for the sum of the terms of a geometric series, which can be found in Theorem 1 in Section 2.4.

The iterative approach has produced the solution to the recurrence relation $H_n = 2H_{n-1} + 1$ with the initial condition $H_1 = 1$. This formula can be proved using mathematical induction. This is left for the reader as an exercise at the end of the section.

A myth created to accompany the puzzle tells of a tower in Hanoi where monks are transferring 64 gold disks from one peg to another, according to the rules of the puzzle. The myth says that the world will end when they finish the puzzle. How long after the monks started will the world end if the monks take one second to move a disk?

From the explicit formula, the monks require

$$2^{64} - 1 = 18{,}446{,}744{,}073{,}709{,}551{,}615$$

moves to transfer the disks. Making one move per second, it will take them more than 500 billion years to complete the transfer, so the world should survive a while longer than it already has. ◄

Remark: Many people have studied variations of the original Tower of Hanoi puzzle discussed in Example 5. Some variations use more pegs, some allow disks to be of the same size, and some restrict the types of allowable disk moves. One of the oldest and most interesting variations is the **Reve's puzzle,**[*] proposed in 1907 by Henry Dudeney in his book *The Canterbury Puzzles*. The Reve's puzzle involves pilgrims challenged by the Reve to move a stack of cheeses of varying sizes from the first of four stools to another stool without ever placing a cheese on one of smaller diameter. The Reve's puzzle, expressed in terms of pegs and disks, follows the same rules as the Tower of Hanoi puzzle, except that four pegs are used. You may find it surprising that no one has been able to establish the minimum number of moves required to solve this puzzle for n disks. However, there is a conjecture, now more than 50 years old, that the minimum number of moves required equals the number of moves used by an algorithm invented by Frame and Stewart in 1939. (See Exercises 27–30 at the end of this section and [St94] for more information.)

Example 6 illustrates how recurrence relations can be used to count bit strings of a specified length that have a certain property.

Example 6   Find a recurrence relation and give initial conditions for the number of bit strings of length n that do not have two consecutive 0s. How many such bit strings are there of length five?

Solution: Let a_n denote the number of bit strings of length n that do not have two consecutive 0s. To obtain a recurrence relation for $\{a_n\}$, note that by the sum rule, the number of bit strings of length n that do not have two consecutive 0s equals the number of such bit strings ending with a 0 plus the number of such bit strings ending with a 1. We will assume that $n \geqslant 3$, so that the bit string has at least three bits.

The bit strings of length n ending with 1 that do not have two consecutive 0s are precisely the bit strings of length $n-1$ with no two consecutive 0s with a 1 added at the end. Consequently, there are a_{n-1} such bit strings.

Bit strings of length n ending with a 0 that do not have two consecutive 0s must have 1 as their $(n-1)$st bit; otherwise they would end with a pair of 0s. It follows that the bit strings of length n ending with a 0 that have no two consecutive 0s are precisely the bit strings of length $n-2$ with no two consecutive 0s with 10 added at the end. Consequently, there are a_{n-2} such bit strings.

We conclude, as illustrated in Figure 4, that

$$a_n = a_{n-1} + a_{n-2}$$

---

[*] *Reve*, more commonly spelled *reeve*, is an archaic word for *governor*.

for $n \geqslant 3$.

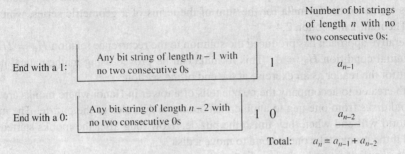

Figure 4   Counting Bit Strings of Length n with No Two Consecutive 0s.

The initial conditions are $a_1 = 2$, because both bit strings of length one, 0 and 1 do not have consecutive 0s, and $a_2 = 3$, because the valid bit strings of length two are 01, 10, and 11. To obtain a_5, we use the recurrence relation three times to find that

$$a_3 = a_2 + a_1 = 3 + 2 = 5,$$
$$a_4 = a_3 + a_2 = 5 + 3 = 8,$$
$$a_5 = a_4 + a_3 = 8 + 5 = 13. \qquad \blacktriangleleft$$

Remark: Note that $\{a_n\}$ satisfies the same recurrence relation as the Fibonacci sequence. Because $a_1 = f_3$ and $a_2 = f_4$ it follows that $a_n = f_{n+2}$.

Example 7 shows how a recurrence relation can be used to model the number of codewords that are allowable using certain validity checks.

Example 7   **Codeword Enumeration**   A computer system considers a string of decimal digits a valid codeword if it contains an even number of 0 digits. For instance, 1230407869 is valid, whereas 120987045608 is not valid. Let a_n be the number of valid n-digit codewords. Find a recurrence relation for a_n.

Solution: Note that $a_1 = 9$ because there are 10 one-digit strings, and only one, namely, the string 0, is not valid. A recurrence relation can be derived for this sequence by considering how a valid n-digit string can be obtained from strings of $n - 1$ digits. There are two ways to form a valid string with n digits from a string with one fewer digit.

First, a valid string of n digits can be obtained by appending a valid string of $n - 1$ digits with a digit other than 0. This appending can be done in nine ways. Hence, a valid string with n digits can be formed in this manner in $9a_{n-1}$ ways.

Second, a valid string of n digits can be obtained by appending a 0 to a string of length $n - 1$ that is not valid. (This produces a string with an even number of 0 digits because the invalid string of length $n - 1$ has an odd number of 0 digits.) The number of ways that this can be done equals the number of invalid $(n - 1)$-digit strings. Because there are 10^{n-1} strings of length $n - 1$, and a_{n-1} are valid, there are $10^{n-1} - a_{n-1}$ valid n-digit strings obtained by appending an invalid string of length $n - 1$ with a 0.

Because all valid strings of length n are produced in one of these two ways, it follows that there are

$$a_n = 9a_{n-1} + (10^{n-1} - a_{n-1})$$
$$= 8a_{n-1} + 10^{n-1}$$

valid strings of length n. $\qquad \blacktriangleleft$

Example 8 establishes a recurrence relation that appears in many different contexts.

Example 8   Find a recurrence relation for C_n, the number of ways to parenthesize the product of $n+1$ numbers, $x_0 \cdot x_1 \cdot x_2 \cdots \cdots x_n$, to specify the order of multiplication. For example, $C_3 = 5$ because there are five ways to parenthesize $x_0 \cdot x_1 \cdot x_2 \cdot x_3$ to determine the order of multiplication:

$$((x_0 \cdot x_1) \cdot x_2) \cdot x_3 \qquad (x_0 \cdot (x_1 \cdot x_2)) \cdot x_3 \qquad (x_0 \cdot x_1) \cdot (x_2 \cdot x_3)$$
$$x_0 \cdot ((x_1 \cdot x_2) \cdot x_3) \qquad x_0 \cdot (x_1 \cdot (x_2 \cdot x_3)).$$

Solution: To develop a recurrence relation for C_n, we note that however we insert parentheses in the product $x_0 \cdot x_1 \cdot x_2 \cdots \cdots x_n$, one "$\cdot$" operator remains outside all parentheses, namely, the operator for the final multiplication to be performed. [For example, in $(x_0 \cdot (x_1 \cdot x_2)) \cdot x_3$, it is the final "$\cdot$", while in $(x_0 \cdot x_1) \cdot (x_2 \cdot x_3)$ it is the second "$\cdot$".] This final operator appears between two of the $n+1$ numbers, say, x_k and x_{k+1}. There are $C_k C_{n-k-1}$ ways to insert parentheses to determine the order of the $n+1$ numbers to be multiplied when the final operator appears between x_k and x_{k+1}, because there are C_k ways to insert parentheses in the product $x_0 \cdot x_1 \cdots \cdots x_k$ to determine the order in which these $k+1$ numbers are to be multiplied and C_{n-k-1} ways to insert parentheses in the product $x_{k+1} \cdot x_{k+2} \cdots \cdots x_n$ to determine the order in which these $n - k$ numbers are to be multiplied. Because this final operator can appear between any two of the $n+1$ numbers, it follows that

$$C_n = C_0 C_{n-1} + C_1 C_{n-2} + \cdots + C_{n-2} C_1 + C_{n-1} C_0$$
$$= \sum_{k=0}^{n-1} C_k C_{n-k-1}.$$

Note that the initial conditions are $C_0 = 1$ and $C_1 = 1$. This recurrence relation can be solved using the method of generating functions, which will be discussed in Section 4.4. It can be shown that $C_n = C(2n, n)/(n + 1)$. (See Exercise 20 at the end of that section.)   ◄

The sequence $\{C_n\}$ is the sequence of **Catalan numbers.** This sequence appears as the solution of many different counting problems besides the one considered here (see the chapter on Catalan numbers in [MiRo91] or [Ro84a] for details).

Exercises

1. Find the first five terms of the sequence defined by each of these recurrence relations and initial conditions.

   a) $a_n = 6a_{n-1}$, $a_0 = 2$

   b) $a_n = a_{n-1}^2$, $a_1 = 2$

   c) $a_n = a_{n-1} + 3a_{n-2}$, $a_0 = 1$, $a_1 = 2$

   d) $a_n = na_{n-1} + n^2 a_{n-2}$, $a_0 = 1$, $a_1 = 1$

   e) $a_n = a_{n-1} + a_{n-3}$, $a_0 = 1$, $a_1 = 2$, $a_2 = 0$

2. Let $a_n = 2^n + 5 \cdot 3^n$ for $n = 0, 1, 2, \ldots$.

   a) Find a_0, a_1, a_2, a_3, and a_4.

   b) Show that $a_2 = 5a_1 - 6a_0$, $a_3 = 5a_2 - 6a_1$, and $a_4 = 5a_3 - 6a_2$.

   c) Show that $a_n = 5a_{n-1} - 6a_{n-2}$ for all integers n with $n \geqslant 2$.

3. Is the sequence $\{a_n\}$ a solution of the recurrence relation $a_n = 8a_{n-1} - 16a_{n-2}$ if

   a) $a_n = 0$?   b) $a_n = 1$?   c) $a_n = 2^n$?   d) $a_n = 4^n$?   e) $a_n = n4^n$?   f) $a_n = 2 \cdot 4^n + 3n4^n$?
   g) $a_n = (-4)^n$?   h) $a_n = n^2 4^n$?

4. Show that the sequence $\{a_n\}$ is a solution of the recurrence relation $a_n = a_{n-1} + 2a_{n-2} + 2n - 9$ if

   a) $a_n = -n+2$.   b) $a_n = 5(-1)^n - n + 2$.   c) $a_n = 3(-1)^n + 2^n - n + 2$.   d) $a_n = 7 \cdot 2^n - n + 2$.

5. Find the solution to each of these recurrence relations and initial conditions. Use an iterative approach such as that used in Example 5.

   a) $a_n = 3a_{n-1}, a_0 = 2$ b) $a_n = a_{n-1} + 2, a_0 = 3$

   c) $a_n = a_{n-1} + n, a_0 = 1$ d) $a_n = a_{n-1} + 2n + 3, a_0 = 4$

   e) $a_n = 2a_{n-1} - 1, a_0 = 1$ f) $a_n = 3a_{n-1} + 1, a_0 = 1$

   g) $a_n = na_{n-1}, a_0 = 5$ h) $a_n = 2na_{n-1}, a_0 = 1$

6. Suppose that the number of bacteria in a colony triples every hour.

   a) Set up a recurrence relation for the number of bacteria after n hours have elapsed.

   b) If 100 bacteria are used to begin a new colony, how many bacteria will be in the colony in 10 hours?

7. A factory makes custom sports cars at an increasing rate. In the first month only one car is made, in the second month two cars are made, and so on, with n cars made in the nth month.

   a) Set up a recurrence relation for the number of cars produced in the first n months by this factory.

   b) How many cars are produced in the first year?

   c) Find an explicit formula for the number of cars produced in the first n months by this factory.

8. Find a recurrence relation for the balance $B(k)$ owed at the end of k months on a loan of \$5000 at a rate of 7% if a payment of \$100 is made each month. [*Hint:* Express $B(k)$ in terms of $B(k-1)$; the monthly interest is $(0.07/12)B(k-1)$.]

9. Use mathematical induction to verify the formula derived in Example 5 for the number of moves required to complete the Tower of Hanoi puzzle.

10. A vending machine dispensing books of stamps accepts only dollar coins, \$1 bills, and \$5 bills.

   a) Find a recurrence relation for the number of ways to deposit n dollars in the vending machine, where the order in which the coins and bills are deposited matters.

   b) What are the initial conditions?

   c) How many ways are there to deposit \$10 for a book of stamps?

11. a) Find a recurrence relation for the number of bit strings of length n that contain a pair of consecutive 0s.

   b) What are the initial conditions?

   c) How many bit strings of length seven contain two consecutive 0s?

12. a) Find a recurrence relation for the number of bit strings of length n that do not contain three consecutive 0s.

   b) What are the initial conditions?

   c) How many bit strings of length seven do not contain three consecutive 0s?

13. a) Find a recurrence relation for the number of ways to climb n stairs if the person climbing the stairs can take one stair or two stairs at a time.

   b) What are the initial conditions?

   c) How many ways can this person climb a flight of eight stairs?

14. a) Find a recurrence relation for the number of ternary strings that do not contain two consecutive 0s.

   b) What are the initial conditions?

   c) How many ternary strings of length six do not contain two consecutive 0s?

*15. a) Find a recurrence relation for the number of ternary strings that do not contain two consecutive 0s or two consecutive 1s.

   b) What are the initial conditions?

   c) How many ternary strings of length six do not contain two consecutive 0s or two consecutive 1s?

*16. a) Find a recurrence relation for the number of ternary strings that do not contain consecutive symbols that are the same.

   b) What are the initial conditions?

   c) How many ternary strings of length six do not contain consecutive symbols that are the same?

17. Messages are transmitted over a communications channel using two signals. The transmittal of one signal requires 1 microsecond, and the transmittal of the other signal requires 2 microseconds.

a) Find a recurrence relation for the number of different messages consisting of sequences of these two signals, where each signal in the message is immediately followed by the next signal, that can be sent in n microseconds.

b) What are the initial conditions?

c) How many different messages can be sent in 10 microseconds using these two signals?

18. a) Find the recurrence relation satisfied by R_n, where R_n is the number of regions that a plane is divided into by n lines, if no two of the lines are parallel and no three of the lines go through the same point.

b) Find R_n using iteration.

*19. a) Find the recurrence relation satisfied by S_n, where S_n is the number of regions into which three-dimensional space is divided by n planes if every three of the planes meet in one point, but no four of the planes go through the same point.

b) Find S_n using iteration.

20. How many bit sequences of length seven contain an even number of 0s?

21. a) Find a recurrence relation for the number of ways to lay out a walkway with slate tiles if the tiles are red, green, or gray, so that no two red tiles are adjacent and tiles of the same color are considered indistinguishable.

b) What are the initial conditions for the recurrence relation in part (a)?

c) How many ways are there to lay out a path of seven tiles as described in part (a)?

*22. Let $S(m, n)$ denote the number of onto functions from a set with m elements to a set with n elements. Show that $S(m, n)$ satisfies the recurrence relation

$$S(m, n) = n^m - \sum_{k=1}^{n-1} C(n, k)S(m, k)$$

whenever $m \geqslant n$ and $n > 1$, with the initial condition $S(m, 1) = 1$.

23. a) Use the recurrence relation developed in Example 8 to determine C_5, the number of ways to parenthesize the product of six numbers so as to determine the order of multiplication.

b) Check your result with the closed formula for C_5 mentioned in the solution of Example 8.

Exercises 24–26 deal with a variation of the **Josephus problem** described by Graham, Knuth, and Patashnik in [GrKnPa94]. This problem is based on an account by the historian Flavius Josephus, who was part of a band of 41 Jewish rebels trapped in a cave by the Romans during the Jewish-Roman war of the first century. The rebels preferred suicide to capture; they decided to form a circle and to repeatedly count off around the circle, killing every third rebel left alive. However, Josephus and another rebel did not want to be killed this way; they determined the positions where they should stand to be the last two rebels remaining alive. The variation we consider begins with n people, numbered 1 to n, standing around a circle. In each stage, every second person still left alive is eliminated until only one survives. We denote the number of the survivor by $J(n)$.

24. Determine the value of $J(n)$ for each integer n with $1 \leqslant n \leqslant 16$.

25. Show that $J(n)$ satisfies the recurrence relation $J(2n) = 2J(n) - 1$ and $J(2n+1) = 2J(n) + 1$, for $n \geqslant 1$, and $J(1) = 1$.

26. Determine $J(100)$, $J(1000)$, and $J(10,000)$ from your formula for $J(n)$.

Exercises 27–30 involve the Reve's puzzle, the variation of the Tower of Hanoi puzzle with four pegs and n disks. Before presenting these exercises, we describe the Frame–Stewart algorithm for moving the disks from peg 1 to peg 4 so that no disk is ever on top of a smaller one. This algorithm, given the number of disks n as input, depends on a choice of an integer k with $1 \leqslant k \leqslant n$. When there is only one disk, move it from peg 1 to peg 4 and stop. For $n > 1$, the algorithm proceeds recursively, using these three steps. Recursively move the stack of the $n - k$ smallest disks from peg 1 to peg 2, using all four pegs. Next move the stack of the k largest disks from peg 1 to peg 4, using the three-peg algorithm from the Tower of Hanoi puzzle without using the peg holding the $n - k$ smallest disks. Finally, recursively move the smallest $n - k$ disks to peg 4, using all four pegs. Frame and Stewart showed that to produce the fewest moves using their algorithm, k should be chosen to be the smallest integer such that n does not exceed $t_k = k(k+1)/2$, the kth triangular number, that is, $t_{k-1} < n \leqslant t_k$. The unsettled conjecture, known as **Frame's conjecture,** is that this algorithm uses the fewest number of moves required to solve the puzzle, no matter how the disks are moved.

27. Show that the Reve's puzzle with four disks can be solved using nine, and no fewer, moves.

*28. Show that if $R(n)$ is the number of moves used by the Frame–Stewart algorithm to solve the Reve's puzzle with n disks, where k is chosen to be the smallest integer with $n \leqslant k(k + 1)/2$, then $R(n)$ satisfies the recurrence relation $R(n) = 2R(n - k) + 2^k - 1$, with $R(0) = 0$ and $R(1) = 1$.

*29. Show that if k is as chosen in Exercise 28, then $R(n) = \sum_{i=1}^{k} i2^{i-1} - (t_k - n)2^{k-1}$.

*30. Show that $R(n)$ is $O(\sqrt{n}2^{\sqrt{2n}})$.

Let $\{a_n\}$ be a sequence of real numbers. The **backward differences** of this sequence are defined recursively as shown next. The **first difference** ∇a_n is

$$\nabla a_n = a_n - a_{n-1}.$$

The $(k + 1)$**st difference** $\nabla^{k+1} a_n$ is obtained from $\nabla^k a_n$ by

$$\nabla^{k+1} a_n = \nabla^k a_n - \nabla^k a_{n-1}.$$

31. Show that $a_{n-2} = a_n - 2\nabla a_n + \nabla^2 a_n$.

32. Express the recurrence relation $a_n = a_{n-1} + a_{n-2}$ in terms of $a_n, \nabla a_n,$ and $\nabla^2 a_n$.

4.2 Solving Linear Recurrence Relations

Introduction

A wide variety of recurrence relations occur in models. Some of these recurrence relations can be solved using iteration or some other ad hoc technique. However, one important class of recurrence relations can be explicitly solved in a systematic way. These are recurrence relations that express the terms of a sequence as linear combinations of previous terms.

Definition 1 A *linear homogeneous recurrence relation of degree k with constant coefficients* is a recurrence relation of the form

$$a_n = c_1 a_{n-1} + c_2 a_{n-2} + \cdots + c_k a_{n-k},$$

where $c_1, c_2, \ldots, c_k$ are real numbers, and $c_k \neq 0$.

The recurrence relation in the definition is **linear** because the right-hand side is a sum of previous terms of the sequence each multiplied by a function of n. The recurrence relation is **homogeneous** because no terms occur that are not multiples of the a_js. The coefficients of the terms of the sequence are all **constants,** rather than functions that depend on n. The **degree** is k because a_n is expressed in terms of the previous k terms of the sequence.

A consequence of the second principle of mathematical induction is that a sequence satisfying the recurrence relation in the definition is uniquely determined by this recurrence relation and the k initial conditions

$$a_0 = C_0, a_1 = C_1, \ldots, a_{k-1} = C_{k-1}.$$

Example 1   The recurrence relation $P_n = (1.11)P_{n-1}$ is a linear homogeneous recurrence relation of degree one. The recurrence relation $f_n = f_{n-1} + f_{n-2}$ is a linear homogeneous recurrence relation of degree two. The recurrence relation $a_n = a_{n-5}$ is a linear homogeneous recurrence relation of degree five.   ◀

Example 2 presents some examples of recurrence relations that are not linear homogeneous recurrence relations with constant coefficients.

Example 2   The recurrence relation $a_n = a_{n-1} + a_{n-2}^2$ is not linear. The recurrence relation $H_n = 2H_{n-1} + 1$ is not homogeneous. The recurrence relation $B_n = nB_{n-1}$ does not have constant coefficients.   ◀

Linear homogeneous recurrence relations are studied for two reasons. First, they often occur in modeling of problems. Second, they can be systematically solved.

Solving Linear Homogeneous Recurrence Relations with Constant Coefficients

The basic approach for solving linear homogeneous recurrence relations is to look for solutions of the form $a_n = r^n$, where r is a constant. Note that $a_n = r^n$ is a solution of the recurrence relation $a_n = c_1 a_{n-1} + c_2 a_{n-2} + \cdots + c_k a_{n-k}$ if and only if

$$r^n = c_1 r^{n-1} + c_2 r^{n-2} + \cdots + c_k r^{n-k}.$$

When both sides of this equation are divided by r^{n-k} and the right-hand side is subtracted from the left, we obtain the equation

$$r^k - c_1 r^{k-1} - c_2 r^{k-2} - \cdots - c_{k-1} r - c_k = 0.$$

Consequently, the sequence $\{a_n\}$ with $a_n = r^n$ is a solution if and only if r is a solution of this last equation, which is called the **characteristic equation** of the recurrence relation. The solutions of this equation are called the **characteristic roots** of the recurrence relation. As we will see, these characteristic roots can be used to give an explicit formula for all the solutions of the recurrence relation.

We will first develop results that deal with linear homogeneous recurrence relations with constant coefficients of degree two. Then corresponding general results when the degree may be greater than two will be stated. Because the proofs needed to establish the results in the general case are more complicated, they will not be given in the text.

We now turn our attention to linear homogeneous recurrence relations of degree two. First, consider the case when there are two distinct characteristic roots.

Theorem 1   Let c_1 and c_2 be real numbers. Suppose that $r^2 - c_1 r - c_2 = 0$ has two distinct roots r_1 and r_2. Then the sequence $\{a_n\}$ is a solution of the recurrence relation $a_n = c_1 a_{n-1} + c_2 a_{n-2}$ if and only if $a_n = \alpha_1 r_1^n + \alpha_2 r_2^n$ for $n = 0, 1, 2, \ldots$, where α_1 and α_2 are constants.

Proof: We must do two things to prove the theorem. First, it must be shown that if r_1 and r_2 are the roots of the characteristic equation, and α_1 and α_2 are constants, then the sequence $\{a_n\}$ with $a_n = \alpha_1 r_1^n + \alpha_2 r_2^n$ is a solution of the recurrence relation. Second, it must be shown that if the sequence $\{a_n\}$ is a solution, then $a_n = \alpha_1 r_1^n + \alpha_2 r_2^n$ for some constants α_1 and α_2.

Now we will show that if $a_n = \alpha_1 r_1^n + \alpha_2 r_2^n$, then the sequence $\{a_n\}$ is a solution of the recurrence relation. Because r_1 and r_2 are roots of $r^2 - c_1 r - c_2 = 0$, it follows that $r_1^2 = c_1 r_1 + c_2$, $r_2^2 = c_1 r_2 + c_2$.

From these equations, we see that

$$
\begin{aligned}
c_1 a_{n-1} + c_2 a_{n-2} &= c_1(\alpha_1 r_1^{n-1} + \alpha_2 r_2^{n-1}) + c_2(\alpha_1 r_1^{n-2} + \alpha_2 r_2^{n-2}) \\
&= \alpha_1 r_1^{n-2}(c_1 r_1 + c_2) + \alpha_2 r_2^{n-2}(c_1 r_2 + c_2) \\
&= \alpha_1 r_1^{n-2} r_1^2 + \alpha_2 r_2^{n-2} r_2^2
\end{aligned}
$$

$$= \alpha_1 r_1^n + \alpha_2 r_2^n$$
$$= a_n.$$

This shows that the sequence $\{a_n\}$ with $a_n = \alpha_1 r_1^n + \alpha_2 r_2^n$ is a solution of the recurrence relation.

To show that every solution $\{a_n\}$ of the recurrence relation $a_n = c_1 a_{n-1} + c_2 a_{n-2}$ has $a_n = \alpha_1 r_1^n + \alpha_2 r_2^n$ for $n = 0, 1, 2, \ldots$, for some constants α_1 and α_2, suppose that $\{a_n\}$ is a solution of the recurrence relation, and the initial conditions $a_0 = C_0$ and $a_1 = C_1$ hold. It will be shown that there are constants α_1 and α_2 such that the sequence $\{a_n\}$ with $a_n = \alpha_1 r_1^n + \alpha_2 r_2^n$ satisfies these same initial conditions. This requires that

$$a_0 = C_0 = \alpha_1 + \alpha_2,$$
$$a_1 = C_1 = \alpha_1 r_1 + \alpha_2 r_2.$$

We can solve these two equations for α_1 and α_2. From the first equation it follows that $\alpha_2 = C_0 - \alpha_1$. Inserting this expression into the second equation gives

$$C_1 = \alpha_1 r_1 + (C_0 - \alpha_1) r_2.$$

Hence,

$$C_1 = \alpha_1 (r_1 - r_2) + C_0 r_2.$$

This shows that

$$\alpha_1 = \frac{C_1 - C_0 r_2}{r_1 - r_2}$$

and

$$\alpha_2 = C_0 - \alpha_1 = C_0 - \frac{C_1 - C_0 r_2}{r_1 - r_2} = \frac{C_0 r_1 - C_1}{r_1 - r_2},$$

where these expressions for α_1 and α_2 depend on the fact that $r_1 \neq r_2$. (When $r_1 = r_2$, this theorem is not true.) Hence, with these values for α_1 and α_2, the sequence $\{a_n\}$ with $\alpha_1 r_1^n + \alpha_2 r_2^n$ satisfies the two initial conditions.

We know that $\{a_n\}$ and $\{\alpha_1 r_1^n + \alpha_2 r_2^n\}$ are both solutions of the recurrence relation $a_n = c_1 a_{n-1} + c_2 a_{n-2}$ and both satisfy the initial conditions when $n = 0$ and $n = 1$. Because there is a unique solution of a linear homogeneous recurrence relation of degree two with two initial conditions, it follows that the two solutions are the same, that is, $a_n = \alpha_1 r_1^n + \alpha_2 r_2^n$ for all nonnegative integers n. We have completed the proof by showing that a solution of the linear homogeneous recurrence relation with constant coefficients of degree two must be of the form $a_n = \alpha_1 r_1^n + \alpha_2 r_2^n$, where α_1 and α_2 are constants.   ◁

The characteristic roots of a linear homogeneous recurrence relation with constant coefficients may be complex numbers. Theorem 1 (and also subsequent theorems in this section) still applies in this case. Recurrence relations with complex characteristic roots will not be discussed in the text. Readers familiar with complex numbers may wish to solve Exercise 20 at the end of this section.

Examples 3 and 4 show how to use Theorem 1 to solve recurrence relations.

Example 3   What is the solution of the recurrence relation

$$a_n = a_{n-1} + 2a_{n-2}$$

with $a_0 = 2$ and $a_1 = 7$?

Solution: Theorem 1 can be used to solve this problem. The characteristic equation of the recurrence relation is $r^2 - r - 2 = 0$. Its roots are $r = 2$ and $r = -1$. Hence, the sequence $\{a_n\}$ is a solution to the recurrence relation if and only if

$$a_n = \alpha_1 2^n + \alpha_2 (-1)^n,$$

for some constants α_1 and α_2. From the initial conditions, it follows that

$$a_0 = 2 = \alpha_1 + \alpha_2,$$
$$a_1 = 7 = \alpha_1 \cdot 2 + \alpha_2 \cdot (-1).$$

Solving these two equations shows that $\alpha_1 = 3$ and $\alpha_2 = -1$. Hence, the solution to the recurrence relation and initial conditions is the sequence $\{a_n\}$ with

$$a_n = 3 \cdot 2^n - (-1)^n.$$ ◀

Example 4   Find an explicit formula for the Fibonacci numbers.
Solution: Recall that the sequence of Fibonacci numbers satisfies the recurrence relation $f_n = f_{n-1} + f_{n-2}$ and also satisfies the initial conditions $f_0 = 0$ and $f_1 = 1$. The roots of the characteristic equation $r^2 - r - 1 = 0$ are $r_1 = (1 + \sqrt{5})/2$ and $r_2 = (1 - \sqrt{5})/2$. Therefore, from Theorem 1 it follows that the Fibonacci numbers are given by

$$f_n = \alpha_1 \left(\frac{1 + \sqrt{5}}{2} \right)^n + \alpha_2 \left(\frac{1 - \sqrt{5}}{2} \right)^n,$$

for some constants α_1 and α_2. The initial conditions $f_0 = 0$ and $f_1 = 1$ can be used to find these constants. We have

$$f_0 = \alpha_1 + \alpha_2 = 0,$$
$$f_1 = \alpha_1 \left(\frac{1 + \sqrt{5}}{2} \right) + \alpha_2 \left(\frac{1 - \sqrt{5}}{2} \right) = 1.$$

The solution to these simultaneous equations for α_1 and α_2 is

$$\alpha_1 = 1/\sqrt{5}, \quad \alpha_2 = -1/\sqrt{5}.$$

Consequently, the Fibonacci numbers are given by

$$f_n = \frac{1}{\sqrt{5}} \left(\frac{1 + \sqrt{5}}{2} \right)^n - \frac{1}{\sqrt{5}} \left(\frac{1 - \sqrt{5}}{2} \right)^n.$$ ◀

Theorem 1 does not apply when there is one characteristic root of multiplicity two. If this happens, then $a_n = nr_0^n$ is another solution of the recurrence relation when r_0 is a root of multiplicity two of the characteristic equation. Theorem 2 shows how to handle this case.

Theorem 2   Let c_1 and c_2 be real numbers with $c_2 \neq 0$. Suppose that $r^2 - c_1 r - c_2 = 0$ has only one root r_0. A sequence $\{a_n\}$ is a solution of the recurrence relation $a_n = c_1 a_{n-1} + c_2 a_{n-2}$ if and only if $a_n = \alpha_1 r_0^n + \alpha_2 n r_0^n$, for $n = 0, 1, 2, \ldots$, where α_1 and α_2 are constants.

The proof of Theorem 2 is left as an exercise at the end of the section. Example 5 illustrates the use of this theorem.

Example 5   What is the solution of the recurrence relation

$$a_n = 6a_{n-1} - 9a_{n-2}$$

with initial conditions $a_0 = 1$ and $a_1 = 6$?
Solution: The only root of $r^2 - 6r + 9 = 0$ is $r = 3$. Hence, the solution to this recurrence relation is

$$a_n = \alpha_1 3^n + \alpha_2 n 3^n$$

for some constants α_1 and α_2. Using the initial conditions, it follows that

$$
\begin{aligned}
a_0 &= 1 = \alpha_1, \\
a_1 &= 6 = \alpha_1 \cdot 3 + \alpha_2 \cdot 3.
\end{aligned}
$$

Solving these two equations shows that $\alpha_1 = 1$ and $\alpha_2 = 1$. Consequently, the solution to this recurrence relation and the initial conditions is

$$
a_n = 3^n + n3^n. \qquad \blacktriangleleft
$$

We will now state the general result about the solution of linear homogeneous recurrence relations with constant coefficients, where the degree may be greater than two, under the assumption that the characteristic equation has distinct roots. The proof of this result will be left as an exercise for the reader.

Theorem 3 Let $c_1, c_2, \ldots, c_k$ be real numbers. Suppose that the characteristic equation

$$
r^k - c_1 r^{k-1} - \cdots - c_k = 0
$$

has k distinct roots $r_1, r_2, \ldots, r_k$. Then a sequence $\{a_n\}$ is a solution of the recurrence relation

$$
a_n = c_1 a_{n-1} + c_2 a_{n-2} + \cdots + c_k a_{n-k}
$$

if and only if

$$
a_n = \alpha_1 r_1^n + \alpha_2 r_2^n + \cdots + \alpha_k r_k^n
$$

for $n = 0, 1, 2, \ldots$, where $\alpha_1, \alpha_2, \ldots, \alpha_k$ are constants.

We illustrate the use of the theorem with Example 6.

Example 6   Find the solution to the recurrence relation

$$
a_n = 6a_{n-1} - 11a_{n-2} + 6a_{n-3}
$$

with the initial conditions $a_0 = 2$, $a_1 = 5$, and $a_2 = 15$.

Solution: The characteristic polynomial of this recurrence relation is

$$
r^3 - 6r^2 + 11r - 6.
$$

The characteristic roots are $r = 1$, $r = 2$, and $r = 3$, because $r^3 - 6r^2 + 11r - 6 = (r - 1)(r - 2)(r - 3)$. Hence, the solutions to this recurrence relation are of the form

$$
a_n = \alpha_1 \cdot 1^n + \alpha_2 \cdot 2^n + \alpha_3 \cdot 3^n.
$$

To find the constants α_1, α_2, and α_3, use the initial conditions. This gives

$$
\begin{aligned}
a_0 &= 2 = \alpha_1 + \alpha_2 + \alpha_3, \\
a_1 &= 5 = \alpha_1 + \alpha_2 \cdot 2 + \alpha_3 \cdot 3, \\
a_2 &= 15 = \alpha_1 + \alpha_2 \cdot 4 + \alpha_3 \cdot 9.
\end{aligned}
$$

When these three simultaneous equations are solved for α_1, α_2, and α_3, we find that $\alpha_1 = 1$, $\alpha_2 = -1$, and $\alpha_3 = 2$. Hence, the unique solution to this recurrence relation and the given initial conditions is the sequence $\{a_n\}$ with

$$
a_n = 1 - 2^n + 2 \cdot 3^n. \qquad \blacktriangleleft
$$

We now state the most general result about linear homogeneous recurrence relations with constant coefficients, allowing the characteristic equation to have multiple roots. The key point is that for each root r of the characteristic equation, the general solution has a summand of the form $P(n)r^n$, where $P(n)$ is a polynomial of degree $m-1$, with m the multiplicity of this root. We leave the proof of this result as a challenging exercise for the reader.

Theorem 4   Let $c_1, c_2, \ldots, c_k$ be real numbers. Suppose that the characteristic equation

$$r^k - c_1 r^{k-1} - \cdots - c_k = 0$$

has t distinct roots $r_1, r_2, \ldots, r_t$ with multiplicities $m_1, m_2, \ldots, m_t$, respectively, so that $m_i \geqslant 1$ for $i = 1, 2, \ldots, t$ and $m_1 + m_2 + \cdots + m_t = k$. Then a sequence $\{a_n\}$ is a solution of the recurrence relation

$$a_n = c_1 a_{n-1} + c_2 a_{n-2} + \cdots + c_k a_{n-k}$$

if and only if

$$a_n = (\alpha_{1,0} + \alpha_{1,1}n + \cdots + \alpha_{1,m_1-1}n^{m_1-1})r_1^n$$
$$+ (\alpha_{2,0} + \alpha_{2,1}n + \cdots + \alpha_{2,m_2-1}n^{m_2-1})r_2^n$$
$$+ \cdots + (\alpha_{t,0} + \alpha_{t,1}n + \cdots + \alpha_{t,m_t-1}n^{m_t-1})r_t^n$$

for $n = 0, 1, 2, \ldots$, where $\alpha_{i,j}$ are constants for $1 \leqslant i \leqslant t$ and $0 \leqslant j \leqslant m_i - 1$.

Example 7 illustrates how Theorem 4 is used to find the general form of a solution of a linear homogeneous recurrence relation when the characteristic equation has several repeated roots.

Example 7   Suppose that the roots of the characteristic equation of a linear homogeneous recurrence relation are 2, 2, 2, 5, 5, and 9 (that is, there are three roots, the root 2 with multiplicity three, the root 5 with multiplicity two, and the root 9 with multiplicity one). What is the form of the general solution?

Solution: By Theorem 4, the general form of the solution is

$$(\alpha_{1,0} + \alpha_{1,1}n + \alpha_{1,2}n^2)2^n + (\alpha_{2,0} + \alpha_{2,1}n)5^n + \alpha_{3,0}9^n. \qquad \blacktriangleleft$$

We now illustrate the use of Theorem 4 to solve a linear homogeneous recurrence relation with constant coefficients when the characteristic equation has a root of multiplicity three.

Example 8   Find the solution to the recurrence relation

$$a_n = -3a_{n-1} - 3a_{n-2} - a_{n-3}$$

with initial conditions $a_0 = 1$, $a_1 = -2$, and $a_2 = -1$.

Solution: The characteristic equation of this recurrence relation is

$$r^3 + 3r^2 + 3r + 1 = 0.$$

Because $r^3 + 3r^2 + 3r + 1 = (r+1)^3$, there is a single root $r = -1$ of multiplicity three of the characteristic equation. By Theorem 4 the solutions of this recurrence relation are of the form

$$a_n = \alpha_{1,0}(-1)^n + \alpha_{1,1}n(-1)^n + \alpha_{1,2}n^2(-1)^n.$$

To find the constants $\alpha_{1,0}, \alpha_{1,1}$, and $\alpha_{1,2}$, use the initial conditions. This gives

$$a_0 = 1 = \alpha_{1,0},$$
$$a_1 = -2 = -\alpha_{1,0} - \alpha_{1,1} - \alpha_{1,2},$$
$$a_2 = -1 = \alpha_{1,0} + 2\alpha_{1,1} + 4\alpha_{1,2}.$$

The simultaneous solution of these three equations is $\alpha_{1,0} = 1$, $\alpha_{1,1} = 3$, and $\alpha_{1,2} = -2$. Hence, the unique solution to this recurrence relation and the given initial conditions is the sequence $\{a_n\}$ with

$$a_n = (1 + 3n - 2n^2)(-1)^n. \qquad \blacktriangleleft$$

Linear Nonhomogeneous Recurrence Relations with Constant Coefficients

We have seen how to solve linear homogeneous recurrence relations with constant coefficients. Is there a relatively simple technique for solving a linear, but not homogeneous, recurrence relation with constant coefficients, such as $a_n = 3a_{n-1} + 2n$? We will see that the answer is yes for certain families of such recurrence relations.

The recurrence relation $a_n = 3a_{n-1} + 2n$ is an example of a **linear nonhomogeneous recurrence relation with constant coefficients,** that is, a recurrence relation of the form

$$a_n = c_1 a_{n-1} + c_2 a_{n-2} + \cdots + c_k a_{n-k} + F(n),$$

where $c_1, c_2, \ldots, c_k$ are real numbers and $F(n)$ is a function not identically zero depending only on n. The recurrence relation

$$a_n = c_1 a_{n-1} + c_2 a_{n-2} + \cdots + c_k a_{n-k}$$

is called the **associated homogeneous recurrence relation.** It plays an important role in the solution of the nonhomogeneous recurrence relation.

Example 9   Each of the recurrence relations $a_n = a_{n-1} + 2^n$, $a_n = a_{n-1} + a_{n-2} + n^2 + n + 1$, $a_n = 3a_{n-1} + n3^n$, and $a_n = a_{n-1} + a_{n-2} + a_{n-3} + n!$ is a linear nonhomogeneous recurrence relation with constant coefficients. The associated linear homogeneous recurrence relations are $a_n = a_{n-1}$, $a_n = a_{n-1} + a_{n-2}$, $a_n = 3a_{n-1}$, and $a_n = a_{n-1} + a_{n-2} + a_{n-3}$, respectively.   ◄

The key fact about linear nonhomogeneous recurrence relations with constant coefficients is that every solution is the sum of a particular solution and a solution of the associated linear homogeneous recurrence relation, as Theorem 5 shows.

Theorem 5   If $\{a_n^{(p)}\}$ is a particular solution of the nonhomogeneous linear recurrence relation with constant coefficients

$$a_n = c_1 a_{n-1} + c_2 a_{n-2} + \cdots + c_k a_{n-k} + F(n),$$

then every solution is of the form $\{a_n^{(p)} + a_n^{(h)}\}$, where $\{a_n^{(h)}\}$ is a solution of the associated homogeneous recurrence relation

$$a_n = c_1 a_{n-1} + c_2 a_{n-2} + \cdots + c_k a_{n-k}.$$

Proof: Because $\{a_n^{(p)}\}$ is a particular solution of the nonhomogeneous recurrence relation, we know that

$$a_n^{(p)} = c_1 a_{n-1}^{(p)} + c_2 a_{n-2}^{(p)} + \cdots + c_k a_{n-k}^{(p)} + F(n).$$

Now suppose that $\{b_n\}$ is a second solution of the nonhomogeneous recurrence relation, so that

$$b_n = c_1 b_{n-1} + c_2 b_{n-2} + \cdots + c_k b_{n-k} + F(n).$$

Subtracting the first of these two equations from the second shows that

$$b_n - a_n^{(p)} = c_1(b_{n-1} - a_{n-1}^{(p)}) + c_2(b_{n-2} - a_{n-2}^{(p)}) + \cdots + c_k(b_{n-k} - a_{n-k}^{(p)}).$$

It follows that $\{b_n - a_n^{(p)}\}$ is a solution of the associated homogeneous linear recurrence, say, $\{a_n^{(h)}\}$. Consequently, $b_n = a_n^{(p)} + a_n^{(h)}$ for all n.   ◄

By Theorem 5, we see that the key to solving nonhomogeneous recurrence relations with constant coefficients is finding a particular solution. Then every solution is a sum of this solution and a solution of the associated homogeneous recurrence relation. Although there is no general method for finding such a solution that works for every function $F(n)$, there are techniques that work for certain types of functions $F(n)$, such as polynomials and powers of constants. This is illustrated in Examples 10 and 11.

Example 10   Find all solutions of the recurrence relation $a_n = 3a_{n-1}+2n$. What is the solution with $a_1 = 3$?

Solution: To solve this linear nonhomogeneous recurrence relation with constant coefficients, we need to solve its associated linear homogeneous equation and to find a particular solution for the given nonhomogeneous equation. The associated linear homogeneous equation is $a_n = 3a_{n-1}$. Its solutions are $a_n^{(h)} = \alpha 3^n$, where α is a constant.

We now find a particular solution. Because $F(n) = 2n$ is a polynomial in n of degree one, a reasonable trial solution is a linear function in n, say, $p_n = cn + d$, where c and d are constants. To determine whether there are any solutions of this form, suppose that $p_n = cn + d$ is such a solution. Then the equation $a_n = 3a_{n-1} + 2n$ becomes $cn + d = 3(c(n-1)+d)+2n$. Simplifying and combining like terms gives $(2+2c)n + (2d-3c) = 0$. It follows that $cn + d$ is a solution if and only if $2 + 2c = 0$ and $2d - 3c = 0$. This shows that $cn + d$ is a solution if and only if $c = -1$ and $d = -3/2$. Consequently, $a_n^{(p)} = -n - 3/2$ is a particular solution.

By Theorem 5 all solutions are of the form

$$a_n = a_n^{(p)} + a_n^{(h)} = -n - \frac{3}{2} + \alpha \cdot 3^n,$$

where α is a constant.

To find the solution with $a_1 = 3$, let $n = 1$ in the formula we obtained for the general solution. We find that $3 = -1 - 3/2 + 3\alpha$, which implies that $\alpha = 11/6$. The solution we seek is $a_n = -n - 3/2 + (11/6)3^n$.   ◄

Example 11   Find all solutions of the recurrence relation

$$a_n = 5a_{n-1} - 6a_{n-2} + 7^n.$$

Solution: This is a linear nonhomogeneous recurrence relation. The solutions of its associated homogeneous recurrence relation

$$a_n = 5a_{n-1} - 6a_{n-2}$$

are $a_n^{(h)} = \alpha_1 \cdot 3^n + \alpha_2 \cdot 2^n$, where α_1 and α_2 are constants. Because $F(n) = 7^n$, a reasonable trial solution is $a_n^{(p)} = C \cdot 7^n$, where C is a constant. Substituting the terms of this sequence into the recurrence relation implies that $C \cdot 7^n = 5C \cdot 7^{n-1} - 6C \cdot 7^{n-2} + 7^n$. Factoring out 7^{n-2}, this equation becomes $49C = 35C - 6C + 49$, which implies that $20C = 49$, or that $C = 49/20$. Hence, $a_n^{(p)} = (49/20)7^n$ is a particular solution. By Theorem 5, all solutions are of the form

$$a_n = \alpha_1 \cdot 3^n + \alpha_2 \cdot 2^n + (49/20)7^n.$$ ◄

In Examples 10 and 11, we made an educated guess that there are solutions of a particular form. In both cases we were able to find particular solutions. This was not an accident. Whenever $F(n)$ is the product of a polynomial in n and the nth power of a constant, we know exactly what form a particular solution has, as stated in Theorem 6. We leave the proof of Theorem 6 as a challenging exercise for the reader.

Theorem 6   Suppose that $\{a_n\}$ satisfies the linear nonhomogeneous recurrence relation

$$a_n = c_1a_{n-1} + c_2a_{n-2} + \cdots + c_ka_{n-k} + F(n),$$

where $c_1, c_2, \ldots, c_k$ are real numbers, and

$$F(n) = (b_t n^t + b_{t-1} n^{t-1} + \cdots + b_1 n + b_0) s^n,$$

where $b_0, b_1, \ldots, b_t$ and s are real numbers. When s is not a root of the characteristic equation of the associated linear homogeneous recurrence relation, there is a particular solution of the form

$$(p_t n^t + p_{t-1} n^{t-1} + \cdots + p_1 n + p_0) s^n.$$

When s is a root of this characteristic equation and its multiplicity is m, there is a particular solution of the form

$$n^m (p_t n^t + p_{t-1} n^{t-1} + \cdots + p_1 n + p_0) s^n.$$

Note that in the case when s is a root of multiplicity m of the characteristic equation of the associated linear homogeneous recurrence relation, the factor n^m ensures that the proposed particular solution will not already be a solution of the associated linear homogeneous recurrence relation. We next provide Example 12 to illustrate the form of a particular solution provided by Theorem 6.

Example 12 What form does a particular solution of the linear nonhomogeneous recurrence relation $a_n = 6a_{n-1} - 9a_{n-2} + F(n)$ have when $F(n) = 3^n$, $F(n) = n3^n$, $F(n) = n^2 2^n$, and $F(n) = (n^2 + 1)3^n$?

Solution: The associated linear homogeneous recurrence relation is $a_n = 6a_{n-1} - 9a_{n-2}$. Its characteristic equation, $r^2 - 6r + 9 = (r - 3)^2 = 0$, has a single root, 3, of multiplicity two. To apply Theorem 6, with $F(n)$ of the form $P(n)s^n$, where $P(n)$ is a polynomial and s is a constant, we need to ask whether s is a root of this characteristic equation.

Because $s = 3$ is a root with multiplicity $m = 2$ but $s = 2$ is not a root, Theorem 6 tells us that a particular solution has the form $p_0 n^2 3^n$ if $F(n) = 3^n$, the form $n^2(p_1 n + p_0)3^n$ if $F(n) = n3^n$, the form $(p_2 n^2 + p_1 n + p_0)2^n$ if $F(n) = n^2 2^n$, and the form $n^2(p_2 n^2 + p_1 n + p_0)3^n$ if $F(n) = (n^2 + 1)3^n$. ◀

Care must be taken when $s = 1$ when solving recurrence relations of the type covered by Theorem 6. In particular, to apply this theorem with $F(n) = b_t n^t + b_{t-1} n^{t-1} + \cdots + b_1 n + b_0$, the parameter s takes the value $s = 1$ (even though the term 1^n does not explicitly appear). By the theorem, the form of the solution then depends on whether 1 is a root of the characteristic equation of the associated linear homogeneous recurrence relation. This is illustrated in Example 13, which shows how Theorem 6 can be used to find a formula for the sum of the first n positive integers.

Example 13 Let a_n be the sum of the first n positive integers, so that

$$a_n = \sum_{k=1}^{n} k.$$

Note that a_n satisfies the linear nonhomogeneous recurrence relation

$$a_n = a_{n-1} + n.$$

(To obtain a_n, the sum of the first n positive integers, from a_{n-1}, the sum of the first $n - 1$ positive integers, we add n.) Note that the initial condition is $a_1 = 1$.

The associated linear homogeneous recurrence relation for a_n is

$$a_n = a_{n-1}.$$

The solutions of this homogeneous recurrence relation are given by $a_n^{(h)} = c(1)^n = c$, where c is a constant. To find all solutions of $a_n = a_{n-1} + n$, we need find only a single particular solution. By Theorem 6, because $F(n) = n = n \cdot (1)^n$ and $s = 1$ is a root of degree one of the characteristic equation of the associated linear homogeneous recurrence relations, there is a particular solution of the form $n(p_1 n + p_0) = p_1 n^2 + p_0 n$.

Inserting this into the recurrence relation gives $p_1n^2 + p_0n = p_1(n-1)^2 + p_0(n-1) + n$. Simplifying, we see that $n(2p_1 - 1) + (p_0 - p_1) = 0$, which means that $2p_1 - 1 = 0$ and $p_0 - p_1 = 0$, so $p_0 = p_1 = 1/2$. Hence,

$$a_n^{(p)} = \frac{n^2}{2} + \frac{n}{2} = \frac{n(n+1)}{2}$$

is a particular solution. Hence, all solutions of the original recurrence relation $a_n = a_{n-1} + n$ are given by $a_n = a_n^{(h)} + a_n^{(p)} = c + n(n+1)/2$. Because $a_1 = 1$, we have $1 = a_1 = c + 1 \cdot 2/2 = c + 1$, so $c = 0$. It follows that $a_n = n(n+1)/2$. (This is the same formula given in Table 2 in Section 2.4 and derived previously.)   ◄

Exercises

1. Determine which of these are linear homogeneous recurrence relations with constant coefficients. Also, find the degree of those that are.

   a) $a_n = 3a_{n-1} + 4a_{n-2} + 5a_{n-3}$ b) $a_n = 2na_{n-1} + a_{n-2}$ c) $a_n = a_{n-1} + a_{n-4}$

   d) $a_n = a_{n-1} + 2$ e) $a_n = a_{n-1}^2 + a_{n-2}$ f) $a_n = a_{n-2}$ g) $a_n = a_{n-1} + n$

2. Solve these recurrence relations together with the initial conditions given.

   a) $a_n = 2a_{n-1}$ for $n \geq 1$, $a_0 = 3$

   b) $a_n = a_{n-1}$ for $n \geq 1$, $a_0 = 2$

   c) $a_n = 5a_{n-1} - 6a_{n-2}$ for $n \geq 2$, $a_0 = 1$, $a_1 = 0$

   d) $a_n = 4a_{n-1} - 4a_{n-2}$ for $n \geq 2$, $a_0 = 6$, $a_1 = 8$

   e) $a_n = -4a_{n-1} - 4a_{n-2}$ for $n \geq 2$, $a_0 = 0$, $a_1 = 1$

   f) $a_n = 4a_{n-2}$ for $n \geq 2$, $a_0 = 0$, $a_1 = 4$

   g) $a_n = a_{n-2}/4$ for $n \geq 2$, $a_0 = 1$, $a_1 = 0$

3. How many different messages can be transmitted in n microseconds using the two signals described in Exercise 17 in Section 4.1?

4. In how many ways can a $2 \times n$ rectangular checkerboard be tiled using 1×2 and 2×2 pieces?

5. A deposit of \$100,000 is made to an investment fund at the beginning of a year. On the last day of each year two dividends are awarded. The first dividend is 20% of the amount in the account during that year. The second dividend is 45% of the amount in the account in the previous year.

   a) Find a recurrence relation for $\{P_n\}$, where P_n is the amount in the account at the end of n years if no money is ever withdrawn.

   b) How much is in the account after n years if no money has been withdrawn?

6. The **Lucas numbers** satisfy the recurrence relation

$$L_n = L_{n-1} + L_{n-2},$$

   and the initial conditions $L_0 = 2$ and $L_1 = 1$.

   a) Show that $L_n = f_{n-1} + f_{n+1}$ for $n = 2, 3, \ldots$, where f_n is the nth Fibonacci number.

   b) Find an explicit formula for the Lucas numbers.

7. Find the solution to $a_n = 7a_{n-2} + 6a_{n-3}$ with $a_0 = 9$, $a_1 = 10$, and $a_2 = 32$.

8. Find the solution to $a_n = 2a_{n-1} + 5a_{n-2} - 6a_{n-3}$ with $a_0 = 7$, $a_1 = -4$, and $a_2 = 8$.

9. Prove this identity relating the Fibonacci numbers and the binomial coefficients:

$$f_{n+1} = C(n, 0) + C(n-1, 1) + \cdots + C(n-k, k),$$

where n is a positive integer and $k = \lfloor n/2 \rfloor$. [*Hint:* Let $a_n = C(n,0) + C(n-1,1) + \cdots + C(n-k,k)$. Show that the sequence $\{a_n\}$ satisfies the same recurrence relation and initial conditions satisfied by the sequence of Fibonacci numbers.]

10. Solve the recurrence relation $a_n = -3a_{n-1} - 3a_{n-2} - a_{n-3}$ with $a_0 = 5$, $a_1 = -9$, and $a_2 = 15$.

11. What is the general form of the solutions of a linear homogeneous recurrence relation if its characteristic equation has roots $1, 1, 1, 1, -2, -2, -2, 3, 3, -4$?

12. Consider the nonhomogeneous linear recurrence relation $a_n = 3a_{n-1} + 2^n$.
    a) Show that $a_n = -2^{n+1}$ is a solution of this recurrence relation.
    b) Use Theorem 5 to find all solutions of this recurrence relation.
    c) Find the solution with $a_0 = 1$.

13. a) Determine values of the constants A and B such that $a_n = An + B$ is a solution of recurrence relation $a_n = 2a_{n-1} + n + 5$.
    b) Use Theorem 5 to find all solutions of this recurrence relation.
    c) Find the solution of this recurrence relation with $a_0 = 4$.

14. What is the general form of the particular solution guaranteed to exist by Theorem 6 of the linear nonhomogeneous recurrence relation $a_n = 8a_{n-2} - 16a_{n-4} + F(n)$ if
    a) $F(n) = n^3$?   b) $F(n) = (-2)^n$?   c) $F(n) = n2^n$?   d) $F(n) = n^2 4^n$?   e) $F(n) = (n^2-2)(-2)^n$?   f) $F(n) = n^4 2^n$?   g) $F(n) = 2$?

15. a) Find all solutions of the recurrence relation $a_n = 2a_{n-1} + 3^n$.
    b) Find the solution of the recurrence relation in part (a) with initial condition $a_1 = 5$.

16. Find all solutions of the recurrence relation $a_n = 5a_{n-1} - 6a_{n-2} + 2^n + 3n$. [*Hint:* Look for a particular solution of the form $qn2^n + p_1 n + p_2$, where q, p_1, and p_2 are constants.]

17. Find all solutions of the recurrence relation $a_n = 4a_{n-1} - 4a_{n-2} + (n+1)2^n$.

18. Find the solution of the recurrence relation $a_n = 4a_{n-1} - 3a_{n-2} + 2^n + n + 3$ with $a_0 = 1$ and $a_1 = 4$.

19. Let a_n be the sum of the first n triangular numbers, that is, $a_n = \sum_{k=1}^{n} t_k$, where $t_k = k(k+1)/2$. Show that $\{a_n\}$ satisfies the linear nonhomogeneous recurrence relation $a_n = a_{n-1} + n(n+1)/2$ and the initial condition $a_1 = 1$. Use Theorem 6 to determine a formula for a_n by solving this recurrence relation.

*20. a) Find the characteristic roots of the linear homogeneous recurrence relation $a_n = a_{n-4}$. (*Note:* These include complex numbers.)
    b) Find the solution of the recurrence relation in part (a) with $a_0 = 1$, $a_1 = 0$, $a_2 = -1$, and $a_3 = 1$.

*21. a) Use the formula found in Example 4 for f_n, the nth Fibonacci number, to show that f_n is the integer closest to
$$\frac{1}{\sqrt{5}} \left(\frac{1+\sqrt{5}}{2} \right)^n.$$
    b) Determine for which n f_n is greater than
$$\frac{1}{\sqrt{5}} \left(\frac{1+\sqrt{5}}{2} \right)^n$$
    and for which n f_n is less than
$$\frac{1}{\sqrt{5}} \left(\frac{1+\sqrt{5}}{2} \right)^n.$$

22. Suppose that each pair of a genetically engineered species of rabbits left on an island produces two new pairs of rabbits at the age of 1 month and six new pairs of rabbits at the age of 2 months and every month afterward. None of the rabbits ever die or leave the island.
    a) Find a recurrence relation for the number of pairs of rabbits on the island n months after one newborn pair is left on the island.
    b) By solving the recurrence relation in (a) determine the number of pairs of rabbits on the island n months after one pair is left on the island.

23. A new employee at an exciting new software company starts with a salary of $50,000 and is promised that at the end of each year her salary will be double her salary of the previous year, with an extra increment of $10,000 for each year she has been with the company.

   a) Construct a recurrence relation for her salary for her nth year of employment.

   b) Solve this recurrence relation to find her salary for her nth year of employment.

**24. Prove Theorem 4.

25. Solve the recurrence relation $T(n) = nT^2(n/2)$ with initial condition $T(1) = 6$. [*Hint:* Let $n = 2^k$ and then make the substitution $a_k = \log T(2^k)$ to obtain a linear nonhomogeneous recurrence relation.]

4.3   Divide-and-Conquer Algorithms and Recurrence Relations

Introduction

Many recursive algorithms take a problem with a given input and divide it into one or more smaller problems. This reduction is successively applied until the solutions of the smaller problems can be found quickly. For instance, we perform a binary search by reducing the search for an element in a list to the search for this element in a list half as long. We successively apply this reduction until one element is left. When we sort a list of integers using the merge sort, we split the list into two halves of equal size and sort each half separately. We then merge the two sorted halves. Another example of this type of recursive algorithm is a procedure for multiplying integers that reduces the problem of the multiplication of two integers to three multiplications of pairs of integers with half as many bits. This reduction is successively applied until integers with one bit are obtained. These procedures are called **divide-and-conquer algorithms** because they *divide* a problem into one or more instances of the same problem of smaller size and they *conquer* the problem by using the solutions of the smaller problems to find a solution of the original problem, perhaps with some additional work.

   In this section we will show how recurrence relations can be used to analyze the computational complexity of divide-and-conquer algorithms. We will use these recurrence relations to estimate the number of operations used by many different divide-and-conquer algorithms, including several that we introduce in this section.

Divide-and-Conquer Recurrence Relations

Suppose that a recursive algorithm divides a problem of size n into a subproblems, where each subproblem is of size n/b (for simplicity, assume that n is a multiple of b; in reality, the smaller problems are often of size equal to the nearest integers either less than or equal to, or greater than or equal to, n/b). Also, suppose that a total of $g(n)$ extra operations are required in the conquer step of the algorithm to combine the solutions of the subproblems into a solution of the original problem. Then, if $f(n)$ represents the number of operations required to solve the problem of size n, it follows that f satisfies the recurrence relation

$$f(n) = af(n/b) + g(n).$$

This is called a **divide-and-conquer recurrence relation.**

   We will first set up the divide-and-conquer recurrence relations that can be used to study the complexity of some important algorithms. Then we will show how to use these divide-and-conquer recurrence relations to estimate the complexity of these algorithms.

Example 1   **Binary Search**   This binary search algorithm reduces the search for an element in a search sequence of size n to the binary search for this element in a search sequence of size $n/2$, when n is even. (Hence, the problem of size n has been reduced to *one* problem of size

$n/2$.) Two comparisons are needed to implement this reduction (one to determine which half of the list to use and the other to determine whether any terms of the list remain). Hence, if $f(n)$ is the number of comparisons required to search for an element in a search sequence of size n, then

$$f(n) = f(n/2) + 2$$

when n is even.   ◄

Example 2   **Finding the Maximum and Minimum of a Sequence**   Consider the following algorithm for locating the maximum and minimum elements of a sequence $a_1, a_2, \ldots, a_n$. If $n = 1$, then a_1 is the maximum and the minimum. If $n > 1$, split the sequence into two sequences, either where both have the same number of elements or where one of the sequences has one more element than the other. The problem is reduced to finding the maximum and minimum of each of the two smaller sequences. The solution to the original problem results from the comparison of the separate maxima and minima of the two smaller sequences to obtain the overall maximum and minimum.

Let $f(n)$ be the total number of comparisons needed to find the maximum and minimum elements of the sequence with n elements. We have shown that a problem of size n can be reduced into two problems of size $n/2$, when n is even, using two comparisons, one to compare the maxima of the two sequences and the other to compare the minima of the two sequences. This gives the recurrence relation

$$f(n) = 2f(n/2) + 2$$

when n is even.   ◄

Example 3   **Merge Sort**   The merge sort algorithm splits a list to be sorted with n items, where n is even, into two lists with $n/2$ elements each, and uses fewer than n comparisons to merge the two sorted lists of $n/2$ items each into one sorted list. Consequently, the number of comparisons used by the merge sort to sort a list of n elements is less than $M(n)$, where the function $M(n)$ satisfies the divide-and-conquer recurrence relation

$$M(n) = 2M(n/2) + n.$$ ◄

Example 4   **Fast Multiplication of Integers**   Surprisingly, there are more efficient algorithms than the conventional algorithm for multiplying integers. One of these algorithms, which uses a divide-and-conquer technique, will be described here. This fast multiplication algorithm proceeds by splitting each of two $2n$-bit integers into two blocks, each with n bits. Then, the original multiplication is reduced from the multiplication of two $2n$-bit integers to three multiplications of n-bit integers, plus shifts and additions.

Suppose that a and b are integers with binary expansions of length $2n$ (add initial bits of zero in these expansions if necessary to make them the same length). Let

$$a = (a_{2n-1} a_{2n-2} \cdots a_1 a_0)_2 \quad \text{and} \quad b = (b_{2n-1} b_{2n-2} \cdots b_1 b_0)_2.$$

Let

$$a = 2^n A_1 + A_0, \quad b = 2^n B_1 + B_0,$$

where

$$A_1 = (a_{2n-1} \cdots a_{n+1} a_n)_2, \quad A_0 = (a_{n-1} \cdots a_1 a_0)_2,$$
$$B_1 = (b_{2n-1} \cdots b_{n+1} b_n)_2, \quad B_0 = (b_{n-1} \cdots b_1 b_0)_2.$$

The algorithm for fast multiplication of integers is based on the fact that ab can be rewritten as

$$ab = (2^{2n} + 2^n) A_1 B_1 + 2^n (A_1 - A_0)(B_0 - B_1) + (2^n + 1) A_0 B_0.$$

The important fact about this identity is that it shows that the multiplication of two $2n$-bit integers can be carried out using three multiplications of n-bit integers, together with additions, subtractions, and shifts. This shows that if $f(n)$ is the total number of bit operations needed to multiply two n-bit integers, then

$$f(2n) = 3f(n) + Cn.$$

The reasoning behind this equation is as follows. The three multiplications of n-bit integers are carried out using $3f(n)$-bit operations. Each of the additions, subtractions, and shifts uses a constant multiple of n-bit operations, and Cn represents the total number of bit operations used by these operations. ◄

Example 5   **Fast Matrix Multiplication** We showed that multiplying two $n \times n$ matrices using the definition of matrix multiplication required n^3 multiplications and $n^2(n-1)$ additions. Consequently, computing the product of two $n \times n$ matrices in this way requires $O(n^3)$ operations (multiplications and additions). Surprisingly, there are more efficient divide-and-conquer algorithms for multiplying two $n \times n$ matrices. Such an algorithm, invented by V. Strassen in 1969, reduces the multiplication of two $n \times n$ matrices, when n is even, to seven multiplications of two $(n/2) \times (n/2)$ matrices and 15 additions of $(n/2) \times (n/2)$ matrices. (See [CoLeRiSt01] for the details of this algorithm.) Hence, if $f(n)$ is the number of operations (multiplications and additions) used, it follows that

$$f(n) = 7f(n/2) + 15n^2/4$$

when n is even. ◄

As Examples 1–5 show, recurrence relations of the form $f(n) = af(n/b) + g(n)$ arise in many different situations. It is possible to derive estimates of the size of functions that satisfy such recurrence relations. Suppose that f satisfies this recurrence relation whenever n is divisible by b. Let $n = b^k$, where k is a positive integer. Then

$$\begin{aligned} f(n) &= af(n/b) + g(n) \\ &= a^2f(n/b^2) + ag(n/b) + g(n) \\ &= a^3f(n/b^3) + a^2g(n/b^2) + ag(n/b) + g(n) \\ &\vdots \\ &= a^kf(n/b^k) + \sum_{j=0}^{k-1} a^j g(n/b^j). \end{aligned}$$

Because $n/b^k = 1$, it follows that

$$f(n) = a^kf(1) + \sum_{j=0}^{k-1} a^j g(n/b^j).$$

We can use this equation for $f(n)$ to estimate the size of functions that satisfy divide-and-conquer relations.

Theorem 1   Let f be an increasing function that satisfies the recurrence relation

$$f(n) = af(n/b) + c$$

whenever n is divisible by b, where $a \geqslant 1$, b is an integer greater than 1, and c is a positive real number. Then

$$f(n) \text{ is } \begin{cases} O(n^{\log_b a}) & \text{if } a > 1, \\ O(\log n) & \text{if } a = 1. \end{cases}$$

Furthermore, when $n = b^k$, where k is a positive integer,

$$f(n) = C_1 n^{\log_b a} + C_2,$$

where $C_1 = f(1) + c/(a-1)$ and $C_2 = -c/(a-1)$.

Proof: First let $n = b^k$. From the expression for $f(n)$ obtained in the discussion preceding the theorem, with $g(n) = c$, we have

$$f(n) = a^k f(1) + \sum_{j=0}^{k-1} a^j c = a^k f(1) + c \sum_{j=0}^{k-1} a^j.$$

First consider the case when $a = 1$. Then

$$f(n) = f(1) + ck.$$

Because $n = b^k$, we have $k = \log_b n$. Hence,

$$f(n) = f(1) + c \log_b n.$$

When n is not a power of b, we have $b^k < n < b^{k+1}$, for a positive integer k. Because f is increasing, it follows that $f(n) \leqslant f(b^{k+1}) = f(1) + c(k+1) = (f(1)+c) + ck \leqslant (f(1)+c) + c \log_b n$. Therefore, in both cases, $f(n)$ is $O(\log n)$ when $a = 1$.

Now suppose that $a > 1$. First assume that $n = b^k$, where k is a positive integer. From the formula for the sum of terms of a geometric progression (Theorem 1 in Section 2.4), it follows that

$$\begin{aligned} f(n) &= a^k f(1) + c(a^k - 1)/(a-1) \\ &= a^k [f(1) + c/(a-1)] - c/(a-1) \\ &= C_1 n^{\log_b a} + C_2, \end{aligned}$$

because $a^k = a^{\log_b n} = n^{\log_b a}$ (see Exercise 4 in Appendix 2), where $C_1 = f(1) + c/(a-1)$ and $C_2 = -c/(a-1)$.

Now suppose that n is not a power of b. Then $b^k < n < b^{k+1}$, where k is a nonnegative integer. Because f is increasing,

$$\begin{aligned} f(n) &\leqslant f(b^{k+1}) = C_1 a^{k+1} + C_2 \\ &\leqslant (C_1 a) a^{\log_b n} + C_2 \\ &\leqslant (C_1 a) n^{\log_b a} + C_2, \end{aligned}$$

because $k \leqslant \log_b n < k+1$.

Hence, we have $f(n)$ is $O(n^{\log_b a})$.   ◁

Examples 6–9 illustrate how Theorem 1 is used.

Example 6   Let $f(n) = 5f(n/2) + 3$ and $f(1) = 7$. Find $f(2^k)$, where k is a positive integer. Also, estimate $f(n)$ if f is an increasing function.

Solution: From the proof of Theorem 1, with $a = 5$, $b = 2$, and $c = 3$, we see that if $n = 2^k$, then

$$\begin{aligned} f(n) &= a^k [f(1) + c/(a-1)] + [-c/(a-1)] \\ &= 5^k [7 + (3/4)] - 3/4 \\ &= 5^k (31/4) - 3/4. \end{aligned}$$

Also, if $f(n)$ is increasing, Theorem 1 shows that $f(n)$ is $O(n^{\log_b a}) = O(n^{\log 5})$.   ◀

We can use Theorem 1 to estimate the computational complexity of the binary search algorithm and the algorithm given in Example 2 for locating the minimum and maximum of a sequence.

Example 7   Estimate the number of comparisons used by a binary search.

Solution: In Example 1 it was shown that $f(n) = f(n/2) + 2$ when n is even, where f is the number of comparisons required to perform a binary search on a sequence of size n. Hence, from Theorem 1, it follows that $f(n)$ is $O(\log n)$.   ◀

Example 8   Estimate the number of comparisons used to locate the maximum and minimum elements in a sequence using the algorithm given in Example 2.

Solution: In Example 2 we showed that $f(n) = 2f(n/2) + 2$, when n is even, where f is the number of comparisons needed by this algorithm. Hence, from Theorem 1, it follows that $f(n)$ is $O(n^{\log 2}) = O(n)$.   ◀

We now state a more general, and more complicated, theorem, which has Theorem 1 as a special case. This theorem (or more powerful versions, including big-Theta estimates) is sometimes known as the Master Theorem because it is useful in analyzing the complexity of many important divide-and-conquer algorithms.

Theorem 2   Master Theorem   Let f be an increasing function that satisfies the recurrence relation

$$f(n) = af(n/b) + cn^d$$

whenever $n = b^k$, where k is a positive integer, $a \geqslant 1$, b is an integer greater than 1, and c and d are real numbers with c positive and d nonnegative. Then

$$f(n) \text{ is } \begin{cases} O(n^d) & \text{if } a < b^d, \\ O(n^d \log n) & \text{if } a = b^d, \\ O(n^{\log_b a}) & \text{if } a > b^d. \end{cases}$$

The proof of Theorem 2 is left for the reader as Exercises 11–13 at the end of this section.

Example 9   Complexity of Merge Sort   In Example 3 we explained that the number of comparisons used by the merge sort to sort a list of n elements is less than $M(n)$, where $M(n) = 2M(n/2) + n$. By the Master Theorem (Theorem 2) we find that $M(n)$ is $O(n \log n)$.   ◀

Example 10   Estimate the number of bit operations needed to multiply two n-bit integers using the fast multiplication algorithm described in Example 4.

Solution: Example 4 shows that $f(n) = 3f(n/2) + Cn$, when n is even, where $f(n)$ is the number of bit operations required to multiply two n-bit integers using the fast multiplication algorithm. Hence, from the Master Theorem (Theorem 2), it follows that $f(n)$ is $O(n^{\log 3})$. Note that $\log 3 \sim 1.6$. Because the conventional algorithm for multiplication uses $O(n^2)$ bit operations, the fast multiplication algorithm is a substantial improvement over the conventional algorithm in terms of time complexity for sufficiently large integers, including large integers that occur in practical applications.   ◀

Example 11   Estimate the number of multiplications and additions required to multiply two $n \times n$ matrices using the matrix multiplication algorithm referred to in Example 5.

Solution: Let $f(n)$ denote the number of additions and multiplications used by the algorithm mentioned in Example 5 to multiply two $n \times n$ matrices. We have $f(n) = 7f(n/2) + 15n^2/4$, when n is even. Hence, from the Master Theorem (Theorem 2), it follows that $f(n)$ is $O(n^{\log 7})$. Note that $\log 7 \sim 2.8$. Because the conventional algorithm for multiplying two $n \times n$ matrices uses $O(n^3)$ additions and multiplications, it follows that for sufficiently large integers n, including those that occur in many practical applications, this algorithm is substantially more efficient in time complexity than the conventional algorithm.   ◀

The closest-pair problem   We conclude this section by introducing a divide-and-conquer algorithm from computational geometry, the part of discrete mathematics devoted to algorithms that solve geometric problems.

Example 12   **The Closest-Pair Problem**   Consider the problem of determining the closest pair of points in a set of n points $(x_1, y_1), \ldots, (x_n, y_n)$ in the plane, where the distance between two points (x_i, y_i) and (x_j, y_j) is the usual Euclidean distance $\sqrt{(x_i - x_j)^2 + (y_i - y_j)^2}$. This problem arises in many applications such as determining the closest pair of airplanes in the air space at a particular altitude being managed by an air traffic controller. How can this closest pair of points be found in an efficient way?

Solution: To solve this problem we can first determine the distance between every pair of points and then find the smallest of these distances. However, this approach requires $O(n^2)$ computations of distances and comparisons because there are $C(n, 2) = n(n - 1)/2$ pairs of points. Surprisingly, there is an elegant divide-and-conquer algorithm that can solve the closest-pair problem for n points using $O(n \log n)$ computations of distances and comparisons. The algorithm we describe here is due to Michael Samos (see [PrSa85]).

For simplicity, we assume that $n = 2^k$, where k is a positive integer. (We avoid some technical considerations that are needed when n is not a power of 2.) When $n = 2$, we have only one pair of points; the distance between these two points is the minimum distance. At the start of the algorithm we use the merge sort twice, once to sort the points in order of increasing x coordinates, and once to sort the points in order of increasing y coordinates. Each of these sorts requires $O(n \log n)$ operations. We will use these sorted lists in each recursive step.

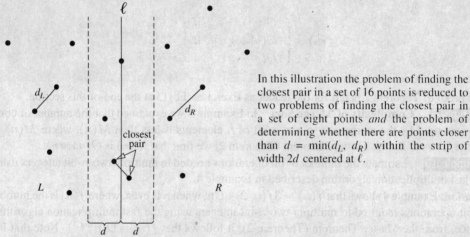

In this illustration the problem of finding the closest pair in a set of 16 points is reduced to two problems of finding the closest pair in a set of eight points *and* the problem of determining whether there are points closer than $d = \min(d_L, d_R)$ within the strip of width $2d$ centered at ℓ.

Figure 1   The Recursive Step of the Algorithm for Solving the Closest-Pair Problem.

The recursive part of the algorithm divides the problem into two subproblems, each involving half as many points. Using the sorted list of the points by their x coordinates, we construct a vertical line ℓ dividing the n points into two parts, a left part and a right part of equal size, each containing $n/2$ points, as shown in Figure 1. (If any points fall on the dividing line ℓ, we divide them among the two parts if necessary.) At subsequent steps of the recursion we need not sort on x coordinates again, because we can select the corresponding sorted subset of all the points. This selection is a task that can be done with $O(n)$ comparisons.

There are three possibilities concerning the positions of the closest points: (1) they are both in the left region L, (2) they are both in the right region R, or (3) one point is in the left region and the other is in the right region. Apply the algorithm recursively to compute d_L and d_R, where d_L is the minimum distance between points in the left region and d_R is the minimum distance between points in the right region. Let $d = \min(d_L, d_R)$. To successfully divide the problem of finding the closest two points in the original set into the two problems of finding the shortest distances between points in the two regions separately, we have to handle the conquer part of the algorithm, which requires that we consider the case where the closest points lie in different regions, that is, one point is in L and the other in R. Because there is a pair of points at distance d where both points lie in R or both points lie in L, for the closest points to lie in different regions requires that they must be a distance less than d apart.

For a point in the left region and a point in the right region to lie at a distance less than d apart, these points must lie in the vertical strip of width $2d$ that has the line ℓ as its center. (Otherwise, the distance between these points is greater than the difference in their x coordinates, which exceeds d.) To examine the points within this strip, we sort the points so that they are listed in order of increasing y coordinates, using the sorted list of the points by their y coordinates. At each recursive step, we form a subset of the points in the region sorted by their y coordinates from the already sorted set of all points sorted by their y coordinates, which can be done with $O(n)$ comparisons.

Beginning with a point in the strip with the smallest y coordinate, we successively examine each point in the strip, computing the distance between this point and all other points in the strip that have larger y coordinates that could lie at a distance less than d from this point. Note that to examine a point p, we need only consider the distances between p and points in the set that lie within the rectangle of height d and width $2d$ with p on its base and with vertical sides at distance d from ℓ.

We can show that there are at most eight points from the set, including p, in or on this $2d \times d$ rectangle. To see this, note that there can be at most one point in each of the eight $d/2 \times d/2$ squares shown in Figure 2. This follows because the farthest apart points can be on or within one of these squares is the diagonal length $d/\sqrt{2}$ (which can be found using the Pythagorean Theorem), which is less than d, and each of these $d/2 \times d/2$ squares lies entirely within the left region or the right region. This means that at this stage we need only compare at most seven distances, the distances between p and the seven or fewer other points in or on the rectangle, with d.

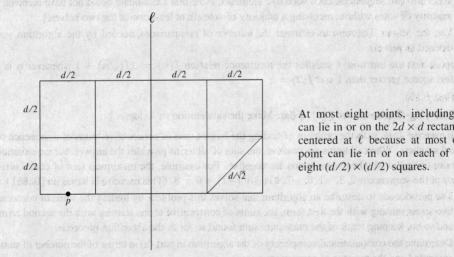

At most eight points, including p, can lie in or on the $2d \times d$ rectangle centered at ℓ because at most one point can lie in or on each of the eight $(d/2) \times (d/2)$ squares.

Figure 2   Showing That There Are at Most Seven Other Points to Consider for Each Point in the Strip.

Because the total number of points in the strip of width $2d$ does not exceed n (the total number of points in the set), at most $7n$ distances need to be compared with d to find the minimum distance between points. That is, there are only $7n$ possible distances that could be less than d. Consequently, once the merge sort has been used to sort the pairs according to their x coordinates and according to their y coordinates, we find that the increasing function $f(n)$ satisfying the recurrence relation

$$f(n) = 2f(n/2) + 7n,$$

where $f(2) = 1$, exceeds the number of comparisons needed to solve the closest-pair problem for n points. By the Master Theorem (Theorem 2), it follows that $f(n)$ is $O(n \log n)$. The two sorts of points by their x coordinates and by their y coordinates each can be done using $O(n \log n)$ comparisons, by using the merge sort, and the sorted subsets of these coordinates at each of the $O(\log n)$ steps of the algorithm can be done using $O(n)$ comparisons each. Thus, we find that the closest-pair problem can be solved using $O(n \log n)$ comparisons.   ◀

Exercises

1. How many comparisons are needed for a binary search in a set of 64 elements?

2. Multiply $(1110)_2$ and $(1010)_2$ using the fast multiplication algorithm.

3. Determine a value for the constant C in Example 4 and use it to estimate the number of bit operations needed to multiply two 64-bit integers using the fast multiplication algorithm.

4. Suppose that $f(n) = f(n/3) + 1$ when n is divisible by 3, and $f(1) = 1$. Find
   a) $f(3)$.   b) $f(27)$.   c) $f(729)$.

5. Suppose that $f(n) = f(n/5) + 3n^2$ when n is divisible by 5, and $f(1) = 4$. Find
   a) $f(5)$.   b) $f(125)$.   c) $f(3125)$.

6. Suppose that the votes of n people for different candidates (where there can be more than two candidates) for a particular office are the elements of a sequence. A person wins the election if this person receives a majority of the votes.
   a) Devise a divide-and-conquer algorithm that determines whether a candidate received a majority and, if so, determine who this candidate is. [*Hint:* Assume that n is even and split the sequence of votes into two sequences, each with $n/2$ elements. Note that a candidate could not have received a majority of votes without receiving a majority of votes in at least one of the two halves.]
   b) Use the Master Theorem to estimate the number of comparisons needed by the algorithm you devised in part (a).

7. Suppose that the function f satisfies the recurrence relation $f(n) = 2f(\sqrt{n}) + 1$ whenever n is a perfect square greater than 1 and $f(2) = 1$.
   a) Find $f(16)$.
   b) Find a big-O estimate for $f(n)$. [*Hint:* Make the substitution $m = \log n$.]

**8. This exercise deals with the problem of finding the largest sum of consecutive terms of a sequence of n real numbers. When all terms are positive, the sum of all terms provides the answer, but the situation is more complicated when some terms are negative. For example, the maximum sum of consecutive terms of the sequence $-2, 3, -1, 6, -7, 4$ is $3 + (-1) + 6 = 8$. (This exercise is based on [Be86].)
   a) Use pseudocode to describe an algorithm that solves this problem by finding the sums of consecutive terms starting with the first term, the sums of consecutive terms starting with the second term, and so on, keeping track of the maximum sum found so far as the algorithm proceeds.
   b) Determine the computational complexity of the algorithm in part (a) in terms of the number of sums computed and the number of comparisons made.
   c) Devise a divide-and-conquer algorithm to solve this problem. [*Hint:* Assume that there are an even number of terms in the sequence and split the sequence into two halves. Explain how to handle the case when the maximum sum of consecutive terms includes terms in both halves.]
   d) Use the algorithm from part (c) to find the maximum sum of consecutive terms of each of the sequences: $-2, 4, -1, 3, 5, -6, 1, 2; 4, 1, -3, 7, -1, -5, 3, -2$; and $-1, 6, 3, -4, -5, 8, -1, 7$.
   e) Find a recurrence relation for the number of sums and comparisons used by the divide-and-conquer algorithm from part (c).

f) Use the Master Theorem to estimate the computational complexity of the divide-and-conquer algorithm. How does it compare in terms of computational complexity with the algorithm from part (a)?

9. Apply the algorithm described in Example 12 for finding the closest pair of points, using the Euclidean distance between points, to find the closest pair of the points $(1, 2)$, $(1, 6)$, $(2, 4)$, $(2, 8)$, $(3, 1)$, $(3, 6)$, $(3, 10)$, $(4, 3)$, $(5, 1)$, $(5, 5)$, $(5, 9)$, $(6, 7)$, $(7, 1)$, $(7, 4)$, $(7, 9)$, and $(8, 6)$.

10. Construct a variation of the algorithm described in Example 12 along with justifications of the steps used by the algorithm to find the smallest distance between two points if the distance between two points is defined to be $d((x_i, y_i), (x_j, y_j)) = \max(|x_i - x_j|, |y_i - y_j|)$.

In Exercises 11–13, assume that f is an increasing function satisfying the recurrence relation $f(n) = af(n/b) + cn^d$, where $a \geqslant 1$, b is an integer greater than 1, and c and d are positive real numbers. These exercises supply a proof of Theorem 2.

*11. Show that if $a = b^d$ and n is a power of b, then $f(n) = f(1)n^d + cn^d \log_b n$.

*12. Show that if $a \neq b^d$ and n is a power of b, then $f(n) = C_1 n^d + C_2 n^{\log_b a}$, where $C_1 = b^d c/(b^d - a)$ and $C_2 = f(1) + b^d c/(a - b^d)$.

*13. Use Exercise 12 to show that if $a > b^d$, then $f(n)$ is $O(n^{\log_b a})$.

4.4 Generating Functions

Introduction

Generating functions are used to represent sequences efficiently by coding the terms of a sequence as coefficients of powers of a variable x in a formal power series. Generating functions can be used to solve many types of counting problems, such as the number of ways to select or distribute objects of different kinds, subject to a variety of constraints, and the number of ways to make change for a dollar using coins of different denominations. Generating functions can be used to solve recurrence relations by translating a recurrence relation for the terms of a sequence into an equation involving a generating function. This equation can then be solved to find a closed form for the generating function. From this closed form, the coefficients of the power series for the generating function can be found, solving the original recurrence relation. Generating functions can also be used to prove combinatorial identities by taking advantage of relatively simple relationships between functions that can be translated into identities involving the terms of sequences. Generating functions are a helpful tool for studying many properties of sequences besides those described in this section, such as their use for establishing asymptotic formulae for the terms of a sequence.

We begin with the definition of the generating function for a sequence.

Definition 1 The *generating function for the sequence* $a_0, a_1, \ldots, a_k, \ldots$ of real numbers is the infinite series

$$G(x) = a_0 + a_1 x + \cdots + a_k x^k + \cdots = \sum_{k=0}^{\infty} a_k x^k.$$

Remark: The generating function for $\{a_k\}$ given in Definition 1 is sometimes called the **ordinary generating function** of $\{a_k\}$ to distinguish it from other types of generating functions for this sequence.

Example 1 The generating functions for the sequences $\{a_k\}$ with $a_k = 3$, $a_k = k + 1$, and $a_k = 2^k$ are $\sum_{k=0}^{\infty} 3x^k$, $\sum_{k=0}^{\infty}(k + 1)x^k$, and $\sum_{k=0}^{\infty} 2^k x^k$; respectively. ◄

We can define generating functions for finite sequences of real numbers by extending a finite sequence $a_0, a_1, \ldots, a_n$ into an infinite sequence by setting $a_{n+1} = 0$, $a_{n+2} = 0$, and so on. The generating function $G(x)$ of this infinite sequence $\{a_n\}$ is a polynomial of degree n because no terms of the form $a_j x^j$ with $j > n$ occur, that is,

$$G(x) = a_0 + a_1 x + \cdots + a_n x^n.$$

Example 2   What is the generating function for the sequence 1, 1, 1, 1, 1, 1?
Solution: The generating function of 1, 1, 1, 1, 1, 1 is

$$1 + x + x^2 + x^3 + x^4 + x^5.$$

By Theorem 1 of Section 2.4 we have

$$(x^6 - 1)/(x - 1) = 1 + x + x^2 + x^3 + x^4 + x^5$$

when $x \neq 1$. Consequently, $G(x) = (x^6 - 1)/(x - 1)$ is the generating function of the sequence 1, 1, 1, 1, 1, 1. [Because the powers of x are only place holders for the terms of the sequence in a generating function, we do not need to worry that $G(1)$ is undefined.]   ◄

Example 3   Let m be a positive integer. Let $a_k = C(m, k)$, for $k = 0, 1, 2, \ldots, m$. What is the generating function for the sequence $a_0, a_1, \ldots, a_m$?
Solution: The generating function for this sequence is

$$G(x) = C(m, 0) + C(m, 1)x + C(m, 2)x^2 + \cdots + C(m, m)x^m.$$

The Binomial Theorem shows that $G(x) = (1 + x)^m$.   ◄

Useful Facts About Power Series

When generating functions are used to solve counting problems, they are usually considered to be **formal power series.** Questions about the convergence of these series are ignored. However, to apply some results from calculus, it is sometimes important to consider for which x the power series converges. The fact that a function has a unique power series around $x = 0$ will also be important. Generally, however, we will not be concerned with questions of convergence or the uniqueness of power series in our discussions. Readers familiar with calculus can consult textbooks on this subject for details about power series, including the convergence of the series we consider here.

We will now state some important facts about infinite series used when working with generating functions. A discussion of these and related results can be found in calculus texts.

Example 4   The function $f(x) = 1/(1-x)$ is the generating function of the sequence 1, 1, 1, 1, ..., because

$$1/(1 - x) = 1 + x + x^2 + \cdots$$

for $|x| < 1$.   ◄

Example 5   The function $f(x) = 1/(1 - ax)$ is the generating function of the sequence $1, a, a^2, a^3, \ldots$, because

$$1/(1 - ax) = 1 + ax + a^2 x^2 + \cdots$$

when $|ax| < 1$, or equivalently, for $|x| < 1/|a|$ for $a \neq 0$.   ◄

We also will need some results on how to add and how to multiply two generating functions. Proofs of these results can be found in calculus texts.

Theorem 1   Let $f(x) = \sum_{k=0}^{\infty} a_k x^k$ and $g(x) = \sum_{k=0}^{\infty} b_k x^k$. Then

$$f(x) + g(x) = \sum_{k=0}^{\infty} (a_k + b_k)x^k \quad \text{and} \quad f(x)g(x) = \sum_{k=0}^{\infty} \left(\sum_{j=0}^{k} a_j b_{k-j} \right) x^k.$$

Remark: Theorem 1 is valid only for power series that converge in an interval, as all series considered in this section do. However, the theory of generating functions is not limited to such series. In the case of series that do not converge, the statements in Theorem 1 can be taken as definitions of addition and multiplication of generating functions.

We will illustrate how Theorem 1 can be used with Example 6.

Example 6 Let $f(x) = 1/(1-x)^2$. Use Example 4 to find the coefficients $a_0, a_1, a_2, \ldots$ in the expansion $f(x) = \sum_{k=0}^{\infty} a_k x^k$.

Solution: From Example 4 we see that

$$1/(1-x) = 1 + x + x^2 + x^3 + \cdots.$$

Hence, from Theorem 1, we have

$$1/(1-x)^2 = \sum_{k=0}^{\infty} \left(\sum_{j=0}^{k} 1 \right) x^k = \sum_{k=0}^{\infty} (k+1)x^k. \quad \blacktriangleleft$$

Remark: This result also can be derived from Example 4 by differentiation. Taking derivatives is a useful technique for producing new identities from existing identities for generating functions.

To use generating functions to solve many important counting problems, we will need to apply the Binomial Theorem for exponents that are not positive integers. Before we state an extended version of the Binomial Theorem, we need to define extended binomial coefficients.

Definition 2 Let u be a real number and k a nonnegative integer. Then the *extended binomial coefficient* $\binom{u}{k}$ is defined by

$$\binom{u}{k} = \begin{cases} u(u-1)\cdots(u-k+1)/k! & \text{if } k > 0, \\ 1 & \text{if } k = 0. \end{cases}$$

Example 7 Find the values of the extended binomial coefficients $\binom{-2}{3}$ and $\binom{1/2}{3}$.

Solution: Taking $u = -2$ and $k = 3$ in Definition 2 gives us

$$\binom{-2}{3} = \frac{(-2)(-3)(-4)}{3!} = -4.$$

Similarly, taking $u = 1/2$ and $k = 3$ gives us

$$\binom{1/2}{3} = \frac{(1/2)(1/2-1)(1/2-2)}{3!}$$
$$= (1/2)(-1/2)(-3/2)/6$$
$$= 1/16. \quad \blacktriangleleft$$

Example 8 provides a useful formula for extended binomial coefficients when the top parameter is a negative integer. It will be useful in our subsequent discussions.

Example 8 When the top parameter is a negative integer, the extended binomial coefficient can be expressed in terms of an ordinary binomial coefficient. To see that this is the case, note that

$$\binom{-n}{r} = \frac{(-n)(-n-1)\cdots(-n-r+1)}{r!} \quad \text{by definition of extended binomial coefficient}$$

$$= \frac{(-1)^r n(n+1)\cdots(n+r-1)}{r!} \quad \text{factoring out } -1 \text{ from each term in the numerator}$$

$$= \frac{(-1)^r (n+r-1)(n+r-2)\cdots n}{r!} \quad \text{by the commutative law for multiplication}$$

$$= \frac{(-1)^r (n+r-1)!}{r!(n-1)!} \quad \text{multiplying both the numerator and denominator by } (n-1)!$$

$$= (-1)^r \binom{n+r-1}{r} \quad \text{by the definition of binomial coefficients}$$

$$= (-1)^r C(n+r-1,r). \quad \text{using alternative notation for binomial coefficients} \quad \blacktriangleleft$$

We now state the extended Binomial Theorem.

Theorem 2   The Extended Binomial Theorem Let x be a real number with $|x| < 1$ and let u be a real number. Then

$$(1+x)^u = \sum_{k=0}^{\infty} \binom{u}{k} x^k.$$

Theorem 2 can be proved using the theory of the Maclaurin series. We leave its proof to the reader with a familiarity with this part of calculus.

Remark: When u is a positive integer, the extended Binomial Theorem reduces to the Binomial Theorem presented in Section 3.4, because in that case $\binom{u}{k} = 0$ if $k > u$.

Example 9 illustrates the use of Theorem 2 when the exponent is a negative integer.

Example 9   Find the generating functions for $(1+x)^{-n}$ and $(1-x)^{-n}$, where n is a positive integer, using the extended Binomial Theorem.

Solution: By the extended Binomial Theorem, it follows that

$$(1+x)^{-n} = \sum_{k=0}^{\infty} \binom{-n}{k} x^k.$$

Using Example 8, which provides a simple formula for $\binom{-n}{k}$, we obtain

$$(1+x)^{-n} = \sum_{k=0}^{\infty} (-1)^k C(n+k-1,k) x^k.$$

Replacing x by $-x$, we find that

$$(1-x)^{-n} = \sum_{k=0}^{\infty} C(n+k-1,k) x^k. \quad \blacktriangleleft$$

Table 1 presents a useful summary of some generating functions that arise frequently.

Remark: Note that the second and third formulae in this table can be deduced from the first formula by substituting ax and x^r for x, respectively. Similarly, the sixth and seventh formulae can be deduced from the fifth formula using the same substitutions. The tenth and eleventh can be deduced from the ninth formula by substituting $-x$ and ax for x, respectively. Also, some of the formulae in this table can be derived from other formulae using methods from calculus (such as differentiation and integration). Students are encouraged to know the core formulae in this table (that is, formulae from which the others can be derived, perhaps the first, fourth, fifth, eighth, ninth, twelfth, and thirteenth formulae) and understand how to derive the other formulae from these core formulae.

Counting Problems And Generating Functions

Generating functions can be used to solve a wide variety of counting problems. In particular, they can be used to count the number of combinations of various types. In Chapter 3 we developed techniques to count the r-combinations from a set with n elements when repetition is allowed and additional constraints may exist. Such problems are equivalent to counting the solutions to equations of the form

$$e_1 + e_2 + \cdots + e_n = C,$$

TABLE 1 Useful Generating Functions.

$G(x)$	a_k
$(1+x)^n = \sum_{k=0}^{n} C(n,k)x^k$ $= 1 + C(n,1)x + C(n,2)x^2 + \cdots + x^n$	$C(n,k)$
$(1+ax)^n = \sum_{k=0}^{n} C(n,k)a^k x^k$ $= 1 + C(n,1)ax + C(n,2)a^2x^2 + \cdots + a^n x^n$	$C(n,k)a^k$
$(1+x^r)^n = \sum_{k=0}^{n} C(n,k)x^{rk}$ $= 1 + C(n,1)x^r + C(n,2)x^{2r} + \cdots + x^{rn}$	$C(n,k/r)$ if $r \mid k$; 0 otherwise
$\dfrac{1-x^{n+1}}{1-x} = \sum_{k=0}^{n} x^k = 1 + x + x^2 + \cdots + x^n$	1 if $k \le n$; 0 otherwise
$\dfrac{1}{1-x} = \sum_{k=0}^{\infty} x^k = 1 + x + x^2 + \cdots$	1
$\dfrac{1}{1-ax} = \sum_{k=0}^{\infty} a^k x^k = 1 + ax + a^2x^2 + \cdots$	a^k
$\dfrac{1}{1-x^r} = \sum_{k=0}^{\infty} x^{rk} = 1 + x^r + x^{2r} + \cdots$	1 if $r \mid k$; 0 otherwise
$\dfrac{1}{(1-x)^2} = \sum_{k=0}^{\infty} (k+1)x^k = 1 + 2x + 3x^2 + \cdots$	$k+1$
$\dfrac{1}{(1-x)^n} = \sum_{k=0}^{\infty} C(n+k-1,k)x^k$ $= 1 + C(n,1)x + C(n+1,2)x^2 + \cdots$	$C(n+k-1,k) = C(n+k-1,n-1)$
$\dfrac{1}{(1+x)^n} = \sum_{k=0}^{\infty} C(n+k-1,k)(-1)^k x^k$ $= 1 - C(n,1)x + C(n+1,2)x^2 - \cdots$	$(-1)^k C(n+k-1,k) = (-1)^k C(n+k-1,n-1)$
$\dfrac{1}{(1-ax)^n} = \sum_{k=0}^{\infty} C(n+k-1,k)a^k x^k$ $= 1 + C(n,1)ax + C(n+1,2)a^2x^2 + \cdots$	$C(n+k-1,k)a^k = C(n+k-1,n-1)a^k$
$e^x = \sum_{k=0}^{\infty} \dfrac{x^k}{k!} = 1 + x + \dfrac{x^2}{2!} + \dfrac{x^3}{3!} + \cdots$	$1/k!$
$\ln(1+x) = \sum_{k=0}^{\infty} \dfrac{(-1)^{k+1}}{k}x^k = x - \dfrac{x^2}{2} + \dfrac{x^3}{3} - \dfrac{x^4}{4} + \cdots$	$(-1)^{k+1}/k$

Note: The series for the last two generating functions can be found in most calculus books when power series are discussed.

where C is a constant and each e_i is a nonnegative integer that may be subject to a specified constraint. Generating functions can also be used to solve counting problems of this type, as Examples 10–12 show.

Example 10   Find the number of solutions of

$$e_1 + e_2 + e_3 = 17,$$

where e_1, e_2, and e_3 are nonnegative integers with $2 \leqslant e_1 \leqslant 5, 3 \leqslant e_2 \leqslant 6$, and $4 \leqslant e_3 \leqslant 7$.
Solution: The number of solutions with the indicated constraints is the coefficient of x^{17} in the expansion of

$$(x^2 + x^3 + x^4 + x^5)(x^3 + x^4 + x^5 + x^6)(x^4 + x^5 + x^6 + x^7).$$

This follows because we obtain a term equal to x^{17} in the product by picking a term in the first sum x^{e_1}, a term in the second sum x^{e_2}, and a term in the third sum x^{e_3}, where the exponents e_1, e_2, and e_3 satisfy the equation $e_1 + e_2 + e_3 = 17$ and the given constraints.

It is not hard to see that the coefficient of x^{17} in this product is 3. Hence, there are three solutions. (Note that the calculating of this coefficient involves about as much work as enumerating all the solutions of the equation with the given constraints. However, the method that this illustrates often can be used to solve wide classes of counting problems with special formulae, as we will see. Furthermore, a computer algebra system can be used to do such computations.)   ◀

Example 11   In how many different ways can eight identical cookies be distributed among three distinct children if each child receives at least two cookies and no more than four cookies?
Solution: Because each child receives at least two but no more than four cookies, for each child there is a factor equal to

$$(x^2 + x^3 + x^4)$$

in the generating function for the sequence $\{c_n\}$, where c_n is the number of ways to distribute n cookies. Because there are three children, this generating function is

$$(x^2 + x^3 + x^4)^3.$$

We need the coefficient of x^8 in this product. The reason is that the x^8 terms in the expansion correspond to the ways that three terms can be selected, with one from each factor, that have exponents adding up to 8. Furthermore, the exponents of the term from the first, second, and third factors are the numbers of cookies the first, second, and third children receive, respectively. Computation shows that this coefficient equals 6. Hence, there are six ways to distribute the cookies so that each child receives at least two, but no more than four, cookies.   ◀

Example 12   Use generating functions to determine the number of ways to insert tokens worth $1, $2, and $5 into a vending machine to pay for an item that costs r dollars in both the cases when the order in which the tokens are inserted does not matter and when the order does matter. (For example, there are two ways to pay for an item that costs $3 when the order in which the tokens are inserted does not matter: inserting three $1 tokens or one $1 token and a $2 token. When the order matters, there are three ways: inserting three $1 tokens, inserting a $1 token and then a $2 token, or inserting a $2 token and then a $1 token.)
Solution: Consider the case when the order in which the tokens are inserted does not matter. Here, all we care about is the number of each token used to produce a total of r dollars. Because we can use any number of $1 tokens, any number of $2 tokens, and any number of $5 tokens, the answer is the coefficient of x^r in the generating function

$$(1 + x + x^2 + x^3 + \cdots)(1 + x^2 + x^4 + x^6 + \cdots)(1 + x^5 + x^{10} + x^{15} + \cdots).$$

(The first factor in this product represents the $1 tokens used, the second the $2 tokens used, and the third the $5 tokens used.) For example, the number of ways to pay for an item costing $7 using $1, $2, and $5 tokens is given by the coefficient of x^7 in this expansion, which equals 6.

When the order in which the tokens are inserted matters, the number of ways to insert exactly n tokens to produce a total of r dollars is the coefficient of x^r in

$$(x + x^2 + x^5)^n,$$

because each of the r tokens may be a \$1 token, a \$2 token, or a \$5 token. Because any number of tokens may be inserted, the number of ways to produce r dollars using \$1, \$2, or \$5 tokens, when the order in which the tokens are inserted matters, is the coefficient of x^r in

$$1 + (x + x^2 + x^5) + (x + x^2 + x^5)^2 + \cdots = \frac{1}{1 - (x + x^2 + x^5)}$$
$$= \frac{1}{1 - x - x^2 - x^5},$$

where we have added the number of ways to insert 0 tokens, 1 token, 2 tokens, 3 tokens, and so on, and where we have used the identity $1/(1 - x) = 1 + x + x^2 + \cdots$ with x replaced with $x + x^2 + x^5$. For example, the number of ways to pay for an item costing \$7 using \$1, \$2, and \$5 tokens, when the order in which the tokens are used matters, is the coefficient of x^7 in this expansion, which equals 26. [*Hint:* To see that this coefficient equals 26 requires the addition of the coefficients of x^7 in the expansions $(x + x^2 + x^5)^k$ for $2 \leqslant k \leqslant 7$. This can be done by hand with considerable computation, or a computer algebra system can be used.]   ◀

Example 13 shows the versatility of generating functions when used to solve problems with differing assumptions.

Example 13   Use generating functions to find the number of k-combinations of a set with n elements. Assume that the Binomial Theorem has already been established.

Solution: Each of the n elements in the set contributes the term $(1 + x)$ to the generating function $f(x) = \sum_{k=0}^{n} a_k x^k$. Here $f(x)$ is the generating function for $\{a_k\}$, where a_k represents the number of k-combinations of a set with n elements. Hence,

$$f(x) = (1 + x)^n.$$

But by the Binomial Theorem, we have

$$f(x) = \sum_{k=0}^{n} \binom{n}{k} x^k,$$

where

$$\binom{n}{k} = \frac{n!}{k!(n - k)!}.$$

Hence, $C(n, k)$, the number of k-combinations of a set with n elements, is

$$\frac{n!}{k!(n - k)!}.$$ ◀

Remark: We proved the Binomial Theorem in Section 3.4 using the formula for the number of r-combinations of a set with n elements. This example shows that the Binomial Theorem, which can be proved by mathematical induction, can be used to derive the formula for the number of r-combinations of a set with n elements.

Example 14   Use generating functions to find the number of r-combinations from a set with n elements when repetition of elements is allowed.

Solution: Let $G(x)$ be the generating function for the sequence $\{a_r\}$, where a_r equals the number of r-combinations of a set with n elements with repetitions allowed. That is, $G(x) = \sum_{r=0}^{\infty} a_r x^r$. Because we can select any number of a particular member of the set with n elements when we form an r-combination with repetition allowed, each of the n elements contributes $(1 + x + x^2 + x^3 + \cdots)$ to a product expansion for $G(x)$. Each element contributes this factor because it may be selected zero times, one time, two times, three times, and so on, when an r-combination is formed (with a total of r elements selected). Because there are n elements in the set and each contributes this same factor to $G(x)$, we have

$$G(x) = (1 + x + x^2 + \cdots)^n.$$

As long as $|x| < 1$, we have $1 + x + x^2 + \cdots = 1/(1 - x)$, so

$$G(x) = 1/(1 - x)^n = (1 - x)^{-n}.$$

Applying the extended Binomial Theorem (Theorem 2), it follows that

$$(1 - x)^{-n} = (1 + (-x))^{-n} = \sum_{r=0}^{\infty} \binom{-n}{r} (-x)^r.$$

The number of r-combinations of a set with n elements with repetitions allowed, when r is a positive integer, is the coefficient a_r of x^r in this sum. Consequently, using Example 8 we find that a_r equals

$$\binom{-n}{r} (-1)^r = (-1)^r C(n + r - 1, r) \cdot (-1)^r$$
$$= C(n + r - 1, r).$$ ◄

Note that the result in Example 14 is the same result we stated as Theorem 2 in Section 3.5.

Example 15   Use generating functions to find the number of ways to select r objects of n different kinds if we must select at least one object of each kind.

Solution: Because we need to select at least one object of each kind, each of the n kinds of objects contributes the factor $(x + x^2 + x^3 + \cdots)$ to the generating function $G(x)$ for the sequence $\{a_r\}$, where a_r is the number of ways to select r objects of n different kinds if we need at least one object of each kind. Hence,

$$G(x) = (x + x^2 + x^3 + \cdots)^n = x^n(1 + x + x^2 + \cdots)^n = x^n/(1 - x)^n.$$

Using the extended Binomial Theorem and Example 8, we have

$$G(x) = x^n/(1 - x)^n$$
$$= x^n \cdot (1 - x)^{-n}$$
$$= x^n \sum_{r=0}^{\infty} \binom{-n}{r} (-x)^r$$
$$= x^n \sum_{r=0}^{\infty} (-1)^r C(n + r - 1, r)(-1)^r x^r$$
$$= \sum_{r=0}^{\infty} C(n + r - 1, r) x^{n+r}$$
$$= \sum_{t=n}^{\infty} C(t - 1, t - n) x^t$$
$$= \sum_{r=n}^{\infty} C(r - 1, r - n) x^r.$$

We have shifted the summation in the next-to-last equality by setting $t = n + r$ so that $t = n$ when $r = 0$ and $n + r - 1 = t - 1$, and then we replaced t by r as the index of summation in the last equality to return to our original notation. Hence, there are $C(r - 1, r - n)$ ways to select r objects of n different kinds if we must select at least one object of each kind.   ◄

Using Generating Functions to Solve Recurrence Relations

We can find the solution to a recurrence relation and its initial conditions by finding an explicit formula for the associated generating function. This is illustrated in Examples 16 and 17.

Example 16 Solve the recurrence relation $a_k = 3a_{k-1}$ for $k = 1, 2, 3, \ldots$ and initial condition $a_0 = 2$.

Solution: Let $G(x)$ be the generating function for the sequence $\{a_k\}$, that is, $G(x) = \sum_{k=0}^{\infty} a_k x^k$. First note that

$$xG(x) = \sum_{k=0}^{\infty} a_k x^{k+1} = \sum_{k=1}^{\infty} a_{k-1} x^k.$$

Using the recurrence relation, we see that

$$G(x) - 3xG(x) = \sum_{k=0}^{\infty} a_k x^k - 3 \sum_{k=1}^{\infty} a_{k-1} x^k$$

$$= a_0 + \sum_{k=1}^{\infty} (a_k - 3a_{k-1}) x^k$$

$$= 2,$$

because $a_0 = 2$ and $a_k = 3a_{k-1}$. Thus,

$$G(x) - 3xG(x) = (1 - 3x)G(x) = 2.$$

Solving for $G(x)$ shows that $G(x) = 2/(1 - 3x)$. Using the identity $1/(1 - ax) = \sum_{k=0}^{\infty} a^k x^k$, from Table 1, we have

$$G(x) = 2 \sum_{k=0}^{\infty} 3^k x^k = \sum_{k=0}^{\infty} 2 \cdot 3^k x^k.$$

Consequently, $a_k = 2 \cdot 3^k$. ◄

Example 17 Suppose that a valid codeword is an n-digit number in decimal notation containing an even number of 0s. Let a_n denote the number of valid codewords of length n. In Example 7 of Section 4.1 we showed that the sequence $\{a_n\}$ satisfies the recurrence relation

$$a_n = 8a_{n-1} + 10^{n-1}$$

and the initial condition $a_1 = 9$. Use generating functions to find an explicit formula for a_n.

Solution: To make our work with generating functions simpler, we extend this sequence by setting $a_0 = 1$; when we assign this value to a_0 and use the recurrence relation, we have $a_1 = 8a_0 + 10^0 = 8 + 1 = 9$, which is consistent with our original initial condition. (It also makes sense because there is one code word of length 0—the empty string.)

We multiply both sides of the recurrence relation by x^n to obtain

$$a_n x^n = 8a_{n-1} x^n + 10^{n-1} x^n.$$

Let $G(x) = \sum_{n=0}^{\infty} a_n x^n$ be the generating function of the sequence $a_0, a_1, a_2, \ldots$. We sum both sides of the last equation starting with $n = 1$, to find that

$$G(x) - 1 = \sum_{n=1}^{\infty} a_n x^n = \sum_{n=1}^{\infty} (8a_{n-1} x^n + 10^{n-1} x^n)$$

$$= 8 \sum_{n=1}^{\infty} a_{n-1} x^n + \sum_{n=1}^{\infty} 10^{n-1} x^n$$

$$= 8x \sum_{n=1}^{\infty} a_{n-1} x^{n-1} + x \sum_{n=1}^{\infty} 10^{n-1} x^{n-1}$$

$$= 8x \sum_{n=0}^{\infty} a_n x^n + x \sum_{n=0}^{\infty} 10^n x^n$$

$$= 8xG(x) + x/(1 - 10x),$$

where we have used Example 5 to evaluate the second summation. Therefore, we have

$$G(x) - 1 = 8xG(x) + x/(1 - 10x).$$

Solving for $G(x)$ shows that

$$G(x) = \frac{1 - 9x}{(1 - 8x)(1 - 10x)}.$$

Expanding the right-hand side of this equation into partial fractions (as is done in the integration of rational functions studied in calculus) gives

$$G(x) = \frac{1}{2} \left(\frac{1}{1 - 8x} + \frac{1}{1 - 10x} \right).$$

Using Example 5 twice (once with $a = 8$ and once with $a = 10$) gives

$$G(x) = \frac{1}{2} \left(\sum_{n=0}^{\infty} 8^n x^n + \sum_{n=0}^{\infty} 10^n x^n \right)$$

$$= \sum_{n=0}^{\infty} \frac{1}{2} (8^n + 10^n) x^n.$$

Consequently, we have shown that

$$a_n = \frac{1}{2} (8^n + 10^n). \qquad \blacktriangleleft$$

Proving Identities via Generating Functions

In Chapter 3 we saw how combinatorial identities could be established using combinatorial proofs. Here we will show that such identities, as well as identities for extended binomial coefficients, can be proved using generating functions. Sometimes the generating function approach is simpler than other approaches, especially when it is simpler to work with the closed form of a generating function than with the terms of the sequence themselves. We illustrate how generating functions can be used to prove identities with Example 18.

Example 18   Use generating functions to show that

$$\sum_{k=0}^{n} C(n, k)^2 = C(2n, n)$$

whenever n is a positive integer.

Solution: First note that by the Binomial Theorem $C(2n, n)$ is the coefficient of x^n in $(1 + x)^{2n}$. However, we also have

$$(1 + x)^{2n} = [(1 + x)^n]^2$$
$$= [C(n, 0) + C(n, 1)x + C(n, 2)x^2 + \cdots + C(n, n)x^n]^2.$$

The coefficient of x^n in this expression is

$$C(n, 0)C(n, n) + C(n, 1)C(n, n - 1) + C(n, 2)C(n, n - 2) + \cdots + C(n, n)C(n, 0).$$

This equals $\sum_{k=0}^{n} C(n,k)^2$, because $C(n, n-k) = C(n,k)$. Because both $C(2n,n)$ and $\sum_{k=0}^{n} C(n,k)^2$ represent the coefficient of x^n in $(1+x)^{2n}$, they must be equal.   ◄

Exercise 22 at the end of this section ask that Pascal's identity and Vandermonde's identity be proved using generating functions.

Exercises

1. Find the generating function for the finite sequence 2, 2, 2, 2, 2, 2.

   In Exercises 2–4, by a **closed form** we mean an algebraic expression not involving a summation over a range of values or the use of ellipses.

2. Find a closed form for the generating function for each of these sequences. (For each sequence, use the most obvious choice of a sequence that follows the pattern of the initial terms listed.)

   a) 0, 2, 2, 2, 2, 2, 2, 0, 0, 0, 0, 0, ...

   b) 0, 0, 0, 1, 1, 1, 1, 1, 1, 1, ...

   c) 0, 1, 0, 0, 1, 0, 0, 1; 0, 0, 1, ...

   d) 2, 4, 8, 16, 32, 64, 128, 256, ...

   e) $\binom{7}{0}, \binom{7}{1}, \binom{7}{2}, \ldots, \binom{7}{7}, 0, 0, 0, 0, 0, \ldots$

   f) 2, −2, 2, −2, 2, −2, 2, −2, ...

   g) 1, 1, 0, 1, 1, 1, 1, 1, 1, 1, ...

   h) 0, 0, 0, 1, 2, 3, 4, ...

3. Find a closed form for the generating function for the sequence $\{a_n\}$, where

   a) $a_n = 5$ for all $n = 0, 1, 2, \ldots$.

   b) $a_n = 3^n$ for all $n = 0, 1, 2, \ldots$.

   c) $a_n = 2$ for $n = 3, 4, 5, \ldots$ and $a_0 = a_1 = a_2 = 0$.

   d) $a_n = 2n + 3$ for all $n = 0, 1, 2, \ldots$.

   e) $a_n = \binom{8}{n}$ for all $n = 0, 1, 2, \ldots$.

   f) $a_n = \binom{n+4}{n}$ for all $n = 0, 1, 2, \ldots$.

4. For each of these generating functions, provide a closed formula for the sequence it determines.

   a) $(3x-4)^3$ b) $(x^3+1)^3$ c) $1/(1-5x)$ d) $x^3/(1+3x)$ e) $x^2+3x+7+(1/(1-x^2))$
   f) $(x^4/(1-x^4)) - x^3 - x^2 - x - 1$ g) $x^2/(1-x)^2$ h) $2e^{2x}$

5. Find the coefficient of x^{10} in the power series of each of these functions.

   a) $(1 + x^5 + x^{10} + x^{15} + \cdots)^3$

   b) $(x^3 + x^4 + x^5 + x^6 + x^7 + \cdots)^3$

   c) $(x^4 + x^5 + x^6)(x^3 + x^4 + x^5 + x^6 + x^7)(1 + x + x^2 + x^3 + x^4 + \cdots)$

   d) $(x^2 + x^4 + x^6 + x^8 + \cdots)(x^3 + x^6 + x^9 + \cdots)(x^4 + x^8 + x^{12} + \cdots)$

   e) $(1 + x^2 + x^4 + x^6 + x^8 + \cdots)(1 + x^4 + x^8 + x^{12} + \cdots)(1 + x^6 + x^{12} + x^{18} + \cdots)$

6. Find the coefficient of x^{10} in the power series of each of these functions.

   a) $1/(1-2x)$ b) $1/(1+x)^2$ c) $1/(1-x)^3$ d) $1/(1+2x)^4$ e) $x^4/(1-3x)^3$

7. Use generating functions to determine the number of different ways 10 identical balloons can be given to four children if each child receives at least two balloons.

8. Use generating functions to determine the number of different ways 15 identical stuffed animals can be given to six children so that each child receives at least one but no more than three stuffed animals.

9. In how many ways can 25 identical donuts be distributed to four police officers so that each officer gets at least three but no more than seven donuts?

10. What is the generating function for the sequence $\{c_k\}$, where c_k is the number of ways to make change for k dollars using $1 bills, $2 bills, $5 bills, and $10 bills?

11. Give a combinatorial interpretation of the coefficient of x^4 in the expansion $(1 + x + x^2 + x^3 + \cdots)^3$. Use this interpretation to find this number.

12. a) What is the generating function for $\{a_k\}$, where a_k is the number of solutions of $x_1 + x_2 + x_3 = k$ when x_1, x_2, and x_3 are integers with $x_1 \geqslant 2, 0 \leqslant x_2 \leqslant 3$, and $2 \leqslant x_3 \leqslant 5$?

   b) Use your answer to part (a) to find a_6.

13. Explain how generating functions can be used to find the number of ways in which postage of r cents can be pasted on an envelope using 3-cent, 4-cent, and 20-cent stamps.

   a) Assume that the order the stamps are pasted on does not matter.

   b) Assume that the stamps are pasted in a row and the order in which they are pasted on matters.

   c) Use your answer to part (a) to determine the number of ways 46 cents of postage can be pasted on an envelope using 3-cent, 4-cent, and 20-cent stamps when the order the stamps are pasted on does not matter. (Use of a computer algebra program is advised.)

   d) Use your answer to part (b) to determine the number of ways 46 cents of postage can be pasted in a row on an envelope using 3-cent, 4-cent, and 20-cent stamps when the order in which the stamps are pasted on matters. (Use of a computer algebra program is advised.)

14. Use generating functions (and a computer algebra package, if available) to find the number of ways to make change for $1 using

   a) dimes and quarters.   b) nickels, dimes, and quarters.

   c) pennies, dimes, and quarters.   d) pennies, nickels, dimes, and quarters.

15. Use generating functions to find the number of ways to make change for $100 using

   a) $10, $20, and $50 bills.

   b) $5, $10, $20, and $50 bills.

   c) $5, $10, $20, and $50 bills if at least one bill of each denomination is used.

   d) $5, $10, and $20 bills if at least one and no more than four of each denomination is used.

16. If $G(x)$ is the generating function for the sequence $\{a_k\}$, what is the generating function for each of these sequences?

   a) $0, 0, 0, a_3, a_4, a_5, \ldots$ (assuming that terms follow the pattern of all but the first three terms)

   b) $a_0, 0, a_1, 0, a_2, 0, \ldots$

   c) $0, 0, 0, 0, a_0, a_1, a_2, \ldots$ (assuming that terms follow the pattern of all but the first four terms)

   d) $a_0, 2a_1, 4a_2, 8a_3, 16a_4, \ldots$

   e) $0, a_0, a_1/2, a_2/3, a_3/4, \ldots$ [*Hint: Calculus required* here.]

   f) $a_0, a_0 + a_1, a_0 + a_1 + a_2, a_0 + a_1 + a_2 + a_3, \ldots$

17. Use generating functions to solve the recurrence relation $a_k = 3a_{k-1} + 2$ with the initial condition $a_0 = 1$.

18. Use generating functions to solve the recurrence relation $a_k = 5a_{k-1} - 6a_{k-2}$ with initial conditions $a_0 = 6$ and $a_1 = 30$.

19. Use generating functions to solve the recurrence relation $a_k = 4a_{k-1} - 4a_{k-2} + k^2$ with initial conditions $a_0 = 2$ and $a_1 = 5$.

20. Use generating functions to find an explicit formula for the Fibonacci numbers.

*21. (*Calculus required*) Let $\{C_n\}$ be the sequence of Catalan numbers, that is, the solution to the recurrence relation $C_n = \sum_{k=0}^{n-1} C_k C_{n-k-1}$ with $C_0 = C_1 = 1$ (see Example 8 in Section 4.1).

   Show that if $G(x)$ is the generating function for the sequence of Catalan numbers, then $xG(x)^2 - G(x) + 1 = 0$. Conclude (using the initial conditions) that $G(x) = (1 - \sqrt{1 - 4x})/(2x)$.

22. Use generating functions to prove Vandermonde's identity: $C(m+n,r) = \sum_{k=0}^{r} C(m, r-k)C(n,k)$, whenever m, n, and r are nonnegative integers with r not exceeding either m or n. [*Hint:* Look at the coefficient of x^r in both sides of $(1+x)^{m+n} = (1+x)^m(1+x)^n$.]

23. Find a closed form for the exponential generating function for the sequence $\{a_n\}$, where
    a) $a_n = 2$.   b) $a_n = (-1)^n$.   c) $a_n = 3^n$.   d) $a_n = n+1$.   e) $a_n = 1/(n+1)$.

24. Find the sequence with each of these functions as its exponential generating function.
    a) $f(x) = e^{-x}$ b) $f(x) = 3x^{2x}$ c) $f(x) = e^{3x} - 3e^{2x}$ d) $f(x) = (1-x) + e^{-2x}$
    e) $f(x) = e^{-2x} - (1/(1-x))$ f) $f(x) = e^{-3x} - (1+x) + (1/(1-2x))$ g) $f(x) = e^{x^2}$

25. A coding system encodes messages using strings of octal (base 8) digits. A codeword is considered valid if and only if it contains an even number of 7s.
    a) Find a linear nonhomogeneous recurrence relation for the number of valid codewords of length n. What are the initial conditions?
    b) Solve this recurrence relation using Theorem 6 in Section 4.2.
    c) Solve this recurrence relation using generating functions.

    Generating functions are useful in studying the number of different types of partitions of an integer n. A **partition** of a positive integer is a way to write this integer as the sum of positive integers where repetition is allowed and the order of the integers in the sum does not matter. For example, the partitions of 5 (with no restrictions) are $1+1+1+1+1, 1+1+1+2, 1+1+3, 1+2+2, 1+4, 2+3$, and 5. Exercises 26–28 illustrate some of these uses.

26. Show that the coefficient $p(n)$ of x^n in the formal power series expansion of $1/((1-x)(1-x^2)(1-x^3)\cdots)$ equals the number of partitions of n.

27. Show that the coefficient $p_d(n)$ of x^n in the formal power series expansion of $(1+x)(1+x^2)(1+x^3)\cdots$ equals the number of partitions of n into distinct parts, that is, the number of ways to write n as the sum of positive integers, where the order does not matter but no repetitions are allowed.

28. Show that if n is a positive integer, then the number of partitions of n into distinct parts equals the number of partitions of n into odd parts with repetitions allowed; that is, $p_o(n) = p_d(n)$. [*Hint:* Show that the generating functions for $p_o(n)$ and $p_d(n)$ are equal.]

29. (*Requires calculus*) Show that if G_X is the probability generating function for a random variable X such that $X(s)$ is a nonnegative integer for all $s \in S$, then
    a) $G_X(1) = 1$.   b) $E(X) = G_X'(1)$.   c) $V(X) = G_X''(1) + G_X'(1) - G_X'(1)^2$.

30. Let m be a positive integer. Let X_m be the random variable whose value is n if the mth success occurs on the $(n+m)$th trial when independent Bernoulli trials are performed, each with probability of success p.

    Find the expected value and the variance of X_m using Exercise 29 and the closed form for the probability generating function in part (a).

4.5   Inclusion–Exclusion

Introduction

A discrete mathematics class contains 30 women and 50 sophomores. How many students in the class are either women or sophomores? This question cannot be answered unless more information is provided. Adding the number of women in the class and the number of sophomores probably does not give the correct answer, because women sophomores are counted twice. This observation shows that the number of students in the class that are either sophomores or women is the sum of the number of women and the number of sophomores in the class minus the number of women sophomores. A technique for solving such counting problems was introduced in Section 3.1. In this section we will generalize the ideas introduced in that section to solve problems that require us to count the number of elements in the union of more than two sets.

The Principle of Inclusion-Exclusion

How many elements are in the union of two finite sets? In Section 2.2 we showed that the number of elements in the union of the two sets A and B is the sum of the numbers of elements in the sets minus the number of elements in their intersection. That is,

$$|A \cup B| = |A| + |B| - |A \cap B|.$$

As we showed in Section 3.1, the formula for the number of elements in the union of two sets is useful in counting problems. Examples 1–3 provide additional illustrations of the usefulness of this formula.

Example 1   In a discrete mathematics class every student is a major in computer science or mathematics, or both. The number of students having computer science as a major (possibly along with mathematics) is 25; the number of students having mathematics as a major (possibly along with computer science) is 13; and the number of students majoring in both computer science and mathematics is 8. How many students are in this class?

Solution: Let A be the set of students in the class majoring in computer science and B be the set of students in the class majoring in mathematics. Then $A \cap B$ is the set of students in the class who are joint mathematics and computer science majors. Because every student in the class is majoring in either computer science or mathematics (or both), it follows that the number of students in the class is $|A \cup B|$. Therefore,

$$|A \cup B| = |A| + |B| - |A \cap B|$$
$$= 25 + 13 - 8$$
$$= 30.$$

Therefore, there are 30 students in the class. This computation is illustrated in Figure 1.   ◄

$$|A \cup B| = |A| + |B| - |A \cap B| = 25 + 13 - 8 = 30$$

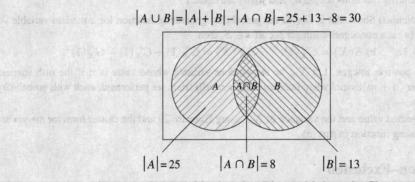

$$|A| = 25 \qquad |A \cap B| = 8 \qquad |B| = 13$$

Figure 1   The Set of Students in a Discrete Mathematics Class.

Example 2   How many positive integers not exceeding 1000 are divisible by 7 or 11?

Solution: Let A be the set of positive integers not exceeding 1000 that are divisible by 7, and let B be the set of positive integers not exceeding 1000 that are divisible by 11. Then $A \cup B$ is the set of integers not exceeding 1000 that are divisible by either 7 or 11, and $A \cap B$ is the set of integers not exceeding 1000 that are divisible by both 7 and 11. We know that among the positive integers not exceeding 1000 there are $\lfloor 1000/7 \rfloor$ integers divisible by 7 and $\lfloor 1000/11 \rfloor$ divisible by 11. Because 7 and 11 are relatively prime, the integers divisible by both 7 and 11 are those divisible by $7 \cdot 11$. Consequently, there are $\lfloor 1000/(11 \cdot 7) \rfloor$ positive integers not exceeding 1000 that are divisible by both 7 and 11. It follows that there are

$$|A \cup B| = |A| + |B| - |A \cap B|$$

$$= \left\lfloor \frac{1000}{7} \right\rfloor + \left\lfloor \frac{1000}{11} \right\rfloor - \left\lfloor \frac{1000}{7 \cdot 11} \right\rfloor$$

$$= 142 + 90 - 12$$

$$= 220$$

positive integers not exceeding 1000 that are divisible by either 7 or 11. This computation is illustrated in Figure 2.   ◄

Example 3 shows how to find the number of elements in a finite universal set that are outside the union of two sets.

$$|A \cup B| = |A| + |B| - |A \cap B| = 142 + 90 - 12 = 220$$

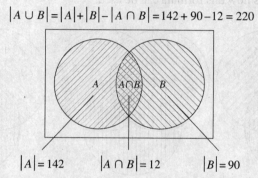

$$|A| = 142 \qquad |A \cap B| = 12 \qquad |B| = 90$$

Figure 2   The Set of Positive Integers Not Exceeding 1000 Divisible by Either 7 or 11.

Example 3   Suppose that there are 1807 freshmen at your school. Of these, 453 are taking a course in computer science, 567 are taking a course in mathematics, and 299 are taking courses in both computer science and mathematics. How many are not taking a course either in computer science or in mathematics?

Solution: To find the number of freshmen who are not taking a course in either mathematics or computer science, subtract the number that are taking a course in either of these subjects from the total number of freshmen. Let A be the set of all freshmen taking a course in computer science, and let B be the set of all freshmen taking a course in mathematics. It follows that $|A| = 453$, $|B| = 567$, and $|A \cap B| = 299$. The number of freshmen taking a course in either computer science or mathematics is

$$|A \cup B| = |A| + |B| - |A \cap B| = 453 + 567 - 299 = 721.$$

Consequently, there are $1807 - 721 = 1086$ freshmen who are not taking a course in computer science or mathematics.   ◄

We will now begin our development of a formula for the number of elements in the union of a finite number of sets. The formula we will develop is called the **principle of inclusion–exclusion.** For concreteness, before we consider unions of n sets, where n is any positive integer, we will derive a formula for the number of elements in the union of three sets A, B, and C. To construct this formula, we note that $|A| + |B| + |C|$ counts each element that is in exactly one of the three sets once, elements that are in exactly two of the sets twice, and elements in all three sets three times. This is illustrated in the first panel in Figure 3.

To remove the overcount of elements in more than one of the sets, we subtract the number of elements in the intersections of all pairs of the three sets. We obtain

$$|A| + |B| + |C| - |A \cap B| - |A \cap C| - |B \cap C|.$$

This expression still counts elements that occur in exactly one of the sets once. An element that occurs in exactly two of the sets is also counted exactly once, because this element will occur in one of the three intersections of sets taken two at a time. However, those elements that occur in all three sets will be counted zero times by this expression, because they occur in all three intersections of sets taken two at a time. This is illustrated in the second panel in Figure 3.

To remedy this undercount, we add the number of elements in the intersection of all three sets. This final expression counts each element once, whether it is in one, two, or three of the sets. Thus,

$$|A \cup B \cup C| = |A| + |B| + |C| - |A \cap B| - |A \cap C| - |B \cap C| + |A \cap B \cap C|.$$

This formula is illustrated in the third panel of Figure 3.

Example 4 illustrates how this formula can be used.

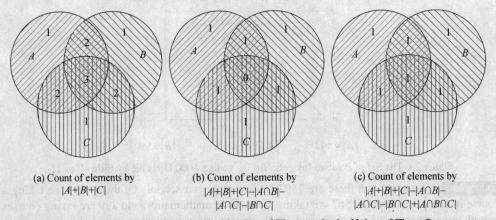

(a) Count of elements by
$|A|+|B|+|C|$

(b) Count of elements by
$|A|+|B|+|C|-|A\cap B|-$
$|A\cap C|-|B\cap C|$

(c) Count of elements by
$|A|+|B|+|C|-|A\cap B|-$
$|A\cap C|-|B\cap C|+|A\cap B\cap C|$

Figure 3   Finding a Formula for the Number of Elements in the Union of Three Sets.

Example 4   A total of 1232 students have taken a course in Spanish, 879 have taken a course in French, and 114 have taken a course in Russian. Further, 103 have taken courses in both Spanish and French, 23 have taken courses in both Spanish and Russian, and 14 have taken courses in both French and Russian. If 2092 students have taken at least one of Spanish, French, and Russian, how many students have taken a course in all three languages?

Solution: Let S be the set of students who have taken a course in Spanish, F the set of students who have taken a course in French, and R the set of students who have taken a course in Russian. Then

$$|S| = 1232, \quad |F| = 879, \quad |R| = 114,$$
$$|S \cap F| = 103, \quad |S \cap R| = 23, \quad |F \cap R| = 14,$$

and

$$|S \cup F \cup R| = 2092.$$

When we insert these quantities into the equation

$$|S \cup F \cup R| = |S| + |F| + |R| - |S \cap F| - |S \cap R| - |F \cap R| + |S \cap F \cap R|$$

we obtain

$$2092 = 1232 + 879 + 114 - 103 - 23 - 14 + |S \cap F \cap R|.$$

We now solve for $|S \cap F \cap R|$. We find that $|S \cap F \cap R| = 7$. Therefore, there are seven students who have taken courses in Spanish, French, and Russian. This is illustrated in Figure 4.   ◄

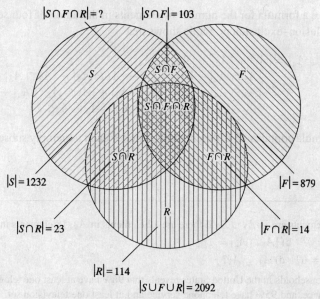

Figure 4   The Set of Students Who Have Taken Courses in Spanish, French, and Russian.

We will now state and prove the inclusion–exclusion principle, which tells us how many elements are in the union of a finite number of finite sets.

Theorem 1   The principle of inclusion–exclusion Let $A_1, A_2, \ldots, A_n$ be finite sets. Then

$$|A_1 \cup A_2 \cup \cdots \cup A_n| = \sum_{1 \leqslant i \leqslant n} |A_i| - \sum_{1 \leqslant i < j \leqslant n} |A_i \cap A_j|$$
$$+ \sum_{1 \leqslant i < j < k \leqslant n} |A_i \cap A_j \cap A_k| - \cdots + (-1)^{n+1} |A_1 \cap A_2 \cap \cdots \cap A_n|.$$

Proof: We will prove the formula by showing that an element in the union is counted exactly once by the right-hand side of the equation. Suppose that a is a member of exactly r of the sets $A_1, A_2, \ldots, A_n$ where $1 \leqslant r \leqslant n$. This element is counted $C(r, 1)$ times by $\Sigma |A_i|$. It is counted $C(r, 2)$ times by $\Sigma |A_i \cap A_j|$. In general, it is counted $C(r, m)$ times by the summation involving m of the sets A_i. Thus, this element is counted exactly

$$C(r, 1) - C(r, 2) + C(r, 3) - \cdots + (-1)^{r+1} C(r, r)$$

times by the expression on the right-hand side of this equation. Our goal is to evaluate this quantity. By Corollary 2 of Section 3.4, we have

$$C(r, 0) - C(r, 1) + C(r, 2) - \cdots + (-1)^r C(r, r) = 0.$$

Hence,

$$1 = C(r, 0) = C(r, 1) - C(r, 2) + \cdots + (-1)^{r+1} C(r, r).$$

Therefore, each element in the union is counted exactly once by the expression on the right-hand side of the equation. This proves the principle of inclusion–exclusion.   ◁

The inclusion–exclusion principle gives a formula for the number of elements in the union of n sets for every positive integer n. There are terms in this formula for the number of elements in the intersection of every nonempty subset of the collection of the n sets. Hence, there are $2^n - 1$ terms in this formula.

Example 5   Give a formula for the number of elements in the union of four sets.

Solution: The inclusion–exclusion principle shows that

$$
\begin{aligned}
|A_1 \cup A_2 \cup A_3 \cup A_4| = &|A_1| + |A_2| + |A_3| + |A_4| \\
&- |A_1 \cap A_2| - |A_1 \cap A_3| - |A_1 \cap A_4| - |A_2 \cap A_3| - |A_2 \cap A_4| \\
&- |A_3 \cap A_4| + |A_1 \cap A_2 \cap A_3| + |A_1 \cap A_2 \cap A_4| + |A_1 \cap A_3 \cap A_4| \\
&+ |A_2 \cap A_3 \cap A_4| - |A_1 \cap A_2 \cap A_3 \cap A_4|.
\end{aligned}
$$

Note that this formula contains 15 different terms, one for each nonempty subset of $\{A_1, A_2, A_3, A_4\}$.   ◀

Exercises

1. How many elements are in $A_1 \cup A_2$ if there are 12 elements in A_1, 18 elements in A_2, and
   a) $A_1 \cap A_2 = \emptyset$?   b) $|A_1 \cap A_2| = 1$?
   c) $|A_1 \cap A_2| = 6$?   d) $A_1 \subseteq A_2$?

2. A survey of households in the United States reveals that 96% have at least one television set, 98% have telephone service, and 95% have telephone service and at least one television set. What percentage of households in the United States have neither telephone service nor a television set?

3. Find the number of elements in $A_1 \cup A_2 \cup A_3$ if there are 100 elements in each set and if
   a) the sets are pairwise disjoint.
   b) there are 50 common elements in each pair of sets and no elements in all three sets.
   c) there are 50 common elements in each pair of sets and 25 elements in all three sets.
   d) the sets are equal.

4. There are 2504 computer science students at a school. Of these, 1876 have taken a course in Pascal, 999 have taken a course in Fortran, and 345 have taken a course in C. Further, 876 have taken courses in both Pascal and Fortran, 231 have taken courses in both Fortran and C, and 290 have taken courses in both Pascal and C. If 189 of these students have taken courses in Fortran, Pascal, and C, how many of these 2504 students have not taken a course in any of these three programming languages?

5. How many students are enrolled in a course either in calculus, discrete mathematics, data structures, or programming languages at a school if there are 507, 292, 312, and 344 students in these courses, respectively; 14 in both calculus and data structures; 213 in both calculus and programming languages; 211 in both discrete mathematics and data structures; 43 in both discrete mathematics and programming languages; and no student may take calculus and discrete mathematics, or data structures and programming languages, concurrently?

6. Find the number of positive integers not exceeding 100 that are either odd or the square of an integer.

7. How many bit strings of length eight do not contain six consecutive 0s?

8. How many permutations of the 10 digits either begin with the 3 digits 987, contain the digits 45 in the fifth and sixth positions, or end with the 3 digits 123?

9. How many elements are in the union of four sets if the sets have 50, 60, 70, and 80 elements, respectively, each pair of the sets has 5 elements in common, each triple of the sets has 1 common element, and no element is in all four sets?

10. Write out the explicit formula given by the principle of inclusion–exclusion for the number of elements in the union of five sets.

11. Write out the explicit formula given by the principle of inclusion–exclusion for the number of elements in the union of six sets when it is known that no three of these sets have a common intersection.

12. Let E_1, E_2, and E_3 be three events from a sample space S. Find a formula for the probability of $E_1 \cup E_2 \cup E_3$.

13. Find the probability that when four numbers from 1 to 100, inclusive, are picked at random with no repetitions allowed, either all are odd, all are divisible by 3, or all are divisible by 5.

14. Find a formula for the probability of the union of five events in a sample space if no four of them can occur at the same time.

15. Find a formula for the probability of the union of n events in a sample space.

4.6   Applications of Inclusion–Exclusion

Introduction

Many counting problems can be solved using the principle of inclusion–exclusion. For instance, we can use this principle to find the number of primes less than a positive integer. Many problems can be solved by counting the number of onto functions from one finite set to another. The inclusion–exclusion principle can be used to find the number of such functions. The famous hatcheck problem can be solved using the principle of inclusion–exclusion. This problem asks for the probability that no person is given the correct hat back by a hatcheck person who gives the hats back randomly.

An Alternative Form of Inclusion-Exclusion

There is an alternative form of the principle of inclusion–exclusion that is useful in counting problems. In particular, this form can be used to solve problems that ask for the number of elements in a set that have none of n properties $P_1, P_2, \ldots, P_n$.

Let A_i be the subset containing the elements that have property P_i. The number of elements with all the properties $P_{i_1}, P_{i_2}, \ldots, P_{i_k}$ will be denoted by $N(P_{i_1} P_{i_2} \cdots P_{i_k})$. Writing these quantities in terms of sets, we have

$$|A_{i_1} \cap A_{i_2} \cap \cdots \cap A_{i_k}| = N(P_{i_1} P_{i_2} \cdots P_{i_k}).$$

If the number of elements with none of the properties $P_1, P_2, \ldots, P_n$ is denoted by $N(P_1' P_2' \cdots P_n')$ and the number of elements in the set is denoted by N, it follows that

$$N(P_1' P_2' \cdots P_n') = N - |A_1 \cup A_2 \cup \cdots \cup A_n|.$$

From the inclusion–exclusion principle, we see that

$$N(P_1' P_2' \cdots P_n') = N - \sum_{1 \leqslant i \leqslant n} N(P_i) + \sum_{1 \leqslant i < j \leqslant n} N(P_i P_j)$$
$$- \sum_{1 \leqslant i < j < k \leqslant n} N(P_i P_j P_k) + \cdots + (-1)^n N(P_1 P_2 \cdots P_n).$$

Example 1 shows how the principle of inclusion–exclusion can be used to determine the number of solutions in integers of an equation with constraints.

Example 1   How many solutions does

$$x_1 + x_2 + x_3 = 11$$

have, where x_1, x_2, and x_3 are nonnegative integers with $x_1 \leqslant 3$, $x_2 \leqslant 4$, and $x_3 \leqslant 6$?
Solution: To apply the principle of inclusion–exclusion, let a solution have property P_1 if $x_1 > 3$, property P_2 if $x_2 > 4$, and property P_3 if $x_3 > 6$. The number of solutions satisfying the inequalities $x_1 \leqslant 3$, $x_2 \leqslant 4$, and $x_3 \leqslant 6$ is

$$N(P_1' P_2' P_3') = N - N(P_1) - N(P_2) - N(P_3) + N(P_1 P_2)$$
$$+ N(P_1 P_3) + N(P_2 P_3) - N(P_1 P_2 P_3).$$

Using the same techniques as in Example 5 of Section 3.5, it follows that

■ N = total number of solutions = $C(3 + 11 - 1, 11) = 78$,

■ $N(P_1)$ = (number of solutions with $x_1 \geqslant 4$) = $C(3 + 7 - 1, 7) = C(9, 7) = 36$,

■ $N(P_2)$ = (number of solutions with $x_2 \geqslant 5$) = $C(3 + 6 - 1, 6) = C(8, 6) = 28$,

■ $N(P_3)$ = (number of solutions with $x_3 \geqslant 7$) = $C(3 + 4 - 1, 4) = C(6, 4) = 15$,

■ $N(P_1 P_2)$ = (number of solutions with $x_1 \geqslant 4$ and $x_2 \geqslant 5$) = $C(3+2-1, 2) = C(4, 2) = 6$,

■ $N(P_1 P_3)$ = (number of solutions with $x_1 \geqslant 4$ and $x_3 \geqslant 7$) = $C(3 + 0 - 1, 0) = 1$,

■ $N(P_2 P_3)$ = (number of solutions with $x_2 \geqslant 5$ and $x_3 \geqslant 7$) = 0,

■ $N(P_1 P_2 P_3)$ = (number of solutions with $x_1 \geqslant 4$, $x_2 \geqslant 5$, and $x_3 \geqslant 7$) = 0.

Inserting these quantities into the formula for $N(P_1' P_2' P_3')$ shows that the number of solutions with $x_1 \leqslant 3$, $x_2 \leqslant 4$, and $x_3 \leqslant 6$ equals

$$N(P_1' P_2' P_3') = 78 - 36 - 28 - 15 + 6 + 1 + 0 - 0 = 6. \qquad \blacktriangleleft$$

The Sieve of Eratosthenes

The principle of inclusion–exclusion can be used to find the number of primes not exceeding a specified positive integer. Recall that a composite integer is divisible by a prime not exceeding its square root. So, to find the number of primes not exceeding 100, first note that composite integers not exceeding 100 must have a prime factor not exceeding 10. Because the only primes less than 10 are 2, 3, 5, and 7, the primes not exceeding 100 are these four primes and those positive integers greater than 1 and not exceeding 100 that are divisible by none of 2, 3, 5, or 7. To apply the principle of inclusion–exclusion, let P_1 be the property that an integer is divisible by 2, let P_2 be the property that an integer is divisible by 3, let P_3 be the property that an integer is divisible by 5, and let P_4 be the property that an integer is divisible by 7. Thus, the number of primes not exceeding 100 is

$$4 + N(P_1' P_2' P_3' P_4').$$

Because there are 99 positive integers greater than 1 and not exceeding 100, the principle of inclusion–exclusion shows that

$$
\begin{aligned}
N(P_1' P_2' P_3' P_4') = {} & 99 - N(P_1) - N(P_2) - N(P_3) - N(P_4) \\
& + N(P_1 P_2) + N(P_1 P_3) + N(P_1 P_4) + N(P_2 P_3) + N(P_2 P_4) + N(P_3 P_4) \\
& - N(P_1 P_2 P_3) - N(P_1 P_2 P_4) - N(P_1 P_3 P_4) - N(P_2 P_3 P_4) \\
& + N(P_1 P_2 P_3 P_4).
\end{aligned}
$$

The number of integers not exceeding 100 (and greater than 1) that are divisible by all the primes in a subset of $\{2, 3, 5, 7\}$ is $\lfloor 100/N \rfloor$, where N is the product of the primes in this subset. (This follows because any two of these primes have no common factor.) Consequently,

$$
\begin{aligned}
N(P_1' P_2' P_3' P_4') = {} & 99 - \left\lfloor \frac{100}{2} \right\rfloor - \left\lfloor \frac{100}{3} \right\rfloor - \left\lfloor \frac{100}{5} \right\rfloor - \left\lfloor \frac{100}{7} \right\rfloor \\
& + \left\lfloor \frac{100}{2 \cdot 3} \right\rfloor + \left\lfloor \frac{100}{2 \cdot 5} \right\rfloor + \left\lfloor \frac{100}{2 \cdot 7} \right\rfloor + \left\lfloor \frac{100}{3 \cdot 5} \right\rfloor + \left\lfloor \frac{100}{3 \cdot 7} \right\rfloor + \left\lfloor \frac{100}{5 \cdot 7} \right\rfloor \\
& - \left\lfloor \frac{100}{2 \cdot 3 \cdot 5} \right\rfloor - \left\lfloor \frac{100}{2 \cdot 3 \cdot 7} \right\rfloor - \left\lfloor \frac{100}{2 \cdot 5 \cdot 7} \right\rfloor - \left\lfloor \frac{100}{3 \cdot 5 \cdot 7} \right\rfloor + \left\lfloor \frac{100}{2 \cdot 3 \cdot 5 \cdot 7} \right\rfloor \\
= {} & 99 - 50 - 33 - 20 - 14 + 16 + 10 + 7 + 6 + 4 + 2 - 3 - 2 - 1 - 0 + 0 \\
= {} & 21.
\end{aligned}
$$

Hence, there are $4 + 21 = 25$ primes not exceeding 100.

The **Sieve of Eratosthenes** is used to find all primes not exceeding a specified positive integer. For instance, the following procedure is used to find the primes not exceeding 100. First the integers that are divisible by 2, other than 2, are deleted. Because 3 is the first integer greater than 2 that is left, all those integers divisible by 3, other than 3, are deleted. Because 5 is the next integer left after 3, those integers divisible by 5, other than 5, are deleted. The next integer left is 7, so those integers divisible by 7, other than 7, are deleted. Because all composite integers not exceeding 100 are divisible by 2, 3, 5, or 7, all remaining integers except 1 are prime. In Table 1, the panels display those integers deleted at each stage, where each integer divisible by 2, other than 2, is underlined in the first panel, each integer divisible by 3, other than 3, is underlined in the second panel, each integer divisible by 5, other than 5, is underlined in the third panel, and each integer divisible by 7, other than 7, is underlined in the fourth panel. The integers not underlined are the primes not exceeding 100.

TABLE 1   The Sieve of Eratosthenes.

Integers divisible by 2 other than 2 receive an underline.

1	2	3	4	5	6	7	8	9	10
11	12	13	14	15	16	17	18	19	20
21	22	23	24	25	26	27	28	29	30
31	32	33	34	35	36	37	38	39	40
41	42	43	44	45	46	47	48	49	50
51	52	53	54	55	56	57	58	59	60
61	62	63	64	65	66	67	68	69	70
71	72	73	74	75	76	77	78	79	80
81	82	83	84	85	86	87	88	89	90
91	92	93	94	95	96	97	98	99	100

Integers divisible by 3 other than 3 receive an underline.

1	2	3	4	5	6	7	8	9	10
11	12	13	14	15	16	17	18	19	20
21	22	23	24	25	26	27	28	29	30
31	32	33	34	35	36	37	38	39	40
41	42	43	44	45	46	47	48	49	50
51	52	53	54	55	56	57	58	59	60
61	62	63	64	65	66	67	68	69	70
71	72	73	74	75	76	77	78	79	80
81	82	83	84	85	86	87	88	89	90
91	92	93	94	95	96	97	98	99	100

Integers divisible by 5 other than 5 receive an underline.

1	2	3	4	5	6	7	8	9	10
11	12	13	14	15	16	17	18	19	20
21	22	23	24	25	26	27	28	29	30
31	32	33	34	35	36	37	38	39	40
41	42	43	44	45	46	47	48	49	50
51	52	53	54	55	56	57	58	59	60
61	62	63	64	65	66	67	68	69	70
71	72	73	74	75	76	77	78	79	80
81	82	83	84	85	86	87	88	89	90
91	92	93	94	95	96	97	98	99	100

Integers divisible by 7 other than 7 receive an underline; integers in color are prime.

1	2	3	4	5	6	7	8	9	10
11	12	13	14	15	16	17	18	19	20
21	22	23	24	25	26	27	28	29	30
31	32	33	34	35	36	37	38	39	40
41	42	43	44	45	46	47	48	49	50
51	52	53	54	55	56	57	58	59	60
61	62	63	64	65	66	67	68	69	70
71	72	73	74	75	76	77	78	79	80
81	82	83	84	85	86	87	88	89	90
91	92	93	94	95	96	97	98	99	100

The Number of Onto Functions

The principle of inclusion–exclusion can also be used to determine the number of onto functions from a set with m elements to a set with n elements. First consider Example 2.

Example 2   How many onto functions are there from a set with six elements to a set with three elements?

Solution: Suppose that the elements in the codomain are b_1, b_2, and b_3. Let P_1, P_2, and P_3 be the properties that b_1, b_2, and b_3 are not in the range of the function, respectively. Note that a function is onto if and only if it has none of the properties P_1, P_2, or P_3. By the inclusion–exclusion principle it follows that the number of onto functions from a set with six elements to a set with three elements is

$$N(P_1'P_2'P_3') = N - [N(P_1) + N(P_2) + N(P_3)]$$
$$+ [N(P_1P_2) + N(P_1P_3) + N(P_2P_3)] - N(P_1P_2P_3),$$

where N is the total number of functions from a set with six elements to one with three elements. We will evaluate each of the terms on the right-hand side of this equation.

From Example 6 of Section 3.1, it follows that $N = 3^6$. Note that $N(P_i)$ is the number of functions that do not have b_i in their range. Hence, there are two choices for the value of the function at each element of the domain. Therefore, $N(P_i) = 2^6$. Furthermore, there are $C(3,1)$ terms of this kind. Note that $N(P_iP_j)$ is the number of functions that do not have b_i and b_j in their range. Hence, there is only one choice for the value of the function at each element of the domain. Therefore, $N(P_iP_j) = 1^6 = 1$. Furthermore, there are $C(3,2)$ terms of this kind. Also, note that $N(P_1P_2P_3) = 0$, because this term is the number of functions that have none of b_1, b_2, and b_3 in their range. Clearly, there are no such functions. Therefore, the number of onto functions from a set with six elements to one with three elements is

$$3^6 - C(3,1)2^6 + C(3,2)1^6 = 729 - 192 + 3 = 540. \qquad \blacktriangleleft$$

The general result that tells us how many onto functions there are from a set with m elements to one with n elements will now be stated. The proof of this result is left as an exercise for the reader.

Theorem 1   Let m and n be positive integers with $m \geqslant n$. Then, there are

$$n^m - C(n,1)(n-1)^m + C(n,2)(n-2)^m - \cdots + (-1)^{n-1}C(n,n-1) \cdot 1^m$$

onto functions from a set with m elements to a set with n elements.

An onto function from a set with m elements to a set with n elements corresponds to a way to distribute the m elements in the domain to n indistinguishable boxes so that no box is empty, and then to associate each of the n elements of the codomain to a box. This means that the number of onto functions from a set with m elements to a set with n elements is the number of ways to distribute m distinguishable objects to n indistinguishable boxes so that no box is empty multiplied by the number of permutations of a set with n elements. Consequently, the number of onto functions from a set with m elements to a set with n elements equals $n!S(m,n)$, where $S(m,n)$ is a *Stirling number of the second kind* defined in Section 3.5. This means that we can use Theorem 1 to deduce the formula given in Section 3.5 for $S(m,n)$. (See Chapter 6 of [MiRo91] for more details about Stirling numbers of the second kind.)

One of the many different applications of Theorem 1 will now be described.

Example 3   How many ways are there to assign five different jobs to four different employees if every employee is assigned at least one job?

Solution: Consider the assignment of jobs as a function from the set of five jobs to the set of four employees. An assignment where every employee gets at least one job is the same as an onto function from the set of jobs to the set of employees. Hence, by Theorem 1 it follows that there are
$$4^5 - C(4,1)3^5 + C(4,2)2^5 - C(4,3)1^5 = 1024 - 972 + 192 - 4 = 240$$

ways to assign the jobs so that each employee is assigned at least one job. $\qquad \blacktriangleleft$

Derangements

The principle of inclusion–exclusion will be used to count the permutations of n objects that leave no objects in their original positions. Consider Example 4.

Example 4   **The Hatcheck Problem**   A new employee checks the hats of n people at a restaurant, forgetting to put claim check numbers on the hats. When customers return for their hats, the checker gives them back hats chosen at random from the remaining hats. What is the probability that no one receives the correct hat?   ◀

Remark: The answer is the number of ways the hats can be arranged so that there is no hat in its original position divided by $n!$, the number of permutations of n hats. We will return to this example after we find the number of permutations of n objects that leave no objects in their original position.

A **derangement** is a permutation of objects that leaves no object in its original position. To solve the problem posed in Example 4 we will need to determine the number of derangements of a set of n objects.

Example 5   The permutation 21453 is a derangement of 12345 because no number is left in its original position. However, 21543 is not a derangement of 12345, because this permutation leaves 4 fixed.   ◀

Let D_n denote the number of derangements of n objects. For instance, $D_3 = 2$, because the derangements of 123 are 231 and 312. We will evaluate D_n, for all positive integers n, using the principle of inclusion–exclusion.

Theorem 2   The number of derangements of a set with n elements is

$$D_n = n! \left[1 - \frac{1}{1!} + \frac{1}{2!} - \frac{1}{3!} + \cdots + (-1)^n \frac{1}{n!} \right].$$

Proof: Let a permutation have property P_i if it fixes element i. The number of derangements is the number of permutations having none of the properties P_i for $i = 1, 2, \ldots, n$. This means that

$$D_n = N(P_1' P_2' \cdots P_n').$$

Using the principle of inclusion–exclusion, it follows that

$$D_n = N - \sum_i N(P_i) + \sum_{i<j} N(P_i P_j) - \sum_{i<j<k} N(P_i P_j P_k)$$
$$+ \cdots + (-1)^n N(P_1 P_2 \cdots P_n),$$

where N is the number of permutations of n elements. This equation states that the number of permutations that fix no elements equals the total number of permutations, less the number that fix at least one element, plus the number that fix at least two elements, less the number that fix at least three elements, and so on. All the quantities that occur on the right-hand side of this equation will now be found.

First, note that $N = n!$, because N is simply the total number of permutations of n elements. Also, $N(P_i) = (n-1)!$. This follows from the product rule, because $N(P_i)$ is the number of permutations that fix element i, so the ith position of the permutation is determined, but each of the remaining positions can be filled arbitrarily. Similarly,

$$N(P_i P_j) = (n-2)!,$$

because this is the number of permutations that fix elements i and j, but where the other $n-2$ elements can be arranged arbitrarily. In general, note that

$$N(P_{i_1} P_{i_2} \cdots P_{i_m}) = (n-m)!,$$

because this is the number of permutations that fix elements $i_1, i_2, \ldots, i_m$, but where the other $n-m$ elements can be arranged arbitrarily. Because there are $C(n, m)$ ways to choose m elements from n, it follows that

$$\sum_{1 \leqslant i \leqslant n} N(P_i) = C(n,1)(n-1)!,$$

$$\sum_{1 \leqslant i < j \leqslant n} N(P_i P_j) = C(n,2)(n-2)!,$$

and in general,

$$\sum_{1 \leqslant i_1 < i_2 < \cdots < i_m \leqslant n} N(P_{i_1} P_{i_2} \cdots P_{i_m}) = C(n,m)(n-m)!.$$

TABLE 2 The Probability of a Derangement.

n	2	3	4	5	6	7
$D_n/n!$	0.50000	0.33333	0.37500	0.36667	0.36806	0.36786

Consequently, inserting these quantities into our formula for D_n gives

$$D_n = n! - C(n,1)(n-1)! + C(n,2)(n-2)! - \cdots + (-1)^n C(n,n)(n-n)!$$

$$= n! - \frac{n!}{1!(n-1)!}(n-1)! + \frac{n!}{2!(n-2)!}(n-2)! - \cdots + (-1)^n \frac{n!}{n!\,0!}0!.$$

Simplifying this expression gives

$$D_n = n! \left[1 - \frac{1}{1!} + \frac{1}{2!} - \cdots + (-1)^n \frac{1}{n!} \right]. \qquad \triangleleft$$

It is now simple to find D_n for a given positive integer n. For instance, using Theorem 2, it follows that

$$D_3 = 3! \left[1 - \frac{1}{1!} + \frac{1}{2!} - \frac{1}{3!} \right] = 6 \left(1 - 1 + \frac{1}{2} - \frac{1}{6} \right) = 2,$$

as we have previously remarked.

The solution of the problem in Example 4 can now be given.

Solution: The probability that no one receives the correct hat is $D_n/n!$. By Theorem 2, this probability is

$$\frac{D_n}{n!} = 1 - \frac{1}{1!} + \frac{1}{2!} - \cdots + (-1)^n \frac{1}{n!}.$$

The values of this probability for $2 \leqslant n \leqslant 7$ are displayed in Table 2.

Using methods from calculus it can be shown that

$$e^{-1} = 1 - \frac{1}{1!} + \frac{1}{2!} - \cdots + (-1)^n \frac{1}{n!} + \cdots \sim 0.368.$$

Because this is an alternating series with terms tending to zero, it follows that as n grows without bound, the probability that no one receives the correct hat converges to $e^{-1} \sim 0.368$. In fact, this probability can be shown to be within $1/(n+1)!$ of e^{-1}.   ◀

Exercises

1. Suppose that in a bushel of 100 apples there are 20 that have worms in them and 15 that have bruises. Only those apples with neither worms nor bruises can be sold. If there are 10 bruised apples that have worms in them, how many of the 100 apples can be sold?

2. How many solutions does the equation $x_1 + x_2 + x_3 = 13$ have where x_1, x_2, and x_3 are nonnegative integers less than 6?

3. Find the number of primes less than 200 using the principle of inclusion–exclusion.

4. How many positive integers less than 10,000 are not the second or higher power of an integer?

5. How many ways are there to distribute six different toys to three different children such that each child gets at least one toy?

6. In how many ways can seven different jobs be assigned to four different employees so that each employee is assigned at least one job and the most difficult job is assigned to the best employee?

7. How many derangements are there of a set with seven elements?

8. A machine that inserts letters into envelopes goes haywire and inserts letters randomly into envelopes. What is the probability that in a group of 100 letters

   a) no letter is put into the correct envelope?

   b) exactly one letter is put into the correct envelope?

   c) exactly 98 letters are put into the correct envelopes?

   d) exactly 99 letters are put into the correct envelopes?

   e) all letters are put into the correct envelopes?

*9. How many ways can the digits 0, 1, 2, 3, 4, 5, 6, 7, 8, 9 be arranged so that no even digit is in its original position?

10. For which positive integers n is D_n, the number of derangements of n objects, even?

*11. Use the principle of inclusion–exclusion to derive a formula for $\phi(n)$ when the prime factorization of n is

$$n = p_1^{a_1} p_2^{a_2} \cdots p_m^{a_m}.$$

12. How many derangements of $\{1, 2, 3, 4, 5, 6\}$ begin with the integers 1, 2, and 3, in some order?

13. Prove Theorem 1.

Key Terms and Results

TERMS

recurrence relation: a formula expressing terms of a sequence, except for some initial terms, as a function of one or more previous terms of the sequence

initial conditions for a recurrence relation: the values of the terms of a sequence satisfying the recurrence relation before this relation takes effect

linear homogeneous recurrence relation with constant coefficients: a recurrence relation that expresses the terms of a sequence, except initial terms, as a linear combination of previous terms

characteristic roots of a linear homogeneous recurrence relation with constant coefficients: the roots of the polynomial associated with a linear homogeneous recurrence relation with constant coefficients

linear nonhomogeneous recurrence relation with constant coefficients: a recurrence relation that expresses the terms of a sequence, except for initial terms, as a linear combination of previous terms plus a function that is not identically zero that depends only on the index

divide-and-conquer algorithm: an algorithm that solves a problem recursively by splitting it into a fixed number of smaller problems of the same type

generating function of a sequence: the formal series that has the nth term of the sequence as the coefficient of x^n

sieve of Eratosthenes: a procedure for finding the primes less than a specified positive integer

derangement: a permutation of objects such that no object is in its original place

RESULTS

the formula for the number of elements in the union of two finite sets:

$$|A \cup B| = |A| + |B| - |A \cap B|$$

the formula for the number of elements in the union of three finite sets:

$$|A \cup B \cup C| = |A| + |B| + |C| - |A \cap B| - |A \cap C|$$
$$- |B \cap C| + |A \cap B \cap C|$$

the principle of inclusion–exclusion:

$$|A_1 \cup A_2 \cup \cdots \cup A_n| = \sum_{1 \leq i \leq n} |A_i| - \sum_{1 \leq i < j \leq n} |A_i \cap A_j|$$

$$+ \sum_{1 \leq i < j < k \leq n} |A_i \cap A_j \cap A_k|$$

$$- \cdots + (-1)^{n+1} |A_1 \cap A_2 \cap \cdots \cap A_n|$$

the number of onto functions from a set with m elements to a set with n elements:

$$n^m - C(n,1)(n-1)^m + C(n,2)(n-2)^m$$
$$- \cdots + (-1)^{n-1} C(n, n-1) \cdot 1^m$$

the number of derangements of n objects:

$$D_n = n! \left[1 - \frac{1}{1!} + \frac{1}{2!} - \cdots + (-1)^n \frac{1}{n!} \right]$$

Review Questions

1. a) What is a recurrence relation?

    b) Find a recurrence relation for the amount of money that will be in an account after n years if $1,000,000 is deposited in an account yielding 9% annually.

2. Explain how the Fibonacci numbers are used to solve Fibonacci's problem about rabbits.

3. a) Find a recurrence relation for the number of steps needed to solve the Tower of Hanoi puzzle.

    b) Show how this recurrence relation can be solved using iteration.

4. a) Explain how to find a recurrence relation for the number of bit strings of length n not containing two consecutive 1s.

    b) Describe another counting problem that has a solution satisfying the same recurrence relation.

5. Define a linear homogeneous recurrence relation of degree k.

6. a) Explain how to solve linear homogeneous recurrence relations of degree 2.

    b) Solve the recurrence relation $a_n = 13a_{n-1} - 22a_{n-2}$ for $n \geq 2$ if $a_0 = 3$ and $a_1 = 15$.

    c) Solve the recurrence relation $a_n = 14a_{n-1} - 49a_{n-2}$ for $n \geq 2$ if $a_0 = 3$ and $a_1 = 35$.

7. a) Explain how to find $f(b^k)$ where k is a positive integer if $f(n)$ satisfies the divide-and-conquer recurrence relation $f(n) = af(n/b) + g(n)$ whenever b divides the positive integer n.

    b) Find $f(256)$ if $f(n) = 3f(n/4) + 5n/4$ and $f(1) = 7$.

8. a) Derive a divide-and-conquer recurrence relation for the number of comparisons used to find a number in a list using a binary search.

    b) Give a big-O estimate for the number of comparisons used by a binary search from the divide-and-conquer recurrence relation you gave in (a) using Theorem 1 in Section 4.3.

9. a) Give a formula for the number of elements in the union of three sets.

   b) Explain why this formula is valid.

   c) Explain how to use the formula from a) to find the number of integers not exceeding 1000 that are divisible by 6, 10, or 15.

   d) Explain how to use the formula from a) to find the number of solutions in nonnegative integers to the equation $x_1 + x_2 + x_3 + x_4 = 22$ with $x_1 < 8$, $x_2 < 6$, and $x_3 < 5$.

10. a) Give a formula for the number of elements in the union of four sets and explain why it is valid.

   b) Suppose the sets A_1, A_2, A_3, and A_4 each contain 25 elements, the intersection of any two of these sets contains 5 elements, the intersection of any three of these sets contains 2 elements, and 1 element is in all four of the sets. How many elements are in the union of the four sets?

11. a) State the principle of inclusion–exclusion.

   b) Outline a proof of this principle.

12. Explain how the principle of inclusion–exclusion can be used to count the number of onto functions from a set with m elements to a set with n elements.

13. a) How can you count the number of ways to assign m jobs to n employees so that each employee is assigned at least one job?

   b) How many ways are there to assign seven jobs to three employees so that each employee is assigned at least one job?

14. Explain how the inclusion–exclusion principle can be used to count the number of primes not exceeding the positive integer n.

15. a) Define a derangement.

   b) Why is counting the number of ways a hatcheck person can return hats to n people, so that no one receives the correct hat, the same as counting the number of derangements of n objects?

   c) Explain how to count the number of derangements of n objects.

Supplementary Exercises

1. A group of 10 people begin a chain letter, with each person sending the letter to four other people. Each of these people sends the letter to four additional people.

   a) Find a recurrence relation for the number of letters sent at the nth stage of this chain letter, if no person ever receives more than one letter.

   b) What are the initial conditions for the recurrence relation in part (a)?

   c) How many letters are sent at the nth stage of the chain letter?

2. A nuclear reactor has created 18 grams of a particular radioactive isotope. Every hour 1% of a radioactive isotope decays.

   a) Set up a recurrence relation for the amount of this isotope left after n hours.

   b) What are the initial conditions for the recurrence relation in part (a)?

   c) Solve this recurrence relation.

3. Every hour the U.S. government prints 10,000 more $1 bills, 4000 more $5 bills, 3000 more $10 bills, 2500 more $20 bills, 1000 more $50 bills, and the same number of $100 bills as it did the previous hour. In the initial hour 1000 of each bill were produced.

   a) Set up a recurrence relation for the amount of money produced in the nth hour.

   b) What are the initial conditions for the recurrence relation in part (a)?

   c) Solve the recurrence relation for the amount of money produced in the nth hour.

   d) Set up a recurrence relation for the total amount of money produced in the first n hours.

   e) Solve the recurrence relation for the total amount of money produced in the first n hours.

4. Suppose that every hour there are two new bacteria in a colony for each bacterium that was present the previous hour, and that all bacteria 2 hours old die. The colony starts with 100 new bacteria.

   a) Set up a recurrence relation for the number of bacteria present after n hours.

   b) What is the solution of this recurrence relation?

   c) When will the colony contain more than 1 million bacteria?

5. Messages are sent over a communications channel using two different signals. One signal requires 2 microseconds for transmittal, and the other signal requires 3 microseconds for transmittal. Each signal of a message is followed immediately by the next signal.

   a) Find a recurrence relation for the number of different signals that can be sent in n microseconds.

   b) What are the initial conditions of the recurrence relation in part (a)?

   c) How many different messages can be sent in 12 microseconds?

6. A small post office has only 4-cent stamps, 6-cent stamps, and 10-cent stamps. Find a recurrence relation for the number of ways to form postage of n cents with these stamps if the order that the stamps are used matters. What are the initial conditions for this recurrence relation?

7. How many ways are there to form these postages using the rules described in Exercise 6?

   a) 12 cents   b) 14 cents   c) 18 cents   d)22 cents

8. Find the solutions of the simultaneous system of congruences

$$a_n = a_{n-1} + b_{n-1}$$
$$b_n = a_{n-1} - b_{n-1}$$

with $a_0 = 1$ and $b_0 = 2$.

9. Solve the recurrence relation $a_n = a_{n-1}^2/a_{n-2}$ if $a_0 = 1$ and $a_1 = 2$. [*Hint:* Take logarithms of both sides to obtain a recurrence relation for the sequence $\log a_n$, $n = 0, 1, 2, \ldots$.]

*10. Solve the recurrence relation $a_n = a_{n-1}^3 a_{n-2}^2$ if $a_0 = 2$ and $a_1 = 2$. (See the hint for Exercise 9.)

11. Find the solution of the recurrence relation $a_n = 3a_{n-1} - 3a_{n-2} + a_{n-3} + 1$ if $a_0 = 2$, $a_1 = 4$, and $a_2 = 8$.

12. Find the solution of the recurrence relation $a_n = 3a_{n-1} - 3a_{n-2} + a_{n-3}$ if $a_0 = 2$, $a_1 = 2$, and $a_2 = 4$.

*13. Suppose that in Example 4 of Section 4.1 a pair of rabbits leaves the island after reproducing twice. Find a recurrence relation for the number of rabbits on the island in the middle of the nth month.

14. Find the solution to the recurrence relation $f(n) = 3f(n/5) + 2n^4$, when n is divisible by 5, for $n = 5^k$, where k is a positive integer and $f(1) = 1$.

15. Estimate the size of f in Exercise 14 if f is an increasing function.

16. Find a recurrence relation that describes the number of comparisons used by the following algorithm: Find the largest and second largest elements of a sequence of n numbers recursively by splitting the sequence into two subsequences with an equal number of terms, or where there is one more term in one subsequence than in the other, at each stage. Stop when subsequences with two terms are reached.

17. Estimate the number of comparisons used by the algorithm described in Exercise 16.

   Let $\{a_n\}$ be a sequence of real numbers. The **forward differences** of this sequence are defined recursively as follows: The **first forward difference** is $\Delta a_n = a_{n+1} - a_n$; the $(k+1)$**st forward difference** $\Delta^{k+1} a_n$ is obtained from $\Delta^k a_n$ by $\Delta^{k+1} a_n = \Delta^k a_{n+1} - \Delta^k a_n$.

18. Find Δa_n, where

   a) $a_n = 3$.   b) $a_n = 4n + 7$.   c) $a_n = n^2 + n + 1$.

19. Let $a_n = 3n^3 + n + 2$. Find $\Delta^k a_n$, where k equals

   a) 2.   b) 3.   c) 4.

*20. Suppose that $a_n = P(n)$, where P is a polynomial of degree d. Prove that $\Delta^{d+1} a_n = 0$ for all nonnegative integers n.

21. Let $\{a_n\}$ and $\{b_n\}$ be sequences of real numbers. Show that

$$\Delta(a_n b_n) = a_{n+1}(\Delta b_n) + b_n(\Delta a_n).$$

22. Show that if $F(x)$ and $G(x)$ are the generating functions for the sequences $\{a_k\}$ and $\{b_k\}$, respectively, and c and d are real numbers, then $(cF + dG)(x)$ is the generating function for $\{ca_k + db_k\}$.

23. (*Requires calculus*) This exercise shows how generating functions can be used to solve the recurrence relation $(n + 1)a_{n+1} = a_n + (1/n!)$ for $n \geqslant 0$ with initial condition $a_0 = 1$.
    a) Let $G(x)$ be the generating function for $\{a_n\}$. Show that $G'(x) = G(x) + e^x$ and $G(0) = 1$.
    b) Show from part (a) that $(e^{-x}G(x))' = 1$, and conclude that $G(x) = xe^x + e^x$.
    c) Use part (b) to find a closed form for a_n.

24. Suppose that 14 students receive an A on the first exam in a discrete mathematics class, and 18 receive an A on the second exam. If 22 students received an A on either the first exam or the second exam, how many students received an A on both exams?

25. There are 323 farms in Monmouth County that have at least one of horses, cows, and sheep. If 224 have horses, 85 have cows, 57 have sheep, and 18 farms have all three types of animals, how many farms have exactly two of these three types of animals?

26. Queries to a database of student records at a college produced the following data: There are 2175 students at the college, 1675 of these are not freshmen, 1074 students have taken a course in calculus, 444 students have taken a course in discrete mathematics, 607 students are not freshmen and have taken calculus, 350 students have taken calculus and discrete mathematics, 201 students are not freshmen and have taken discrete mathematics, and 143 students are not freshmen and have taken both calculus and discrete mathematics. Can all the responses to the queries be correct?

27. Students in the school of mathematics at a university major in one or more of the following four areas: applied mathematics (AM), pure mathematics (PM), operations research (OR), and computer science (CS). How many students are in this school if (including joint majors) there are 23 students majoring in AM; 17 students majoring in PM; 44 in OR; 63 in CS; 5 in AM and PM; 8 in AM and CS; 4 in AM and OR; 6 in PM and CS; 5 in PM and OR; 14 in OR and CS; 2 in PM, OR, and CS; 2 in AM, OR, and CS; 1 in PM, AM, and OR; 1 in PM, AM, and CS; and 1 in all four fields.

28. How many terms are needed when the inclusion–exclusion principle is used to express the number of elements in the union of seven sets if no more than five of these sets have a common element?

29. How many solutions in positive integers are there to the equation $x_1 + x_2 + x_3 = 20$ with $2 < x_1 < 6$, $6 < x_2 < 10$, and $0 < x_3 < 5$?

30. How many positive integers less than 1,000,000 are
    a) divisible by 2, 3, or 5?
    b) not divisible by 7, 11, or 13?
    c) divisible by 3 but not by 7?

31. How many positive integers less than 200 are
    a) second or higher powers of integers?
    b) either second or higher powers of integers or primes?
    c) not divisible by the square of an integer greater than 1?
    d) not divisible by the cube of an integer greater than 1?
    e) not divisible by three or more primes?

*32. How many ways are there to assign six different jobs to three different employees if the hardest job is assigned to the most experienced employee and the easiest job is assigned to the least experienced employee?

33. What is the probability that exactly one person is given back the correct hat by a hatcheck person who gives n people their hats back at random?

34. How many bit strings of length six do not contain four consecutive 1s?

35. What is the probability that a bit string of length six contains at least four 1s?

Computer Projects

Write programs with these input and output.

1. Given a positive integer n, list all the moves required in the Tower of Hanoi puzzle to move n disks from one peg to another according to the rules of the puzzle.

2. Given a positive integer n and an integer k with $1 \leqslant k \leqslant n$, list all the moves used by the Frame–Stewart algorithm to move n disks from one peg to another using four pegs according to the rules of the puzzle.

3. Given a positive integer n, list all the bit sequences of length n that do not have a pair of consecutive 0s.

4. Given a positive integer n, write out all ways to parenthesize the product of $n + 1$ variables.

5. Given a recurrence relation $a_n = c_1 a_{n-1} + c_2 a_{n-2}$, where c_1 and c_2 are real numbers, initial conditions $a_0 = C_0$ and $a_1 = C_1$, and a positive integer k, find a_k using iteration.

6. Given a recurrence relation $a_n = c_1 a_{n-1} + c_2 a_{n-2}$ and initial conditions $a_0 = C_0$ and $a_1 = C_1$, determine the unique solution.

7. Given a recurrence relation of the form $f(n) = af(n/b) + c$, where a is a real number, b is a positive integer, and c is a real number, and a positive integer k, find $f(b^k)$ using iteration.

8. Given the number of elements in the intersection of three sets, the number of elements in each pairwise intersection of these sets, and the number of elements in each set, find the number of elements in their union.

9. Given a positive integer n, produce the formula for the number of elements in the union of n sets.

10. Given positive integers m and n, find the number of onto functions from a set with m elements to a set with n elements.

11. Given a positive integer n, list all the derangements of the set $\{1, 2, 3, \ldots, n\}$.

Computations and Explorations

Use a computational program or programs you have written to do these exercises.

1. Find the exact value of f_{100}, f_{500}, and f_{1000}, where f_n is the nth Fibonacci number.

2. Find the smallest Fibonacci number greater than 1,000,000, greater than 1,000,000,000, and greater than 1,000,000,000,000.

3. Find as many prime Fibonacci numbers as you can. It is unknown whether there are infinitely many of these.

4. Write out all the moves required to solve the Tower of Hanoi puzzle with 10 disks.

5. Write out all the moves required to use the Frame–Stewart algorithm to move 20 disks from one peg to another peg using four pegs according to the rules of the Reve's puzzle.

6. Verify the Frame conjecture for solving the Reve's puzzle for n disks for as many integers n as possible by showing that the puzzle cannot be solved using fewer moves than are made by the Frame–Stewart algorithm with the optimal choice of k.

7. Compute the number of operations required to multiply two integers with n bits for various integers n including 16, 64, 256, and 1024 using the fast multiplication described in Section 4.3 and the standard algorithm for multiplying integers .

8. Compute the number of operations required to multiply two $n \times n$ matrices for various integers n including 4, 16, 64, and 128 using the fast matrix multiplication described in Section 4.3 and the standard algorithm for multiplying matrices.

9. Use the sieve of Eratosthenes to find all the primes not exceeding 1000.

10. Find the number of primes not exceeding 10,000 using the method described in Section 4.6 to find the number of primes not exceeding 100.

11. List all the derangements of $\{1, 2, 3, 4, 5, 6, 7, 8\}$.

12. Compute the probability that a permutation of n objects is a derangement for all positive integers not exceeding 20 and determine how quickly these probabilities approach the number e.

Writing Projects

Respond with essays using outside sources.

1. Find the original source where Fibonacci presented his puzzle about modeling rabbit populations. Discuss this problem and other problems posed by Fibonacci and give some information about Fibonacci himself.

2. Explain how the Fibonacci numbers arise in a variety of applications, such as in phyllotaxis, the study of arrangement of leaves in plants, in the study of reflections by mirrors, and so on.

3. Describe different variations of the Tower of Hanoi puzzle, including those with more than three pegs (including the Reve's puzzle discussed in the text and exercises), those where disk moves are restricted, and those where disks may have the same size. Include what is known about the number of moves required to solve each variation.

4. Discuss as many different problems as possible where the Catalan numbers arise.

5. Describe the solution of Ulam's problem involving searching with one lie found by Andrzej Pelc.

6. Discuss variations of Ulam's problem involving searching with more than one lie and what is known about this problem.

7. Define the convex hull of a set of points in the plane and describe divide-and-conquer algorithms for finding the convex hull of a set of points in the plane.

8. Look up the definition of the *lucky numbers*. Explain how they are found using a sieve technique similar to the sieve of Eratosthenes. Find all the lucky numbers less than 1000.

9. Describe how sieve methods are used in number theory. What kind of results have been established using such methods?

10. Look up the rules of the old French card game of *rencontres*. Describe these rules and describe the work of Pierre Raymond de Montmort on *le problème de rencontres*.

11. Describe how exponential generating functions can be used to solve a variety of counting problems.

12. Describe the Polyá theory of counting and the kind of counting problems that can be solved using this theory.

13. The *problème des ménages* (the problem of the households) asks for the number of ways to arrange n couples around a table so that the sexes alternate and no husband and wife are seated together. Explain the method used by E. Lucas to solve this problem.

14. Explain how *rook polynomials* can be used to solve counting problems.

Chapter 5

Relations

Relationships between elements of sets occur in many contexts. Every day we deal with relationships such as those between a business and its telephone number, an employee and his or her salary, a person and a relative, and so on. In mathematics we study relationships such as those between a positive integer and one that it divides, an integer and one that it is congruent to modulo 5, a real number and one that is larger than it, a real number x and the value $f(x)$ where f is a function, and so on. Relationships such as that between a program and a variable it uses and that between a computer language and a valid statement in this language often arise in computer science.

Relationships between elements of sets are represented using the structure called a relation, which is just a subset of the Cartesian product of the sets. Relations can be used to solve problems such as determining which pairs of cities are linked by airline flights in a network, finding a viable order for the different phases of a complicated project, or producing a useful way to store information in computer databases.

In some computer languages, only the first 31 characters of the name of a variable matter. The relation consisting of ordered pairs of strings where the first string has the same initial 31 characters as the second string is an example of a special type of relation, known as an equivalence relation. Equivalence relations arise throughout mathematics and computer science. We will study equivalence relations, and other special types of relations, in this chapter.

5.1 Relations and Their Properties

Introduction

The most direct way to express a relationship between elements of two sets is to use ordered pairs made up of two related elements. For this reason, sets of ordered pairs are called binary relations. In this section we introduce the basic terminology used to describe binary relations. Later in this chapter we will use relations to solve problems involving communications networks, project scheduling, and identifying elements in sets with common properties.

Definition 1 Let A and B be sets. A *binary relation from A to B* is a subset of $A \times B$.

In other words, a binary relation from A to B is a set R of ordered pairs where the first element of each ordered pair comes from A and the second element comes from B. We use the notation $a\,R\,b$ to denote that $(a, b) \in R$ and $a\,\cancel{R}\,b$ to denote that $(a, b) \notin R$. Moreover, when (a, b) belongs to R, a is said to be **related to** b by R.

Binary relations represent relationships between the elements of two sets. We will introduce n-ary relations, which express relationships among elements of more than two sets, later in this chapter. We will omit the word *binary* when there is no danger of confusion.

Examples 1–3 illustrate the notion of a relation.

Example 1 Let A be the set of students in your school, and let B be the set of courses. Let R be the relation that consists of those pairs (a, b), where a is a student enrolled in course b. For instance, if Jason Goodfriend and Deborah Sherman are enrolled in CS518, the pairs (Jason Goodfriend, CS518) and (Deborah Sherman, CS518) belong to R. If Jason Goodfriend is also enrolled in CS510, then the pair (Jason Goodfriend, CS510) is also in R. However, if Deborah Sherman is not enrolled in CS510, then the pair (Deborah Sherman, CS510) is not in R.

Note that if a student is not currently enrolled in any courses there will be no pairs in R that have this student as the first element. Similarly, if a course is not currently being offered there will be no pairs in R that have this course as their second element.   ◀

Example 2   Let A be the set of all cities, and let B be the set of the 50 states in the United States of America. Define the relation R by specifying that (a, b) belongs to R if city a is in state b. For instance, (Boulder, Colorado), (Bangor, Maine), (Ann Arbor, Michigan), (Middletown, New Jersey), (Middletown, New York), (Cupertino, California), and (Red Bank, New Jersey) are in R.   ◀

Example 3   Let $A = \{0, 1, 2\}$ and $B = \{a, b\}$. Then $\{(0, a), (0, b), (1, a), (2, b)\}$ is a relation from A to B. This means, for instance, that $0\,R\,a$, but that $1\,\not R\,b$. Relations can be represented graphically, as shown in Figure 1, using arrows to represent ordered pairs. Another way to represent this relation is to use a table, which is also done in Figure 1. We will discuss representations of relations in more detail in Section 8.3.   ◀

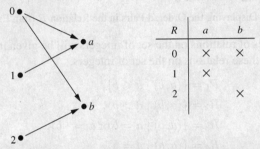

R	a	b
0	×	×
1	×	
2		×

Figure 1   Displaying the Ordered Pairs in the Relation R from Example 3.

Functions as Relations

Recall that a function f from a set A to a set B (as defined in Section 2.3) assigns exactly one element of B to each element of A. The graph of f is the set of ordered pairs (a, b) such that $b = f(a)$. Because the graph of f is a subset of $A \times B$, it is a relation from A to B. Moreover, the graph of a function has the property that every element of A is the first element of exactly one ordered pair of the graph.

Conversely, if R is a relation from A to B such that every element in A is the first element of exactly one ordered pair of R, then a function can be defined with R as its graph. This can be done by assigning to an element a of A the unique element $b \in B$ such that $(a, b) \in R$. (Note that the relation R in Example 2 is not the graph of a function because Middletown occurs more than once as the first element of an ordered pair in R.)

A relation can be used to express a one-to-many relationship between the elements of the sets A and B (as in Example 2), where an element of A may be related to more than one element of B. A function represents a relation where exactly one element of B is related to each element of A.

Relations are a generalization of functions; they can be used to express a much wider class of relationships between sets.

Relations on a Set

Relations from a set A to itself are of special interest.

Definition 2   A *relation on the set A* is a relation from A to A.

In other words, a relation on a set A is a subset of $A \times A$.

Example 4   Let A be the set $\{1, 2, 3, 4\}$. Which ordered pairs are in the relation $R = \{(a, b) \mid$ a divides $b\}$?

Solution: Because (a, b) is in R if and only if a and b are positive integers not exceeding 4 such that a divides b, we see that

$$R = \{(1, 1), (1, 2), (1, 3), (1, 4), (2, 2), (2, 4), (3, 3), (4, 4)\}.$$

The pairs in this relation are displayed both graphically and in tabular form in Figure 2.   ◄

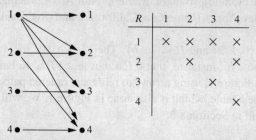

R	1	2	3	4
1	×	×	×	×
2		×		×
3			×	
4				×

Figure 2   Displaying the Ordered Pairs in the Relation R from Example 4.

Next, some examples of relations on the set of integers will be given in Example 5.

Example 5   Consider these relations on the set of integers:

$$R_1 = \{(a, b) \mid a \leqslant b\},$$
$$R_2 = \{(a, b) \mid a > b\},$$
$$R_3 = \{(a, b) \mid a = b \text{ or } a = -b\},$$
$$R_4 = \{(a, b) \mid a = b\},$$
$$R_5 = \{(a, b) \mid a = b + 1\},$$
$$R_6 = \{(a, b) \mid a + b \leqslant 3\}.$$

Which of these relations contain each of the pairs $(1, 1)$, $(1, 2)$, $(2, 1)$, $(1, -1)$, and $(2, 2)$?

Remark: Unlike the relations in Examples 1–4, these are relations on an infinite set.

Solution: The pair $(1, 1)$ is in R_1, R_3, R_4, and R_6; $(1, 2)$ is in R_1 and R_6; $(2, 1)$ is in R_2, R_5, and R_6; $(1, -1)$ is in R_2, R_3, and R_6; and finally, $(2, 2)$ is in R_1, R_3, and R_4.   ◄

It is not hard to determine the number of relations on a finite set, because a relation on a set A is simply a subset of $A \times A$.

Example 6   How many relations are there on a set with n elements?

Solution: A relation on a set A is a subset of $A \times A$. Because $A \times A$ has n^2 elements when A has n elements, and a set with m elements has 2^m subsets, there are 2^{n^2} subsets of $A \times A$. Thus, there are 2^{n^2} relations on a set with n elements. For example, there are $2^{3^2} = 2^9 = 512$ relations on the set $\{a, b, c\}$.   ◄

Properties of Relations

There are several properties that are used to classify relations on a set. We will introduce the most important of these here.

In some relations an element is always related to itself. For instance, let R be the relation on the set of all people consisting of pairs (x, y) where x and y have the same mother and the same father. Then xRx for every person x.

Definition 3   A relation R on a set A is called *reflexive* if $(a, a) \in R$ for every element $a \in A$.

Remark: Using quantifiers we see that the relation R on the set A is reflexive if $\forall a((a, a) \in R)$, where the universe of discourse is the set of all elements in A.

We see that a relation on A is reflexive if every element of A is related to itself. Examples 7–9 illustrate the concept of a reflexive relation.

Example 7 Consider the following relations on $\{1, 2, 3, 4\}$:

$$R_1 = \{(1,1), (1,2), (2,1), (2,2), (3,4), (4,1), (4,4)\},$$
$$R_2 = \{(1,1), (1,2), (2,1)\},$$
$$R_3 = \{(1,1), (1,2), (1,4), (2,1), (2,2), (3,3), (4,1), (4,4)\},$$
$$R_4 = \{(2,1), (3,1), (3,2), (4,1), (4,2), (4,3)\},$$
$$R_5 = \{(1,1), (1,2), (1,3), (1,4), (2,2), (2,3), (2,4), (3,3), (3,4), (4,4)\},$$
$$R_6 = \{(3,4)\}.$$

Which of these relations are reflexive?

Solution: The relations R_3 and R_5 are reflexive because they both contain all pairs of the form (a, a), namely, $(1, 1)$, $(2, 2)$, $(3, 3)$, and $(4, 4)$. The other relations are not reflexive because they do not contain all of these ordered pairs. In particular, R_1, R_2, R_4, and R_6 are not reflexive because $(3, 3)$ is not in any of these relations. ◄

Example 8 Which of the relations from Example 5 are reflexive?

Solution: The reflexive relations from Example 5 are R_1 (because $a \leqslant a$ for every integer a), R_3, and R_4. For each of the other relations in this example it is easy to find a pair of the form (a, a) that is not in the relation. (This is left as an exercise for the reader.) ◄

Example 9 Is the "divides" relation on the set of positive integers reflexive?

Solution: Because $a \mid a$ whenever a is a positive integer, the "divides" relation is reflexive. (Note that if we replace the set of positive integers with the set of all integers the relation is not reflexive because 0 does not divide 0.) ◄

In some relations an element is related to a second element if and only if the second element is also related to the first element. The relation consisting of pairs (x, y), where x and y are students at your school with at least one common class has this property. Other relations have the property that if an element is related to a second element, then this second element is not related to the first. The relation consisting of the pairs (x, y), where x and y are students at your school, where x has a higher grade point average than y has this property.

Definition 4 A relation R on a set A is called *symmetric* if $(b, a) \in R$ whenever $(a, b) \in R$, for all $a, b \in A$. A relation R on a set A such that for all $a, b \in A$, if $(a, b) \in R$ and $(b, a) \in R$, then $a = b$ is called *antisymmetric*.

Remark: Using quantifiers, we see that the relation R on the set A is symmetric if $\forall a \forall b ((a, b) \in R \rightarrow (b, a) \in R)$. Similarly, the relation R on the set A is antisymmetric if $\forall a \forall b (((a, b) \in R \wedge (b, a) \in R) \rightarrow (a = b))$.

That is, a relation is symmetric if and only if a is related to b implies that b is related to a. A relation is antisymmetric if and only if there are no pairs of distinct elements a and b with a related to b and b related to a. That is, the only way to have a related to b and b related to a is for a and b to be the same element. The terms *symmetric* and *antisymmetric* are not opposites, because a relation can have both of these properties or may lack both of them. A relation cannot be both symmetric and antisymmetric if it contains some pair of the form (a, b), where $a \neq b$.

Remark: Although relatively few of the 2^{n^2} relations on a set with n elements are symmetric or antisymmetric, as counting arguments can show, many important relations have one of these properties. (See Exercise 21.)

Example 10 Which of the relations from Example 7 are symmetric and which are antisymmetric?

Solution: The relations R_2 and R_3 are symmetric, because in each case (b, a) belongs to the relation whenever (a, b) does. For R_2, the only thing to check is that both $(2, 1)$ and $(1, 2)$ are in the relation. For R_3, it is necessary to check that both $(1,2)$ and $(2,1)$ belong to the relation, and $(1,4)$ and $(4,1)$ belong to the relation. The reader should verify that none of the other relations is symmetric. This is done by finding a pair (a,b) such that it is in the relation but (b,a) is not.

R_4, R_5, and R_6 are all antisymmetric. For each of these relations there is no pair of elements a and b with $a \neq b$ such that both (a,b) and (b,a) belong to the relation. The reader should verify that none of the other relations is antisymmetric. This is done by finding a pair (a,b) with $a \neq b$ such that (a,b) and (b,a) are both in the relation.   ◀

Example 11   Which of the relations from Example 5 are symmetric and which are antisymmetric?

Solution: The relations R_3, R_4, and R_6 are symmetric. R_3 is symmetric, for if $a = b$ or $a = -b$, then $b = a$ or $b = -a$. R_4 is symmetric because $a = b$ implies that $b = a$. R_6 is symmetric because $a+b \leqslant 3$ implies that $b+a \leqslant 3$. The reader should verify that none of the other relations is symmetric.

The relations R_1, R_2, R_4, and R_5 are antisymmetric. R_1 is antisymmetric because the inequalities $a \leqslant b$ and $b \leqslant a$ imply that $a = b$. R_2 is antisymmetric because it is impossible for $a > b$ and $b > a$. R_4 is antisymmetric, because two elements are related with respect to R_4 if and only if they are equal. R_5 is antisymmetric because it is impossible that $a = b+1$ and $b = a+1$. The reader should verify that none of the other relations is antisymmetric.   ◀

Example 12   Is the "divides" relation on the set of positive integers symmetric? Is it antisymmetric?

Solution: This relation is not symmetric because $1 \,|\, 2$, but $2 \nmid 1$. It is antisymmetric, for if a and b are positive integers with $a \,|\, b$ and $b \,|\, a$, then $a = b$ (the verification of this is left as an exercise for the reader).   ◀

Let R be the relation consisting of all pairs (x,y) of students at your school, where x has taken more credits than y. Suppose that x is related to y and y is related to z. This means that x has taken more credits than y and y has taken more credits than z. We can conclude that x has taken more credits than z, so that x is related to z. What we have shown is that R has the transitive property, which is defined as follows.

Definition 5   A relation R on a set A is called *transitive* if whenever $(a,b) \in R$ and $(b,c) \in R$, then $(a,c) \in R$, for all $a,b,c \in A$.

Remark: Using quantifiers we see that the relation R on a set A is transitive if we have $\forall a \forall b \forall c$ $(((a,b) \in R \land (b,c) \in R) \to (a,c) \in R)$.

Example 13   Which of the relations in Example 7 are transitive?

Solution: R_4, R_5, and R_6 are transitive. For each of these relations, we can show that it is transitive by verifying that if (a,b) and (b,c) belong to this relation, then (a,c) also does. For instance, R_4 is transitive, because $(3,2)$ and $(2,1)$, $(4,2)$ and $(2,1)$, $(4,3)$ and $(3,1)$, and $(4,3)$ and $(3,2)$ are the only such sets of pairs, and $(3,1)$, $(4,1)$, and $(4,2)$ belong to R_4. The reader should verify that R_5 and R_6 are transitive.

R_1 is not transitive because $(3,4)$ and $(4,1)$ belong to R_1, but $(3,1)$ does not. R_2 is not transitive because $(2,1)$ and $(1,2)$ belong to R_2, but $(2,2)$ does not. R_3 is not transitive because $(4,1)$ and $(1,2)$ belong to R_3, but $(4,2)$ does not.   ◀

Example 14   Which of the relations in Example 5 are transitive?

Solution: The relations R_1, R_2, R_3, and R_4 are transitive. R_1 is transitive because $a \leqslant b$ and $b \leqslant c$ imply that $a \leqslant c$. R_2 is transitive because $a > b$ and $b > c$ imply that $a > c$. R_3 is transitive because $a = \pm b$ and $b = \pm c$ imply that $a = \pm c$. R_4 is clearly transitive, as the reader should verify. R_5 is not transitive because $(2,1)$ and $(1,0)$ belong to R_5, but $(2,0)$ does not. R_6 is not transitive because $(2,1)$ and $(1,2)$ belong to R_6, but $(2,2)$ does not.   ◀

Example 15   Is the "divides" relation on the set of positive integers transitive?

Solution: Suppose that a divides b and b divides c. Then there are positive integers k and l such that $b = ak$ and $c = bl$. Hence, $c = a(kl)$, so a divides c. It follows that this relation is transitive.
◀

We can use counting techniques to determine the number of relations with specific properties. Finding the number of relations with a particular property provides information about how common this property is in the set of all relations on a set with n elements.

Example 16   How many reflexive relations are there on a set with n elements?

Solution: A relation R on a set A is a subset of $A \times A$. Consequently, a relation is determined by specifying whether each of the n^2 ordered pairs in $A \times A$ is in R. However, if R is reflexive, each of the n ordered pairs (a, a) for $a \in A$ must be in R. Each of the other $n(n - 1)$ ordered pairs of the form (a, b), where $a \neq b$, may or may not be in R. Hence, by the product rule for counting, there are $2^{n(n-1)}$ reflexive relations [this is the number of ways to choose whether each element (a, b), with $a \neq b$, belongs to R].
◀

The number of symmetric relations and the number of antisymmetric relations on a set with n elements can be found using reasoning similar to that in Example 16 (see Exercise 21 at the end of this section). Counting the transitive relations on a set with n elements is a problem beyond the scope of this book.

Combining Relations

Because relations from A to B are subsets of $A \times B$, two relations from A to B can be combined in any way two sets can be combined. Consider Examples 17–19.

Example 17   Let $A = \{1, 2, 3\}$ and $B = \{1, 2, 3, 4\}$. The relations $R_1 = \{(1, 1), (2, 2), (3, 3)\}$ and $R_2 = \{(1, 1), (1, 2), (1, 3), (1, 4)\}$ can be combined to obtain

$$R_1 \cup R_2 = \{(1, 1), (1, 2), (1, 3), (1, 4), (2, 2), (3, 3)\},$$
$$R_1 \cap R_2 = \{(1, 1)\},$$
$$R_1 - R_2 = \{(2, 2), (3, 3)\},$$
$$R_2 - R_1 = \{(1, 2), (1, 3), (1, 4)\}.$$
◀

Example 18   Let A and B be the set of all students and the set of all courses at a school, respectively. Suppose that R_1 consists of all ordered pairs (a, b), where a is a student who has taken course b, and R_2 consists of all ordered pairs (a, b), where a is a student who requires course b to graduate. What are the relations $R_1 \cup R_2$, $R_1 \cap R_2$, $R_1 \oplus R_2$, $R_1 - R_2$, and $R_2 - R_1$?

Solution: The relation $R_1 \cup R_2$ consists of all ordered pairs (a, b), where a is a student who either has taken course b or needs course b to graduate, and $R_1 \cap R_2$ is the set of all ordered pairs (a, b), where a is a student who has taken course b and needs this course to graduate. Also, $R_1 \oplus R_2$ consists of all ordered pairs (a, b), where student a has taken course b but does not need it to graduate or needs course b to graduate but has not taken it. $R_1 - R_2$ is the set of ordered pairs (a, b), where a has taken course b but does not need it to graduate; that is, b is an elective course that a has taken. $R_2 - R_1$ is the set of all ordered pairs (a, b), where b is a course that a needs to graduate but has not taken.
◀

Example 19   Let R_1 be the "less than" relation on the set of real numbers and let R_2 be the "greater than" relation on the set of real numbers, that is, $R_1 = \{(x, y) \mid x < y\}$ and $R_2 = \{(x, y) \mid x > y\}$. What are $R_1 \cup R_2$, $R_1 \cap R_2$, $R_1 - R_2$, $R_2 - R_1$, and $R_1 \oplus R_2$?

Solution: We note that $(x, y) \in R_1 \cup R_2$ if and only if $(x, y) \in R_1$ or $(x, y) \in R_2$. Hence, $(x, y) \in R_1 \cup R_2$ if and only if $x < y$ or $x > y$. Because the condition $x < y$ or $x > y$ is the same as the condition $x \neq y$, it follows that $R_1 \cup R_2 = \{(x, y) \mid x \neq y\}$. In other words, the union of the "less than" relation and the "greater than" relation is the "not equals" relation.

Next, note that it is impossible for a pair (x, y) to belong to both R_1 and R_2 because it is impossible for $x < y$ and $x > y$. It follows that $R_1 \cap R_2 = \emptyset$. We also see that $R_1 - R_2 = R_1$,

$R_2 - R_1 = R_2$, and $R_1 \oplus R_2 = R_1 \cup R_2 - R_1 \cap R_2 = \{(x,y) \mid x \neq y\}$.   ◄

There is another way that relations are combined that is analogous to the composition of functions.

Definition 6   Let R be a relation from a set A to a set B and S a relation from B to a set C. The *composite* of R and S is the relation consisting of ordered pairs (a,c), where $a \in A$, $c \in C$, and for which there exists an element $b \in B$ such that $(a,b) \in R$ and $(b,c) \in S$. We denote the composite of R and S by $S \circ R$.

Computing the composite of two relations requires that we find elements that are the second element of ordered pairs in the first relation and the first element of ordered pairs in the second relation, as Examples 20 and 21 illustrate.

Example 20   What is the composite of the relations R and S, where R is the relation from $\{1,2,3\}$ to $\{1,2,3,4\}$ with $R = \{(1,1),(1,4),(2,3),(3,1),(3,4)\}$ and S is the relation from $\{1,2,3,4\}$ to $\{0,1,2\}$ with $S = \{(1,0),(2,0),(3,1),(3,2),(4,1)\}$?

Solution: $S \circ R$ is constructed using all ordered pairs in R and ordered pairs in S, where the second element of the ordered pair in R agrees with the first element of the ordered pair in S. For example, the ordered pairs $(2,3)$ in R and $(3,1)$ in S produce the ordered pair $(2,1)$ in $S \circ R$. Computing all the ordered pairs in the composite, we find

$$S \circ R = \{(1,0),(1,1),(2,1),(2,2),(3,0),(3,1)\}.$$ ◄

Example 21   **Composing the Parent Relation with Itself**   Let R be the relation on the set of all people such that $(a,b) \in R$ if person a is a parent of person b. Then $(a,c) \in R \circ R$ if and only if there is a person b such that $(a,b) \in R$ and $(b,c) \in R$, that is, if and only if there is a person b such that a is a parent of b and b is a parent of c. In other words, $(a,c) \in R \circ R$ if and only if a is a grandparent of c.   ◄

The powers of a relation R can be recursively defined from the definition of a composite of two relations.

Definition 7   Let R be a relation on the set A. The powers $R^n, n = 1,2,3,\ldots$, are defined recursively by

$$R^1 = R \qquad \text{and} \qquad R^{n+1} = R^n \circ R.$$

The definition shows that $R^2 = R \circ R$, $R^3 = R^2 \circ R = (R \circ R) \circ R$, and so on.

Example 22   Let $R = \{(1,1),(2,1),(3,2),(4,3)\}$. Find the powers $R^n, n = 2,3,4,\ldots$.
Solution: Because $R^2 = R \circ R$, we find that $R^2 = \{(1,1),(2,1),(3,1),(4,2)\}$. Furthermore, because $R^3 = R^2 \circ R$, $R^3 = \{(1,1),(2,1),(3,1),(4,1)\}$. Additional computation shows that R^4 is the same as R^3, so $R^4 = \{(1,1),(2,1),(3,1),(4,1)\}$. It also follows that $R^n = R^3$ for $n = 5,6,7,\ldots$. The reader should verify this.   ◄

The following theorem shows that the powers of a transitive relation are subsets of this relation. It will be used in Section 5.4.

Theorem 1   The relation R on a set A is transitive if and only if $R^n \subseteq R$ for $n = 1,2,3,\ldots$.

Proof: We first prove the "if" part of the theorem. We suppose that $R^n \subseteq R$ for $n = 1,2,3,\ldots$. In particular, $R^2 \subseteq R$. To see that this implies R is transitive, note that if $(a,b) \in R$ and $(b,c) \in R$, then by the definition of composition, $(a,c) \in R^2$. Because $R^2 \subseteq R$, this means that $(a,c) \in R$. Hence, R is transitive.

We will use mathematical induction to prove the only if part of the theorem. Note that this part of the theorem is trivially true for $n = 1$.

Assume that $R^n \subseteq R$, where n is a positive integer. This is the inductive hypothesis. To complete the inductive step we must show that this implies that R^{n+1} is also a subset of R. To show this, assume that $(a,b) \in R^{n+1}$. Then, because $R^{n+1} = R^n \circ R$, there is an element x with

$x \in A$ such that $(a, x) \in R$ and $(x, b) \in R^n$. The inductive hypothesis, namely, that $R^n \subseteq R$, implies that $(x, b) \in R$. Furthermore, because R is transitive, and $(a, x) \in R$ and $(x, b) \in R$, it follows that $(a, b) \in R$. This shows that $R^{n+1} \subseteq R$, completing the proof. ◁

Exercises

1. List the ordered pairs in the relation R from $A = \{0, 1, 2, 3, 4\}$ to $B = \{0, 1, 2, 3\}$, where $(a, b) \in R$ if and only if
   a) $a = b$.   b) $a + b = 4$.   c) $a > b$.   d) $a \mid b$.   e) $\gcd(a, b) = 1$.   f) $\mathrm{lcm}(a, b) = 2$.

2. For each of these relations on the set $\{1, 2, 3, 4\}$, decide whether it is reflexive, whether it is symmetric, whether it is antisymmetric, and whether it is transitive.
   a) $\{(2, 2), (2, 3), (2, 4), (3, 2), (3, 3), (3, 4)\}$ b) $\{(1, 1), (1, 2), (2, 1), (2, 2), (3, 3), (4, 4)\}$
   c) $\{(2, 4), (4, 2)\}$ d) $\{(1, 2), (2, 3), (3, 4)\}$ e) $\{(1, 1), (2, 2), (3, 3), (4, 4)\}$
   f) $\{(1, 3), (1, 4), (2, 3), (2, 4), (3, 1), (3, 4)\}$

3. Determine whether the relation R on the set of all Web pages is reflexive, symmetric, antisymmetric, and/or transitive, where $(a, b) \in R$ if and only if
   a) everyone who has visited Web page a has also visited Web page b.
   b) there are no common links found on both Web page a and Web page b.
   c) there is at least one common link on Web page a and Web page b.
   d) there is a Web page that includes links to both Web page a and Web page b.

4. Determine whether the relation R on the set of all integers is reflexive, symmetric, antisymmetric, and/or transitive, where $(x, y) \in R$ if and only if
   a) $x \neq y$.   b) $xy \geqslant 1$.   c) $x = y + 1$ or $x = y - 1$.
   d) $x \equiv y \pmod 7$.   e) x is a multiple of y.
   f) x and y are both negative or both nonnegative.   g) $x = y^2$.   h) $x \geqslant y^2$.

5. Which relations in Exercise 2 are irreflexive?

6. Which relations in Exercise 3 are irreflexive?

7. Can a relation on a set be neither reflexive nor irreflexive?

8. Give an example of an irreflexive relation on the set of all people.
   A relation R is called **asymmetric** if $(a, b) \in R$ implies that $(b, a) \notin R$. Exercise 9 explore the notion of an asymmetric relation.

9. Use quantifiers to express what it means for a relation to be asymmetric.

10. How many different relations are there from a set with m elements to a set with n elements?

11. Let R be the relation $R = \{(a, b) \mid a \text{ divides } b\}$ on the set of positive integers. Find
    a) R^{-1}.   b) $\overline{R}$.

12. Suppose that the function f from A to B is a one-to-one correspondence. Let R be the relation that equals the graph of f. That is, $R = \{(a, f(a)) \mid a \in A\}$. What is the inverse relation R^{-1}?

13. Let A be the set of students at your school and B the set of books in the school library. Let R_1 and R_2 be the relations consisting of all ordered pairs (a, b), where student a is required to read book b in a course, and where student a has read book b, respectively. Describe the ordered pairs in each of these relations.
    a) $R_1 \cup R_2$ b) $R_1 \cap R_2$ c) $R_1 \oplus R_2$ d) $R_1 - R_2$ e) $R_2 - R_1$

14. Let R be the relation on the set of people consisting of pairs (a, b), where a is a parent of b. Let S be the relation on the set of people consisting of pairs (a, b), where a and b are siblings (brothers or sisters). What are $S \circ R$ and $R \circ S$?
    Exercises 15–16 deal with these relations on the set of real numbers:
    $$R_1 = \{(a, b) \in \mathbf{R}^2 \mid a > b\}, \text{ the "greater than" relation,}$$
    $$R_2 = \{(a, b) \in \mathbf{R}^2 \mid a \geqslant b\}, \text{ the "greater than or equal to" relation,}$$
    $$R_3 = \{(a, b) \in \mathbf{R}^2 \mid a < b\}, \text{ the "less than" relation,}$$
    $$R_4 = \{(a, b) \in \mathbf{R}^2 \mid a \leqslant b\}, \text{ the "less than or equal to" relation,}$$

$$R_5 = \{(a, b) \in \mathbf{R}^2 \mid a = b\}, \text{the "equal to" relation},$$
$$R_6 = \{(a, b) \in \mathbf{R}^2 \mid a \neq b\}, \text{the "unequal to" relation}.$$

15. Find
  a) $R_2 \cup R_4$.   b) $R_3 \cup R_6$.   c) $R_3 \cap R_6$.   d) $R_4 \cap R_6$.
  e) $R_3 - R_6$.   f) $R_6 - R_3$.   g) $R_2 \oplus R_6$.   h) $R_3 \oplus R_5$.

16. Find
  a) $R_2 \circ R_1$.   b) $R_2 \circ R_2$.   c) $R_3 \circ R_5$.   d) $R_4 \circ R_1$.
  e) $R_5 \circ R_3$.   f) $R_3 \circ R_6$.   g) $R_4 \circ R_6$.   h) $R_6 \circ R_6$.

17. Let R be the relation on the set of people with doctorates such that $(a, b) \in R$ if and only if a was the thesis advisor of b. When is an ordered pair (a, b) in R^2? When is an ordered pair (a, b) in R^n, when n is a positive integer? (Note that every person with a doctorate has a thesis advisor.)

18. Let R_1 and R_2 be the "congruent modulo 3" and the "congruent modulo 4" relations, respectively, on the set of integers. That is, $R_1 = \{(a, b) \mid a \equiv b \pmod{3}\}$ and $R_2 = \{(a, b) \mid a \equiv b \pmod{4}\}$. Find
  a) $R_1 \cup R_2$.   b) $R_1 \cap R_2$.   c) $R_1 - R_2$.   d) $R_2 - R_1$.   e) $R_1 \oplus R_2$.

19. How many of the 16 different relations on $\{0, 1\}$ contain the pair $(0, 1)$?

20. a) How many relations are there on the set $\{a, b, c, d\}$?
  b) How many relations are there on the set $\{a, b, c, d\}$ that contain the pair (a, a)?

*21. How many relations are there on a set with n elements that are
  a) symmetric?   b) antisymmetric?   c) asymmetric?   d) irreflexive?
  e) reflexive and symmetric?   f) neither reflexive nor irreflexive?

22. Find the error in the "proof" of the following "theorem." "Theorem": Let R be a relation on a set A that is symmetric and transitive. Then R is reflexive.
  "Proof": Let $a \in A$. Take an element $b \in A$ such that $(a, b) \in R$. Because R is symmetric, we also have $(b, a) \in R$. Now using the transitive property, we can conclude that $(a, a) \in R$ because $(a, b) \in R$ and $(b, a) \in R$.

23. Show that the relation R on a set A is symmetric if and only if $R = R^{-1}$, where R^{-1} is the inverse relation.

24. Show that the relation R on a set A is reflexive if and only if the inverse relation R^{-1} is reflexive.

25. Let R be a relation that is reflexive and transitive. Prove that $R^n = R$ for all positive integers n.

26. Let R be a reflexive relation on a set A. Show that R^n is reflexive for all positive integers n.

27. Suppose that the relation R is irreflexive. Is R^2 necessarily irreflexive? Give a reason for your answer.

5.2 n-ary Relations and Their Applications

Introduction

Relationships among elements of more than two sets often arise. For instance, there is a relationship involving the name of a student, the student's major, and the student's grade point average. Similarly, there is a relationship involving the airline, flight number, starting point, destination, departure time, and arrival time of a flight. An example of such a relationship in mathematics involves three integers, where the first integer is larger than the second integer, which is larger than the third. Another example is the betweenness relationship involving points on a line, such that three points are related when the second point is between the first and the third.

We will study relationships among elements from more than two sets in this section. These relationships are called **n-ary relations.** These relations are used to represent computer databases. These representations help us answer queries about the information stored in databases, such as: Which flights land at O'Hare Airport between 3 A.M. and 4 A.M.? Which students at your school are sophomores majoring in mathematics or computer science and have greater than a 3.0 average? Which employees of a company have worked for the company less than 5 years and make more than $50,000?

n-ary Relations

We begin with the basic definition on which the theory of relational databases rests.

Definition 1 Let $A_1, A_2, \ldots, A_n$ be sets. An *n-ary relation* on these sets is a subset of $A_1 \times A_2 \times \cdots \times A_n$. The sets $A_1, A_2, \ldots, A_n$ are called the *domains* of the relation, and n is called its *degree*.

Example 1 Let R be the relation on $\mathbf{N} \times \mathbf{N} \times \mathbf{N}$ consisting of triples (a, b, c), where a, b, and c are integers with $a < b < c$. Then $(1, 2, 3) \in R$, but $(2, 4, 3) \notin R$. The degree of this relation is 3. Its domains are all equal to the set of natural numbers. ◄

Example 2 Let R be the relation on $\mathbf{Z} \times \mathbf{Z} \times \mathbf{Z}$ consisting of all triples of integers (a, b, c) in which a, b, and c form an arithmetic progression. That is, $(a, b, c) \in R$ if and only if there is an integer k such that $b = a + k$ and $c = a + 2k$, or equivalently, such that $b - a = k$ and $c - b = k$. Note that $(1, 3, 5) \in R$ because $3 = 1 + 2$ and $5 = 1 + 2 \cdot 2$, but $(2, 5, 9) \notin R$ because $5 - 2 = 3$ while $9 - 5 = 4$. This relation has degree 3 and its domains are all equal to the set of integers. ◄

Example 3 Let R be the relation on $\mathbf{Z} \times \mathbf{Z} \times \mathbf{Z}^+$ consisting of triples (a, b, m), where a, b, and m are integers with $m \geqslant 1$ and $a \equiv b \pmod{m}$. Then $(8, 2, 3), (-1, 9, 5)$, and $(14, 0, 7)$ all belong to R, but $(7, 2, 3), (-2, -8, 5)$, and $(11, 0, 6)$ do not belong to R because $8 \equiv 2 \pmod 3$, $-1 \equiv 9 \pmod 5$, and $14 \equiv 0 \pmod 7$, but $7 \not\equiv 2 \pmod 3$, $-2 \not\equiv -8 \pmod 5$, and $11 \not\equiv 0 \pmod 6$. This relation has degree 3 and its first two domains are the set of all integers and its third domain is the set of positive integers. ◄

Example 4 Let R be the relation consisting of 5-tuples (A, N, S, D, T) representing airplane flights, where A is the airline, N is the flight number, S is the starting point, D is the destination, and T is the departure time. For instance, if Nadir Express Airlines has flight 963 from Newark to Bangor at 15:00, then (Nadir, 963, Newark, Bangor, 15:00) belongs to R. The degree of this relation is 5, and its domains are the set of all airlines, the set of flight numbers, the set of cities, the set of cities (again), and the set of times. ◄

Databases and Relations

The time required to manipulate information in a database depends on how this information is stored. The operations of adding and deleting records, updating records, searching for records, and combining records from overlapping databases are performed millions of times each day in a large database. Because of the importance of these operations, various methods for representing databases have been developed. We will discuss one of these methods, called the **relational data model**, based on the concept of a relation.

A database consists of **records,** which are *n*-tuples, made up of **fields.** The fields are the entries of the *n*-tuples. For instance, a database of student records may be made up of fields containing the name, student number, major, and grade point average of the student. The relational data model represents a database of records as an *n*-ary relation. Thus, student records are represented as 4-tuples of the form (*STUDENT NAME, ID NUMBER, MAJOR, GPA*). A sample database of six such records is

(Ackermann, 231455, Computer Science, 3.88)
(Adams, 888323, Physics, 3.45)
(Chou, 102147, Computer Science, 3.49)
(Goodfriend, 453876, Mathematics, 3.45)
(Rao, 678543, Mathematics, 3.90)
(Stevens, 786576, Psychology, 2.99).

Relations used to represent databases are also called **tables,** because these relations are often displayed as tables. Each column of the table corresponds to an *attribute* of the database. For instance, the same database of students is displayed in Table 1. The attributes of this database are Student Name, ID Number, Major, and GPA.

TABLE 1 Students.

Student_name	ID_number	Major	GPA
Ackermann	231455	Computer Science	3.88
Adams	888323	Physics	3.45
Chou	102147	Computer Science	3.49
Goodfriend	453876	Mathematics	3.45
Rao	678543	Mathematics	3.90
Stevens	786576	Psychology	2.99

A domain of an n-ary relation is called a **primary key** when the value of the n-tuple from this domain determines the n-tuple. That is, a domain is a primary key when no two n-tuples in the relation have the same value from this domain.

Records are often added to or deleted from databases. Because of this, the property that a domain is a primary key is time-dependent. Consequently, a primary key should be chosen that remains one whenever the database is changed. The current collection of n-tuples in a relation is called the **extension** of the relation. The more permanent part of a database, including the name and attributes of the database, is called its **intension.** When selecting a primary key, the goal should be to select a key that can serve as a primary key for all possible extensions of the database. To do this, it is necessary to examine the intension of the database to understand the set of possible n-tuples that can occur in an extension.

Example 5   Which domains are primary keys for the n-ary relation displayed in Table 1, assuming that no n-tuples will be added in the future?

Solution: Because there is only one 4-tuple in this table for each student name, the domain of student names is a primary key. Similarly, the ID numbers in this table are unique, so the domain of ID numbers is also a primary key. However, the domain of major fields of study is not a primary key, because more than one 4-tuple contains the same major field of study. The domain of grade point averages is also not a primary key, because there are two 4-tuples containing the same GPA. ◄

Combinations of domains can also uniquely identify n-tuples in an n-ary relation. When the values of a set of domains determine an n-tuple in a relation, the Cartesian product of these domains is called a **composite key.**

Example 6   Is the Cartesian product of the domain of major fields of study and the domain of GPAs a composite key for the n-ary relation from Table 1, assuming that no n-tuples are ever added?

Solution: Because no two 4-tuples from this table have both the same major and the same GPA, this Cartesian product is a composite key. ◄

Because primary and composite keys are used to identify records uniquely in a database, it is important that keys remain valid when new records are added to the database. Hence, checks should be made to ensure that every new record has values that are different in the appropriate field, or fields, from all other records in this table. For instance, it makes sense to use the student identification number as a key for student records if no two students ever have the same student identification number. A university should not use the name field as a key, because two students may have the same name (such as John Smith).

Operations on n-ary Relations

There are a variety of operations on n-ary relations that can be used to form new n-ary relations. Applied together, these operations can answer queries on databases that ask for all tuples that satisfy certain conditions.

The most basic operation on an *n*-ary relation is determining all *n*-tuples in the *n*-ary relation that satisfy certain conditions. For example, we may want to find all the records of all computer science majors in a database of student records. We may want to find all students who have a grade point average above 3.5 in this same database. We may want to find the records of all computer science majors who have a grade point average above 3.5 in this database. To perform such tasks we use the selection operator.

Definition 2   Let R be an *n*-ary relation and C a condition that elements in R may satisfy. Then the *selection operator* s_C maps the *n*-ary relation R to the *n*-ary relation of all *n*-tuples from R that satisfy the condition C.

Example 7   To find the records of computer science majors in the *n*-ary relation R shown in Table 1, we use the operator s_{C_1}, where C_1 is the condition Major = "Computer Science." The result is the two 4-tuples (Ackermann, 231455, Computer Science, 3.88) and (Chou, 102147, Computer Science, 3.49). Similarly, to find the records of students who have a grade point average above 3.5 in this database, we use the operator s_{C_2}, where C_2 is the condition GPA > 3.5. The result is the two 4-tuples (Ackermann, 231455, Computer Science, 3.88) and (Rao, 678543, Mathematics, 3.90). Finally, to find the records of computer science majors who have a GPA above 3.5, we use the operator s_{C_3}, where C_3 is the condition (Major = "Computer Science" $\land$ GPA > 3.5). The result consists of the single 4-tuple (Ackermann, 231455, Computer Science, 3.88).   ◄

Projections are used to form new *n*-ary relations by deleting the same fields in every record of the relation.

Definition 3   The *projection* $P_{i_1 i_2, \ldots, i_m}$ where $i_1 < i_2 < \cdots < i_m$, maps the *n*-tuple $(a_1, a_2, \ldots, a_n)$ to the *m*-tuple $(a_{i_1}, a_{i_2}, \ldots, a_{i_m})$, where $m \leqslant n$.

In other words, the projection $P_{i_1, i_2, \ldots, i_m}$ deletes $n - m$ of the components of an *n*-tuple, leaving the i_1th, i_2th, ..., and i_mth components.

Example 8   What results when the projection $P_{1,3}$ is applied to the 4-tuples $(2, 3, 0, 4)$, (Jane Doe, 234111001, Geography, 3.14), and (a_1, a_2, a_3, a_4)?

Solution: The projection $P_{1,3}$ sends these 4-tuples to $(2, 0)$, (Jane Doe, Geography), and (a_1, a_3), respectively.   ◄

Example 9 illustrates how new relations are produced using projections.

Example 9   What relation results when the projection $P_{1,4}$ is applied to the relation in Table 1?

Solution: When the projection $P_{1,4}$ is used, the second and third columns of the table are deleted, and pairs representing student names and grade point averages are obtained. Table 2 displays the results of this projection.   ◄

Fewer rows may result when a projection is applied to the table for a relation. This happens when some of the *n*-tuples in the relation have identical values in each of the m components of the projection, and only disagree in components deleted by the projection. For instance, consider the following example.

Example 10   What is the table obtained when the projection $P_{1,2}$ is applied to the relation in Table 3?

Solution: Table 4 displays the relation obtained when $P_{1,2}$ is applied to Table 3. Note that there are fewer rows after this projection is applied.   ◄

The **join** operation is used to combine two tables into one when these tables share some identical fields. For instance, a table containing fields for airline, flight number, and gate, and another table containing fields for flight number, gate, and departure time can be combined into a table containing fields for airline, flight number, gate, and departure time.

TABLE 2 GPAs.	
Student_name	*GPA*
Ackermann	3.88
Adams	3.45
Chou	3.49
Goodfriend	3.45
Rao	3.90
Stevens	2.99

TABLE 3 Enrollments.		
Student	*Major*	*Course*
Glauser	Biology	BI 290
Glauser	Biology	MS 475
Glauser	Biology	PY 410
Marcus	Mathematics	MS 511
Marcus	Mathematics	MS 603
Marcus	Mathematics	CS 322
Miller	Computer Science	MS 575
Miller	Computer Science	CS 455

TABLE 4 Majors.	
Student	*Major*
Glauser	Biology
Marcus	Mathematics
Miller	Computer Science

Definition 4 Let R be a relation of degree m and S a relation of degree n. The *join* $J_p(R, S)$, where $p \leqslant m$ and $p \leqslant n$, is a relation of degree $m + n - p$ that consists of all $(m + n - p)$-tuples $(a_1, a_2, \ldots, a_{m-p}, c_1, c_2, \ldots, c_p, b_1, b_2, \ldots, b_{n-p})$, where the m-tuple $(a_1, a_2, \ldots, a_{m-p}, c_1, c_2, \ldots, c_p)$ belongs to R and the n-tuple $(c_1, c_2, \ldots, c_p, b_1, b_2, \ldots, b_{n-p})$ belongs to S.

In other words, the join operator J_p produces a new relation from two relations by combining all m-tuples of the first relation with all n-tuples of the second relation, where the last p components of the m-tuples agree with the first p components of the n-tuples.

Example 11   What relation results when the join operator J_2 is used to combine the relation displayed in Tables 5 and 6?

TABLE 5 Teaching_assignments.		
Professor	*Department*	*Course_ number*
Cruz	Zoology	335
Cruz	Zoology	412
Farber	Psychology	501
Farber	Psychology	617
Grammer	Physics	544
Grammer	Physics	551
Rosen	Computer Science	518
Rosen	Mathematics	575

TABLE 6 Class_schedule.			
Department	*Course_ number*	*Room*	*Time*
Computer Science	518	N521	2:00 P.M.
Mathematics	575	N502	3:00 P.M.
Mathematics	611	N521	4:00 P.M.
Physics	544	B505	4:00 P.M.
Psychology	501	A100	3:00 P.M.
Psychology	617	A110	11:00 A.M.
Zoology	335	A100	9:00 A.M.
Zoology	412	A100	8:00 A.M.

Solution: The join J_2 produces the relation shown in Table 7.   ◄

TABLE 7 Teaching_schedule.				
Professor	*Department*	*Course_number*	*Room*	*Time*
Cruz	Zoology	335	A100	9:00 A.M.
Cruz	Zoology	412	A100	8:00 A.M.
Farber	Psychology	501	A100	3:00 P.M.
Farber	Psychology	617	A110	11:00 A.M.
Grammer	Physics	544	B505	4:00 P.M.
Rosen	Computer Science	518	N521	2:00 P.M.
Rosen	Mathematics	575	N502	3:00 P.M.

There are other operators besides projections and joins that produce new relations from existing relations. A description of these operations can be found in books on database theory.

SQL

The database query language SQL (short for structured query language) can be used to carry out the operations we have described in this section. Example 12 illustrates how SQL commands are related to operations on *n*-ary relations.

Example 12   We will illustrate how SQL is used to express queries by showing how SQL can be employed to make a query about airline flights using Table 8. The SQL statement

```
SELECT Departure_time
FROM Flights
WHERE Destination='Detroit'
```

is used to find the projection P_5 (on the Departure_time attribute) of the selection of 5-tuples in the Flights database that satisfy the condition: Destination = 'Detroit'. The output would be a list containing the times of flights that have Detroit as their destination, namely, 08:10, 08:47, and 09:44. SQL uses the FROM clause to identify the *n*-ary relation the query is applied to, the WHERE clause to specify the condition of the selection operation, and the SELECT clause to specify the projection operation that is to be applied. (*Beware:* SQL uses SELECT to represent a projection, rather than a selection operation. This is an unfortunate example of conflicting terminology.)   ◀

TABLE 8 Flights.

Airline	Flight_number	Gate	Destination	Departure_time
Nadir	122	34	Detroit	08:10
Acme	221	22	Denver	08:17
Acme	122	33	Anchorage	08:22
Acme	323	34	Honolulu	08:30
Nadir	199	13	Detroit	08:47
Acme	222	22	Denver	09:10
Nadir	322	34	Detroit	09:44

Example 13 shows how SQL queries can be made involving more than one table.

Example 13   The SQL statement

```
SELECT Professor, Time
FROM Teaching_assignments, Class_schedule
WHERE Department='Mathematics'
```

is used to find the projection $P_{1,5}$ of the 5-tuples in the database (shown in Table 7), which is the join J_2 of the Teaching_assignments and Class_schedule databases in Tables 5 and 6, respectively, which satisfy the condition: Department = Mathematics. The output would consist of the single 2-tuple (Rosen, 3:00 P.M.). The SQL FROM clause is used here to find the join of two different databases.   ◀

We have only touched on the basic concepts of relational databases in this section. More information can be found in [AhUl95].

Exercises

1. List the triples in the relation $\{(a, b, c) \mid a, b,$ and c are integers with $0 < a < b < c < 5\}$.

2. List the 5-tuples in the relation in Table 8.

3. Assuming that no new *n*-tuples are added, find a composite key with two fields containing the *Airline* field for the database in Table 8.

4. The 3-tuples in a 3-ary relation represent the following attributes of a student database: student ID number, name, phone number.
   a) Is student ID number likely to be a primary key?
   b) Is name likely to be a primary key?
   c) Is phone number likely to be a primary key?

5. The 5-tuples in a 5-ary relation represent these attributes of all people in the United States: name, Social Security number, street address, city, state.
   a) Determine a primary key for this relation.
   b) Under what conditions would (name, street address) be a composite key?
   c) Under what conditions would (name, street address, city) be a composite key?

6. What do you obtain when you apply the selection operator s_C, where C is the condition Destination = Detroit, to the database in Table 8?

7. What do you obtain when you apply the selection operator s_C, where C is the condition (Airline = Nadir) $\vee$ (Destination = Denver), to the database in Table 8?

8. Which projection mapping is used to delete the first, second, and fourth components of a 6-tuple?

9. Display the table produced by applying the projection $P_{1,4}$ to Table 8.

10. Construct the table obtained by applying the join operator J_2 to the relations in Tables 9 and 10.

TABLE 9 Part_needs.

Supplier	Part_number	Project
23	1092	1
23	1101	3
23	9048	4
31	4975	3
31	3477	2
32	6984	4
32	9191	2
33	1001	1

TABLE 10 Parts_inventory.

Part_number	Project	Quantity	Color_code
1001	1	14	8
1092	1	2	2
1101	3	1	1
3477	2	25	2
4975	3	6	2
6984	4	10	1
9048	4	12	2
9191	2	80	4

11. Show that if C_1 and C_2 are conditions that elements of the n-ary relation R may satisfy, then $s_{C_1}(s_{C_2}(R)) = s_{C_2}(s_{C_1}(R))$.

12. Show that if C is a condition that elements of the n-ary relations R and S may satisfy, then $s_C(R \cap S) = s_C(R) \cap s_C(S)$.

13. Show that if R and S are both n-ary relations, then $P_{i_1,i_2,\ldots,i_m}(R \cup S) = P_{i_1,i_2,\ldots,i_m}(R) \cup P_{i_1,i_2,\ldots,i_m}(S)$.

14. Give an example to show that if R and S are both n-ary relations, then $P_{i_1,i_2,\ldots,i_m}(R - S)$ may be different from $P_{i_1,i_2,\ldots,i_m}(R) - P_{i_1,i_2,\ldots,i_m}(S)$.

15. a) What are the operations that correspond to the query expressed using this SQL statement?

```
SELECT Supplier, Project
FROM Part_needs, Parts_inventory
WHERE Quantity ≤ 10
```

   b) What is the output of this query given the databases in Tables 9 and 10 as input?

16. Determine whether there is a primary key for the relation in Example 3.

5.3 Representing Relations

Introduction

In this section, and in the remainder of this chapter, all relations we study will be binary relations. Because of this, in this section and in the rest of this chapter, the word relation will always refer to a binary relation. There are many ways to represent a relation between finite sets. As we have seen in Section 5.1, one way is to list its ordered pairs. Another way to represent a relation is to use a table, as we did in Example 3 in Section 5.1. In this section we will discuss two alternative methods for representing relations. One method uses zero–one matrices. The other method uses pictorial representations called directed graphs, which we will discuss later in this section.

Generally, matrices are appropriate for the representation of relations in computer programs. On the other hand, people often find the representation of relations using directed graphs useful for understanding the properties of these relations.

Representing Relations Using Matrices

A relation between finite sets can be represented using a zero–one matrix. Suppose that R is a relation from $A = \{a_1, a_2, \ldots, a_m\}$ to $B = \{b_1, b_2, \ldots, b_n\}$. (Here the elements of the sets A and B have been listed in a particular, but arbitrary, order. Furthermore, when $A = B$ we use the same ordering for A and B.) The relation R can be represented by the matrix $\mathbf{M}_R = [m_{ij}]$, where

$$m_{ij} = \begin{cases} 1 & \text{if } (a_i, b_j) \in R, \\ 0 & \text{if } (a_i, b_j) \notin R. \end{cases}$$

In other words, the zero–one matrix representing R has a 1 as its (i, j) entry when a_i is related to b_j, and a 0 in this position if a_i is not related to b_j. (Such a representation depends on the orderings used for A and B.)

The use of matrices to represent relations is illustrated in Examples 1–6.

Example 1   Suppose that $A = \{1, 2, 3\}$ and $B = \{1, 2\}$. Let R be the relation from A to B containing (a, b) if $a \in A$, $b \in B$, and $a > b$. What is the matrix representing R if $a_1 = 1$, $a_2 = 2$, and $a_3 = 3$, and $b_1 = 1$ and $b_2 = 2$?

Solution: Because $R = \{(2, 1), (3, 1), (3, 2)\}$, the matrix for R is

$$\mathbf{M}_R = \begin{bmatrix} 0 & 0 \\ 1 & 0 \\ 1 & 1 \end{bmatrix}.$$

The 1s in $\mathbf{M}_R$ show that the pairs $(2, 1)$, $(3, 1)$, and $(3, 2)$ belong to R. The 0s show that no other pairs belong to R.   ◄

Example 2   Let $A = \{a_1, a_2, a_3\}$ and $B = \{b_1, b_2, b_3, b_4, b_5\}$. Which ordered pairs are in the relation R represented by the matrix

$$\mathbf{M}_R = \begin{bmatrix} 0 & 1 & 0 & 0 & 0 \\ 1 & 0 & 1 & 1 & 0 \\ 1 & 0 & 1 & 0 & 1 \end{bmatrix} ?$$

Solution: Because R consists of those ordered pairs (a_i, b_j) with $m_{ij} = 1$, it follows that

$$R = \{(a_1, b_2), (a_2, b_1), (a_2, b_3), (a_2, b_4), (a_3, b_1), (a_3, b_3), (a_3, b_5)\}. \quad ◄$$

The matrix of a relation on a set, which is a square matrix, can be used to determine whether the relation has certain properties. Recall that a relation R on A is reflexive if $(a, a) \in R$ whenever $a \in A$. Thus, R is reflexive if and only if $(a_i, a_i) \in R$ for $i = 1, 2, \ldots, n$. Hence, R is reflexive if and only if $m_{ii} = 1$, for $i = 1, 2, \ldots, n$. In other words, R is reflexive if all the elements on the main diagonal of $\mathbf{M}_R$ are equal to 1, as shown in Figure 1.

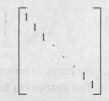

Figure 1   The Zero–One Matrix for a Reflexive Relation.

The relation R is symmetric if $(a, b) \in R$ implies that $(b, a) \in R$. Consequently, the relation R on the set $A =$

$\{a_1, a_2, \ldots, a_n\}$ is symmetric if and only if $(a_j, a_i) \in R$ whenever $(a_i, a_j) \in R$. In terms of the entries of $\mathbf{M}_R$, R is symmetric if and only if $m_{ji} = 1$ whenever $m_{ij} = 1$. This also means $m_{ji} = 0$ whenever $m_{ij} = 0$. Consequently, R is symmetric if and only if $m_{ij} = m_{ji}$, for all pairs of integers i and j with $i = 1, 2, \ldots, n$ and $j = 1, 2, \ldots, n$. Recalling the definition of the transpose of a matrix from Section 3.8, we see that R is symmetric if and only if

$$\mathbf{M}_R = (\mathbf{M}_R)^t,$$

that is, if $\mathbf{M}_R$ is a symmetric matrix. The form of the matrix for a symmetric relation is illustrated in Figure 2(a).

The relation R is antisymmetric if and only if $(a, b) \in R$ and $(b, a) \in R$ imply that $a = b$. Consequently, the matrix of an antisymmetric relation has the property that if $m_{ij} = 1$ with $i \neq j$, then $m_{ji} = 0$. Or, in other words, either $m_{ij} = 0$ or $m_{ji} = 0$ when $i \neq j$. The form of the matrix for an antisymmetric relation is illustrated in Figure 2(b).

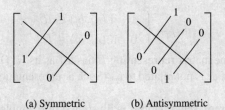

(a) Symmetric   (b) Antisymmetric

Figure 2   The Zero–One Matrices for Symmetric and Antisymmetric Relations.

Example 3   Suppose that the relation R on a set is represented by the matrix

$$\mathbf{M}_R = \begin{bmatrix} 1 & 1 & 0 \\ 1 & 1 & 1 \\ 0 & 1 & 1 \end{bmatrix}.$$

Is R reflexive, symmetric, and/or antisymmetric?
Solution: Because all the diagonal elements of this matrix are equal to 1, R is reflexive. Moreover, because $\mathbf{M}_R$ is symmetric, it follows that R is symmetric. It is also easy to see that R is not antisymmetric.   ◄

The Boolean operations join and meet can be used to find the matrices representing the union and the intersection of two relations. Suppose that R_1 and R_2 are relations on a set A represented by the matrices $\mathbf{M}_{R_1}$ and $\mathbf{M}_{R_2}$, respectively. The matrix representing the union of these relations has a 1 in the positions where either $\mathbf{M}_{R_1}$ or $\mathbf{M}_{R_2}$ has a 1. The matrix representing the intersection of these relations has a 1 in the positions where both $\mathbf{M}_{R_1}$ and $\mathbf{M}_{R_2}$ have a 1. Thus, the matrices representing the union and intersection of these relations are

$$\mathbf{M}_{R_1 \cup R_2} = \mathbf{M}_{R_1} \vee \mathbf{M}_{R_2} \quad \text{and} \quad \mathbf{M}_{R_1 \cap R_2} = \mathbf{M}_{R_1} \wedge \mathbf{M}_{R_2}.$$

Example 4   Suppose that the relations R_1 and R_2 on a set A are represented by the matrices

$$\mathbf{M}_{R_1} = \begin{bmatrix} 1 & 0 & 1 \\ 1 & 0 & 0 \\ 0 & 1 & 0 \end{bmatrix} \quad \text{and} \quad \mathbf{M}_{R_2} = \begin{bmatrix} 1 & 0 & 1 \\ 0 & 1 & 1 \\ 1 & 0 & 0 \end{bmatrix}.$$

What are the matrices representing $R_1 \cup R_2$ and $R_1 \cap R_2$?
Solution: The matrices of these relations are

$$\mathbf{M}_{R_1 \cup R_2} = \mathbf{M}_{R_1} \vee \mathbf{M}_{R_2} = \begin{bmatrix} 1 & 0 & 1 \\ 1 & 1 & 1 \\ 1 & 1 & 0 \end{bmatrix},$$

$$\mathbf{M}_{R_1 \cap R_2} = \mathbf{M}_{R_1} \wedge \mathbf{M}_{R_2} = \begin{bmatrix} 1 & 0 & 1 \\ 0 & 0 & 0 \\ 0 & 0 & 0 \end{bmatrix}.$$

◄

We now turn our attention to determining the matrix for the composite of relations. This matrix can be found using the Boolean product of the matrices for these relations. In particular, suppose that R is a relation from A to B and S is a relation from B to C. Suppose that A, B, and C have m, n, and p elements, respectively. Let the zero–one matrices for $S \circ R$, R, and S be $\mathbf{M}_{S \circ R} = [t_{ij}]$, $\mathbf{M}_R = [r_{ij}]$, and $\mathbf{M}_S = [s_{ij}]$, respectively (these matrices have sizes $m \times p$, $m \times n$, and $n \times p$, respectively). The ordered pair (a_i, c_j) belongs to $S \circ R$ if and only if there is an element b_k such that (a_i, b_k) belongs to R and (b_k, c_j) belongs to S. It follows that $t_{ij} = 1$ if and only if $r_{ik} = s_{kj} = 1$ for some k. From the definition of the Boolean product, this means that

$$\mathbf{M}_{S \circ R} = \mathbf{M}_R \odot \mathbf{M}_S.$$

Example 5 Find the matrix representing the relations $S \circ R$, where the matrices representing R and S are

$$\mathbf{M}_R = \begin{bmatrix} 1 & 0 & 1 \\ 1 & 1 & 0 \\ 0 & 0 & 0 \end{bmatrix} \quad \text{and} \quad \mathbf{M}_S = \begin{bmatrix} 0 & 1 & 0 \\ 0 & 0 & 1 \\ 1 & 0 & 1 \end{bmatrix}.$$

Solution: The matrix for $S \circ R$ is

$$\mathbf{M}_{S \circ R} = \mathbf{M}_R \odot \mathbf{M}_S = \begin{bmatrix} 1 & 1 & 1 \\ 0 & 1 & 1 \\ 0 & 0 & 0 \end{bmatrix}.$$

◄

The matrix representing the composite of two relations can be used to find the matrix for $\mathbf{M}_{R^n}$. In particular,

$$\mathbf{M}_{R^n} = \mathbf{M}_R^{[n]},$$

from the definition of Boolean powers. Exercise 16 at the end of this section asks for a proof of this formula.

Example 6 Find the matrix representing the relation R^2, where the matrix representing R is

$$\mathbf{M}_R = \begin{bmatrix} 0 & 1 & 0 \\ 0 & 1 & 1 \\ 1 & 0 & 0 \end{bmatrix}.$$

Solution: The matrix for R^2 is

$$\mathbf{M}_{R^2} = \mathbf{M}_R^{[2]} = \begin{bmatrix} 0 & 1 & 1 \\ 1 & 1 & 1 \\ 0 & 1 & 0 \end{bmatrix}.$$

Representing Relations Using Digraphs

We have shown that a relation can be represented by listing all of its ordered pairs or by using a zero–one matrix. There is another important way of representing a relation using a pictorial representation. Each element of the set is represented by a point, and each ordered pair is represented using an arc with its direction indicated by an arrow. We use such pictorial representations when we think of relations on a finite set as **directed graphs,** or **digraphs.**

Definition 1 A *directed graph,* or *digraph,* consists of a set V of *vertices* (or *nodes*) together with a set E of ordered pairs of elements of V called *edges* (or *arcs*). The vertex a is called the *initial vertex* of the edge (a, b), and the vertex b is called the *terminal vertex* of this edge.

An edge of the form (a, a) is represented using an arc from the vertex a back to itself. Such an edge is called a **loop.**

Example 7   The directed graph with vertices a, b, c, and d, and edges (a, b), (a, d), (b, b), (b, d), (c, a), (c, b), and (d, b) is displayed in Figure 3.   ◄

The relation R on a set A is represented by the directed graph that has the elements of A as its vertices and the ordered pairs (a, b), where $(a, b) \in R$, as edges. This assignment sets up a one-to-one correspondence between the relations on a set A and the directed graphs with A as their set of vertices. Thus, every statement about relations corresponds to a statement about directed graphs, and vice versa. Directed graphs give a visual display of information about relations. As such, they are often used to study relations and their properties. (Note

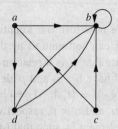

Figure 3   A Directed Graph.

that relations from a set A to a set B can be represented by a directed graph where there is a vertex for each element of A and a vertex for each element of B, as shown in Section 5.1. However, when $A = B$, such representation provides much less insight than the digraph representations described here.) The use of directed graphs to represent relations on a set is illustrated in Examples 8–10.

Example 8   The directed graph of the relation

$$R = \{(1,1), (1,3), (2,1), (2,3), (2,4), (3,1), (3,2), (4,1)\}$$

on the set $\{1, 2, 3, 4\}$ is shown in Figure 4.   ◄

Example 9   What are the ordered pairs in the relation R represented by the directed graph shown in Figure 5?

Solution: The ordered pairs (x, y) in the relation are

$$R = \{(1,3), (1,4), (2,1), (2,2), (2,3), (3,1), (3,3), (4,1), (4,3)\}.$$

Each of these pairs corresponds to an edge of the directed graph, with $(2,2)$ and $(3,3)$ corresponding to loops.   ◄

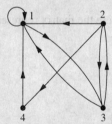

Figure 4   The Directed Graph of the Relation R.

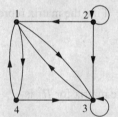

Figure 5   The Directed Graph of the Relation R.

The directed graph representing a relation can be used to determine whether the relation has various properties. For instance, a relation is reflexive if and only if there is a loop at every vertex of the directed graph, so that every ordered pair of the form (x, x) occurs in the relation. A relation is symmetric if and only if for every edge between distinct vertices in its digraph there is an edge in the opposite direction, so that (y, x) is in the relation whenever (x, y) is in the relation. Similarly, a relation is antisymmetric if and only if there are never two edges in opposite directions between distinct vertices. Finally, a relation is transitive if and only if whenever there is an edge from a vertex x to a vertex y and an edge from a vertex y to a vertex z, there is an edge from x to z (completing a triangle where each side is a directed edge with the correct direction).

Remark: Note that a symmetric relation can be represented by an undirected graph, which is a graph where edges do not have directions. We will study undirected graphs in Chapter 6.

Example 10   Determine whether the relations for the directed graphs shown in Figure 6 are reflexive, symmetric, antisymmetric, and/or transitive.

Solution: Because there are loops at every vertex of the directed graph of R, it is reflexive. R is neither symmetric nor antisymmetric because there is an edge from a to b but not one from b to a, but there are edges in both directions connecting b and c. Finally, R is not transitive because there is an edge from a to b and an edge from b to c, but no edge from a to c.

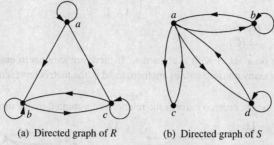

(a) Directed graph of R (b) Directed graph of S

Figure 6   The Directed Graphs of the Relations R and S.

Because loops are not present at all the vertices of the directed graph of S, this relation is not reflexive. It is symmetric and not antisymmetric, because every edge between distinct vertices is accompanied by an edge in the opposite direction. It is also not hard to see from the directed graph that S is not transitive, because (c, a) and (a, b) belong to S, but (c, b) does not belong to S.   ◄

Exercises

1. Represent each of these relations on $\{1, 2, 3\}$ with a matrix (with the elements of this set listed in increasing order).

   a) $\{(1, 1), (1, 2), (1, 3)\}$ b) $\{(1, 2), (2, 1), (2, 2), (3, 3)\}$

   c) $\{(1, 1), (1, 2), (1, 3), (2, 2), (2, 3), (3, 3)\}$ d) $\{(1, 3), (3, 1)\}$

2. List the ordered pairs in the relations on $\{1, 2, 3\}$ corresponding to these matrices (where the rows and columns correspond to the integers listed in increasing order).

   a) $\begin{bmatrix} 1 & 0 & 1 \\ 0 & 1 & 0 \\ 1 & 0 & 1 \end{bmatrix}$ b) $\begin{bmatrix} 0 & 1 & 0 \\ 0 & 1 & 0 \\ 0 & 1 & 0 \end{bmatrix}$ c) $\begin{bmatrix} 1 & 1 & 1 \\ 1 & 0 & 1 \\ 1 & 1 & 1 \end{bmatrix}$

3. How can the matrix representing a relation R on a set A be used to determine whether the relation is irreflexive?

4. Determine whether the relations represented by the matrices in Exercise 2 are reflexive, irreflexive, symmetric, antisymmetric, and/or transitive.

5. How many nonzero entries does the matrix representing the relation R on $A = \{1, 2, 3, \ldots, 100\}$ consisting of the first 100 positive integers have if R is

   a) $\{(a, b) \mid a > b\}$?   b) $\{(a, b) \mid a \neq b\}$?   c) $\{(a, b) \mid a = b + 1\}$?

   d) $\{(a, b) \mid a = 1\}$?   e) $\{(a, b) \mid ab = 1\}$?

6. How can the matrix for $\overline{R}$, the complement of the relation R, be found from the matrix representing R, when R is a relation on a finite set A?

7. Let R be the relation represented by the matrix

$$M_R = \begin{bmatrix} 0 & 1 & 1 \\ 1 & 1 & 0 \\ 1 & 0 & 1 \end{bmatrix}.$$

Find the matrix representing
a) R^{-1}.   b) $\overline{R}$.   c) R^2.

8. Let R be the relation represented by the matrix

$$\mathbf{M}_R = \begin{bmatrix} 0 & 1 & 0 \\ 0 & 0 & 1 \\ 1 & 1 & 0 \end{bmatrix}.$$

Find the matrices that represent
a) R^2.   b) R^3.   c) R^4.

9. Let R be a relation on a set A with n elements. If there are k nonzero entries in $\mathbf{M}_R$, the matrix representing R, how many nonzero entries are there in $\mathbf{M}_{\overline{R}}$, the matrix representing $\overline{R}$, the complement of R?

In Exercises 10–12 list the ordered pairs in the relations represented by the directed graphs.

10.   11.   12.

      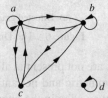

13. How can the directed graph of a relation R on a finite set A be used to determine whether a relation is asymmetric?

14. Determine whether the relations represented by the directed graphs shown in Exercises 10–11 are reflexive, irreflexive, symmetric, antisymmetric, and/or transitive.

15. Let R be a relation on a set A. Explain how to use the directed graph representing R to obtain the directed graph representing the inverse relation R^{-1}.

16. Show that if $\mathbf{M}_R$ is the matrix representing the relation R, then $\mathbf{M}_R^{[n]}$ is the matrix representing the relation R^n.

5.4   Closures of Relations

Introduction

A computer network has data centers in Boston, Chicago, Denver, Detroit, New York, and San Diego. There are direct, one-way telephone lines from Boston to Chicago, from Boston to Detroit, from Chicago to Detroit, from Detroit to Denver, and from New York to San Diego. Let R be the relation containing (a, b) if there is a telephone line from the data center in a to that in b. How can we determine if there is some (possibly indirect) link composed of one or more telephone lines from one center to another? Because not all links are direct, such as the link from Boston to Denver that goes through Detroit, R cannot be used directly to answer this. In the language of relations, R is not transitive, so it does not contain all the pairs that can be linked. As we will show in this section, we can find all pairs of data centers that have a link by constructing a transitive relation S containing R such that S is a subset of every transitive relation containing R. Here, S is the smallest transitive relation that contains R. This relation is called the **transitive closure** of R.

In general, let R be a relation on a set A. R may or may not have some property $\mathbf{P}$, such as reflexivity, symmetry, or transitivity. If there is a relation S with property $\mathbf{P}$ containing R such that S is a subset of every relation with property $\mathbf{P}$ containing R, then S is called the **closure** of R with respect to $\mathbf{P}$. (Note that the closure of a relation with respect to a property may not exist; see Exercises 8 and 17 at the end of this section.) We will show how reflexive, symmetric, and transitive closures of relations can be found.

Closures

The relation $R = \{(1,1),(1,2),(2,1),(3,2)\}$ on the set $A = \{1,2,3\}$ is not reflexive. How can we produce a reflexive relation containing R that is as small as possible? This can be done by adding $(2,2)$ and $(3,3)$ to R, because these are the only pairs of the form (a,a) that are not in R. Clearly, this new relation contains R. Furthermore, *any* reflexive relation that contains R must also contain $(2,2)$ and $(3,3)$. Because this relation contains R, is reflexive, and is contained within every reflexive relation that contains R, it is called the **reflexive closure** of R.

As this example illustrates, given a relation R on a set A, the reflexive closure of R can be formed by adding to R all pairs of the form (a,a) with $a \in A$, not already in R. The addition of these pairs produces a new relation that is reflexive, contains R, and is contained within any reflexive relation containing R. We see that the reflexive closure of R equals $R \cup \Delta$, where $\Delta = \{(a,a) \mid a \in A\}$ is the **diagonal relation** on A. (The reader should verify this.)

Example 1   What is the reflexive closure of the relation $R = \{(a,b) \mid a < b\}$ on the set of integers?

Solution: The reflexive closure of R is

$$R \cup \Delta = \{(a,b) \mid a < b\} \cup \{(a,a) \mid a \in \mathbf{Z}\} = \{(a,b) \mid a \leqslant b\}. \qquad \blacktriangleleft$$

The relation $\{(1,1),(1,2),(2,2),(2,3),(3,1),(3,2)\}$ on $\{1,2,3\}$ is not symmetric. How can we produce a symmetric relation that is as small as possible and contains R? To do this, we need only add $(2,1)$ and $(1,3)$, because these are the only pairs of the form (b,a) with $(a,b) \in R$ that are not in R. This new relation is symmetric and contains R. Furthermore, *any* symmetric relation that contains R must contain this new relation, because a symmetric relation that contains R must contain $(2,1)$ and $(1,3)$. Consequently, this new relation is called the **symmetric closure** of R.

As this example illustrates, the symmetric closure of a relation R can be constructed by adding all ordered pairs of the form (b,a), where (a,b) is in the relation, that are not already present in R. Adding these pairs produces a relation that is symmetric, that contains R, and that is contained in any symmetric relation that contains R. The symmetric closure of a relation can be constructed by taking the union of a relation with its inverse; that is, $R \cup R^{-1}$ is the symmetric closure of R, where $R^{-1} = \{(b,a) \mid (a,b) \in R\}$. The reader should verify this statement.

Example 2   What is the symmetric closure of the relation $R = \{(a,b) \mid a > b\}$ on the set of positive integers?

Solution: The symmetric closure of R is the relation

$$R \cup R^{-1} = \{(a,b) \mid a > b\} \cup \{(b,a) \mid a > b\} = \{(a,b) \mid a \neq b\}.$$

This last equality follows because R contains all ordered pairs of positive integers where the first element is greater than the second element and R^{-1} contains all ordered pairs of positive integers where the first element is less than the second. $\qquad \blacktriangleleft$

Suppose that a relation R is not transitive. How can we produce a transitive relation that contains R such that this new relation is contained within any transitive relation that contains R? Can the transitive closure of a relation R be produced by adding all the pairs of the form (a,c), where (a,b) and (b,c) are already in the relation? Consider the relation $R = \{(1,3),(1,4),(2,1),(3,2)\}$ on the set $\{1,2,3,4\}$. This relation is not transitive because it does not contain all pairs of the form (a,c) where (a,b) and (b,c) are in R. The pairs of this form not in R are $(1,2)$, $(2,3)$, $(2,4)$, and $(3,1)$. Adding these pairs does *not* produce a transitive relation, because the resulting relation contains $(3,1)$ and $(1,4)$ but does not contain $(3,4)$. This shows that constructing the transitive closure of a relation is more complicated than constructing either the reflexive or symmetric closure. The rest of this section develops algorithms for constructing transitive closures.

As will be shown later in this section, the transitive closure of a relation can be found by adding new ordered pairs that must be present and then repeating this process until no new ordered pairs are needed.

Paths in Directed Graphs

We will see that representing relations by directed graphs helps in the construction of transitive closures. We now introduce some terminology that we will use for this purpose.

A path in a directed graph is obtained by traversing along edges (in the same direction as indicated by the arrow on the edge).

Definition 1   A *path* from a to b in the directed graph G is a sequence of edges (x_0, x_1), (x_1, x_2), (x_2, x_3), ..., (x_{n-1}, x_n) in G, where n is a nonnegative integer, and $x_0 = a$ and $x_n = b$, that is, a sequence of edges where the terminal vertex of an edge is the same as the initial vertex in the next edge in the path. This path is denoted by $x_0, x_1, x_2, \ldots, x_{n-1}, x_n$ and has *length n*. We view the empty set of edges as a path from a to a. A path of length $n \geqslant 1$ that begins and ends at the same vertex is called a *circuit* or *cycle*.

A path in a directed graph can pass through a vertex more than once. Moreover, an edge in a directed graph can occur more than once in a path.

Example 3   Which of the following are paths in the directed graph shown in Figure 1: a, b, e, d; a, e, c, d, b; b, a, c, b, a, a, b; d, c; c, b, a; e, b, a, b, a, b, e? What are the lengths of those that are paths? Which of the paths in this list are circuits?

Solution: Because each of (a, b), (b, e), and (e, d) is an edge, a, b, e, d is a path of length three. Because (c, d) is not an edge, a, e, c, d, b is not a path. Also, b, a, c, b, a, a, b is a path of length six because (b, a), (a, c), (c, b), (b, a), (a, a), and (a, b) are all edges. We see that d, c is a path of length one, because (d, c) is an edge. Also c, b, a is a path of length two, because (c, b) and (b, a) are edges. All of (e, b), (b, a), (a, b), (b, a), (a, b), and (b, e) are edges, so e, b, a, b, a, b, e is a path of length six.

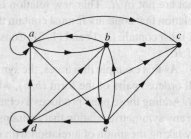

Figure 1   A Directed Graph.

The two paths b, a, c, b, a, a, b and e, b, a, b, a, b, e are circuits because they begin and end at the same vertex. The paths a, b, e, d; c, b, a; and d, c are not circuits.   ◀

The term *path* also applies to relations. Carrying over the definition from directed graphs to relations, there is a **path** from a to b in R if there is a sequence of elements $a, x_1, x_2, \ldots, x_{n-1}, b$ with $(a, x_1) \in R$, $(x_1, x_2) \in R, \ldots$, and $(x_{n-1}, b) \in R$. Theorem 1 can be obtained from the definition of a path in a relation.

Theorem 1   Let R be a relation on a set A. There is a path of length n, where n is a positive integer, from a to b if and only if $(a, b) \in R^n$.

Proof: We will use mathematical induction. By definition, there is a path from a to b of length one if and only if $(a, b) \in R$, so the theorem is true when $n = 1$.

Assume that the theorem is true for the positive integer n. This is the inductive hypothesis. There is a path of length $n + 1$ from a to b if and only if there is an element $c \in A$ such that there is a path of length one from a to c, so $(a, c) \in R$, and a path of length n from c to b, that is, $(c, b) \in R^n$. Consequently, by the induction hypothesis, there is a path of length $n + 1$ from a to b if and only if there is an element c with $(a, c) \in R$ and $(c, b) \in R^n$. But there is such an element if and only if $(a, b) \in R^{n+1}$. Therefore, there is a path of length $n + 1$ from a to b if and only if $(a, b) \in R^{n+1}$. This completes the proof.   ◁

Transitive Closures

We now show that finding the transitive closure of a relation is equivalent to determining which pairs of vertices in the associated directed graph are connected by a path. With this in mind, we define a new relation.

Definition 2   Let R be a relation on a set A. The *connectivity relation* R^* consists of the pairs (a, b) such that there is a path of length at least one from a to b in R.

Because R^n consists of the pairs (a, b) such that there is a path of length n from a to b, it follows that R^* is the union of all the sets R^n. In other words,

$$R^* = \bigcup_{n=1}^{\infty} R^n.$$

The connectivity relation is useful in many models.

Example 4   Let R be the relation on the set of all people in the world that contains (a, b) if a has met b. What is R^n, where n is a positive integer greater than one? What is R^*?

Solution: The relation R^2 contains (a, b) if there is a person c such that $(a, c) \in R$ and $(c, b) \in R$, that is, if there is a person c such that a has met c and c has met b. Similarly, R^n consists of those pairs (a, b) such that there are people $x_1, x_2, \ldots, x_{n-1}$ such that a has met x_1, x_1 has met $x_2, \ldots$, and x_{n-1} has met b.

The relation R^* contains (a, b) if there is a sequence of people, starting with a and ending with b, such that each person in the sequence has met the next person in the sequence. (There are many interesting conjectures about R^*. Do you think that this connectivity relation includes the pair with you as the first element and the president of Mongolia as the second element? We will use graphs to model this application in Chapter 6.)   ◀

Example 5   Let R be the relation on the set of all subway stops in New York City that contains (a, b) if it is possible to travel from stop a to stop b without changing trains. What is R^n when n is a positive integer? What is R^*?

Solution: The relation R^n contains (a, b) if it is possible to travel from stop a to stop b by making $n - 1$ changes of trains. The relation R^* consists of the ordered pairs (a, b) where it is possible to travel from stop a to stop b making as many changes of trains as necessary. (The reader should verify these statements.)   ◀'

Example 6   Let R be the relation on the set of all states in the United States that contains (a, b) if state a and state b have a common border. What is R^n, where n is a positive integer? What is R^*?

Solution: The relation R^n consists of the pairs (a, b), where it is possible to go from state a to state b by crossing exactly n state borders. R^* consists of the ordered pairs (a, b), where it is possible to go from state a to state b crossing as many borders as necessary. (The reader should verify these statements.) The only ordered pairs not in R^* are those containing states that are not connected to the continental United States (i.e., those pairs containing Alaska or Hawaii).   ◀

Theorem 2 shows that the transitive closure of a relation and the associated connectivity relation are the same.

Theorem 2   The transitive closure of a relation R equals the connectivity relation R^*.

Proof: Note that R^* contains R by definition. To show that R^* is the transitive closure of R we must also show that R^* is transitive and that $R^* \subseteq S$ whenever S is a transitive relation that contains R.

First, we show that R^* is transitive. If $(a, b) \in R^*$ and $(b, c) \in R^*$, then there are paths from a to b and from b to c in R. We obtain a path from a to c by starting with the path from a to b and following it with the path from b to c. Hence, $(a, c) \in R^*$. It follows that R^* is transitive.

Now suppose that S is a transitive relation containing R. Because S is transitive, S^n also is transitive (the reader should verify this) and $S^n \subseteq S$ (by Theorem 1 of Section 5.1). Furthermore, because

$$S^* = \bigcup_{k=1}^{\infty} S^k$$

and $S^k \subseteq S$, it follows that $S^* \subseteq S$. Now note that if $R \subseteq S$, then $R^* \subseteq S^*$, because any path in R is also a path in S. Consequently, $R^* \subseteq S^* \subseteq S$. Thus, any transitive relation that contains R must also contain R^*. Therefore, R^* is the transitive closure of R.   ◁

Now that we know that the transitive closure equals the connectivity relation, we turn our attention to the problem of computing this relation. We do not need to examine arbitrarily long paths to determine whether there is a path between two vertices in a finite directed graph. As Lemma 1 shows, it is sufficient to examine paths containing no more than n edges, where n is the number of elements in the set.

Lemma 1 Let A be a set with n elements, and let R be a relation on A. If there is a path of length at least one in R from a to b, then there is such a path with length not exceeding n. Moreover, when $a \neq b$, if there is a path of length at least one in R from a to b, then there is such a path with length not exceeding $n - 1$.

Proof: Suppose there is a path from a to b in R. Let m be the length of the shortest such path. Suppose that $x_0, x_1, x_2, \ldots, x_{m-1}, x_m$, where $x_0 = a$ and $x_m = b$, is such a path.

Suppose that $a = b$ and that $m > n$, so that $m \geqslant n + 1$. By the pigeonhole principle, because there are n vertices in A, among the m vertices $x_0, x_1, \ldots, x_{m-1}$, at least two are equal (see Figure 2).

Suppose that $x_i = x_j$ with $0 \leqslant i < j \leqslant m - 1$. Then the path contains a circuit from x_i to itself. This circuit can be deleted from the path from a to b, leaving a path, namely, $x_0, x_1, \ldots, x_i, x_{j+1}, \ldots, x_{m-1}, x_m$, from a to b of shorter length. Hence, the path of shortest length must have length less than or equal to n.

The case where $a \neq b$ is left as an exercise for the reader.   ◁

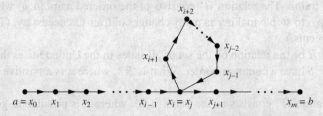

Figure 2   Producing a Path with Length Not Exceeding n.

From Lemma 1, we see that the transitive closure of R is the union of $R, R^2, R^3, \ldots$, and R^n. This follows because there is a path in R^* between two vertices if and only if there is a path between these vertices in R^i, for some positive integer i with $i \leqslant n$. Because

$$R^* = R \cup R^2 \cup R^3 \cup \cdots \cup R^n$$

and the zero–one matrix representing a union of relations is the join of the zero–one matrices of these relations, the zero–one matrix for the transitive closure is the join of the zero–one matrices of the first n powers of the zero–one matrix of R.

Theorem 3 Let $\mathbf{M}_R$ be the zero–one matrix of the relation R on a set with n elements. Then the zero–one matrix of the transitive closure R^* is

$$\mathbf{M}_{R^*} = \mathbf{M}_R \vee \mathbf{M}_R^{[2]} \vee \mathbf{M}_R^{[3]} \vee \cdots \vee \mathbf{M}_R^{[n]}.$$

Example 7   Find the zero–one matrix of the transitive closure of the relation R where

$$\mathbf{M}_R = \begin{bmatrix} 1 & 0 & 1 \\ 0 & 1 & 0 \\ 1 & 1 & 0 \end{bmatrix}.$$

Solution: From Theorem 3, it follows that the zero–one matrix of R^* is

$$\mathbf{M}_{R^*} = \mathbf{M}_R \vee \mathbf{M}_R^{[2]} \vee \mathbf{M}_R^{[3]}.$$

Because

$$\mathbf{M}_R^{[2]} = \begin{bmatrix} 1 & 1 & 1 \\ 0 & 1 & 0 \\ 1 & 1 & 1 \end{bmatrix} \quad \text{and} \quad \mathbf{M}_R^{[3]} = \begin{bmatrix} 1 & 1 & 1 \\ 0 & 1 & 0 \\ 1 & 1 & 1 \end{bmatrix},$$

it follows that

$$\mathbf{M}_{R^*} = \begin{bmatrix} 1 & 0 & 1 \\ 0 & 1 & 0 \\ 1 & 1 & 0 \end{bmatrix} \vee \begin{bmatrix} 1 & 1 & 1 \\ 0 & 1 & 0 \\ 1 & 1 & 1 \end{bmatrix} \vee \begin{bmatrix} 1 & 1 & 1 \\ 0 & 1 & 0 \\ 1 & 1 & 1 \end{bmatrix} = \begin{bmatrix} 1 & 1 & 1 \\ 0 & 1 & 0 \\ 1 & 1 & 1 \end{bmatrix}.$$

◀

Theorem 3 can be used as a basis for an algorithm for computing the matrix of the relation R^*. To find this matrix, the successive Boolean powers of $\mathbf{M}_R$, up to the nth power, are computed. As each power is calculated, its join with the join of all smaller powers is formed. When this is done with the nth power, the matrix for R^* has been found. This procedure is displayed as Algorithm 1.

Algorithm 1   A Procedure for Computing the Transitive Closure.

procedure *transitive closure* ($\mathbf{M}_R$: zero–one $n \times n$ matrix)
$\mathbf{A} := \mathbf{M}_R$
$\mathbf{B} := \mathbf{A}$
for $i := 2$ **to** n
begin
    $\mathbf{A} := \mathbf{A} \odot \mathbf{M}_R$
    $\mathbf{B} := \mathbf{B} \vee \mathbf{A}$
end {$\mathbf{B}$ is the zero–one matrix for R^*}

We can easily find the number of bit operations used by Algorithm 1 to determine the transitive closure of a relation. Computing the Boolean powers $\mathbf{M}_R, \mathbf{M}_R^{[2]}, \ldots, \mathbf{M}_R^{[n]}$ requires that $n - 1$ Boolean products of $n \times n$ zero–one matrices be found. Each of these Boolean products can be found using $n^2(2n - 1)$ bit operations. Hence, these products can be computed using $n^2(2n - 1)(n - 1)$ bit operations.

To find $\mathbf{M}_{R^*}$ from the n Boolean powers of $\mathbf{M}_R$, $n - 1$ joins of zero–one matrices need to be found. Computing each of these joins uses n^2 bit operations. Hence, $(n - 1)n^2$ bit operations are used in this part of the computation. Therefore, when Algorithm 1 is used, the matrix of the transitive closure of a relation on a set with n elements can be found using $n^2(2n - 1)(n - 1) + (n - 1)n^2 = 2n^3(n - 1)$, which is $O(n^4)$ bit operations. The remainder of this section describes a more efficient algorithm for finding transitive closures.

Warshall's Algorithm

Warshall's algorithm, named after Stephen Warshall, who described this algorithm in 1960, is an efficient method for computing the transitive closure of a relation. Algorithm 1 can find the transitive closure of a relation on a set with n elements using $2n^3(n-1)$ bit operations. However, the transitive closure can be found by Warshall's algorithm using only $2n^3$ bit operations.

Remark: Warshall's algorithm is sometimes called the Roy–Warshall algorithm, because Bernard Roy described this algorithm in 1959.

Suppose that R is a relation on a set with n elements. Let $v_1, v_2, \ldots, v_n$ be an arbitrary listing of these n elements. The concept of the **interior vertices** of a path is used in Warshall's algorithm. If $a, x_1, x_2, \ldots, x_{m-1}, b$ is a path, its interior vertices are $x_1, x_2, \ldots, x_{m-1}$, that is, all the vertices of the path that occur somewhere other than as the first and last vertices in the path. For instance, the interior vertices of a path a, c, d, f, g, h, b, j in a directed graph are c, d, f, g, h, and b. The interior vertices of a, c, d, a, f, b are c, d, a, and f. (Note that the first vertex in the path is not an interior vertex unless it is visited again by the path, except as the last vertex. Similarly, the last vertex in the path is not an interior vertex unless it was visited previously by the path, except as the first vertex.)

Warshall's algorithm is based on the construction of a sequence of zero–one matrices. These matrices are $\mathbf{W}_0, \mathbf{W}_1, \ldots, \mathbf{W}_n$, where $\mathbf{W}_0 = \mathbf{M}_R$ is the zero–one matrix of this relation, and $\mathbf{W}_k = [w_{ij}^{(k)}]$, where $w_{ij}^{(k)} = 1$ if there is a path from v_i to v_j such that all the interior vertices of this path are in the set $\{v_1, v_2, \ldots, v_k\}$ (the first k vertices in the list) and is 0 otherwise. (The first and last vertices in the path may be outside the set of the first k vertices in the list.) Note that $\mathbf{W}_n = \mathbf{M}_{R^*}$, because the (i, j)th entry of $\mathbf{M}_{R^*}$ is 1 if and only if there is a path from v_i to v_j, with all interior vertices in the set $\{v_1, v_2, \ldots, v_n\}$ (but these are the only vertices in the directed graph). Example 8 illustrates what the matrix $\mathbf{W}_k$ represents.

Example 8   Let R be the relation with directed graph shown in Figure 3. Let a, b, c, d be a listing of the elements of the set. Find the matrices $\mathbf{W}_0, \mathbf{W}_1, \mathbf{W}_2, \mathbf{W}_3$, and $\mathbf{W}_4$. The matrix $\mathbf{W}_4$ is the transitive closure of R.

Solution: Let $v_1 = a$, $v_2 = b$, $v_3 = c$, and $v_4 = d$. $\mathbf{W}_0$ is the matrix of the relation. Hence,

$$\mathbf{W}_0 = \begin{bmatrix} 0 & 0 & 0 & 1 \\ 1 & 0 & 1 & 0 \\ 1 & 0 & 0 & 1 \\ 0 & 0 & 1 & 0 \end{bmatrix}.$$

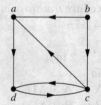

Figure 3   The Directed Graph of
the Relation R.

$\mathbf{W}_1$ has 1 as its (i, j)th entry if there is a path from v_i to v_j that has only $v_1 = a$ as an interior vertex. Note that all paths of length one can still be used because they have no interior vertices.

Also, there is now an allowable path from b to d, namely, b, a, d. Hence,

$$\mathbf{W}_1 = \begin{bmatrix} 0 & 0 & 0 & 1 \\ 1 & 0 & 1 & 1 \\ 1 & 0 & 0 & 1 \\ 0 & 0 & 1 & 0 \end{bmatrix}.$$

$\mathbf{W}_2$ has 1 as its (i, j)th entry if there is a path from v_i to v_j that has only $v_1 = a$ and/or $v_2 = b$ as its interior vertices, if any. Because there are no edges that have b as a terminal vertex, no new paths are obtained when we permit b to be an interior vertex. Hence, $\mathbf{W}_2 = \mathbf{W}_1$.

$\mathbf{W}_3$ has 1 as its (i, j)th entry if there is a path from v_i to v_j that has only $v_1 = a$, $v_2 = b$, and/or $v_3 = c$ as its interior vertices, if any. We now have paths from d to a, namely, d, c, a, and from d to d, namely, d, c, d. Hence,

$$\mathbf{W}_3 = \begin{bmatrix} 0 & 0 & 0 & 1 \\ 1 & 0 & 1 & 1 \\ 1 & 0 & 0 & 1 \\ 1 & 0 & 1 & 1 \end{bmatrix}.$$

Finally, $\mathbf{W}_4$ has 1 as its (i, j)th entry if there is a path from v_i to v_j that has $v_1 = a$, $v_2 = b$, $v_3 = c$, and/or $v_4 = d$ as interior vertices, if any. Because these are all the vertices of the graph, this entry is 1 if and only if there is a path from v_i to v_j. Hence,

$$\mathbf{W}_4 = \begin{bmatrix} 1 & 0 & 1 & 1 \\ 1 & 0 & 1 & 1 \\ 1 & 0 & 1 & 1 \\ 1 & 0 & 1 & 1 \end{bmatrix}.$$

This last matrix, $\mathbf{W}_4$, is the matrix of the transitive closure.   ◀

Warshall's algorithm computes $\mathbf{M}_{R^*}$ by efficiently computing $\mathbf{W}_0 = \mathbf{M}_R$, $\mathbf{W}_1$, $\mathbf{W}_2$, ..., $\mathbf{W}_n = \mathbf{M}_{R^*}$. This observation shows that we can compute $\mathbf{W}_k$ directly from $\mathbf{W}_{k-1}$: There is a path from v_i to v_j with no vertices other than $v_1, v_2, \ldots, v_k$ as interior vertices if and only if either there is a path from v_i to v_j with its interior vertices among the first $k-1$ vertices in the list, or there are paths from v_i to v_k and from v_k to v_j that have interior vertices only among the first $k-1$ vertices in the list. That is, either a path from v_i to v_j already existed before v_k was permitted as an interior vertex, or allowing v_k as an interior vertex produces a path that goes from v_i to v_k and then from v_k to v_j. These two cases are shown in Figure 4.

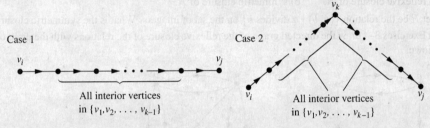

Case 1

v_i v_j

All interior vertices
in $\{v_1, v_2, \ldots, v_{k-1}\}$

Case 2

v_k

v_i All interior vertices v_j
in $\{v_1, v_2, \ldots, v_{k-1}\}$

Figure 4   Adding v_k to the Set of Allowable Interior Vertices.

The first type of path exists if and only if $w_{ij}^{[k-1]} = 1$, and the second type of path exists if and only if both $w_{ik}^{[k-1]}$ and $w_{kj}^{[k-1]}$ are 1. Hence, $w_{ij}^{[k]}$ is 1 if and only if either $w_{ij}^{[k-1]}$ is 1 or both $w_{ik}^{[k-1]}$ and $w_{kj}^{[k-1]}$ are 1. This gives us Lemma 2.

Lemma 2   Let $\mathbf{W}_k = [w_{ij}^{[k]}]$ be the zero–one matrix that has a 1 in its (i, j)th position if and only if there is a path from v_i to v_j with interior vertices from the set $\{v_1, v_2, \ldots, v_k\}$. Then

$$w_{ij}^{[k]} = w_{ij}^{[k-1]} \vee (w_{ik}^{[k-1]} \wedge w_{kj}^{[k-1]}),$$

whenever i, j, and k are positive integers not exceeding n.

Lemma 2 gives us the means to compute efficiently the matrices $\mathbf{W}_k$, $k = 1, 2, \ldots, n$. We display the pseudocode for Warshall's algorithm, using Lemma 2, as Algorithm 2.

Algorithm 2   Warshall Algorithm.

procedure *Warshall* ($\mathbf{M}_R : n \times n$ zero–one matrix)
$\mathbf{W} := \mathbf{M}_R$
for $k := 1$ **to** n
begin
    for $i := 1$ **to** n
    begin

> for $j := 1$ to n
> $w_{ij} := w_{ij} \lor (w_{ik} \land w_{kj})$
> **end**
> **end** $\{\mathbf{W} = [w_{ij}]$ is $\mathbf{M}_{R^*}\}$

The computational complexity of Warshall's algorithm can easily be computed in terms of bit operations. To find the entry $w_{ij}^{[k]}$ from the entries $w_{ij}^{[k-1]}, w_{ik}^{[k-1]}$, and $w_{kj}^{[k-1]}$ using Lemma 2 requires two bit operations. To find all n^2 entries of $\mathbf{W}_k$ from those of $\mathbf{W}_{k-1}$ requires $2n^2$ bit operations. Because Warshall's algorithm begins with $\mathbf{W}_0 = \mathbf{M}_R$ and computes the sequence of n zero–one matrices $\mathbf{W}_1, \mathbf{W}_2, \ldots, \mathbf{W}_n = \mathbf{M}_{R^*}$, the total number of bit operations used is $n \cdot 2n^2 = 2n^3$.

Exercises

1. Let R be the relation on the set $\{0, 1, 2, 3\}$ containing the ordered pairs $(0, 1)$, $(1, 1)$, $(1, 2)$, $(2, 0)$, $(2, 2)$, and $(3, 0)$. Find the
   a) reflexive closure of R.   b) symmetric closure of R.

2. Let R be the relation $\{(a, b) \mid a \text{ divides } b\}$ on the set of integers. What is the symmetric closure of R?

In Exercises 3–4 draw the directed graph of the reflexive closure of the relations with the directed graph shown.

3. 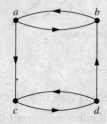   4.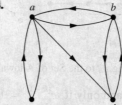

5. Find the directed graphs of the symmetric closures of the relations with directed graphs shown in Exercises 3–4.

6. Find the directed graph of the smallest relation that is both reflexive and symmetric for each of the relations with directed graphs shown in Exercises 3–4.

7. Suppose that the relation R on the finite set A is represented by the matrix $\mathbf{M}_R$. Show that the matrix that represents the symmetric closure of R is $\mathbf{M}_R \lor \mathbf{M}_R^t$.

8. When is it possible to define the "irreflexive closure" of a relation R, that is, a relation that contains R, is irreflexive, and is contained in every irreflexive relation that contains R?

9. Let R be the relation on the set $\{1, 2, 3, 4, 5\}$ containing the ordered pairs $(1, 3)$, $(2, 4)$, $(3, 1)$, $(3, 5)$, $(4, 3)$, $(5, 1)$, $(5, 2)$, and $(5, 4)$. Find
   a) R^2.   b) R^3.   c) R^4.   d) R^5.   e) R^6.   f) R^*.

10. Let R be the relation on the set of all students containing the ordered pair (a, b) if a and b are in at least one common class and $a \neq b$. When is (a, b) in
    a) R^2?   b) R^3?   c) R^*?

11. Suppose that the relation R is symmetric. Show that R^* is symmetric.

12. Use Algorithm 1 to find the transitive closures of these relations on $\{1, 2, 3, 4\}$.
    a) $\{(1, 2), (2, 1), (2, 3), (3, 4), (4, 1)\}$ b) $\{(2, 1), (2, 3), (3, 1), (3, 4), (4, 1), (4, 3)\}$
    c) $\{(1, 2), (1, 3), (1, 4), (2, 3), (2, 4), (3, 4)\}$
    d) $\{(1, 1), (1, 4), (2, 1), (2, 3), (3, 1), (3, 2), (3, 4), (4, 2)\}$

13. Use Warshall's algorithm to find the transitive closures of the relations in Exercise 12.

14. Find the smallest relation containing the relation $\{(1, 2), (1, 4), (3, 3), (4, 1)\}$ that is
   a) reflexive and transitive.   b) symmetric and transitive.   c) reflexive, symmetric, and transitive.

15. Algorithms have been devised that use $O(n^{2.8})$ bit operations to compute the Boolean product of two $n \times n$ zero–one matrices. Assuming that these algorithms can be used, give big-O estimates for the number of bit operations using Algorithm 1 and using Warshall's algorithm to find the transitive closure of a relation on a set with n elements.

16. Adapt Algorithm 1 to find the reflexive closure of the transitive closure of a relation on a set with n elements.

17. Show that the closure with respect to the property **P** of the relation $R = \{(0, 0), (0, 1), (1, 1), (2, 2)\}$ on the set $\{0, 1, 2\}$ does not exist if **P** is the property
   a) "is not reflexive."   b) "has an odd number of elements."

5.5   Equivalence Relations

Introduction

In some programming languages the names of variables can contain an unlimited number of characters. However, there is a limit on the number of characters that are checked when a compiler determines whether two variables are equal. For instance, in traditional C, only the first eight characters of a variable name are checked by the compiler. (These characters are uppercase or lowercase letters, digits, or underscores.) Consequently, the compiler considers strings longer than eight characters that agree in their first eight characters the same. Let R be the relation on the set of strings of characters such that sRt, where s and t are two strings, if s and t are at least eight characters long and the first eight characters of s and t agree, or $s = t$. It is easy to see that R is reflexive, symmetric, and transitive. Moreover, R divides the set of all strings into classes, where all strings in a particular class are considered the same by a compiler for traditional C.

The integers a and b are related by the "congruence modulo 4" relation when 4 divides $a - b$. We will show later that this relation is reflexive, symmetric, and transitive. It is not hard to see that a is related to b if and only if a and b have the same remainder when divided by 4. It follows that this relation splits the set of integers into four different classes. When we care only what remainder an integer leaves when it is divided by 4, we need only know which class it is in, not its particular value.

These two relations, R and congruence modulo 4, are examples of equivalence relations, namely, relations that are reflexive, symmetric, and transitive. In this section we will show that such relations split sets into disjoint classes of equivalent elements. Equivalence relations arise whenever we care only whether an element of a set is in a certain class of elements, instead of caring about its particular identity.

Equivalence Relations

In this section we will study relations with a particular combination of properties that allows them to be used to relate objects that are similar in some way.

Definition 1   A relation on a set A is called an *equivalence relation* if it is reflexive, symmetric, and transitive.

Equivalence relations are important throughout mathematics and computer science. One reason for this is that in an equivalence relation, when two elements are related it makes sense to say they are equivalent.

Definition 2   Two elements a and b that are related by an equivalence relation are called *equivalent*. The notation $a \sim b$ is often used to denote that a and b are equivalent elements with respect to a particular equivalence relation.

For the notion of equivalent elements to make sense, every element should be equivalent to itself, as the reflexive property guarantees for an equivalence relation. It makes sense to say that a and b are related (not just that a is related to b) by an equivalence relation, because when a is related to b, by the symmetric property, b is related to a. Furthermore, because an equivalence relation is transitive, if a and b are equivalent and b and c are equivalent, it follows that a and c are equivalent.

Examples 1–5 illustrate the notion of an equivalence relation.

Example 1   Let R be the relation on the set of integers such that aRb if and only if $a = b$ or $a = -b$. In Section 5.1 we showed that R is reflexive, symmetric, and transitive. It follows that R is an equivalence relation.   ◀

Example 2   Let R be the relation on the set of real numbers such that aRb if and only if $a - b$ is an integer. Is R an equivalence relation?

Solution: Because $a - a = 0$ is an integer for all real numbers a, aRa for all real numbers a. Hence, R is reflexive. Now suppose that aRb. Then $a - b$ is an integer, so $b - a$ is also an integer. Hence, bRa. It follows that R is symmetric. If aRb and bRc, then $a - b$ and $b - c$ are integers. Therefore, $a - c = (a - b) + (b - c)$ is also an integer. Hence, aRc. Thus, R is transitive. Consequently, R is an equivalence relation.   ◀

One of the most widely used equivalence relations is congruence modulo m, where m is a positive integer greater than 1.

Example 3   **Congruence Modulo m**   Let m be a positive integer with $m > 1$. Show that the relation

$$R = \{(a, b) \mid a \equiv b \;(\text{mod } m)\}$$

is an equivalence relation on the set of integers.

Solution: Recall that $a \equiv b \;(\text{mod } m)$ if and only if m divides $a - b$. Note that $a - a = 0$ is divisible by m, because $0 = 0 \cdot m$. Hence, $a \equiv a \;(\text{mod } m)$, so congruence modulo m is reflexive. Now suppose that $a \equiv b \;(\text{mod } m)$. Then $a - b$ is divisible by m, so $a - b = km$, where k is an integer. It follows that $b - a = (-k)m$, so $b \equiv a \;(\text{mod } m)$. Hence, congruence modulo m is symmetric. Next, suppose that $a \equiv b \;(\text{mod } m)$ and $b \equiv c \;(\text{mod } m)$. Then m divides both $a - b$ and $b - c$. Therefore, there are integers k and l with $a - b = km$ and $b - c = lm$. Adding these two equations shows that $a - c = (a - b) + (b - c) = km + lm = (k + l)m$. Thus, $a \equiv c \;(\text{mod } m)$. Therefore, congruence modulo m is transitive. It follows that congruence modulo m is an equivalence relation.   ◀

Example 4   Suppose that R is the relation on the set of strings of English letters such that aRb if and only if $l(a) = l(b)$, where $l(x)$ is the length of the string x. Is R an equivalence relation?

Solution: Because $l(a) = l(a)$, it follows that aRa whenever a is a string, so that R is reflexive. Next, suppose that aRb, so that $l(a) = l(b)$. Then bRa, because $l(b) = l(a)$. Hence, R is symmetric. Finally, suppose that aRb and bRc. Then $l(a) = l(b)$ and $l(b) = l(c)$. Hence, $l(a) = l(c)$, so aRc. Consequently, R is transitive. Because R is reflexive, symmetric, and transitive, it is an equivalence relation.   ◀

Example 5   Let n be a positive integer and S a set of strings. Suppose that R_n is the relation on S such that $sR_n t$ if and only if $s = t$, or both s and t have at least n characters and the first n characters of s and t are the same. That is, a string of fewer than n characters is related only to itself; a string s with at least n characters is related to a string t if and only if t has at least n characters and t begins with the n characters at the start of s. For example, let $n = 3$ and let S be the set of all bit strings. Then $sR_3 t$ either when $s = t$ or both s and t are bit strings of length 3 or more that begin with the same three bits. For instance, $01 R_3 01$ and $00111 R_3 00101$, but $01 \not{R}_3 010$ and $01011 \not{R}_3 01110$.

Show that for every set S of strings and every positive integer n, R_n is an equivalence relation on S.

Solution: The relation R_n is reflexive because $s = s$, so that $sR_n s$ whenever s is a string in S. If $sR_n t$, then either $s = t$ or s and t are both at least n characters long that begin with the same n characters. This means that $tR_n s$. We conclude that R_n is symmetric.

Now suppose that $sR_n t$ and $tR_n u$. Then either $s = t$ or s and t are at least n characters long and s and t begin with the same n characters, and either $t = u$ or t and u are at least n characters long and t and u begin with the same n characters. From this, we can deduce that either $s = u$ or both s and u are n characters long and s and u begin with the same n characters (because in this case we know that s, t, and u are all at least n characters long and both s and u begin with the same n characters that t does). Consequently, R_n is transitive. It follows that R_n is an equivalence relation.   ◄

In Examples 6 and 7 we look at two relations that are not equivalence relations.

Example 6   Show that the "divides" relation on the set of positive integers in not an equivalence relation.

Solution: By Examples 9 and 15 in Section 5.1, we know that the "divides" relation is reflexive and transitive. However, by Example 12 in Section 5.1, we know that this relation is not symmetric (for instance, $2 \mid 4$ but $4 \nmid 2$). We conclude that the "divides" relation on the set of positive integers is not an equivalence relation.   ◄

Example 7   Let R be the relation on the set of real numbers such that xRy if and only if x and y are real numbers that differ by less than 1, that is $|x - y| < 1$. Show that R is not an equivalence relation.

Solution: R is reflexive because $|x - x| = 0 < 1$ whenever $x \in \mathbf{R}$. R is symmetric, for if xRy, where x and y are real numbers, then $|x - y| < 1$, which tells us that $|y - x| = |x - y| < 1$, so that yRx. However, R is not an equivalence relation because it is not transitive. Take $x = 2.8$, $y = 1.9$, and $z = 1.1$, so that $|x - y| = |2.8 - 1.9| = 0.9 < 1$, $|y - z| = |1.9 - 1.1| = 0.8 < 1$, but $|x - z| = |2.8 - 1.1| = 1.7 > 1$. That is, $2.8\,R\,1.9$, $1.9\,R\,1.1$, but $2.8\,\cancel{R}\,1.1$.   ◄

Equivalence Classes

Let A be the set of all students in your school who graduated from high school. Consider the relation R on A that consists of all pairs (x, y), where x and y graduated from the same high school. Given a student x, we can form the set of all students equivalent to x with respect to R. This set consists of all students who graduated from the same high school as x did. This subset of A is called an equivalence class of the relation.

Definition 3   Let R be an equivalence relation on a set A. The set of all elements that are related to an element a of A is called the *equivalence class* of a. The equivalence class of a with respect to R is denoted by $[a]_R$. When only one relation is under consideration, we can delete the subscript R and write $[a]$ for this equivalence class.

In other words, if R is an equivalence relation on a set A, the equivalence class of the element a is

$$[a]_R = \{s \mid (a, s) \in R\}.$$

If $b \in [a]_R$, then b is called a **representative** of this equivalence class. Any element of a class can be used as a representative of this class. That is, there is nothing special about the particular element chosen as the representative of the class.

Example 8   What is the equivalence class of an integer for the equivalence relation of Example 1?

Solution: Because an integer is equivalent to itself and its negative in this equivalence relation, it follows that $[a] = \{-a, a\}$. This set contains two distinct integers unless $a = 0$. For instance, $[7] = \{-7, 7\}$, $[-5] = \{-5, 5\}$, and $[0] = \{0\}$.   ◄

Example 9   What are the equivalence classes of 0 and 1 for congruence modulo 4?

Solution: The equivalence class of 0 contains all integers a such that $a \equiv 0 \pmod 4$. The integers in this class are those divisible by 4. Hence, the equivalence class of 0 for this relation is

$$[0] = \{\ldots, -8, -4, 0, 4, 8, \ldots\}.$$

The equivalence class of 1 contains all the integers a such that $a \equiv 1 \pmod 4$. The integers in this class are those that have a remainder of 1 when divided by 4. Hence, the equivalence class of 1 for this relation is

$$[1] = \{\ldots, -7, -3, 1, 5, 9, \ldots\}. \qquad \blacktriangleleft$$

In Example 9 the equivalence classes of 0 and 1 with respect to congruence modulo 4 were found. Example 9 can easily be generalized, replacing 4 with any positive integer m. The equivalence classes of the relation congruence modulo m are called the **congruence classes modulo** m. The congruence class of an integer a modulo m is denoted by $[a]_m$, so $[a]_m = \{\ldots, a - 2m, a - m, a, a + m, a + 2m, \ldots\}$. For instance, from Example 9 it follows that $[0]_4 = \{\ldots, -8, -4, 0, 4, 8, \ldots\}$ and $[1]_4 = \{\ldots, -7, -3, 1, 5, 9, \ldots\}$.

Example 10   What is the equivalence class of the string 0111 with respect to the equivalence relation R_3 from Example 5 on the set of all bit strings? (Recall that sR_3t if and only if s and t are bit strings with $s = t$ or s and t are strings of at least three bits that start with the same three bits.)

Solution: The bit strings equivalent to 0111 are the bit strings with at least three bits that begin with 011. These are the bit strings 011, 0110, 0111, 01100, 01101, 01110, 01111, and so on. Consequently,

$$[011]_{R_3} = \{011, 0110, 0111, 01100, 01101, 01110, 01111, \ldots\}. \qquad \blacktriangleleft$$

Example 11   **Identifiers in the C Programming Language**   In the C programming language, an **identifier** is the name of a variable, a function, or another type of entity. Each identifier is a nonempty string of characters where each character is a lowercase or an uppercase English letter, a digit, or an underscore, and the first character is a lowercase or an uppercase English letter. Identifiers can be any length. This allows developers to use as many characters as they want to name an entity, such as a variable. However, for compilers for some versions of C, there is a limit on the number of characters checked when two names are compared to see whether they refer to the same thing. For example, Standard C compilers consider two identifiers the same when they agree in their first 31 characters. Consequently, developers must be careful not to use identifiers with the same initial 31 characters for different things. We see that two identifiers are considered the same when they are related by the relation R_{31} in Example 5. Using Example 5, we know that R_{31}, on the set of all identifiers in Standard C, is an equivalence relation.

What are the equivalence classes of the each of the identifiers Number_of_tropical_ storms, Number_of_named_tropical_storms, and Number_of_named_tropical_storms_in_the_Atlantic_in_ 2005?

Solution: Note that when an identifier is less than 31 characters long, by the definition of R_{31}, its equivalence class contains only itself. Because the identifier Number_of_tropical_storms is 25 characters long, its equivalence class contains exactly one element, namely, itself.

The identifier Number_of_named_tropical_storms is exactly 31 characters long. An identifier is equivalent to it when it starts with these same 31 characters. Consequently, every identifier at least 31 characters long that starts with Number_of_named_tropical_storms is equivalent to this identifier. It follows that the equivalence class of Number_of_named_tropical_storms is the set of all identifiers that begin with the 31 characters Number_of_named_tropical_storms.

An identifier is equivalent to the Number_of_named_tropical_storms_in_the_Atlantic_in_ 2005 if and only if it begins with its first 31 characters. Because these characters are Number_of_named_ tropical_storms, we see that an identifier is equivalent to Number_of_named_tropical_storms_in_ the_Atlantic_in_ 2005 if and only if it is equivalent to Number_of_named_tropical_storms. It follows that these last two identifiers have the same equivalence class.   ◄

Equivalence Classes and Partitions

Let A be the set of students at your school who are majoring in exactly one subject, and let R be the relation on A consisting of pairs (x, y), where x and y are students with the same major. Then R is an equivalence relation, as the reader should verify. We can see that R splits all students in A into a collection of disjoint subsets, where each subset contains students with a specified major. For instance, one subset contains all students majoring (just) in computer science, and a second subset contains all students majoring in history. Furthermore, these subsets are equivalence classes of R. This example illustrates how the equivalence classes of an equivalence relation partition a set into disjoint, nonempty subsets. We will make these notions more precise in the following discussion.

Let R be a relation on the set A. Theorem 1 shows that the equivalence classes of two elements of A are either identical or disjoint.

Theorem 1   Let R be an equivalence relation on a set A. These statements for elements a and b of A are equivalent:
    (i) aRb (ii) $[a] = [b]$ (iii) $[a] \cap [b] \neq \emptyset$

Proof: We first show that (i) implies (ii). Assume that aRb. We will prove that $[a] = [b]$ by showing $[a] \subseteq [b]$ and $[b] \subseteq [a]$. Suppose $c \in [a]$. Then aRc. Because aRb and R is symmetric, we know that bRa. Furthermore, because R is transitive and bRa and aRc, it follows that bRc. Hence, $c \in [b]$. This shows that $[a] \subseteq [b]$. The proof that $[b] \subseteq [a]$ is similar; it is left as an exercise for the reader.

Second, we will show that (ii) implies (iii). Assume that $[a] = [b]$. It follows that $[a] \cap [b] \neq \emptyset$ because $[a]$ is nonempty (because $a \in [a]$ because R is reflexive).

Next, we will show that (iii) implies (i). Suppose that $[a] \cap [b] \neq \emptyset$. Then there is an element c with $c \in [a]$ and $c \in [b]$. In other words, aRc and bRc. By the symmetric property, cRb. Then by transitivity, because aRc and cRb, we have aRb.

Because (i) implies (ii), (ii) implies (iii), and (iii) implies (i), the three statements, (i), (ii), and (iii), are equivalent.   ◁

We are now in a position to show how an equivalence relation *partitions* a set. Let R be an equivalence relation on a set A. The union of the equivalence classes of R is all of A, because an element a of A is in its own equivalence class, namely, $[a]_R$. In other words,

$$\bigcup_{a \in A} [a]_R = A.$$

In addition, from Theorem 1, it follows that these equivalence classes are either equal or disjoint, so

$$[a]_R \cap [b]_R = \emptyset,$$

when $[a]_R \neq [b]_R$.

These two observations show that the equivalence classes form a partition of A, because they split A into disjoint subsets. More precisely, a **partition** of a set S is a collection of disjoint nonempty subsets of S that have S as their union. In other words, the collection of subsets A_i, $i \in I$ (where I is an index set) forms a partition of S if and only if

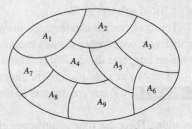

Figure 1   A Partition of a Set.

$$A_i \neq \emptyset \text{ for } i \in I,$$

$$A_i \cap A_j = \emptyset \text{ when } i \neq j,$$

and

$$\bigcup_{i \in I} A_i = S.$$

(Here the notation $\bigcup_{i \in I} A_i$ represents the union of the sets A_i for all $i \in I$.) Figure 1 illustrates the concept of a partition of a set.

Example 12   Suppose that $S = \{1, 2, 3, 4, 5, 6\}$. The collection of sets $A_1 = \{1, 2, 3\}$, $A_2 = \{4, 5\}$, and $A_3 = \{6\}$ forms a partition of S, because these sets are disjoint and their union is S.
◀

We have seen that the equivalence classes of an equivalence relation on a set form a partition of the set. The subsets in this partition are the equivalence classes. Conversely, every partition of a set can be used to form an equivalence relation. Two elements are equivalent with respect to this relation if and only if they are in the same subset of the partition.

To see this, assume that $\{A_i \mid i \in I\}$ is a partition on S. Let R be the relation on S consisting of the pair (x, y), where x and y belong to the same subset A_i in the partition. To show that R is an equivalence relation we must show that R is reflexive, symmetric, and transitive.

We see that $(a, a) \in R$ for every $a \in S$, because a is in the same subset as itself. Hence, R is reflexive. If $(a, b) \in R$, then b and a are in the same subset of the partition, so that $(b, a) \in R$ as well. Hence, R is symmetric. If $(a, b) \in R$ and $(b, c) \in R$, then a and b are in the same subset in the partition, X, and b and c are in the same subset of the partition, Y. Because the subsets of the partition are disjoint and b belongs to X and Y, it follows that $X = Y$. Consequently, a and c belong to the same subset of the partition, so $(a, c) \in R$. Thus, R is transitive.

It follows that R is an equivalence relation. The equivalence classes of R consist of subsets of S containing related elements, and by the definition of R, these are the subsets of the partition. Theorem 2 summarizes the connections we have established between equivalence relations and partitions.

Theorem 2   Let R be an equivalence relation on a set S. Then the equivalence classes of R form a partition of S. Conversely, given a partition $\{A_i \mid i \in I\}$ of the set S, there is an equivalence relation R that has the sets A_i, $i \in I$, as its equivalence classes.

Example 13 shows how to construct an equivalence relation from a partition.

Example 13   List the ordered pairs in the equivalence relation R produced by the partition $A_1 = \{1, 2, 3\}$, $A_2 = \{4, 5\}$, and $A_3 = \{6\}$ of $S = \{1, 2, 3, 4, 5, 6\}$, given in Example 12.
Solution: The subsets in the partition are the equivalence classes of R. The pair $(a, b) \in R$ if and only if a and b are in the same subset of the partition. The pairs $(1, 1)$, $(1, 2)$, $(1, 3)$, $(2, 1)$, $(2, 2)$, $(2, 3)$, $(3, 1)$, $(3, 2)$, and $(3, 3)$ belong to R because $A_1 = \{1, 2, 3\}$ is an equivalence class; the pairs $(4, 4)$, $(4, 5)$, $(5, 4)$, and $(5, 5)$ belong to R because $A_2 = \{4, 5\}$ is an equivalence class; and finally the pair $(6, 6)$ belongs to R because $\{6\}$ is an equivalence class. No pair other than those listed belongs to R.
◀

The congruence classes modulo m provide a useful illustration of Theorem 2. There are m different congruence classes modulo m, corresponding to the m different remainders possible when an integer is divided by m. These m congruence classes are denoted by $[0]_m, [1]_m, \ldots, [m-1]_m$. They form a partition of the set of integers.

Example 14   What are the sets in the partition of the integers arising from congruence modulo 4?
Solution: There are four congruence classes, corresponding to $[0]_4$, $[1]_4$, $[2]_4$, and $[3]_4$. They are the sets

$$[0]_4 = \{\ldots, -8, -4, 0, 4, 8, \ldots\},$$
$$[1]_4 = \{\ldots, -7, -3, 1, 5, 9, \ldots\},$$
$$[2]_4 = \{\ldots, -6, -2, 2, 6, 10, \ldots\},$$
$$[3]_4 = \{\ldots, -5, -1, 3, 7, 11, \ldots\}.$$

These congruence classes are disjoint, and every integer is in exactly one of them. In other words, as Theorem 2 says, these congruence classes form a partition. ◄

We now provide an example of a partition of the set of all strings arising from an equivalence relation on this set.

Example 15   Let R_3 be the relation from Example 5. What are the sets in the partition of the set of all bit strings arising from the relation R_3 on the set of all bit strings? (Recall that sR_3t, where s and t are bit strings, if $s = t$ or s and t are bit strings with at least three bits that agree in their first three bits.)

Solution: Note that every bit string of length less than three is equivalent only to itself. Hence $[\lambda]_{R_3} = \{\lambda\}$, $[0]_{R_3} = \{0\}$, $[1]_{R_3} = \{1\}$, $[00]_{R_3} = \{00\}$, $[01]_{R_3} = \{01\}$, $[10]_{R_3} = \{10\}$, and $[11]_{R_3} = \{11\}$. Note that every bit string of length three or more is equivalent to one of the eight bit strings $000, 001, 010, 011, 100, 101, 110$, and 111. We have

$$[000]_{R_3} = \{000, 0000, 0001, 00000, 00001, 00010, 00011, \ldots\},$$
$$[001]_{R_3} = \{001, 0010, 0011, 00100, 00101, 00110, 00111, \ldots\},$$
$$[010]_{R_3} = \{010, 0100, 0101, 01000, 01001, 01010, 01011, \ldots\},$$
$$[011]_{R_3} = \{011, 0110, 0111, 01100, 01101, 01110, 01111, \ldots\},$$
$$[100]_{R_3} = \{100, 1000, 1001, 10000, 10001, 10010, 10011, \ldots\},$$
$$[101]_{R_3} = \{101, 1010, 1011, 10100, 10101, 10110, 10111, \ldots\},$$
$$[110]_{R_3} = \{110, 1100, 1101, 11000, 11001, 11010, 11011, \ldots\}, \text{ and}$$
$$[111]_{R_3} = \{111, 1110, 1111, 11100, 11101, 11110, 11111, \ldots\}.$$

These 15 equivalence classes are disjoint and every bit string is in exactly one of them. As Theorem 2 tells us, these equivalence classes partition the set of all bit strings. ◄

Exercises

1. Which of these relations on $\{0, 1, 2, 3\}$ are equivalence relations? Determine the properties of an equivalence relation that the others lack.
   a) $\{(0, 0), (1, 1), (2, 2), (3, 3)\}$ b) $\{(0, 0), (0, 2), (2, 0), (2, 2), (2, 3), (3, 2), (3, 3)\}$
   c) $\{(0, 0), (1, 1), (1, 2), (2, 1), (2, 2), (3, 3)\}$
   d) $\{(0, 0), (1, 1), (1, 3), (2, 2), (2, 3), (3, 1), (3, 2), (3, 3)\}$
   e) $\{(0, 0), (0, 1), (0, 2), (1, 0), (1, 1), (1, 2), (2, 0), (2, 2), (3, 3)\}$

2. Which of these relations on the set of all functions from $\mathbf{Z}$ to $\mathbf{Z}$ are equivalence relations? Determine the properties of an equivalence relation that the others lack.
   a) $\{(f, g) \mid f(1) = g(1)\}$ b) $\{(f, g) \mid f(0) = g(0) \text{ or } f(1) = g(1)\}$
   c) $\{(f, g) \mid f(x) - g(x) = 1 \text{ for all } x \in \mathbf{Z}\}$
   d) $\{(f, g) \mid \text{for some } C \in \mathbf{Z}, \text{ for all } x \in \mathbf{Z}, f(x) - g(x) = C\}$
   e) $\{(f, g) \mid f(0) = g(1) \text{ and } f(1) = g(0)\}$

3. Define three equivalence relations on the set of buildings on a college campus. Determine the equivalence classes for each of these equivalence relations.

4. Show that the relation of logical equivalence on the set of all compound propositions is an equivalence relation. What are the equivalence classes of **F** and of **T**?

5. Suppose that A is a nonempty set, and f is a function that has A as its domain. Let R be the relation on A consisting of all ordered pairs (x, y) such that $f(x) = f(y)$.
   a) Show that R is an equivalence relation on A.   b) What are the equivalence classes of R?

6. Show that the relation R consisting of all pairs (x, y) such that x and y are bit strings of length three or more that agree in their first three bits is an equivalence relation on the set of all bit strings of length three or more.

7. Show that the relation R consisting of all pairs (x, y) such that x and y are bit strings that agree in their first and third bits is an equivalence relation on the set of all bit strings of length three or more.

8. Let R be the relation on the set of ordered pairs of positive integers such that $((a, b), (c, d)) \in R$ if and only if $a + d = b + c$. Show that R is an equivalence relation.

9. *(Requires calculus)*
   a) Show that the relation R on the set of all differentiable functions from **R** to **R** consisting of all pairs (f, g) such that $f'(x) = g'(x)$ for all real numbers x is an equivalence relation.
   b) Which functions are in the same equivalence class as the function $f(x) = x^2$?

10. Let R be the relation on the set of all URLs (or Web addresses) such that $x \, R \, y$ if and only if the Web page at x is the same as the Web page at y. Show that R is an equivalence relation.
    In Exercises 11–12 determine whether the relation with the directed graphs shown is an equivalence relation.

11.
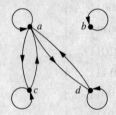

12.
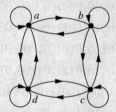

13. Show that the relation R on the set of all bit strings such that $s \, R \, t$ if and only if s and t contain the same number of 1s is an equivalence relation.

14. What is the equivalence class of the bit string 011 for the equivalence relation in Exercise 13?

15. What is the congruence class $[n]_5$ (that is, the equivalence class of n with respect to congruence modulo 5) when n is
    a) 2?   b) 3?   c) 6?   d) −3?

16. Give a description of each of the congruence classes modulo 6.

17. a) What is the equivalence class of $(1, 2)$ with respect to the equivalence relation in Exercise 8?
    b) Give an interpretation of the equivalence classes for the equivalence relation R in Exercise 8. [*Hint:* Look at the difference $a - b$ corresponding to (a, b).]

18. Which of these collections of subsets are partitions of $\{1, 2, 3, 4, 5, 6\}$?
    a) $\{1, 2\}, \{2, 3, 4\}, \{4, 5, 6\}$ b) $\{1\}, \{2, 3, 6\}, \{4\}, \{5\}$
    c) $\{2, 4, 6\}, \{1, 3, 5\}$ d) $\{1, 4, 5\}, \{2, 6\}$

19. Which of these collections of subsets are partitions on the set of bit strings of length 8?
    a) the set of bit strings that begin with 1, the set of bit strings that begin with 00, and the set of bit strings that begin with 01
    b) the set of bit strings that contain the string 00, the set of bit strings that contain the string 01, the set of bit strings that contain the string 10, and the set of bit strings that contain the string 11
    c) the set of bit strings that end with 00, the set of bit strings that end with 01, the set of bit strings that end with 10, and the set of bit strings that end with 11
    d) the set of bit strings that end with 111, the set of bit strings that end with 011, and the set of bit strings that end with 00
    e) the set of bit strings that have $3k$ ones, where k is a nonnegative integer; the set of bit strings that contain $3k + 1$ ones, where k is a nonnegative integer; and the set of bit strings that contain $3k + 2$ ones, where k is a nonnegative integer

20. Which of these are partitions of the set $\mathbf{Z} \times \mathbf{Z}$ of ordered pairs of integers?

    a) the set of pairs (x, y), where x or y is odd; the set of pairs (x, y), where x is even; and the set of pairs (x, y), where y is even

    b) the set of pairs (x, y), where both x and y are odd; the set of pairs (x, y), where exactly one of x and y is odd; and the set of pairs (x, y), where both x and y are even

    c) the set of pairs (x, y), where x is positive; the set of pairs (x, y), where y is positive; and the set of pairs (x, y), where both x and y are negative

    d) the set of pairs (x, y), where $3 \mid x$ and $3 \mid y$; the set of pairs (x, y), where $3 \mid x$ and $3 \nmid y$; the set of pairs (x, y), where $3 \nmid x$ and $3 \mid y$; and the set of pairs (x, y), where $3 \nmid x$ and $3 \nmid y$

    e) the set of pairs (x, y), where $x > 0$ and $y > 0$; the set of pairs (x, y), where $x > 0$ and $y \leqslant 0$; the set of pairs (x, y), where $x \leqslant 0$ and $y > 0$; and the set of pairs (x, y), where $x \leqslant 0$ and $y \leqslant 0$

    f) the set of pairs (x, y), where $x \neq 0$ and $y \neq 0$; the set of pairs (x, y), where $x = 0$ and $y \neq 0$; and the set of pairs (x, y), where $x \neq 0$ and $y = 0$

21. List the ordered pairs in the equivalence relations produced by these partitions of $\{0, 1, 2, 3, 4, 5\}$.

    a) $\{0\}, \{1, 2\}, \{3, 4, 5\}$ b) $\{0, 1\}, \{2, 3\}, \{4, 5\}$

    c) $\{0, 1, 2\}, \{3, 4, 5\}$ d) $\{0\}, \{1\}, \{2\}, \{3\}, \{4\}, \{5\}$

22. Show that the partition formed from congruence classes modulo 6 is a refinement of the partition formed from congruence classes modulo 3.

23. Show that the partition of the set of bit strings of length 16 formed by equivalence classes of bit strings that agree on the last eight bits is a refinement of the partition formed from the equivalence classes of bit strings that agree on the last four bits.

    In Exercise 24, R_n refers to the family of equivalence relations defined in Example 5. Recall that $s \, R_n \, t$, where s and t are two strings if $s = t$ or s and t are strings with at least n characters that agree in their first n characters.

24. Show that the partition of the set of all identifiers in C formed by the equivalence classes of identifiers with respect to the equivalence relation R_{31} is a refinement of the partition formed by equivalence classes of identifiers with respect to the equivalence relation R_8. (Compilers for "old" C consider identifiers the same when their names agree in their first eight characters, while compilers in standard C consider identifiers the same when their names agree in their first 31 characters.)

25. Find the smallest equivalence relation on the set $\{a, b, c, d, e\}$ containing the relation $\{(a, b), (a, c), (d, e)\}$.

26. Consider the equivalence relation from Example 3, namely, $R = \{(x, y) \mid x - y \text{ is an integer}\}$.

    a) What is the equivalence class of 1 for this equivalence relation?

    b) What is the equivalence class of 1/2 for this equivalence relation?

*27. Let R be the relation on the set of all colorings of the 2×2 checkerboard where each of the four squares is colored either red or blue so that (C_1, C_2), where C_1 and C_2 are 2×2 checkerboards with each of their four squares colored blue or red, belongs to R if and only if C_2 can be obtained from C_1 either by rotating the checkerboard or by rotating it and then reflecting it.

    a) Show that R is an equivalence relation.   b) What are the equivalence classes of R?

28. Determine the number of different equivalence relations on a set with three elements by listing them.

*29. Do we necessarily get an equivalence relation when we form the transitive closure of the symmetric closure of the reflexive closure of a relation?

30. Suppose we use Theorem 2 to form a partition P from an equivalence relation R. What is the equivalence relation R' that results if we use Theorem 2 again to form an equivalence relation from P?

31. Devise an algorithm to find the smallest equivalence relation containing a given relation.

5.6   Partial Orderings

Introduction

We often use relations to order some or all of the elements of sets. For instance, we order words using the relation containing pairs of words (x, y), where x comes before y in the dictionary. We schedule projects using the relation consisting of pairs (x, y), where x and y are tasks in a project such that x must be completed before y begins. We order the set of integers using the relation containing the pairs (x, y), where x is less than y. When we add all of the pairs of the form (x, x) to these relations, we obtain a relation that is reflexive, antisymmetric, and transitive. These are properties that characterize relations used to order the elements of sets.

Definition 1   A relation R on a set S is called a *partial ordering* or *partial order* if it is reflexive, antisymmetric, and transitive. A set S together with a partial ordering R is called a *partially ordered set*, or *poset*, and is denoted by (S, R). Members of S are called *elements* of the poset.

We give examples of posets in Examples 1–3.

Example 1   Show that the "greater than or equal" relation ($\geq$) is a partial ordering on the set of integers.

Solution: Because $a \geq a$ for every integer a, $\geq$ is reflexive. If $a \geq b$ and $b \geq a$, then $a = b$. Hence, $\geq$ is antisymmetric. Finally, $\geq$ is transitive because $a \geq b$ and $b \geq c$ imply that $a \geq c$. It follows that $\geq$ is a partial ordering on the set of integers and $(\mathbf{Z}, \geq)$ is a poset.   ◀

Example 2   The divisibility relation $\mid$ is a partial ordering on the set of positive integers, because it is reflexive, antisymmetric, and transitive, as was shown in Section 5.1. We see that $(\mathbf{Z}^+, \mid)$ is a poset. Recall that ($\mathbf{Z}^+$ denotes the set of positive integers.)   ◀

Example 3   Show that the inclusion relation $\subseteq$ is a partial ordering on the power set of a set S.
Solution: Because $A \subseteq A$ whenever A is a subset of S, $\subseteq$ is reflexive. It is antisymmetric because $A \subseteq B$ and $B \subseteq A$ imply that $A = B$. Finally, $\subseteq$ is transitive, because $A \subseteq B$ and $B \subseteq C$ imply that $A \subseteq C$. Hence, $\subseteq$ is a partial ordering on $P(S)$, and $(P(S), \subseteq)$ is a poset.   ◀

Example 4 illustrates a relation that is not a partial ordering.

Example 4   Let R be the relation on the set of people such that xRy if x and y are people and x is older than y. Show that R is not a partial ordering.
Solution: Note that R is antisymmetric because if a person x is older than a person y, then y is not older than x. That is, if xRy, then $y\not\!Rx$. The relation R is transitive because if person x is older than person y and y is older than person z, then x is older than z. That is, if xRy and yRz, then xRz. However, R is not reflexive, because no person is older than himself or herself. That is, $x\not\!Rx$ for all people x. It follows that R is not a partial ordering.   ◀

In different posets different symbols such as $\leq$, $\subseteq$, and $\mid$, are used for a partial ordering. However, we need a symbol that we can use when we discuss the ordering relation in an arbitrary poset. Customarily, the notation $a \preccurlyeq b$ is used to denote that $(a, b) \in R$ in an arbitrary poset (S, R). This notation is used because the "less than or equal to" relation on the set of real numbers is the most familiar example of a partial ordering and the symbol $\preccurlyeq$ is similar to the $\leq$ symbol. (Note that the symbol $\preccurlyeq$ is used to denote the relation in *any* poset, not just the "less than or equals" relation.) The notation $a \prec b$ denotes that $a \preccurlyeq b$, but $a \neq b$. Also, we say "a is less than b" or "b is greater than a" if $a \prec b$.

When a and b are elements of the poset $(S, \preccurlyeq)$, it is not necessary that either $a \preccurlyeq b$ or $b \preccurlyeq a$. For instance, in $(P(\mathbf{Z}), \subseteq)$, $\{1, 2\}$ is not related to $\{1, 3\}$, and vice versa, because neither set is contained within the other. Similarly, in $(\mathbf{Z}^+, \mid)$, 2 is not related to 3 and 3 is not related to 2, because $2 \nmid 3$ and $3 \nmid 2$. This leads to Definition 2.

Definition 2   The elements a and b of a poset $(S, \preccurlyeq)$ are called *comparable* if either $a \preccurlyeq b$ or $b \preccurlyeq a$. When a and b are elements of S such that neither $a \preccurlyeq b$ nor $b \preccurlyeq a$, a and b are called *incomparable*.

Example 5   In the poset $(\mathbf{Z}^+, \mid)$, are the integers 3 and 9 comparable? Are 5 and 7 comparable?
Solution: The integers 3 and 9 are comparable, because $3 \mid 9$. The integers 5 and 7 are incomparable, because $5 \nmid 7$ and $7 \nmid 5$.   ◀

The adjective "partial" is used to describe partial orderings because pairs of elements may be incomparable. When every two elements in the set are comparable, the relation is called a **total ordering**.

Definition 3 If $(S, \preccurlyeq)$ is a poset and every two elements of S are comparable, S is called a *totally ordered* or *linearly ordered set,* and $\preccurlyeq$ is called a *total order* or a *linear order.* A totally ordered set is also called a *chain.*

Example 6 The poset $(\mathbf{Z}, \leqslant)$ is totally ordered, because $a \leqslant b$ or $b \leqslant a$ whenever a and b are integers. ◀

Example 7 The poset $(\mathbf{Z}^+, |)$ is not totally ordered because it contains elements that are incomparable, such as 5 and 7. ◀

We noted that $(\mathbf{Z}^+, \leqslant)$ is well-ordered, where $\leqslant$ is the usual "less than or equal to" relation. We now define well-ordered sets.

Definition 4 $(S, \preccurlyeq)$ is a *well-ordered set* if it is a poset such that $\preccurlyeq$ is a total ordering and every nonempty subset of S has a least element.

Example 8 The set of ordered pairs of positive integers, $\mathbf{Z}^+ \times \mathbf{Z}^+$, with $(a_1, a_2) \preccurlyeq (b_1, b_2)$ if $a_1 < b_1$, or if $a_1 = b_1$ and $a_2 \leqslant b_2$ (the lexicographic ordering), is a well-ordered set. The verification of this is left as an exercise at the end of this section. The set $\mathbf{Z}$, with the usual $\leqslant$ ordering, is not well-ordered because the set of negative integers, which is a subset of $\mathbf{Z}$, has no least element. ◀

We now state and prove that this proof technique is valid.

Theorem 1 **The Principle Of Well-Ordered Induction** Suppose that S is a well-ordered set. Then $P(x)$ is true for all $x \in S$, if
Inductive Step: For every $y \in S$, if $P(x)$ is true for all $x \in S$ with $x \prec y$, then $P(y)$ is true.

Proof: Suppose it is not the case that $P(x)$ is true for all $x \in S$. Then there is an element $y \in S$ such that $P(y)$ is false. Consequently, the set $A = \{x \in S \mid P(x) \text{ is false}\}$ is nonempty. Because S is well ordered, A has a least element a. By the choice of a as a least element of A, we know that $P(x)$ is true for all $x \in S$ with $x \prec a$. This implies by the inductive step $P(a)$ is true. This contradiction shows that $P(x)$ must be true for all $x \in S$. ◁

Remark: We do not need a basis step in a proof using the principle of well-ordered induction because if x_0 is the least element of a well ordered set, the inductive step tells us that $P(x_0)$ is true. This follows because there are no elements $x \in S$ with $x \prec x_0$, so we know (using a vacuous proof) that $P(x)$ is true for all $x \in S$ with $x \prec x_0$.

The principle of well-ordered induction is a versatile technique for proving results about well-ordered sets. Even when it is possible to use mathematical induction for the set of positive integers to prove a theorem, it may be simpler to use the principle of well-ordered induction, we proved a result about the well-ordered set $(\mathbf{N} \times \mathbf{N}, \preccurlyeq)$ where $\preccurlyeq$ is lexicographic ordering on $\mathbf{N} \times \mathbf{N}$.

Lexicographic Order

The words in a dictionary are listed in alphabetic, or lexicographic, order, which is based on the ordering of the letters in the alphabet. This is a special case of an ordering of strings on a set constructed from a partial ordering on the set. We will show how this construction works in any poset.

First, we will show how to construct a partial ordering on the Cartesian product of two posets, $(A_1, \preccurlyeq_1)$ and $(A_2, \preccurlyeq_2)$. The **lexicographic ordering** $\preccurlyeq$ on $A_1 \times A_2$ is defined by specifying that one pair is less than a second pair if the first entry of the first pair is less than (in A_1) the first entry of the second pair, or if the first entries are equal, but the second entry of this pair is less than (in A_2) the second entry of the second pair. In other words, (a_1, a_2) is less than (b_1, b_2), that is,

$$(a_1, a_2) \prec (b_1, b_2),$$

either if $a_1 \prec_1 b_1$ or if both $a_1 = b_1$ and $a_2 \prec_2 b_2$.

We obtain a partial ordering $\preccurlyeq$ by adding equality to the ordering $\prec$ on $A_1 \times A_2$. The verification of this is left as an exercise.

Example 9   Determine whether $(3,5) \prec (4,8)$, whether $(3,8) \prec (4,5)$, and whether $(4,9) \prec (4, 11)$ in the poset $(\mathbf{Z} \times \mathbf{Z}, \preccurlyeq)$, where $\preccurlyeq$ is the lexicographic ordering constructed from the usual $\leqslant$ relation on $\mathbf{Z}$.

Solution: Because $3 < 4$, it follows that $(3,5) \prec (4,8)$ and that $(3,8) \prec (4,5)$. We have $(4,9) \prec (4,11)$, because the first entries of $(4,9)$ and $(4,11)$ are the same but $9 < 11$. ◀

In Figure 1 the ordered pairs in $\mathbf{Z}^+ \times \mathbf{Z}^+$ that are less than $(3,4)$ are highlighted. A lexicographic ordering can be defined on the Cartesian product of n posets $(A_1, \preccurlyeq_1), (A_2, \preccurlyeq_2), \ldots, (A_n, \preccurlyeq_n)$. Define the partial ordering $\preccurlyeq$ on $A_1 \times A_2 \times \cdots \times A_n$ by

$$(a_1, a_2, \ldots, a_n) \prec (b_1, b_2, \ldots, b_n)$$

if $a_1 \prec_1 b_1$, or if there is an integer $i > 0$ such that $a_1 = b_1, \ldots, a_i = b_i$, and $a_{i+1} \prec_{i+1} b_{i+1}$. In other words, one n-tuple is less than a second n-tuple if the entry of the first n-tuple in the first position where the two n-tuples disagree is less than the entry in that position in the second n-tuple.

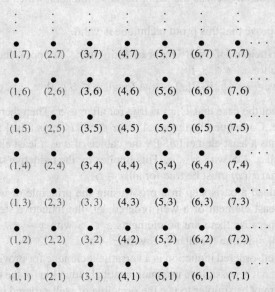

Figure 1   The Ordered Pairs Less Than $(3,4)$ in Lexicographic Order.

Example 10   Note that $(1,2,3,5) \prec (1,2,4,3)$, because the entries in the first two positions of these 4-tuples agree, but in the third position the entry in the first 4-tuple, 3, is less than that in the second 4-tuple, 4. (Here the ordering on 4-tuples is the lexicographic ordering that comes from the usual "less than or equals" relation on the set of integers.) ◀

We can now define lexicographic ordering of strings. Consider the strings $a_1 a_2 \ldots a_m$ and $b_1 b_2 \ldots b_n$ on a partially ordered set S. Suppose these strings are not equal. Let t be the minimum of m and n. The definition of lexicographic ordering is that the string $a_1 a_2 \ldots a_m$ is less than $b_1 b_2 \ldots b_n$ if and only if

$$(a_1, a_2, \ldots, a_t) \prec (b_1, b_2, \ldots, b_t), \text{ or}$$
$$(a_1, a_2, \ldots, a_t) = (b_1, b_2, \ldots, b_t) \text{ and } m < n,$$

where $\prec$ in this inequality represents the lexicographic ordering of S^t. In other words, to determine the ordering of two different strings, the longer string is truncated to the length of the shorter string, namely, to $t = \min(m, n)$ terms. Then the t-tuples made up of the first t terms of each string are compared using the lexicographic ordering on S^t. One string is less than another string if the t-tuple corresponding to the first string is less than the t-tuple of the second string, or if these two t-tuples are the same, but the second string is longer. The verification that this is a partial ordering is left as an exercise for the reader.

Example 11   Consider the set of strings of lowercase English letters. Using the ordering of letters in the alphabet, a lexicographic ordering on the set of strings can be constructed. A string is less than a second string if the letter in the first string in the first position where the strings differ comes before the letter in the second string in this position, or if the first string and the second string agree in all positions, but the second string has more letters. This ordering is the same as that used in dictionaries. For example,

$$discreet \prec discrete,$$

because these strings differ first in the seventh position, and $e \prec t$. Also,

$$discreet \prec discreetness,$$

because the first eight letters agree, but the second string is longer. Furthermore,

$$discrete \prec discretion,$$

because

$$discrete \prec discreti. \qquad \blacktriangleleft$$

Hasse Diagrams

Many edges in the directed graph for a finite poset do not have to be shown because they must be present. For instance, consider the directed graph for the partial ordering $\{(a, b) \mid a \leqslant b\}$ on the set $\{1, 2, 3, 4\}$, shown in Figure 2(a). Because this relation is a partial ordering, it is reflexive, and its directed graph has loops at all vertices. Consequently, we do not have to show these loops because they must be present; in Figure 2(b) loops are not shown. Because a partial ordering is transitive, we do not have to show those edges that must be present because of transitivity. For example, in Figure 2(c) the edges $(1, 3)$, $(1, 4)$, and $(2, 4)$ are not shown because they must be present. If we assume that all edges are pointed "upward" (as they are drawn in the figure), we do not have to show the directions of the edges; Figure 2(c) does not show directions.

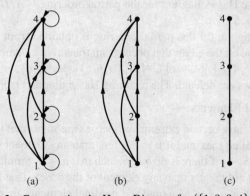

(a)   (b)   (c)

Figure 2   Constructing the Hasse Diagram for $(\{1, 2, 3, 4\}, \leqslant)$.

In general, we can represent a partial ordering on a finite set using this procedure: Start with the directed graph for this relation. Because a partial ordering is reflexive, a loop is present at every vertex. Remove these loops. Remove all edges that must be in the partial ordering because of the presence of other edges and transitivity. For instance, if (a, b) and (b, c) are in the partial ordering, remove the edge (a, c), because it must be present also. Furthermore, if (c, d) is also in the partial ordering, remove the edge (a, d), because it must be present also. Finally, arrange each edge so that its initial vertex is below its terminal vertex (as it is drawn on paper). Remove all the arrows on the directed edges, because all edges point "upward" toward their terminal vertex. (The edges left correspond to pairs in the covering relation of the poset.)

These steps are well defined, and only a finite number of steps need to be carried out for a finite poset. When all the steps have been taken, the resulting diagram contains sufficient information to find the partial ordering. This diagram is called a **Hasse diagram,** named after the twentieth-century German mathematician Helmut Hasse.

Example 12   Draw the Hasse diagram representing the partial ordering $\{(a, b) \mid a$ divides $b\}$ on $\{1, 2, 3, 4, 6, 8, 12\}$.

Solution: Begin with the digraph for this partial order, as shown in Figure 3(a). Remove all loops, as shown in Figure 3(b). Then delete all the edges implied by the transitive property. These are $(1, 4), (1, 6), (1, 8), (1, 12), (2, 8), (2, 12),$ and $(3, 12)$. Arrange all edges to point upward, and delete all arrows to obtain the Hasse diagram. The resulting Hasse diagram is shown in Figure 3(c).   ◄

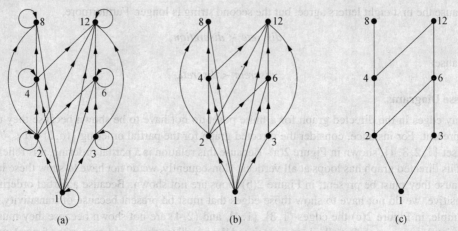

(a)   (b)   (c)

Figure 3   Constructing the Hasse Diagram of $(\{1, 2, 3, 4, 6, 8, 12\}, |)$.

Example 13   Draw the Hasse diagram for the partial ordering $\{(A, B) \mid A \subseteq B\}$ on the power set $P(S)$ where $S = \{a, b, c\}$.

Solution: The Hasse diagram for this partial ordering is obtained from the associated digraph by deleting all the loops and all the edges that occur from transitivity, namely, $(\emptyset, \{a, b\})$, $(\emptyset, \{a, c\})$, $(\emptyset, \{b, c\})$, $(\emptyset, \{a, b, c\})$, $(\{a\}, \{a, b, c\})$, $(\{b\}, \{a, b, c\})$, and $(\{c\}, \{a, b, c\})$. Finally all edges point upward, and arrows are deleted. The resulting Hasse diagram is illustrated in Figure 4.   ◄

Maximal and Minimal Elements

Elements of posets that have certain extremal properties are important for many applications. An element of a poset is called maximal if it is not less than any element of the poset. That is, a is **maximal** in the poset $(S, \preccurlyeq)$ if there is no $b \in S$ such that $a \prec b$. Similarly, an element of a poset is called minimal if it is not greater than any element of the poset. That is, a is **minimal** if there is no element $b \in S$ such that $b \prec a$. Maximal and minimal elements are easy to spot using a Hasse diagram. They are the "top" and "bottom" elements in the diagram.

Example 14   Which elements of the poset $(\{2, 4, 5, 10, 12, 20, 25\}, |)$ are maximal, and which are minimal?

Solution: The Hasse diagram in Figure 5 for this poset shows that the maximal elements are 12, 20, and 25, and the minimal elements are 2 and 5. As this example shows, a poset can have more than one maximal element and more than one minimal element.   ◀

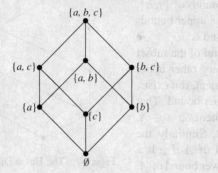   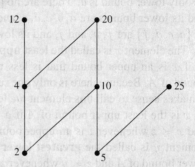

Figure 4   The Hasse Diagram of $(P(\{a, b, c\}), \subseteq)$.   Figure 5   The Hasse Diagram of a Poset.

Sometimes there is an element in a poset that is greater than every other element. Such an element is called the greatest element. That is, a is the **greatest element** of the poset $(S, \preccurlyeq)$ if $b \preccurlyeq a$ for all $b \in S$. The greatest element is unique when it exists. Likewise, an element is called the least element if it is less than all the other elements in the poset. That is, a is the **least element** of $(S, \preccurlyeq)$ if $a \preccurlyeq b$ for all $b \in S$. The least element is unique when it exists.

Example 15   Determine whether the posets represented by each of the Hasse diagrams in Figure 6 have a greatest element and a least element.

Solution: The least element of the poset with Hasse diagram (a) is a. This poset has no greatest element. The poset with Hasse diagram (b) has neither a least nor a greatest element. The poset with Hasse diagram (c) has no least element. Its greatest element is d. The poset with Hasse diagram (d) has least element a and greatest element d.   ◀

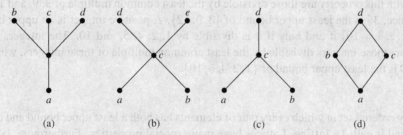

Figure 6   Hasse Diagrams of Four Posets.

Example 16   Let S be a set. Determine whether there is a greatest element and a least element in the poset $(P(S), \subseteq)$.

Solution: The least element is the empty set, because $\emptyset \subseteq T$ for any subset T of S. The set S is the greatest element in this poset, because $T \subseteq S$ whenever T is a subset of S.   ◀

Example 17   Is there a greatest element and a least element in the poset $(\mathbf{Z}^+, |)$?

Solution: The integer 1 is the least element because $1|n$ whenever n is a positive integer. Because there is no integer that is divisible by all positive integers, there is no greatest element.   ◀

Sometimes it is possible to find an element that is greater than or equal to all the elements in a subset A of a poset $(S, \preccurlyeq)$. If u is an element of S such that $a \preccurlyeq u$ for all elements $a \in A$, then u is called an **upper bound** of A. Likewise, there may be an element less than or equal to all the elements in A. If l is an element of S such that $l \preccurlyeq a$ for all elements $a \in A$, then l is called a **lower bound** of A.

Example 18   Find the lower and upper bounds of the subsets $\{a, b, c\}$, $\{j, h\}$, and $\{a, c, d, f\}$ in the poset with the Hasse diagram shown in Figure 7.

Solution: The upper bounds of $\{a, b, c\}$ are e, f, j, and h, and its only lower bound is a. There are no upper bounds of $\{j, h\}$, and its lower bounds are a, b, c, d, e, and f. The upper bounds of $\{a, c, d, f\}$ are f, h, and j, and its lower bound is a.   ◄

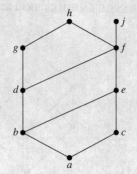

Figure 7   The Hasse Diagram of a Poset.

The element x is called the **least upper bound** of the subset A if x is an upper bound that is less than every other upper bound of A. Because there is only one such element, if it exists, it makes sense to call this element *the* least upper bound. That is, x is the least upper bound of A if $a \preccurlyeq x$ whenever $a \in A$, and $x \preccurlyeq z$ whenever z is an upper bound of A. Similarly, the element y is called the **greatest lower bound** of A if y is a lower bound of A and $z \preccurlyeq y$ whenever z is a lower bound of A. The greatest lower bound of A is unique if it exists. The greatest lower bound and least upper bound of a subset A are denoted by $\mathrm{glb}(A)$ and $\mathrm{lub}(A)$, respectively.

Example 19   Find the greatest lower bound and the least upper bound of $\{b, d, g\}$, if they exist, in the poset shown in Figure 7.

Solution: The upper bounds of $\{b, d, g\}$ are g and h. Because $g \prec h$, g is the least upper bound. The lower bounds of $\{b, d, g\}$ are a and b. Because $a \prec b$, b is the greatest lower bound.   ◄

Example 20   Find the greatest lower bound and the least upper bound of the sets $\{3, 9, 12\}$ and $\{1, 2, 4, 5, 10\}$, if they exist, in the poset $(\mathbf{Z}^+, |)$.

Solution: An integer is a lower bound of $\{3, 9, 12\}$ if 3, 9, and 12 are divisible by this integer. The only such integers are 1 and 3. Because $1 \mid 3$, 3 is the greatest lower bound of $\{3, 9, 12\}$. The only lower bound for the set $\{1, 2, 4, 5, 10\}$ with respect to $\mid$ is the element 1. Hence, 1 is the greatest lower bound for $\{1, 2, 4, 5, 10\}$.

An integer is an upper bound for $\{3, 9, 12\}$ if and only if it is divisible by 3, 9, and 12. The integers with this property are those divisible by the least common multiple of 3, 9, and 12, which is 36. Hence, 36 is the least upper bound of $\{3, 9, 12\}$. A positive integer is an upper bound for the set $\{1, 2, 4, 5, 10\}$ if and only if it is divisible by 1, 2, 4, 5, and 10. The integers with this property are those integers divisible by the least common multiple of these integers, which is 20. Hence, 20 is the least upper bound of $\{1, 2, 4, 5, 10\}$.   ◄

Lattices

A partially ordered set in which every pair of elements has both a least upper bound and a greatest lower bound is called a **lattice.** Lattices have many special properties. Furthermore, lattices are used in many different applications such as models of information flow and play an important role in Boolean algebra.

Example 21   Determine whether the posets represented by each of the Hasse diagrams in Figure 8 are lattices.

Solution: The posets represented by the Hasse diagrams in (a) and (c) are both lattices because in each poset every pair of elements has both a least upper bound and a greatest lower bound, as the reader should verify. On the other hand, the poset with the Hasse diagram shown in (b) is not a lattice, because the elements b and c have no least upper bound. To see this, note that each of the elements d, e, and f is an upper bound, but none of these three elements precedes the other two with respect to the ordering of this poset.   ◄

Example 22   Is the poset $(\mathbf{Z}^+, |)$ a lattice?

Solution: Let a and b be two positive integers. The least upper bound and greatest lower bound of these two integers are the least common multiple and the greatest common divisor of these

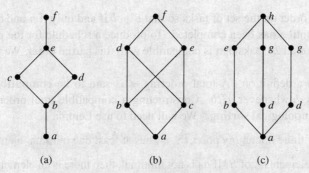

Figure 8   Hasse Diagrams of Three Posets.

integers, respectively, as the reader should verify. It follows that this poset is a lattice.   ◄

Example 23   Determine whether the posets $(\{1, 2, 3, 4, 5\}, |)$ and $(\{1, 2, 4, 8, 16\}, |)$ are lattices.
Solution: Because 2 and 3 have no upper bounds in $(\{1, 2, 3, 4, 5\}, |)$, they certainly do not have a least upper bound. Hence, the first poset is not a lattice.

Every two elements of the second poset have both a least upper bound and a greatest lower bound. The least upper bound of two elements in this poset is the larger of the elements and the greatest lower bound of two elements is the smaller of the elements, as the reader should verify. Hence, this second poset is a lattice.   ◄

Example 24   Determine whether $(P(S), \subseteq)$ is a lattice where S is a set.
Solution: Let A and B be two subsets of S. The least upper bound and the greatest lower bound of A and B are $A \cup B$ and $A \cap B$, respectively, as the reader can show. Hence, $(P(S), \subseteq)$ is a lattice.   ◄

Example 25   **The Lattice Model of Information Flow**   In many settings the flow of information from one person or computer program to another is restricted via security clearances. We can use a lattice model to represent different information flow policies. For example, one common information flow policy is the *multilevel security policy* used in government and military systems. Each piece of information is assigned to a security class, and each security class is represented by a pair (A, C) where A is an *authority level* and C is a *category*. People and computer programs are then allowed access to information from a specific restricted set of security classes.

The typical authority levels used in the U.S. government are unclassified (0), confidential (1), secret (2), and top secret (3). Categories used in security classes are the subsets of a set of all *compartments* relevant to a particular area of interest. Each compartment represents a particular subject area. For example, if the set of compartments is {*spies, moles, double agents*}, then there are eight different categories, one for each of the eight subsets of the set of compartments, such as {*spies, moles*}.

We can order security classes by specifying that $(A_1, C_1) \preccurlyeq (A_2, C_2)$ if and only if $A_1 \leqslant A_2$ and $C_1 \subseteq C_2$. Information is permitted to flow from security class (A_1, C_1) into security class (A_2, C_2) if and only if $(A_1, C_1) \preccurlyeq (A_2, C_2)$. For example, information is permitted to flow from the security class (*secret*, {*spies, moles*}) into the security class (*top secret*, {*spies, moles, double agents*}), whereas information is not allowed to flow from the security class (*top secret*, {*spies, moles*}) into either of the security classes (*secret*, {*spies, moles, double agents*}) or (*top secret*, {*spies*}).

We leave it to the reader to show that the set of all security classes with the ordering defined in this example forms a lattice.   ◄

Topological Sorting

Suppose that a project is made up of 20 different tasks. Some tasks can be completed only after others have been finished. How can an order be found for these tasks? To model this problem we set up a partial order on the set of tasks so that $a \prec b$ if and only if a and b are tasks where b cannot be started until a has been completed. To produce a schedule for the project, we need to produce an order for all 20 tasks that is compatible with this partial order. We will show how this can be done.

We begin with a definition. A total ordering $\preccurlyeq$ is said to be **compatible** with the partial ordering R if $a \preccurlyeq b$ whenever aRb. Constructing a compatible total ordering from a partial ordering is called **topological sorting**.* We will need to use Lemma 1.

Lemma 1   Every finite nonempty poset $(S, \preccurlyeq)$ has at least one minimal element.

Proof: Choose an element a_0 of S. If a_0 is not minimal, then there is an element a_1 with $a_1 \prec a_0$. If a_1 is not minimal, there is an element a_2 with $a_2 \prec a_1$. Continue this process, so that if a_n is not minimal, there is an element a_{n+1} with $a_{n+1} \prec a_n$. Because there are only a finite number of elements in the poset, this process must end with a minimal element a_n.   ◁

The topological sorting algorithm we will describe works for any finite nonempty poset. To define a total ordering on the poset $(A, \preccurlyeq)$, first choose a minimal element a_1; such an element exists by Lemma 1. Next, note that $(A - \{a_1\}, \preccurlyeq)$ is also a poset, as the reader should verify. (Here by $\preccurlyeq$ we mean the restriction of the original relation $\preccurlyeq$ on A to $A - \{a_1\}$.) If it is nonempty, choose a minimal element a_2 of this poset. Then remove a_2 as well, and if there are additional elements left, choose a minimal element a_3 in $A - \{a_1, a_2\}$. Continue this process by choosing a_{k+1} to be a minimal element in $A - \{a_1, a_2, \ldots, a_k\}$, as long as elements remain.

Because A is a finite set, this process must terminate. The end product is a sequence of elements $a_1, a_2, \ldots, a_n$. The desired total ordering $\preccurlyeq_t$ is defined by

$$a_1 \prec_t a_2 \prec_t \cdots \prec_t a_n.$$

This total ordering is compatible with the original partial ordering. To see this, note that if $b \prec c$ in the original partial ordering, c is chosen as the minimal element at a phase of the algorithm where b has already been removed, for otherwise c would not be a minimal element. Pseudocode for this topological sorting algorithm is shown in Algorithm 1.

Algorithm 1   Topological Sorting

procedure *topological sort* $((S, \preccurlyeq)$: finite poset)
$k := 1$
while $S \neq \emptyset$
begin
    $a_k := $ a minimal element of S {such an element exists by Lemma 1}
    $S := S - \{a_k\}$
    $k := k + 1$
end $\{a_1, a_2, \ldots, a_n$ is a compatible total ordering of $S\}$

Example 26   Find a compatible total ordering for the poset $(\{1, 2, 4, 5, 12, 20\}, |)$.
Solution: The first step is to choose a minimal element. This must be 1, because it is the only minimal element. Next, select a minimal element of $(\{2, 4, 5, 12, 20\}, |)$. There are two minimal elements in this poset, namely, 2 and 5. We select 5. The remaining elements are $\{2, 4, 12, 20\}$. The only minimal element at this stage is 2. Next, 4 is chosen because it is the only minimal

---

*"Topological sorting" is terminology used by computer scientists; mathematicians use the terminology "linearization of a partial ordering" for the same thing. In mathematics, topology is the branch of geometry dealing with properties of geometric figures that hold for all figures that can be transformed into one another by continuous bijections. In computer science, a topology is any arrangement of objects that can be connected with edges.

element of $(\{4, 12, 20\}, |)$. Because both 12 and 20 are minimal elements of $(\{12, 20\}, |)$, either can be chosen next. We select 20, which leaves 12 as the last element left. This produces the total ordering

$$1 \prec 5 \prec 2 \prec 4 \prec 20 \prec 12.$$

The steps used by this sorting algorithm are displayed in Figure 9.

◄

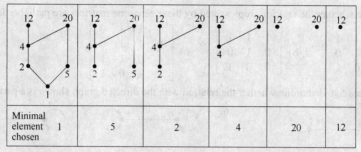

Figure 9   A Topological Sort of $(\{1, 2, 4, 5, 12, 20\}, |)$.

Topological sorting has an application to the scheduling of projects.

Example 27   A development project at a computer company requires the completion of seven tasks. Some of these tasks can be started only after other tasks are finished. A partial ordering on tasks is set up by considering task $X \prec$ task Y if task Y cannot be started until task X has been completed. The Hasse diagram for the seven tasks, with respect to this partial ordering, is shown in Figure 10. Find an order in which these tasks can be carried out to complete the project.

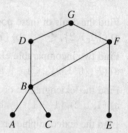

Figure 10   The Hasse Diagram for Seven Tasks.

Solution: An ordering of the seven tasks can be obtained by performing a topological sort. The steps of a sort are illustrated in Figure 11. The result of this sort, $A \prec C \prec B \prec E \prec F \prec D \prec G$, gives one possible order for the tasks.   ◄

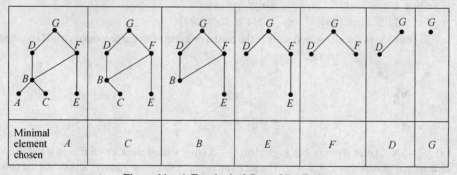

Figure 11   A Topological Sort of the Tasks.

Exercises

1. Which of these relations on $\{0, 1, 2, 3\}$ are partial orderings? Determine the properties of a partial ordering that the others lack.

   a) $\{(0, 0), (1, 1), (2, 2), (3, 3)\}$ b) $\{(0, 0), (1, 1), (2, 0), (2, 2), (2, 3), (3, 2), (3, 3)\}$
   c) $\{(0, 0), (1, 1), (1, 2), (2, 2), (3, 3)\}$ d) $\{(0, 0), (1, 1), (1, 2), (1, 3), (2, 2), (2, 3), (3, 3)\}$
   e) $\{(0, 0), (0, 1), (0, 2), (1, 0), (1, 1), (1, 2), (2, 0), (2, 2), (3, 3)\}$

2. Is (S, R) a poset if S is the set of all people in the world and $(a, b) \in R$, where a and b are people, if
   a) a is taller than b?   b) a is not taller than b?
   c) $a = b$ or a is an ancestor of b?   d) a and b have a common friend?

3. Which of these are posets?
   a) $(\mathbf{Z}, =)$ b) $(\mathbf{Z}, \neq)$ c) $(\mathbf{Z}, \geqslant)$ d) $(\mathbf{Z}, \nmid)$

4. Determine whether the relations represented by these zero–one matrices are partial orders.

a) $\begin{bmatrix} 1 & 1 & 1 \\ 1 & 1 & 0 \\ 0 & 0 & 1 \end{bmatrix}$ b) $\begin{bmatrix} 1 & 1 & 1 \\ 0 & 1 & 0 \\ 0 & 0 & 1 \end{bmatrix}$ c) $\begin{bmatrix} 1 & 1 & 1 & 0 \\ 0 & 1 & 1 & 0 \\ 0 & 0 & 1 & 1 \\ 1 & 1 & 0 & 1 \end{bmatrix}$

In Exercises 5–6 determine whether the relation with the directed graph shown is a partial order.

5.

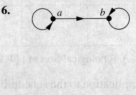

6.

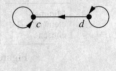

7. Find the duals of these posets.
   a) $(\{0, 1, 2\}, \leqslant)$ b) $(\mathbf{Z}, \geqslant)$ c) $(P(\mathbf{Z}), \supseteq)$ d) $(\mathbf{Z}^+, |)$

8. Find two incomparable elements in these posets.
   a) $(P(\{0, 1, 2\}), \subseteq)$ b) $(\{1, 2, 4, 6, 8\}, |)$

9. Find the lexicographic ordering of these n-tuples:
   a) $(1, 1, 2), (1, 2, 1)$ b) $(0, 1, 2, 3), (0, 1, 3, 2)$ c) $(1, 0, 1, 0, 1), (0, 1, 1, 1, 0)$

10. Find the lexicographic ordering of the bit strings 0, 01, 11, 001, 010, 011, 0001, and 0101 based on the ordering $0 < 1$.

11. Draw the Hasse diagram for the "less than or equal to" relation on $\{0, 2, 5, 10, 11, 15\}$.

12. Draw the Hasse diagram for divisibility on the set
   a) $\{1, 2, 3, 4, 5, 6, 7, 8\}$.   b) $\{1, 2, 3, 5, 7, 11, 13\}$.
   c) $\{1, 2, 3, 6, 12, 24, 36, 48\}$.   d) $\{1, 2, 4, 8, 16, 32, 64\}$.

In Exercises 13–14 list all ordered pairs in the partial ordering with the accompanying Hasse diagram.

13.   **14.**

Let $(S, \preccurlyeq)$ be a poset. We say that an element $y \in S$ **covers** an element $x \in S$ if $x \prec y$ and there is no element $z \in S$ such that $x \prec z \prec y$. The set of pairs (x, y) such that y covers x is called the **covering relation** of $(S, \preccurlyeq)$.

15. What is the covering relation of the partial ordering $\{(A, B) \mid A \subseteq B\}$ on the power set of S, where $S = \{a, b, c\}$?

16. Show that a finite poset can be reconstructed from its covering relation. [*Hint:* Show that the poset is the reflexive transitive closure of its covering relation.]

17. Answer these questions for the poset $(\{3, 5, 9, 15, 24, 45\}, |)$.
   a) Find the maximal elements.   b) Find the minimal elements.
   c) Is there a greatest element?   d) Is there a least element?
   e) Find all upper bounds of $\{3, 5\}$.   f) Find the least upper bound of $\{3, 5\}$, if it exists.

g) Find all lower bounds of $\{15, 45\}$.   h) Find the greatest lower bound of $\{15, 45\}$, if it exists.

18. Answer these questions for the poset $(\{\{1\}, \{2\}, \{4\}, \{1,2\}, \{1,4\}, \{2,4\}, \{3,4\}, \{1,3,4\}, \{2,3,4\}\}, \subseteq)$.
    a) Find the maximal elements.   b) Find the minimal elements.
    c) Is there a greatest element?   d) Is there a least element?
    e) Find all upper bounds of $\{\{2\}, \{4\}\}$.   f) Find the least upper bound of $\{\{2\}, \{4\}\}$, if it exists.
    g) Find all lower bounds of $\{\{1, 3, 4\}, \{2, 3, 4\}\}$.
    h) Find the greatest lower bound of $\{\{1, 3, 4\}, \{2, 3, 4\}\}$, if it exists.

19. Show that lexicographic order is a partial ordering on the Cartesian product of two posets.

20. Suppose that $(S, \preccurlyeq_1)$ and $(T, \preccurlyeq_2)$ are posets. Show that $(S \times T, \preccurlyeq)$ is a poset where $(s, t) \preccurlyeq (u, v)$ if and only if $s \preccurlyeq_1 u$ and $t \preccurlyeq_2 v$.

21. a) Show that there is exactly one maximal element in a poset with a greatest element.
    b) Show that there is exactly one minimal element in a poset with a least element.

22. Determine whether the posets with these Hasse diagrams are lattices.

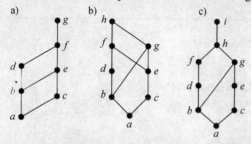

23. Show that every nonempty finite subset of a lattice has a least upper bound and a greatest lower bound.

24. In a company, the lattice model of information flow is used to control sensitive information with security classes represented by ordered pairs (A, C). Here A is an authority level, which may be nonproprietary (0), proprietary (1), restricted (2), or registered (3). A category C is a subset of the set of all projects $\{Cheetah, Impala, Puma\}$. (Names of animals are often used as code names for projects in companies.)
    a) Is information permitted to flow from $(Proprietary, \{Cheetah, Puma\})$ into $(Restricted, \{Puma\})$?
    b) Is information permitted to flow from $(Restricted, \{Cheetah\})$ into $(Registered, \{Cheetah, Impala\})$?
    c) Into which classes is information from $(Proprietary, \{Cheetah, Puma\})$ permitted to flow?
    d) From which classes is information permitted to flow into the security class $(Restricted, \{Impala, Puma\})$?

*25. Show that the set of all partitions of a set S with the relation $P_1 \preccurlyeq P_2$ if the partition P_1 is a refinement of the partition P_2 is a lattice. (See the preamble to Exercise 22 of Section 5.5.)

26. Show that every finite lattice has a least element and a greatest element.

27. Verify that $(\mathbf{Z}^+ \times \mathbf{Z}^+, \preccurlyeq)$ is a well-ordered set, where $\preccurlyeq$ is lexicographic order, as claimed in Example 8.

28. Show that the poset $(\mathbf{Z}, \preccurlyeq)$, where $x \prec y$ if and only if $|x| < |y|$ is well-founded but is not a totally ordered set.

29. Show that the poset of rational numbers with the usual "less than or equal to" relation, $(\mathbf{Q}, \leqslant)$, is a dense poset.

30. Show that a poset is well-ordered if and only if it is totally ordered and well-founded.

31. Find an order different from that constructed in Example 27 for completing the tasks in the development project.

32. Find an ordering of the tasks of a software project if the Hasse diagram for the tasks of the project is as shown.

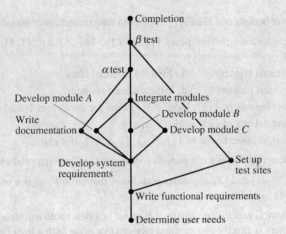

Key Terms and Results

TERMS

binary relation from A to B: a subset of $A \times B$

relation on A: a binary relation from A to itself (i.e., a subset of $A \times A$)

$S \circ R$: composite of R and S

R^{-1}: inverse relation of R

R^n: nth power of R

reflexive: a relation R on A is reflexive if $(a, a) \in R$ for all $a \in A$

symmetric: a relation R on A is symmetric if $(b, a) \in R$ whenever $(a, b) \in R$

antisymmetric: a relation R on A is antisymmetric if $a = b$ whenever $(a, b) \in R$ and $(b, a) \in R$

transitive: a relation R on A is transitive if $(a, b) \in R$ and $(b, c) \in R$ implies that $(a, c) \in R$

n-ary relation on $A_1, A_2, \ldots, A_n$: a subset of $A_1 \times A_2 \times \cdots \times A_n$

relational data model: a model for representing databases using n-ary relations

primary key: a domain of an n-ary relation such that an n-tuple is uniquely determined by its value for this domain

composite key: the Cartesian product of domains of an n-ary relation such that an n-tuple is uniquely determined by its values in these domains

selection operator: a function that selects the n-tuples in an n-ary relation that satisfy a specified condition

projection: a function that produces relations of smaller degree from an n-ary relation by deleting fields

join: a function that combines n-ary relations that agree on certain fields

directed graph or digraph: a set of elements called vertices and ordered pairs of these elements, called edges

loop: an edge of the form (a, a)

closure of a relation R with respect to a property P: the relation S (if it exists) that contains R, has property **P**, and is contained within any relation that contains R and has property **P**

path in a digraph: a sequence of edges $(a, x_1), (x_1, x_2), \ldots, (x_{n-2}, x_{n-1}), (x_{n-1}, b)$ such that the terminal vertex of each edge is the initial vertex of the succeeding edge in the sequence

circuit (or cycle) in a digraph: a path that begins and ends at the same vertex

R^* (connectivity relation): the relation consisting of those ordered pairs (a, b) such that there is a path from a to b

equivalence relation: a reflexive, symmetric, and transitive relation

equivalent: if R is an equivalence relation, a is equivalent to b if aRb

$[a]_R$ (equivalence class of a with respect to R): the set of all elements of A that are equivalent to a

$[a]_m$ (congruence class modulo m): the set of integers congruent to a modulo m

partition of a set S: a collection of pairwise disjoint nonempty subsets that have S as their union

partial ordering: a relation that is reflexive, antisymmetric, and transitive

poset (S, R): a set S and a partial ordering R on this set

comparable: the elements a and b in the poset $(A, \preccurlyeq)$ are comparable if $a \preccurlyeq b$ or $b \preccurlyeq a$

incomparable: elements in a poset that are not comparable

total (or linear) ordering: a partial ordering for which every pair of elements are comparable

totally (or linearly) ordered set: a poset with a total (or linear) ordering

well-ordered set: a poset $(S, \preccurlyeq)$, where $\preccurlyeq$ is a total order and every nonempty subset of S has a least element

lexicographic order: a partial ordering of Cartesian products or strings

Hasse diagram: a graphical representation of a poset where loops and all edges resulting from the transitive property are not shown, and the direction of the edges is indicated by the position of the vertices

maximal element: an element of a poset that is not less than any other element of the poset

minimal element: an element of a poset that is not greater than any other element of the poset

greatest element: an element of a poset greater than or equal to all other elements in this set

least element: an element of a poset less than or equal to all other elements in this set

upper bound of a set: an element in a poset greater than all other elements in the set

lower bound of a set: an element in a poset less than all other elements in the set

least upper bound of a set: an upper bound of the set that is less than all other upper bounds

greatest lower bound of a set: a lower bound of the set that is greater than all other lower bounds

lattice: a partially ordered set in which every two elements have a greatest lower bound and a least upper bound

compatible total ordering for a partial ordering: a total ordering that contains the given partial ordering

topological sort: the construction of a total ordering compatible with a given partial ordering

RESULTS

The reflexive closure of a relation R on the set A equals $R \cup \Delta$, where $\Delta = \{(a, a) \mid a \in A\}$.

The symmetric closure of a relation R on the set A equals $R \cup R^{-1}$, where $R^{-1} = \{(b, a) \mid (a, b) \in R\}$.

The transitive closure of a relation equals the connectivity relation formed from this relation.

Warshall's algorithm for finding the transitive closure of a relation.

Let R be an equivalence relation. Then the following three statements are equivalent: (1) $a \, R \, b$; (2) $[a]_R \cap [b]_R \neq \emptyset$; (3) $[a]_R = [b]_R$.

The equivalence classes of an equivalence relation on a set A form a partition of A. Conversely, an equivalence relation can be constructed from any partition so that the equivalence classes are the subsets in the partition.

The principle of well-ordered induction.

The topological sorting algorithm.

Review Questions

1. a) What is a relation on a set?
   b) How many relations are there on a set with n elements?
2. a) What is a reflexive relation?
   b) What is a symmetric relation?
   c) What is an antisymmetric relation?
   d) What is a transitive relation?
3. Give an example of a relation on the set $\{1, 2, 3, 4\}$ that is
   a) reflexive, symmetric, and not transitive.
   b) not reflexive, symmetric, and transitive.
   c) reflexive, antisymmetric, and not transitive.
   d) reflexive, symmetric, and transitive.
   e) reflexive, antisymmetric, and transitive.

4. a) How many reflexive relations are there on a set with n elements?

b) How many symmetric relations are there on a set with n elements?

c) How many antisymmetric relations are there on a set with n elements?

5. a) Explain how an n-ary relation can be used to represent information about students at a university.

b) How can the 5-ary relation containing names of students, their addresses, telephone numbers, majors, and grade point averages be used to form a 3-ary relation containing the names of students, their majors, and their grade point averages?

c) How can the 4-ary relation containing names of students, their addresses, telephone numbers, and majors and the 4-ary relation containing names of students, their student numbers, majors, and numbers of credit hours be combined into a single n-ary relation?

6. a) Explain how to use a zero–one matrix to represent a relation on a finite set.

b) Explain how to use the zero–one matrix representing a relation to determine whether the relation is reflexive, symmetric, and/or antisymmetric.

7. a) Explain how to use a directed graph to represent a relation on a finite set.

b) Explain how to use the directed graph representing a relation to determine whether a relation is reflexive, symmetric, and/or antisymmetric.

8. a) Define the reflexive closure and the symmetric closure of a relation.

b) How can you construct the reflexive closure of a relation?

c) How can you construct the symmetric closure of a relation?

d) Find the reflexive closure and the symmetric closure of the relation $\{(1, 2), (2, 3), (2, 4), (3, 1)\}$ on the set $\{1, 2, 3, 4\}$.

9. a) Define the transitive closure of a relation.

b) Can the transitive closure of a relation be obtained by including all pairs (a, c) such that (a, b) and (b, c) belong to the relation?

c) Describe two algorithms for finding the transitive closure of a relation.

d) Find the transitive closure of the relation $\{(1,1), (1,3), (2,1), (2,3), (2,4), (3,2), (3,4), (4,1)\}$.

10. a) Define an equivalence relation.

b) Which relations on the set $\{a, b, c, d\}$ are equivalence relations and contain (a, b) and (b, d)?

11. a) Show that congruence modulo m is an equivalence relation whenever m is a positive integer.

b) Show that the relation $\{(a, b) \mid a \equiv \pm b \pmod 7\}$ is an equivalence relation on the set of integers.

12. a) What are the equivalence classes of an equivalence relation?

b) What are the equivalence classes of the "congruent modulo 5" relation?

c) What are the equivalence classes of the equivalence relation in Question 11(b)?

13. Explain the relationship between equivalence relations on a set and partitions of this set.

14. a) Define a partial ordering.

b) Show that the divisibility relation on the set of positive integers is a partial order.

15. Explain how partial orderings on the sets A_1 and A_2 can be used to define a partial ordering on the set $A_1 \times A_2$.

16. a) Explain how to construct the Hasse diagram of a partial order on a finite set.

b) Draw the Hasse diagram of the divisibility relation on the set $\{2, 3, 5, 9, 12, 15, 18\}$.

17. a) Define a maximal element of a poset and the greatest element of a poset.

b) Give an example of a poset that has three maximal elements.

c) Give an example of a poset with a greatest element.

18. a) Define a lattice.

b) Give an example of a poset with five elements that is a lattice and an example of a poset with five elements that is not a lattice.

19. a) Show that every finite subset of a lattice has a greatest lower bound and a least upper bound.

b) Show that every lattice with a finite number of elements has a least element and a greatest element.

20. a) Define a well-ordered set.

b) Describe an algorithm for producing a well-ordered set from a partially ordered set.

c) Explain how the algorithm from (b) can be used to order the tasks in a project if each task can be done only after one or more of the other tasks have been completed.

Supplementary Exercises

1. Let S be the set of all strings of English letters. Determine whether these relations are reflexive, irreflexive, symmetric, antisymmetric, and/or transitive.
   a) $R_1 = \{(a, b) \mid a \text{ and } b \text{ have no letters in common}\}$
   b) $R_2 = \{(a, b) \mid a \text{ and } b \text{ are not the same length}\}$
   c) $R_3 = \{(a, b) \mid a \text{ is longer than } b\}$

2. Construct a relation on the set $\{a, b, c, d\}$ that is
   a) reflexive, symmetric, but not transitive.
   b) irreflexive, symmetric, and transitive.
   c) irreflexive, antisymmetric, and not transitive.
   d) reflexive, neither symmetric nor antisymmetric, and transitive.
   e) neither reflexive, irreflexive, symmetric, antisymmetric, nor transitive.

3. Show that the relation R on $\mathbf{Z} \times \mathbf{Z}$ defined by $(a, b) \, R \, (c, d)$ if and only if $a + d = b + c$ is an equivalence relation.

4. Show that a subset of an antisymmetric relation is also antisymmetric.

5. Let R be a reflexive relation on a set A. Show that $R \subseteq R^2$.

6. Suppose that R_1 and R_2 are reflexive relations on a set A. Show that $R_1 \oplus R_2$ is irreflexive.

7. Suppose that R_1 and R_2 are reflexive relations on a set A. Is $R_1 \cap R_2$ also reflexive? Is $R_1 \cup R_2$ also reflexive?

8. Suppose that R is a symmetric relation on a set A. Is $\overline{R}$ also symmetric?

9. Let R_1 and R_2 be symmetric relations. Is $R_1 \cap R_2$ also symmetric? Is $R_1 \cup R_2$ also symmetric?

10. A relation R is called **circular** if aRb and bRc imply that cRa. Show that R is reflexive and circular if and only if it is an equivalence relation.

11. Show that a primary key in an n-ary relation is a primary key in any projection of this relation that contains this key as one of its fields.

12. Is the primary key in an n-ary relation also a primary key in a larger relation obtained by taking the join of this relation with a second relation?

13. Show that the reflexive closure of the symmetric closure of a relation is the same as the symmetric closure of its reflexive closure.

14. Let R be the relation on the set of all mathematicians that contains the ordered pair (a, b) if and only if a and b have written a paper together.
    a) Describe the relation R^2.
    b) Describe the relation R^*.
    c) The **Erdős number** of a mathematician is 1 if this mathematician wrote a paper with the prolific Hungarian mathematician Paul Erdős, it is 2 if this mathematician did not write a joint paper with Erdős but wrote a joint paper with someone who wrote a joint paper with Erdős, and so on (except that the Erdős number of Erdős himself is 0). Give a definition of the Erdős number in terms of paths in R.

15. a) Give an example to show that the transitive closure of the symmetric closure of a relation is not necessarily the same as the symmetric closure of the transitive closure of this relation.
    b) Show, however, that the transitive closure of the symmetric closure of a relation must contain the symmetric closure of the transitive closure of this relation.

16. a) Let S be the set of subroutines of a computer program. Define the relation R by $\mathbf{P} \, R \, \mathbf{Q}$ if subroutine $\mathbf{P}$ calls subroutine $\mathbf{Q}$ during its execution. Describe the transitive closure of R.
    b) For which subroutines $\mathbf{P}$ does $(\mathbf{P}, \mathbf{P})$ belong to the transitive closure of R?
    c) Describe the reflexive closure of the transitive closure of R.

17. Suppose that R and S are relations on a set A with $R \subseteq S$ such that the closures of R and S with respect to a property $\mathbf{P}$ both exist. Show that the closure of R with respect to $\mathbf{P}$ is a subset of the closure of S with respect to $\mathbf{P}$.

18. Show that the symmetric closure of the union of two relations is the union of their symmetric closures.

*19. Devise an algorithm, based on the concept of interior vertices, that finds the length of the longest path between two vertices in a directed graph, or determines that there are arbitrarily long paths between these vertices.

20. Which of these are equivalence relations on the set of all people?
    a) $\{(x, y) \mid x$ and y have the same sign of the zodiac$\}$
    b) $\{(x, y) \mid x$ and y were born in the same year$\}$
    c) $\{(x, y) \mid x$ and y have been in the same city$\}$

*21. How many different equivalence relations with exactly three different equivalence classes are there on a set with five elements?

22. Show that $\{(x, y) \mid x - y \in \mathbf{Q}\}$ is an equivalence relation on the set of real numbers, where $\mathbf{Q}$ denotes the set of rational numbers. What are $[1]$, $[\frac{1}{2}]$, and $[\pi]$?

23. Suppose that $P_1 = \{A_1, A_2, \ldots, A_m\}$ and $P_2 = \{B_1, B_2, \ldots, B_n\}$ are both partitions of the set S. Show that the collection of nonempty subsets of the form $A_i \cap B_j$ is a partition of S that is a refinement of both P_1 and P_2 (see the preamble to Exercise 22 of Section 5.5).

*24. Show that the transitive closure of the symmetric closure of the reflexive closure of a relation R is the smallest equivalence relation that contains R.

25. Let $\mathbf{R}(S)$ be the set of all relations on a set S. Define the relation $\preccurlyeq$ on $\mathbf{R}(S)$ by $R_1 \preccurlyeq R_2$ if $R_1 \subseteq R_2$, where R_1 and R_2 are relations on S. Show that $(\mathbf{R}(S), \preccurlyeq)$ is a poset.

26. Let $\mathbf{P}(S)$ be the set of all partitions of the set S. Define the relation $\preccurlyeq$ on $\mathbf{P}(S)$ by $P_1 \preccurlyeq P_2$ if P_1 is a refinement of P_2 (see Exercise 22 of Section 5.5). Show that $(\mathbf{P}(S), \preccurlyeq)$ is a poset.

27. Schedule the tasks needed to cook a Chinese meal by specifying their order, if the Hasse diagram representing these tasks is as shown here.

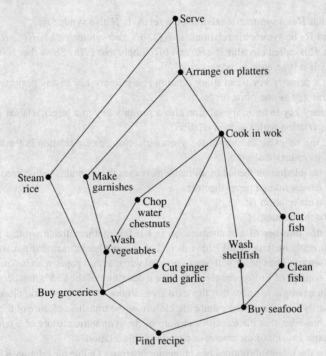

A subset of a poset such that every two elements of this subset are comparable is called a **chain.** A subset of a poset is called an **antichain** if every two elements of this subset are incomparable.

28. Find all chains in the posets with the Hasse diagrams shown in Exercises 13–14 in Section 5.6.

29. Find all antichains in the posets with the Hasse diagrams shown in Exercises 13–14 in Section 5.6.

30. Find an antichain with the greatest number of elements in the poset.

31. Show that every maximal chain in a finite poset $(S, \preccurlyeq)$ contains a minimal element of S. (A maximal chain is a chain that is not a subset of a larger chain.)

**32. Show that every finite poset can be partitioned into k chains, where k is the largest number of elements in an antichain in this poset.

*33. Show that in any group of $mn + 1$ people there is either a list of $m + 1$ people where a person in the list (except for the first person listed) is a descendant of the previous person on the list, or there are $n + 1$ people such that none of these people is a descendant of any of the other n people. [*Hint:* Use Exercise 32.]

Suppose that $(S, \preceq)$ is a well-founded partially ordered set. The *principle of well-founded induction* states that $P(x)$ is true for all $x \in S$ if $\forall x (\forall y (y \prec x \rightarrow P(y)) \rightarrow P(x))$.

34. Show that no separate basis case is needed for the principle of well-founded induction. That is, $P(u)$ is true for all minimal elements u in S if $\forall x (\forall y (y \prec x \rightarrow P(y)) \rightarrow P(x))$.

*35. Show that the principle of well-founded induction is valid.

A relation R on a set A is a **quasi-ordering** on A if R is reflexive and transitive.

36. Let R be the relation on the set of all functions from $\mathbf{Z}^+$ to $\mathbf{Z}^+$ such that (f, g) belongs to R if and only if f is $O(g)$. Show that R is a quasi-ordering.

37. Let R be a quasi-ordering on a set A. Show that $R \cap R^{-1}$ is an equivalence relation.

*38. Let R be a quasi-ordering and let S be the relation on the set of equivalence classes of $R \cap R^{-1}$ such that (C, D) belongs to S, where C and D are equivalence classes of R, if and only if there are elements c of C and d of D such that (c, d) belongs to R. Show that S is a partial ordering.

Let L be a lattice. Define the **meet** ($\wedge$) and **join** ($\vee$) operations by $x \wedge y = \text{glb}(x, y)$ and $x \vee y = \text{lub}(x, y)$.

39. Show that the following properties hold for all elements x, y, and z of a lattice L.
   a) $x \wedge y = y \wedge x$ and $x \vee y = y \vee x$ **(commutative laws)**
   b) $(x \wedge y) \wedge z = x \wedge (y \wedge z)$ and $(x \vee y) \vee z = x \vee (y \vee z)$ **(associative laws)**
   c) $x \wedge (x \vee y) = x$ and $x \vee (x \wedge y) = x$ **(absorption laws)**
   d) $x \wedge x = x$ and $x \vee x = x$ **(idempotent laws)**

40. Show that if x and y are elements of a lattice L, then $x \vee y = y$ if and only if $x \wedge y = x$.

A lattice L is **bounded** if it has both an **upper bound**, denoted by 1, such that $x \preceq 1$ for all $x \in L$ and a **lower bound**, denoted by 0, such that $0 \preceq x$ for all $x \in L$.

41. Show that if L is a bounded lattice with upper bound 1 and lower bound 0 then these properties hold for all elements $x \in L$.
   a) $x \vee 1 = 1$ b) $x \wedge 1 = x$ c) $x \vee 0 = x$ d) $x \wedge 0 = 0$

42. Show that every finite lattice is bounded.

A lattice is called **distributive** if $x \vee (y \wedge z) = (x \vee y) \wedge (x \vee z)$ and $x \wedge (y \vee z) = (x \wedge y) \vee (x \wedge z)$ for all x, y, and z in L.

*43. Give an example of a lattice that is not distributive.

44. Show that the lattice $(P(S), \subseteq)$ where $P(S)$ is the power set of a finite set S is distributive.

45. Is the lattice $(\mathbf{Z}^+, |)$ distributive?

The **complement** of an element a of a bounded lattice L with upper bound 1 and lower bound 0 is an element b such that $a \vee b = 1$ and $a \wedge b = 0$. Such a lattice is **complemented** if every element of the lattice has a complement.

46. Give an example of a finite lattice where at least one element has more than one complement and at least one element has no complement.

47. Show that the lattice $(P(S), \subseteq)$ where $P(S)$ is the power set of a finite set S is complemented.

*48. Show that if L is a finite distributive lattice, then an element of L has at most one complement.

The game of Chomp, introduced in Example 12 in Section 1.7, can be generalized for play on any finite partially ordered set $(S, \preceq)$ with a least element a. In this game, a move consists of selecting an element x in S and removing x and all elements larger than it from S. The loser is the player who is forced to select the least element a.

49. Show that the game of Chomp with cookies arranged in an $m \times n$ rectangular grid, described in Example 12 in Section 1.7, is the same as the game of Chomp on the poset $(S, |)$, where S is the set of all positive integers that divide $p^{m-1} q^{n-1}$, where p and q are distinct primes.

50. Show that if $(S, \preceq)$ has a greatest element b, then a winning strategy for Chomp on this poset exists. [*Hint:* Generalize the argument in Example 12 in Section 1.7.]

Computer Projects

Write programs with these input and output.

1. Given the matrix representing a relation on a finite set, determine whether the relation is reflexive and/or irreflexive.
2. Given the matrix representing a relation on a finite set, determine whether the relation is symmetric and/or antisymmetric.
3. Given the matrix representing a relation on a finite set, determine whether the relation is transitive.
4. Given a positive integer n, display all the relations on a set with n elements.
*5. Given a positive integer n, determine the number of transitive relations on a set with n elements.
*6. Given a positive integer n, determine the number of equivalence relations on a set with n elements.
*7. Given a positive integer n, display all the equivalence relations on the set of the n smallest positive integers.
8. Given an n-ary relation, find the projection of this relation when specified fields are deleted.
9. Given an m-ary relation and an n-ary relation, and a set of common fields, find the join of these relations with respect to these common fields.
10. Given the matrix representing a relation on a finite set, find the matrix representing the reflexive closure of this relation.
11. Given the matrix representing a relation on a finite set, find the matrix representing the symmetric closure of this relation.
12. Given the matrix representing a relation on a finite set, find the matrix representing the transitive closure of this relation by computing the join of the powers of the matrix representing the relation.
13. Given the matrix representing a relation on a finite set, find the matrix representing the transitive closure of this relation using Warshall's algorithm.
14. Given the matrix representing a relation on a finite set, find the matrix representing the smallest equivalence relation containing this relation.
15. Given a partial ordering on a finite set, find a total ordering compatible with it using topological sorting.

Computations and Explorations

Use a computational program or programs you have written to do these exercises.

1. Display all the different relations on a set with four elements.
2. Display all the different reflexive and symmetric relations on a set with six elements.
3. Display all the reflexive and transitive relations on a set with five elements.
*4. Determine how many transitive relations there are on a set with n elements for all positive integers n with $n \leqslant 7$.
5. Find the transitive closure of a relation of your choice on a set with at least 20 elements. Either use a relation that corresponds to direct links in a particular transportation or communications network or use a randomly generated relation.
6. Compute the number of different equivalence relations on a set with n elements for all positive integers n not exceeding 20.
7. Display all the equivalence relations on a set with seven elements.
*8. Display all the partial orders on a set with five elements.
*9. Display all the lattices on a set with five elements.

Writing Projects

Respond to these questions with essays using outside sources.

1. Discuss the concept of a fuzzy relation. How are fuzzy relations used?

2. Describe the basic principles of relational databases, going beyond what was covered in Section 5.2. How widely used are relational databases as compared with other types of databases?

3. Look up the original papers by Warshall and by Roy (in French) in which they develop algorithms for finding transitive closures. Discuss their approaches. Why do you suppose that what we call Warshall's algorithm was discovered independently by more than one person?

4. Describe how equivalence classes can be used to define the rational numbers as classes of pairs of integers and how the basic arithmetic operations on rational numbers can be defined following this approach.

5. Explain how Helmut Hasse used what we now call Hasse diagrams.

6. Describe some of the mechanisms used to enforce information flow policies in computer operating systems.

7. Discuss the use of the Program Evaluation and Review Technique (PERT) to schedule the tasks of a large complicated project. How widely is PERT used?

8. Discuss the use of the Critical Path Method (CPM) to find the shortest time for the completion of a project. How widely is CPM used?

9. Discuss the concept of *duality* in a lattice. Explain how duality can be used to establish new results.

10. Explain what is meant by a *modular lattice*. Describe some of the properties of modular lattices and describe how modular lattices arise in the study of projective geometry.

Chapter 6
Graphs

Graphs are discrete structures consisting of vertices and edges that connect these vertices. Problems in almost every conceivable discipline can be solved using graph models. We will give examples to show how graphs are used as models in a variety of areas. For instance, we will show how graphs are used to represent the competition of different species in an ecological niche, how graphs are used to represent who influences whom in an organization, and how graphs are used to represent the outcomes of round-robin tournaments. We will describe how graphs can be used to model acquaintanceships between people, collaboration between researchers, telephone calls between telephone numbers, and links between websites. We will show how graphs can be used to model roadmaps and the assignment of jobs to employees of an organization.

Using graph models, we can determine whether it is possible to walk down all the streets in a city without going down a street twice, and we can find the number of colors needed to color the regions of a map. Graphs can be used to determine whether a circuit can be implemented on a planar circuit board. We can distinguish between two chemical compounds with the same molecular formula but different structures using graphs. We can determine whether two computers are connected by a communications link using graph models of computer networks. Graphs with weights assigned to their edges can be used to solve problems such as finding the shortest path between two cities in a transportation network. We can also use graphs to schedule exams and assign channels to television stations. This chapter will introduce the basic concepts of graph theory and present many different graph models. To solve the wide variety of problems that can be studied using graphs, we will introduce many different graph algorithms. We will also study the complexity of these algorithms.

6.1 Graphs and Graph Models

We begin with the definition of a graph.

Definition 1 A *graph* $G = (V, E)$ consists of V, a nonempty set of *vertices* (or *nodes*) and E, a set of *edges*. Each edge has either one or two vertices associated with it, called its *endpoints*. An edge is said to *connect* its endpoints.

Remark: The set of vertices V of a graph G may be infinite. A graph with an infinite vertex set is called an **infinite graph,** and in comparison, a graph with a finite vertex set is called a **finite graph.** In this book we will usually consider only finite graphs.

Now suppose that a network is made up of data centers and communication links between computers. We can represent the location of each data center by a point and each communications link by a line segment, as shown in Figure 1.

This computer network can be modeled using a graph in which the vertices of the graph represent the data centers and the edges represent communication links. In general, we visualize graphs by using points to represent vertices and line segments, possibly curved, to represent edges, where the endpoints of a line segment representing an edge are the points representing the endpoints of the edge. When we draw a graph, we generally try to draw edges so that they do not cross. However, this is not necessary because any depiction using points to represent vertices and any form of connection between vertices can be used. Indeed, there are some graphs that cannot be drawn in the plane without edges crossing (see Section 6.7). The key point is that the way we draw a graph is arbitrary, as long as the correct connections between vertices are depicted.

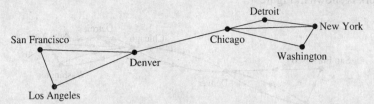

Figure 1   A Computer Network.

Note that each edge of the graph representing this computer network connects two different vertices. That is, no edge connects a vertex to itself. Furthermore, no two different edges connect the same pair of vertices. A graph in which each edge connects two different vertices and where no two edges connect the same pair of vertices is called a **simple graph.** Note that in a simple graph, each edge is associated to an unordered pair of vertices, and no other edge is associated to this same edge. Consequently, when there is an edge of a simple graph associated to $\{u, v\}$, we can also say, without possible confusion, that $\{u, v\}$ is an edge of the graph.

A computer network may contain multiple links between data centers, as shown in Figure 2. To model such networks we need graphs that have more than one edge connecting the same pair of vertices. Graphs that may have **multiple edges** connecting the same vertices are called **multigraphs.** When there are m different edges associated to the same unordered pair of vertices $\{u, v\}$, we also say that $\{u, v\}$ is an edge of multiplicity m. That is, we can think of this set of edges as m different copies of an edge $\{u, v\}$.

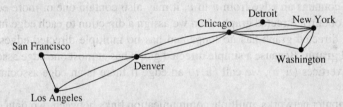

Figure 2   A Computer Network with Multiple Links between Data Centers.

Sometimes a communications link connects a data center with itself, perhaps a feedback loop for diagnostic purposes. Such a network is illustrated in Figure 3. To model this network we need to include edges that connect a vertex to itself. Such edges are called **loops.** Graphs that may include loops, and possibly multiple edges connecting the same pair of vertices, are sometimes called **pseudographs.**

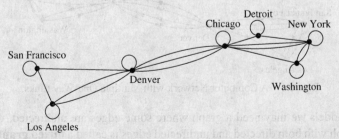

Figure 3   A Computer Network with Diagnostic Links.

So far the graphs we have introduced are **undirected graphs.** Their edges are also said to be **undirected.** However, to construct a graph model, we may find it necessary to assign directions to the edges of a graph. For example, in a computer network, some links may operate in only one direction (such links are called single duplex lines). This may be the case if there is a large amount of traffic sent to some data centers, with little or no traffic going in the opposite direction. Such a network is shown in Figure 4.

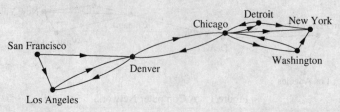

Figure 4   A Communications Network with One-Way Communications Links.

To model such a computer network we use a directed graph. Each edge of a directed graph is associated to an ordered pair. The definition of directed graph we give here is more general than the one we used in Chapter 5, where we used directed graphs to represent relations.

Definition 2   A *directed graph* (or *digraph*) (V, E) consists of a nonempty set of vertices V and a set of *directed edges* (or *arcs*) E. Each directed edge is associated with an ordered pair of vertices. The directed edge associated with the ordered pair (u, v) is said to *start* at u and *end* at v.

When we depict a directed graph with a line drawing, we use an arrow pointing from u to v to indicate the direction of an edge that starts at u and ends at v. A directed graph may contain loops and it may contain multiple directed edges that start and end at the same vertices. A directed graph may also contain directed edges that connect vertices u and v in both directions; that is, when a digraph contains an edge from u to v, it may also contain one or more edges from v to u. Note that we obtain a directed graph when we assign a direction to each edge in an undirected graph. When a directed graph has no loops and has no multiple directed edges, it is called a **simple directed graph.** Because a simple directed graph has at most one edge associated to each ordered pair of vertices (u, v), we call (u, v) an edge if there is an edge associated to it in the graph.

In some computer networks, multiple communication links between two data centers may be present, as illustrated in Figure 5. Directed graphs that may have **multiple directed edges** from a vertex to a second (possibly the same) vertex are to used model such networks. We called such graphs **directed multigraphs.** When there are m directed edges, each associated to an ordered pair of vertices (u, v), we say that (u, v) is an edge of **multiplicity** m.

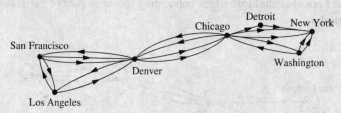

Figure 5   A Computer Network with Multiple One-Way Links.

For some models we may need a graph where some edges are undirected, while others are directed. A graph with both directed and undirected edges is called a **mixed graph.** For example, a mixed graph might be used to model a computer network containing links that operate in both directions and other links that operate only in one direction.

This terminology for the various types of graphs is summarized in Table 1. We will sometimes use the term **graph** as a general term to describe graphs with directed or undirected edges (or both), with or without loops, and with or without multiple edges. At other times, when the context is clear, we will use the term graph to refer only to undirected graphs.

TABLE 1 Graph Terminology.

Type	Edges	Multiple Edges Allowed?	Loops Allowed?
Simple graph	Undirected	No	No
Multigraph	Undirected	Yes	No
Pseudograph	Undirected	Yes	Yes
Simple directed graph	Directed	No	No
Directed multigraph	Directed	Yes	Yes
Mixed graph	Directed and undirected	Yes	Yes

Because of the relatively modern interest in graph theory, and because it has applications to a wide variety of disciplines, many different terminologies of graph theory have been introduced. The reader should determine how such terms are being used whenever they are encountered. The terminology used by mathematicians to describe graphs has been increasingly standardized, but the terminology used to discuss graphs when they are used in other disciplines is still quite varied.

Although the terminology used to describe graphs may vary, three key questions can help us understand the structure of a graph:

- Are the edges of the graph undirected or directed (or both)?
- If the graph is undirected, are multiple edges present that connect the same pair of vertices? If the graph is directed, are multiple directed edges present?
- Are loops present?

Answering such questions helps us understand graphs. It is less important to remember the particular terminology used.

Graph Models

Graphs are used in a wide variety of models. We will present a few graph models from diverse fields here. Others will be introduced in subsequent sections of this and later chapters. When we build a graph model, we need to make sure that we have correctly answered the three key questions we posed about the structure of a graph.

Example 1   Niche Overlap Graphs in Ecology Graphs are used in many models involving the interaction of different species of animals. For instance, the competition between species in an ecosystem can be modeled using a **niche overlap graph.** Each species is represented by a vertex. An undirected edge connects two vertices if the two species represented by these vertices compete (that is, some of the food resources they use are the same). A niche overlap graph is a simple graph because no loops or multiple edges are needed in this model. The graph in Figure 6 models the ecosystem of a forest. We see from this graph that squirrels and raccoons compete but that crows and shrews do not.   ◄

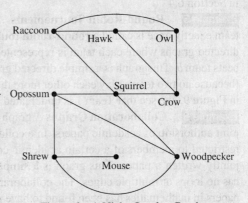

Figure 6   A Niche Overlap Graph.

Example 2   Acquaintanceship Graphs We can use graph models to represent various relationships between people. For example, we can use a simple graph to represent whether two people know each other, that is, whether they are acquainted. Each person in a particular group of people is represented by a vertex. An undirected edge is used to connect two people when these people know each other. No multiple edges and usually no loops are used. (If we want to include the notion of self-knowledge, we would include loops.) A small acquaintanceship graph is shown in Figure 7. The acquaintanceship graph of all people in the world has more than six billion vertices and probably more than one trillion edges! We will discuss this graph further in Section 6.4.   ◄

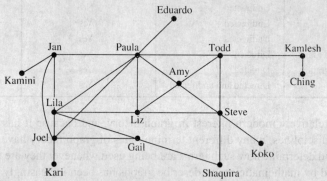

Figure 7   An Acquaintanceship Graph.

Example 3   **Influence Graphs**   In studies of group behavior it is observed that certain people can influence the thinking of others. A directed graph called an **influence graph** can be used to model this behavior. Each person of the group is represented by a vertex. There is a directed edge from vertex a to vertex b when the person represented by vertex a influences the person represented by vertex b. This graph does not contain loops and it does not contain multiple directed edges. An example of an influence graph for members of a group is shown in Figure 8. In the group modeled by this influence graph, Deborah can influence Brian, Fred, and Linda, but no one can influence her. Also, Yvonne and Brian can influence each other.   ◄

Example 4   **The Hollywood Graph**   The **Hollywood graph** represents actors by vertices and connects two vertices when the actors represented by these vertices have worked together on a movie. This graph is a simple graph because its edges are undirected, it contains no multiple edges, and it contains no loops. According to the Internet Movie Database, in Janurary 2006 the Hollywood graph had 637,099 vertices representing actors who have appeared in 339,896 films, and had more than 20 million edges. We will discuss some aspects of the Hollywood graph later in Section 6.4.   ◄

Example 5   **Round-Robin Tournaments**   A tournament where each team plays each other team exactly once is called a **round-robin tournament.** Such tournaments can be modeled using directed graphs where each team is represented by a vertex. Note that (a, b) is an edge if team a beats team b. This graph is a simple directed graph, containing no loops or multiple directed edges (because no two teams play each other more than once). Such a directed graph model is presented in Figure 9. We see that Team 1 is undefeated in this tournament, and Team 3 is winless.   ◄

Example 6   **Collaboration Graphs**   A graph called a **collaboration graph** can be used to model joint authorship of academic papers. In a collaboration graph, vertices represent people (perhaps restricted to members of a certain academic community) and edges link two people if they have jointly written a paper. This graph is a simple graph because it contains undirected edges and has no loops or multiple edges. The collaboration graph for people working together on research papers in mathematics has been found to have more than 400,000 vertices and 675,000 edges. We will have more to say about this graph in Section 6.4.   ◄

Example 7   **Call Graphs**   Graphs can be used to model telephone calls made in a network, such as a long-distance telephone network. In particular, a directed multigraph can be used to model calls where each telephone number is represented by a vertex and each telephone call is represented by a directed edge. The edge representing a call starts at the telephone number from which the call was made and ends at the telephone number to which the call was made. We need directed edges because the direction in which the call is made matters. We need multiple directed edges because we want to represent each call made from a particular telephone number to a second number.

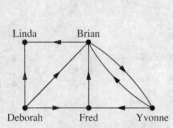

Figure 8   An Influence Graph.

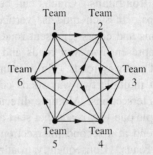

Figure 9   A Graph Model of a Round-Robin Tournament.

A small telephone call graph is displayed in Figure 10(a), representing seven telephone numbers. This graph shows, for instance, that three calls have been made from 732-555-1234 to 732-555-9876 and two in the other direction, but no calls have been made from 732-555-4444 to any of the other six numbers except 732-555-0011. When we care only whether there has been a call connecting two telephone numbers, we use an undirected graph with an edge connecting telephone numbers when there has been a call between these numbers. This version of the call graph is displayed in Figure 10(b).

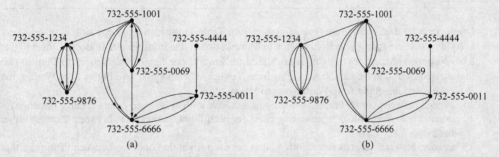

Figure 10   A Call Graph.

Call graphs that model actual calling activities can be huge. For example, one call graph studied at AT&T, which models calls during 20 days, has about 290 million vertices and 4 billion edges. We will discuss call graphs further in Section 6.4. ◀

Example 8   **The Web Graph**   The World Wide Web can be modeled as a directed graph where each Web page is represented by a vertex and where an edge starts at the Web page a and ends at the Web page b if there is a link on a pointing to b. Because new Web pages are created and others removed somewhere on the Web almost every second, the Web graph changes on an almost continual basis. Currently the Web graph has more than three billion vertices and 20 billion edges. Many people are studying the properties of the Web graph to better understand the nature of the Web. We will return to Web graphs in Section 6.4, and in Chapter 7 we will explain how the Web graph is used by the Web crawlers that search engines use to create indices of Web pages. ◀

Example 9   **Precedence Graphs and Concurrent Processing**   Computer programs can be executed more rapidly by executing certain statements concurrently. It is important not to execute a statement that requires results of statements not yet executed. The dependence of statements on previous statements can be represented by a directed graph. Each statement is represented by a vertex, and there is an edge from one vertex to a second vertex if the statement represented by the second vertex cannot be executed before the statement represented by the first vertex has been executed. This graph is called a **precedence graph.** A computer program and its graph are displayed in Figure 11. For instance, the graph shows that statement S_5 cannot be executed before statements S_1, S_2, and S_4 are executed.   ◀

Example 10   **Roadmaps**   Graphs can be used to model roadmaps. In such models, vertices represent intersections and edges represent roads. Undirected edges represent two-way roads and directed edges represent one-way roads. Multiple undirected edges represent multiple two-way roads connecting the same two intersections. Multiple directed edges represent multiple one-way roads that start at one intersection and end at a second intersection. Loops represent loop roads. Consequently, roadmaps depicting only two-way roads and no loop roads, and in which no two roads connect the same pair of intersections, can be represented using a simple undirected

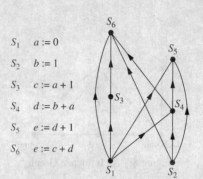

$S_1 \quad a := 0$

$S_2 \quad b := 1$

$S_3 \quad c := a + 1$

$S_4 \quad d := b + a$

$S_5 \quad e := d + 1$

$S_6 \quad e := c + d$

Figure 11   A Precedence Graph.

graph. Roadmaps depicting only one-way roads and no loop roads, and where no two roads start at the same intersection and end at the same intersection, can be modeled using simple directed graphs. Mixed graphs are needed to depict roadmaps that include both one-way and two-way roads.   ◀

Exercises

1. Draw graph models, stating the type of graph (from Table 1) used, to represent airline routes where every day there are four flights from Boston to Newark, two flights from Newark to Boston, three flights from Newark to Miami, two flights from Miami to Newark, one flight from Newark to Detroit, two flights from Detroit to Newark, three flights from Newark to Washington, two flights from Washington to Newark, and one flight from Washington to Miami, with
   a) an edge between vertices representing cities that have a flight between them (in either direction).
   b) an edge between vertices representing cities for each flight that operates between them (in either direction).
   c) an edge between vertices representing cities for each flight that operates between them (in either direction), plus a loop for a special sightseeing trip that takes off and lands in Miami.
   d) an edge from a vertex representing a city where a flight starts to the vertex representing the city where it ends.
   e) an edge for each flight from a vertex representing a city where the flight begins to the vertex representing the city where the flight ends.

   For Exercises 2–5, determine whether the graph shown has directed or undirected edges, whether it has multiple edges, and whether it has one or more loops. Use your answers to determine the type of graph in Table 1 this graph is.

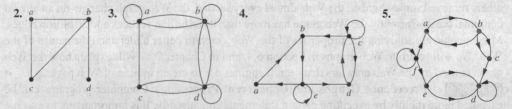

6. Let G be a simple graph. Show that the relation R on the set of vertices of G such that uRv if and only if there is an edge associated to $\{u, v\}$ is a symmetric, irreflexive relation on G.

7. The **intersection graph** of a collection of sets $A_1, A_2, \ldots, A_n$ is the graph that has a vertex for each of these sets and has an edge connecting the vertices representing two sets if these sets have a nonempty intersection. Construct the intersection graph of these collections of sets.

   a) $A_1 = \{0, 2, 4, 6, 8\}$, $A_2 = \{0, 1, 2, 3, 4\}$,

   $\quad A_3 = \{1, 3, 5, 7, 9\}$, $A_4 = \{5, 6, 7, 8, 9\}$,

   $\quad A_5 = \{0, 1, 8, 9\}$

   b) $A_1 = \{\ldots, -4, -3, -2, -1, 0\}$,

   $\quad A_2 = \{\ldots, -2, -1, 0, 1, 2, \ldots\}$,

   $\quad A_3 = \{\ldots, -6, -4, -2, 0, 2, 4, 6, \ldots\}$,

   $\quad A_4 = \{\ldots, -5, -3, -1, 1, 3, 5, \ldots\}$,

   $\quad A_5 = \{\ldots, -6, -3, 0, 3, 6, \ldots\}$

   c) $A_1 = \{x \mid x < 0\}$,

   $\quad A_2 = \{x \mid -1 < x < 0\}$,

   $\quad A_3 = \{x \mid 0 < x < 1\}$,

   $\quad A_4 = \{x \mid -1 < x < 1\}$,

   $\quad A_5 = \{x \mid x > -1\}$,

   $\quad A_6 = \mathbf{R}$

8. Construct a niche overlap graph for six species of birds, where the hermit thrush competes with the robin and with the blue jay, the robin also competes with the mockingbird, the mockingbird also competes with the blue jay, and the nuthatch competes with the hairy woodpecker.

9. We can use a graph to represent whether two people were alive at the same time. Draw such a graph to represent whether each pair of the mathematicians and computer scientists with biographies in the first four chapters of this book who died before 1900 were contemporaneous. (Assume two people lived at the same time if they were alive during the same year.)

10. Construct an influence graph for the board members of a company if the President can influence the Director of Research and Development, the Director of Marketing, and the Director of Operations; the Director of Research and Development can influence the Director of Operations; the Director of Marketing can influence the Director of Operations; and no one can influence, or be influenced by, the Chief Financial Officer.

11. In a round-robin tournament the Tigers beat the Blue Jays, the Tigers beat the Cardinals, the Tigers beat the Orioles, the Blue Jays beat the Cardinals, the Blue Jays beat the Orioles, and the Cardinals beat the Orioles. Model this outcome with a directed graph.

12. Explain how the two telephone call graphs for calls made during the month of January and calls made during the month of February can be used to determine the new telephone numbers of people who have changed their telephone numbers.

13. How can a graph that models e-mail messages sent in a network be used to find people who have recently changed their primary e-mail address?

14. Describe a graph model that represents whether each person at a party knows the name of each other person at the party. Should the edges be directed or undirected? Should multiple edges be allowed? Should loops be allowed?

15. Describe a graph model that represents traditional marriages between men and women. Does this graph have any special properties?

16. Construct a precedence graph for the following program:

$$S_1: x := 0$$
$$S_2: x := x + 1$$
$$S_3: y := 2$$
$$S_4: z := y$$
$$S_5: x := x + 2$$
$$S_6: y := x + z$$
$$S_7: z := 4$$

17. Describe a discrete structure based on a graph that can be used to model relationships between pairs of individuals in a group, where each individual may either like, dislike, or be neutral about another individual, and the reverse relationship may be different. [*Hint:* Add structure to a directed graph. Treat separately the edges in opposite directions between vertices representing two individuals.]

6.2   Graph Terminology and Special Types of Graphs

Introduction

We introduce some of the basic vocabulary of graph theory in this section. We will use this vocabulary later in this chapter when we solve many different types of problems. One such problem involves determining whether a graph can be drawn in the plane so that no two of its edges cross. Another example is deciding whether there is a one-to-one correspondence between the vertices of two graphs that produces a one-to-one correspondence between the edges of the graphs. We will also introduce several important families of graphs often used as examples and in models. Several important applications will be described where these special types of graphs arise.

Basic Terminology

First, we give some terminology that describes the vertices and edges of undirected graphs.

Definition 1   Two vertices u and v in an undirected graph G are called *adjacent* (or *neighbors*) in G if u and v are endpoints of an edge of G. If e is associated with $\{u, v\}$, the edge e is called *incident with* the vertices u and v. The edge e is also said to *connect* u and v. The vertices u and v are called *endpoints* of an edge associated with $\{u, v\}$.

To keep track of how many edges are incident to a vertex, we make the following definition.

Definition 2   The *degree of a vertex in an undirected graph* is the number of edges incident with it, except that a loop at a vertex contributes twice to the degree of that vertex. The degree of the vertex v is denoted by $\deg(v)$.

Example 1   What are the degrees of the vertices in the graphs G and H displayed in Figure 1?
Solution: In G, $\deg(a) = 2$, $\deg(b) = \deg(c) = \deg(f) = 4$, $\deg(d) = 1$, $\deg(e) = 3$, and $\deg(g) = 0$. In H, $\deg(a) = 4$, $\deg(b) = \deg(e) = 6$, $\deg(c) = 1$, and $\deg(d) = 5$.   ◄

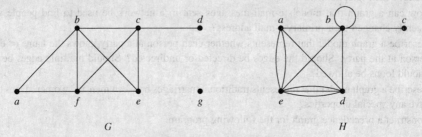

G H

Figure 1   The Undirected Graphs G and H.

A vertex of degree zero is called **isolated.** It follows that an isolated vertex is not adjacent to any vertex. Vertex g in graph G in Example 1 is isolated. A vertex is **pendant** if and only if it has degree one. Consequently, a pendant vertex is adjacent to exactly one other vertex. Vertex d in graph G in Example 1 is pendant.

Examining the degrees of vertices in a graph model can provide useful information about the model, as Example 2 shows.

Example 2   What does the degree of a vertex in a niche overlap graph (introduced in Example 1 in Section 6.1) represent? Which vertices in this graph are pendant and which are isolated? Use the niche overlap graph shown in Figure 6 of Section 6.1 to interpret your answers.
Solution: There is an edge between two vertices in a niche overlap graph if and only if the two species represented by these vertices compete. Hence, the degree of a vertex in a niche overlap

graph is the number of species in the ecosystem that compete with the species represented by this vertex. A vertex is pendant if the species competes with exactly one other species in the ecosystem. Finally, the vertex representing a species is isolated if this species does not compete with any other species in the ecosystem.

For instance, the degree of the vertex representing the squirrel in Figure 6 in Section 6.1 is four, because the squirrel competes with four other species: the crow, the opossum, the raccoon, and the woodpecker. In the graph in Figure 6, the mouse is the only species represented by a pendant vertex, because the mouse competes only with the shrew and all other species compete with at least two other species. The vertex representing a species is pendant if this species competes with only one other species. There are no isolated vertices in the graph in Figure 6 because every species in this ecosystem competes with at least one other species.   ◀

What do we get when we add the degrees of all the vertices of a graph $G = (V, E)$? Each edge contributes two to the sum of the degrees of the vertices because an edge is incident with exactly two (possibly equal) vertices. This means that the sum of the degrees of the vertices is twice the number of edges. We have the result in Theorem 1, which is sometimes called the Handshaking Theorem, because of the analogy between an edge having two endpoints and a handshake involving two hands.

Theorem 1   The handshaking theorem   Let $G = (V, E)$ be an undirected graph with e edges. Then

$$2e = \sum_{v \in V} \deg(v).$$

(Note that this applies even if multiple edges and loops are present.)

Example 3   How many edges are there in a graph with 10 vertices each of degree six?
Solution: Because the sum of the degrees of the vertices is $6 \cdot 10 = 60$, it follows that $2e = 60$. Therefore, $e = 30$.   ◀

Theorem 1 shows that the sum of the degrees of the vertices of an undirected graph is even. This simple fact has many consequences, one of which is given as Theorem 2.

Theorem 2   An undirected graph has an even number of vertices of odd degree.

Proof: Let V_1 and V_2 be the set of vertices of even degree and the set of vertices of odd degree, respectively, in an undirected graph $G = (V, E)$. Then

$$2e = \sum_{v \in V} \deg(v) = \sum_{v \in V_1} \deg(v) + \sum_{v \in V_2} \deg(v).$$

Because $\deg(v)$ is even for $v \in V_1$, the first term in the right-hand side of the last equality is even. Furthermore, the sum of the two terms on the right-hand side of the last equality is even, because this sum is $2e$. Hence, the second term in the sum is also even. Because all the terms in this sum are odd, there must be an even number of such terms. Thus, there are an even number of vertices of odd degree.   ◁

Terminology for graphs with directed edges reflects the fact that edges in directed graphs have directions.

Definition 3   When (u, v) is an edge of the graph G with directed edges, u is said to be *adjacent to* v and v is said to be *adjacent from u*. The vertex u is called the *initial vertex* of (u, v), and v is called the *terminal* or *end vertex* of (u, v). The initial vertex and terminal vertex of a loop are the same.

Because the edges in graphs with directed edges are ordered pairs, the definition of the degree of a vertex can be refined to reflect the number of edges with this vertex as the initial vertex and as the terminal vertex.

Definition 4 In a graph with directed edges the *in-degree of a vertex* v, denoted by $\deg^-(v)$, is the number of edges with v as their terminal vertex. The *out-degree of* v, denoted by $\deg^+(v)$, is the number of edges with v as their initial vertex. (Note that a loop at a vertex contributes 1 to both the in-degree and the out-degree of this vertex.)

Example 4 Find the in-degree and out-degree of each vertex in the graph G with directed edges shown in Figure 2.

Solution: The in-degrees in G are $\deg^-(a) = 2$, $\deg^-(b) = 2$, $\deg^-(c) = 3$, $\deg^-(d) = 2$, $\deg^-(e) = 3$, and $\deg^-(f) = 0$. The out-degrees are $\deg^+(a) = 4$, $\deg^+(b) = 1$, $\deg^+(c) = 2$, $\deg^+(d) = 2$, $\deg^+(e) = 3$, and $\deg^+(f) = 0$. ◄

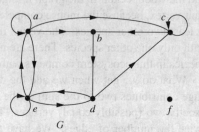

Figure 2   The Directed Graph G.

Because each edge has an initial vertex and a terminal vertex, the sum of the in-degrees and the sum of the out-degrees of all vertices in a graph with directed edges are the same. Both of these sums are the number of edges in the graph. This result is stated as Theorem 3.

Theorem 3 Let $G = (V, E)$ be a graph with directed edges. Then

$$\sum_{v \in V} \deg^-(v) = \sum_{v \in V} \deg^+(v) = |E|.$$

There are many properties of a graph with directed edges that do not depend on the direction of its edges. Consequently, it is often useful to ignore these directions. The undirected graph that results from ignoring directions of edges is called the **underlying undirected graph.** A graph with directed edges and its underlying undirected graph have the same number of edges.

Some Special Simple Graphs

We will now introduce several classes of simple graphs. These graphs are often used as examples and arise in many applications.

Example 5 **Complete Graphs** The **complete graph on n vertices,** denoted by K_n, is the simple graph that contains exactly one edge between each pair of distinct vertices. The graphs K_n, for $n = 1, 2, 3, 4, 5, 6$, are displayed in Figure 3. ◄

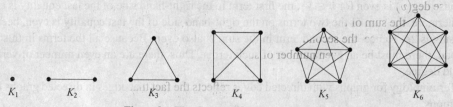

K_1 K_2 K_3 K_4 K_5 K_6

Figure 3   The Graphs K_n for $1 \leqslant n \leqslant 6$.

Example 6 **Cycles** The **cycle C_n,** $n \geqslant 3$, consists of n vertices $v_1, v_2, \ldots, v_n$ and edges $\{v_1, v_2\}, \{v_2, v_3\}, \ldots, \{v_{n-1}, v_n\}$, and $\{v_n, v_1\}$. The cycles C_3, C_4, C_5, and C_6 are displayed in Figure 4. ◄

Example 7 **Wheels** We obtain the **wheel W_n** when we add an additional vertex to the cycle C_n, for $n \geqslant 3$, and connect this new vertex to each of the n vertices in C_n, by new edges. The wheels W_3, W_4, W_5, and W_6 are displayed in Figure 5. ◄

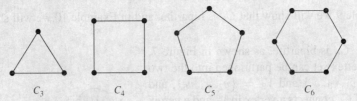

Figure 4   The Cycles C_3, C_4, C_5, and C_6.

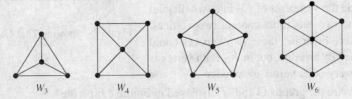

Figure 5   The Wheels W_3, W_4, W_5, and W_6.

Example 8   *n*-**Cubes**   The *n*-**dimensional hypercube**, or *n*-**cube**, denoted by Q_n, is the graph that has vertices representing the 2^n bit strings of length n. Two vertices are adjacent if and only if the bit strings that they represent differ in exactly one bit position. The graphs Q_1, Q_2, and Q_3 are displayed in Figure 6. Note that you can construct the $(n + 1)$-cube Q_{n+1} from the *n*-cube Q_n by making two copies of Q_n, prefacing the labels on the vertices with a 0 in one copy of Q_n and with a 1 in the other copy of Q_n, and adding edges connecting two vertices that have labels differing only in the first bit. In Figure 6, Q_3 is constructed from Q_2 by drawing two copies of Q_2 as the top and bottom faces of Q_3, adding 0 at the beginning of the label of each vertex in the bottom face and 1 at the beginning of the label of each vertex in the top face. (Here, by *face* we mean a face of a cube in three-dimensional space. Think of drawing the graph Q_3 in three-dimensional space with copies of Q_2 as the top and bottom faces of a cube and then drawing the projection of the resulting depiction in the plane.)   ◄

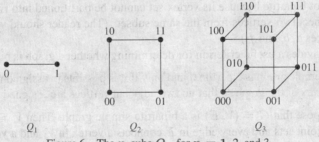

Figure 6   The *n*-cube Q_n for $n = 1, 2$, and 3.

Bipartite Graphs

Sometimes a graph has the property that its vertex set can be divided into two disjoint subsets such that each edge connects a vertex in one of these subsets to a vertex in the other subset. For example, consider the graph representing marriages between men and women in a village, where each person is represented by a vertex and a marriage is represented by an edge. In this graph, each edge connects a vertex in the subset of vertices representing males and a vertex in the subset of vertices representing females. This leads us to Definition 5.

Definition 5   A simple graph G is called *bipartite* if its vertex set V can be partitioned into two disjoint sets V_1 and V_2 such that every edge in the graph connects a vertex in V_1 and a vertex in V_2 (so that no edge in G connects either two vertices in V_1 or two vertices in V_2). When this condition holds, we call the pair (V_1, V_2) a *bipartition* of the vertex set V of G.

In Example 9 we will show that C_6 is bipartite, and in Example 10 we will show that K_3 is not bipartite.

Example 9 C_6 is bipartite, as shown in Figure 7, because its vertex set can be partitioned into the two sets $V_1 = \{v_1, v_3, v_5\}$ and $V_2 = \{v_2, v_4, v_6\}$, and every edge of C_6 connects a vertex in V_1 and a vertex in V_2.   ◄

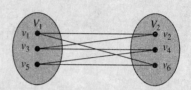

Figure 7   Showing That C_6 Is Bipartite.

Example 10 K_3 is not bipartite. To verify this, note that if we divide the vertex set of K_3 into two disjoint sets, one of the two sets must contain two vertices. If the graph were bipartite, these two vertices could not be connected by an edge, but in K_3 each vertex is connected to every other vertex by an edge.   ◄

Example 11   Are the graphs G and H displayed in Figure 8 bipartite?

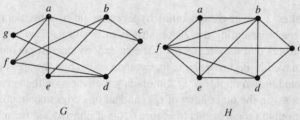

G   H

Figure 8   The Undirected Graphs G and H.

Solution: Graph G is bipartite because its vertex set is the union of two disjoint sets, $\{a, b, d\}$ and $\{c, e, f, g\}$, and each edge connects a vertex in one of these subsets to a vertex in the other subset. (Note that for G to be bipartite it is not necessary that every vertex in $\{a, b, d\}$ be adjacent to every vertex in $\{c, e, f, g\}$. For instance, b and g are not adjacent.)

Graph H is not bipartite because its vertex set cannot be partitioned into two subsets so that edges do not connect two vertices from the same subset. (The reader should verify this by considering the vertices a, b, and f.)   ◄

Theorem 4 provides a useful criterion for determining whether a graph is bipartite.

Theorem 4   A simple graph is bipartite if and only if it is possible to assign one of two different colors to each vertex of the graph so that no two adjacent vertices are assigned the same color.

Proof: First, suppose that $G = (V, E)$ is a bipartite simple graph. Then $V = V_1 \cup V_2$, where V_1 and V_2 are disjoint sets and every edge in E connects a vertex in V_1 and a vertex in V_2. If we assign one color to each vertex in V_1 and a second color to each vertex in V_2, then no two adjacent vertices are assigned the same color.

Now suppose that it is possible to assign colors to the vertices of the graph using just two colors so that no two adjacent vertices are assigned the same color. Let V_1 be the set of vertices assigned one color and V_2 be the set of vertices assigned the other color. Then, V_1 and V_2 are disjoint and $V = V_1 \cup V_2$. Furthermore, every edge connects a vertex in V_1 and a vertex in V_2 because no two adjacent vertices are either both in V_1 or both in V_2. Consequently, G is bipartite.   ◄

We illustrate how Theorem 4 can used to determine whether a graph is bipartite in Example 12.

Example 12   Use Theorem 4 to determine whether the graphs in Example 11 are bipartite.
Solution: We first consider the graph G. We will try to assign one of two colors, say red and blue, to each vertex in G so that no edge in G connects a red vertex and a blue vertex. Without loss of

generality we begin by arbitrarily assigning red to a. Then, we must assign blue to c, e, f, and g, because each of these vertices is adjacent to a. To avoid having an edge with two blue endpoints, we must assign red to all the vertices adjacent to either c, e, f, or g. This means that we must assign red to both b and d (and means that a must be assigned red, which it already has been). We have now assigned colors to all vertices, with a, b, and d red and c, e, f, and g blue. Checking all edges, we see that every edge connects a red vertex and a blue vertex. Hence, by Theorem 4 the graph G is bipartite.

Next, we will try to assign either red or blue to each vertex in H so that no edge in H connects a red vertex and a blue vertex. Without loss of generality we arbitrarily assign red to a. Then, we must assign blue to b, e, and f, because each is adjacent to a. But this is not possible because e and f are adjacent, so both cannot be assigned blue. This argument shows that we cannot assign one of two colors to each of the vertices of H so that no adjacent vertices are assigned the same color. It follows by Theorem 4 that H is not bipartite.   ◀

Theorem 4 is an example of a result in the part of graph theory known as graph colorings. Graph colorings is an important part of graph theory with important applications. We will study graph colorings further in Section 6.8.

Another useful criterion for determing whether a graph is bipartite is based on the notion of a path, a topic we study in Section 6.4. A graph is bipartite if and only if it is not possible to start at a vertex and return to this vertex by traversing an odd number of distinct edges. We will make this notion more precise when we discuss paths and circuits in graphs in Section 6.4 (see Exercise 26 in that section).

Example 13   **Complete Bipartite Graphs**   The **complete bipartite graph** $K_{m,n}$ is the graph that has its vertex set partitioned into two subsets of m and n vertices, respectively. There is an edge between two vertices if and only if one vertex is in the first subset and the other vertex is in the second subset. The complete bipartite graphs $K_{2,3}$, $K_{3,3}$, $K_{3,5}$, and $K_{2,6}$ are displayed in Figure 9.   ◀

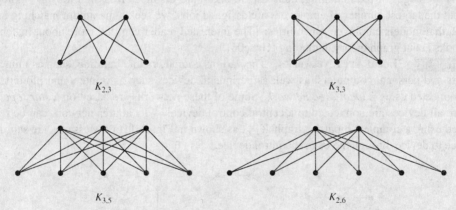

Figure 9   Some Complete Bipartite Graphs.

Some Applications of Special Types of Graphs

We will show how bipartite graphs and special types of graphs are used in models in Examples 14–16.

Example 14   **Job Assignments**   Suppose that there are m employees in a group and j different jobs that need to be done where $m \leqslant j$. Each employee is trained to do one or more of these j jobs. We can use a graph to model employee capabilities. We represent each employee by a vertex and each job by a vertex. For each employee, we include an edge from the vertex representing that employee to the vertices representing all jobs that the employee has been trained to do. Note that the vertex set of this graph can be partitioned into two disjoint sets, the set of vertices representing employees and the set of vertices representing jobs, and each edge connects a vertex representing an employee to a vertex representing a job. Consequently, this graph is bipartite.

For example, suppose that a group has four employees: Alvarez, Berkowitz, Chen, and Davis; and suppose that four jobs need to be done to complete a project: requirements, architecture, implementation, and testing. Suppose that Alvarez has been trained to do requirements and testing; Berkowitz has been trained to do architecture, implementation, and testing; Chen has been trained to do requirements, architecture, and implementation; and Davis has only been trained to do requirements. We can model these capabilities of employees using the bipartite graph shown in Figure 10.

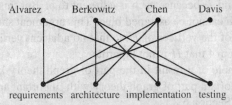

Figure 10   Modeling the Jobs for Which Employees Have Been Trained.

To complete the project, we must assign jobs to the employees so that every job has an employee assigned to it and no employee is assigned more than one job. In this case, we can assign Alvarez to do testing, Berkowitz to do implementation, Chen to do architecture, and Davis to do requirements, as shown in Figure 10 (where colored lines show this assignment of jobs).   ◄

Finding an assignment of jobs to employees can be thought of as finding a matching in the graph model. A **matching** in a simple graph is a subset of the set of edges of the graph such that no two edges are incident with the same vertex; a **maximal matching** is a matching with the largest number of edges. In other words, a matching is a subset of edges such that if $\{s, t\}$ and $\{u, v\}$ are edges of the matching, then s, t, u, and v are distinct. To assign jobs to employees so that the largest number of employees are assigned jobs, we seek a maximum matching in the graph that models employee capabilities. (The interested reader can find more about matchings in books about graph theory, including [GrYe06].)

Example 15   **Local Area Networks**   The various computers in a building, such as minicomputers and personal computers, as well as peripheral devices such as printers and plotters, can be connected using a *local area network*. Some of these networks are based on a *star topology*, where all devices are connected to a central control device. A local area network can be represented using a complete bipartite graph $K_{1,n}$, as shown in Figure 11(a). Messages are sent from device to device through the central control device.

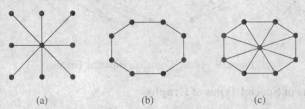

(a)   (b)   (c)

Figure 11   Star, Ring, and Hybrid Topologies for Local Area Networks.

Other local area networks are based on a *ring topology*, where each device is connected to exactly two others. Local area networks with a ring topology are modeled using n-cycles, C_n, as shown in Figure 11(b). Messages are sent from device to device around the cycle until the intended recipient of a message is reached.

Finally, some local area networks use a hybrid of these two topologies. Messages may be sent around the ring, or through a central device. This redundancy makes the network more reliable.

Local area networks with this redundancy can be modeled using wheels W_n, as shown in Figure 11(c).   ◄

Example 16   **Interconnection Networks for Parallel Computation**   For many years, computers executed programs one operation at a time. Consequently, the algorithms written to solve problems were designed to perform one step at a time; such algorithms are called **serial.** (Almost all algorithms described in this book are serial.) However, many computationally intense problems, such as weather simulations, medical imaging, and cryptanalysis, cannot be solved in a reasonable amount of time using serial operations, even on a supercomputer. Furthermore, there is a physical limit to how fast a computer can carry out basic operations, so there will always be problems that cannot be solved in a reasonable length of time using serial operations.

Parallel processing, which uses computers made up of many separate processors, each with its own memory, helps overcome the limitations of computers with a single processor. **Parallel algorithms,** which break a problem into a number of subproblems that can be solved concurrently, can then be devised to rapidly solve problems using a computer with multiple processors. In a parallel algorithm, a single instruction stream controls the execution of the algorithm, sending subproblems to different processors, and directs the input and output of these subproblems to the appropriate processors.

When parallel processing is used, one processor may need output generated by another processor. Consequently, these processors need to be interconnected. We can use the appropriate type of graph to represent the interconnection network of the processors in a computer with multiple processors. In the following discussion, we will describe the most commonly used types of interconnection networks for parallel processors. The type of interconnection network used to implement a particular parallel algorithm depends on the requirements for exchange of data between processors, the desired speed, and, of course, the available hardware.

The simplest, but most expensive, network-interconnecting processors include a two-way link between each pair of processors. This network can be represented by K_n, the complete graph on n vertices, when there are n processors. However, there are serious problems with this type of interconnection network because the required number of connections is so large. In reality, the number of direct connections to a processor is limited, so when there are a large number of processors, a processor cannot be linked directly to all others. For example, when there are 64 processors, $C(64, 2) = 2016$ connections would be required, and each processor would have to be directly connected to 63 others.

On the other hand, perhaps the simplest way to interconnect n processors is to use an arrangement known as a **linear array.** Each processor P_i, other than P_1 and P_n, is connected to its neighbors P_{i-1} and P_{i+1} via a two-way link. P_1 is connected only to P_2, and P_n is connected only to P_{n-1}. The linear array for six processors is shown in Figure 12. The advantage of a linear array is that each processor has at most two direct connections to other processors. The disadvantage is that it is sometimes necessary to use a large number of intermediate links, called **hops,** for processors to share information.

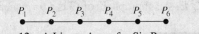

Figure 12   A Linear Array for Six Processors.

The **mesh network** (or **two-dimensional array**) is a commonly used interconnection network. In such a network, the number of processors is a perfect square, say $n = m^2$. The n processors are labeled $P(i, j), 0 \leqslant i \leqslant m - 1, 0 \leqslant j \leqslant m - 1$. Two-way links connect processor $P(i, j)$ with its four neighbors, processors $P(i \pm 1, j)$ and $P(i, j \pm 1)$, as long as these are processors in the mesh. (Note that four processors, on the corners of the mesh, have only two adjacent processors, and other processors on the boundaries have only three neighbors. Sometimes a variant of a mesh network in which every processor has exactly four connections is used.) The mesh network limits the number of links for each processor. Communication between some pairs of processors requires $O(\sqrt{n}) = O(m)$ intermediate links. (See Exercise 33 at the end of this section.) The graph representing the mesh network for 16 processors is shown in Figure 13.

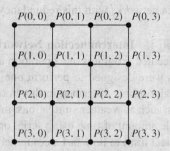

Figure 13   A Mesh Network for 16 Processors.

One important type of interconnection network is the hypercube. For such a network, the number of processors is a power of 2, $n = 2^m$. The n processors are labeled $P_0, P_1, \ldots, P_{n-1}$. Each processor has two-way connections to m other processors. Processor P_i is linked to the processors with indices whose binary representations differ from the binary representation of i in exactly one bit. The hypercube network balances the number of direct connections for each processor and the number of intermediate connections required so that processors can communicate. Many computers have been built using a hypercube network, and many parallel algorithms have been devised that use a hypercube network. The graph Q_m, the m-cube, represents the hypercube network with $n = 2^m$ processors. Figure 14 displays the hypercube network for eight processors. (Figure 14 displays a different way to draw Q_3 than was shown in Figure 6.) ◄

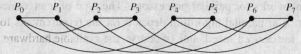

Figure 14   A Hypercube Network for Eight Processors.

New Graphs from Old

Sometimes we need only part of a graph to solve a problem. For instance, we may care only about the part of a large computer network that involves the computer centers in New York, Denver, Detroit, and Atlanta. Then we can ignore the other computer centers and all telephone lines not linking two of these specific four computer centers. In the graph model for the large network, we can remove the vertices corresponding to the computer centers other than the four of interest, and we can remove all edges incident with a vertex that was removed. When edges and vertices are removed from a graph, without removing endpoints of any remaining edges, a smaller graph is obtained. Such a graph is called a **subgraph** of the original graph.

Definition 6   A *subgraph of a graph* $G = (V, E)$ is a graph $H = (W, F)$, where $W \subseteq V$ and $F \subseteq E$. A subgraph H of G is a *proper subgraph* of G if $H \neq G$.

Example 17   The graph G shown in Figure 15 is a subgraph of K_5. ◄

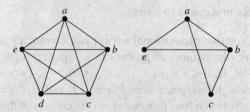

Figure 15   A Subgraph of K_5.

Two or more graphs can be combined in various ways. The new graph that contains all the vertices and edges of these graphs is called the **union** of the graphs. We will give a more formal definition for the union of two simple graphs.

Definition 7   The *union* of two simple graphs $G_1 = (V_1, E_1)$ and $G_2 = (V_2, E_2)$ is the simple graph with vertex set $V_1 \cup V_2$ and edge set $E_1 \cup E_2$. The union of G_1 and G_2 is denoted by $G_1 \cup G_2$.

Example 18   Find the union of the graphs G_1 and G_2 shown in Figure 16(a).   ◀

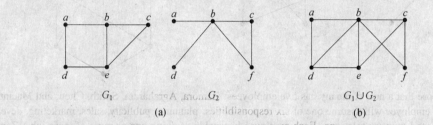

G_1 G_2 $G_1 \cup G_2$

(a)   (b)

Figure 16   (a) The Simple Graphs G_1 and G_2; (b) Their Union $G_1 \cup G_2$.

Solution: The vertex set of the union $G_1 \cup G_2$ is the union of the two vertex sets, namely, $\{a, b, c, d, e, f\}$. The edge set of the union is the union of the two edge sets. The union is displayed in Figure 16(b).

Exercises

In Exercises 1–2 find the number of vertices, the number of edges, and the degree of each vertex in the given undirected graph. Identify all isolated and pendant vertices.

1. 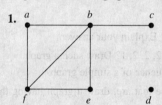   **2.**

3. Can a simple graph exist with 15 vertices each of degree five?

In Exercises 4–5 determine the number of vertices and edges and find the in-degree and out-degree of each vertex for the given directed multigraph.

4. 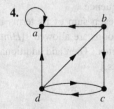   **5.**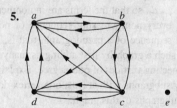

6. Construct the underlying undirected graph for the graph with directed edges in Figure 2.

7. What does the degree of a vertex represent in a collaboration graph? What do isolated and pendant vertices represent?

8. What do the in-degree and the out-degree of a vertex in a telephone call graph, as described in Example 7 of Section 6.1, represent? What does the degree of a vertex in the undirected version of this graph represent?

9. What do the in-degree and the out-degree of a vertex in a directed graph modeling a round-robin tournament represent?

In Exercises 10–12 determine whether the graph is bipartite. You may find it useful to apply Theorem 4 and answer the question by determining whether it is possible to assign either red or blue to each vertex so that no two adjacent vertices are assigned the same color.

10.   **11.**   **12.**

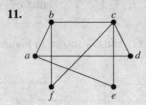 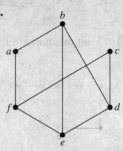

13. Suppose that a new company has five employees: Zamora, Agraharam, Smith, Chou, and Macintyre. Each employee will assume one of six responsiblities: planning, publicity, sales, marketing, development, and industry relations. Each employee is capable of doing one or more of these jobs: Zamora could do planning, sales, marketing, or industry relations; Agraharam could do planning or development; Smith could do publicity, sales, or industry relations; Chou could do planning, sales, or industry relations; and Macintyre could do planning, publicity, sales, or industry relations.

    a) Model the capabilities of these employees using a bipartite graph.

    b) Find an assignment of responsibilites such that each employee is assigned a responsibility.

14. How many vertices and how many edges do these graphs have?

    a) K_n b) C_n c) W_n d) $K_{m,n}$ e) Q_n

    The **degree sequence** of a graph is the sequence of the degrees of the vertices of the graph in nonincreasing order. For example, the degree sequence of the graph G in Example 1 in this section is 4, 4, 4, 3, 2, 1, 0.

15. Find the degree sequence of each of the following graphs.

    a) K_4 b) C_4 c) W_4 d) $K_{2,3}$ e) Q_3

16. What is the degree sequence of K_n, where n is a positive integer? Explain your answer.

17. How many edges does a graph have if its degree sequence is 5, 2, 2, 2, 2, 1? Draw such a graph.

    A sequence $d_1, d_2, \ldots, d_n$ is called **graphic** if it is the degree sequence of a simple graph.

18. Determine whether each of these sequences is graphic. For those that are, draw a graph having the given degree sequence.

    a) 3, 3, 3, 3, 2   b) 5, 4, 3, 2, 1   c) 4, 4, 3, 2, 1   d) 4, 4, 3, 3, 3   e) 3, 2, 2, 1, 0   f) 1, 1, 1, 1, 1

*19. Show that a sequence $d_1, d_2, \ldots, d_n$ of nonnegative integers in nonincreasing order is a graphic sequence if and only if the sequence obtained by reordering the terms of the sequence $d_2 - 1, \ldots, d_{d_1+1} - 1, d_{d_1+2}, \ldots, d_n$ so that the terms are in nonincreasing order is a graphic sequence.

20. Show that every nonincreasing sequence of nonnegative integers with an even sum of its terms is the degree sequence of a pseudograph, that is, an undirected graph where loops are allowed. [*Hint:* Construct such a graph by first adding as many loops as possible at each vertex. Then add additional edges connecting vertices of odd degree. Explain why this construction works.]

21. How many subgraphs with at least one vertex does K_3 have?

22. Draw all subgraphs of this graph.

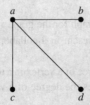

A simple graph is called **regular** if every vertex of this graph has the same degree. A regular graph is called n-**regular** if every vertex in this graph has degree n.

23. For which values of n are these graphs regular?

   a) K_n b) C_n c) W_n d) Q_n

24. How many vertices does a regular graph of degree four with 10 edges have?

In Exercise 25 find the union of the given pair of simple graphs. (Assume edges with the same endpoints are the same.)

25.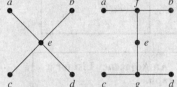

26. The **complementary graph** $\overline{G}$ of a simple graph G has the same vertices as G. Two vertices are adjacent in $\overline{G}$ if and only if they are not adjacent in G. Describe each of these graphs.

   a) $\overline{K_n}$ b) $\overline{K_{m,n}}$ c) $\overline{C_n}$ d) $\overline{Q_n}$

27. If the simple graph G has v vertices and e edges, how many edges does $\overline{G}$ have?

28. If the degree sequence of the simple graph G is $d_1, d_2, \ldots, d_n$, what is the degree sequence of $\overline{G}$?

29. Show that if G is a simple graph with n vertices, then the union of G and $\overline{G}$ is K_n.

30. Draw the converse of each of the graphs in Exercises 4–5 in Section 6.1.

31. Show that the graph G is its own converse if and only if the relation associated with G (see Section 5.3) is symmetric.

32. Draw the mesh network for interconnecting nine parallel processors.

33. Show that every pair of processors in a mesh network of $n = m^2$ processors can communicate using $O(\sqrt{n}) = O(m)$ hops between directly connected processors.

6.3   Representing Graphs and Graph Isomorphism

Introduction

There are many useful ways to represent graphs. As we will see throughout this chapter, in working with a graph it is helpful to be able to choose its most convenient representation. In this section we will show how to represent graphs in several different ways.

Sometimes, two graphs have exactly the same form, in the sense that there is a one-to-one correspondence between their vertex sets that preserves edges. In such a case, we say that the two graphs are **isomorphic.** Determining whether two graphs are isomorphic is an important problem of graph theory that we will study in this section.

Representing Graphs

One way to represent a graph without multiple edges is to list all the edges of this graph. Another way to represent a graph with no multiple edges is to use **adjacency lists,** which specify the vertices that are adjacent to each vertex of the graph.

Example 1   Use adjacency lists to describe the simple graph given in Figure 1.

Solution: Table 1 lists those vertices adjacent to each of the vertices of the graph.   ◄

Example 2   Represent the directed graph shown in Figure 2 by listing all the vertices that are the terminal vertices of edges starting at each vertex of the graph.

Solution: Table 2 represents the directed graph shown in Figure 2.   ◄

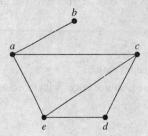

Figure 1   A Simple Graph.

TABLE 1 An Adjacency List for a Simple Graph.	
Vertex	Adjacent Vertices
a	b, c, e
b	a
c	a, d, e
d	c, e
e	a, c, d

Figure 2   A Directed Graph.

TABLE 2 An Adjacency List for a Directed Graph.	
Initial Vertex	Terminal Vertices
a	b, c, d, e
b	b, d
c	a, c, e
d	
e	b, c, d

Adjacency Matrices

Carrying out graph algorithms using the representation of graphs by lists of edges, or by adjacency lists, can be cumbersome if there are many edges in the graph. To simplify computation, graphs can be represented using matrices. Two types of matrices commonly used to represent graphs will be presented here. One is based on the adjacency of vertices, and the other is based on incidence of vertices and edges.

Suppose that $G = (V, E)$ is a simple graph where $|V| = n$. Suppose that the vertices of G are listed arbitrarily as $v_1, v_2, \ldots, v_n$. The **adjacency matrix** $\mathbf{A}$ (or $\mathbf{A}_G$) of G, with respect to this listing of the vertices, is the n x n zero–one matrix with 1 as its (i, j)th entry when v_i and v_j are adjacent, and 0 as its (i, j)th entry when they are not adjacent. In other words, if its adjacency matrix is $\mathbf{A} = [a_{ij}]$, then

$$a_{ij} = \begin{cases} 1 & \text{if } \{v_i, v_j\} \text{ is an edge of } G, \\ 0 & \text{otherwise.} \end{cases}$$

Example 3   Use an adjacency matrix to represent the graph shown in Figure 3.

Solution: We order the vertices as a, b, c, d. The matrix representing this graph is

$$\begin{bmatrix} 0 & 1 & 1 & 1 \\ 1 & 0 & 1 & 0 \\ 1 & 1 & 0 & 0 \\ 1 & 0 & 0 & 0 \end{bmatrix}.$$ ◀

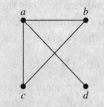

Figure 3   Simple Graph.

Example 4   Draw a graph with the adjacency matrix

$$\begin{bmatrix} 0 & 1 & 1 & 0 \\ 1 & 0 & 0 & 1 \\ 1 & 0 & 0 & 1 \\ 0 & 1 & 1 & 0 \end{bmatrix}$$

with respect to the ordering of vertices a, b, c, d.

Solution: A graph with this adjacency matrix is shown in Figure 4.   ◄

Note that an adjacency matrix of a graph is based on the ordering chosen for the vertices. Hence, there are as many as $n!$ different adjacency matrices for a graph with n vertices, because there are $n!$ different orderings of n vertices.

The adjacency matrix of a simple graph is symmetric, that is, $a_{ij} = a_{ji}$, because both of these entries are 1 when v_i and v_j are adjacent, and both are 0 otherwise. Furthermore, because a simple graph has no loops, each entry $a_{ii}, i = 1, 2, 3, \ldots, n$, is 0.

Adjacency matrices can also be used to represent undirected graphs with loops and with multiple edges. A loop at the vertex a_i is represented by a 1 at the (i, i)th position of the adjacency matrix. When multiple edges are present, the adjacency matrix is no longer a zero–one matrix, because the

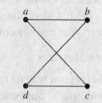

Figure 4   A Graph with the Given Adjacency Matrix.

(i, j)th entry of this matrix equals the number of edges that are associated to $\{a_i, a_j\}$. All undirected graphs, including multigraphs and pseudographs, have symmetric adjacency matrices.

Example 5   Use an adjacency matrix to represent the pseudograph shown in Figure 5.

Solution: The adjacency matrix using the ordering of vertices a, b, c, d is

$$\begin{bmatrix} 0 & 3 & 0 & 2 \\ 3 & 0 & 1 & 1 \\ 0 & 1 & 1 & 2 \\ 2 & 1 & 2 & 0 \end{bmatrix}.$$

◄

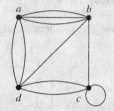

Figure 5   A Pseudograph.

We used zero–one matrices in Chapter 5 to represent directed graphs. The matrix for a directed graph $G = (V, E)$ has a 1 in its (i, j)th position if there is an edge from v_i to v_j, where $v_1, v_2, \ldots, v_n$ is an arbitrary listing of the vertices of the directed graph. In other words, if $\mathbf{A} = [a_{ij}]$ is the adjacency matrix for the directed graph with respect to this listing of the vertices, then

$$a_{ij} = \begin{cases} 1 & \text{if } (v_i, v_j) \text{ is an edge of } G, \\ 0 & \text{otherwise.} \end{cases}$$

The adjacency matrix for a directed graph does not have to be symmetric, because there may not be an edge from a_j to a_i when there is an edge from a_i to a_j.

Adjacency matrices can also be used to represent directed multigraphs. Again, such matrices are not zero–one matrices when there are multiple edges in the same direction connecting two vertices. In the adjacency matrix for a directed multigraph, a_{ij} equals the number of edges that are associated to (v_i, v_j).

Trade-offs between adjacency lists and adjacency matrices   When a simple graph contains relatively few edges, that is, when it is **sparse,** it is usually preferable to use adjacency lists rather than an adjacency matrix to represent the graph. For example, if each vertex has degree not exceeding c, where c is a constant much smaller than n, then each adjacency list contains c or fewer vertices. Hence, there are no more than cn items in all these adjacency lists. On the other hand, the adjacency matrix for the graph has n^2 entries. Note, however, that the adjacency matrix of a sparse graph is a **sparse matrix,** that is, a matrix with few nonzero entries, and there are special techniques for representing, and computing with, sparse matrices.

Now suppose that a simple graph is **dense,** that is, suppose that it contains many edges, such as a graph that contains more than half of all possible edges. In this case, using an adjacency matrix to represent the graph is usually preferable over using adjacency lists. To see why, we compare the complexity of determining whether the possible edge $\{v_i, v_j\}$ is present. Using an adjacency matrix, we can determine whether this edge is present by examining the (i, j)th entry in the matrix. This entry is 1 if the graph contains this edge and is 0 otherwise. Consequently, we need make only one comparison, namely, comparing this entry with 0, to determine whether this edge is present. On the other hand, when we use adjacency lists to represent the graph, we need to search the list of vertices adjacent to either v_i or v_j to determine whether this edge is present. This can require $\Theta(|V|)$ comparisons when many edges are present.

Incidence Matrices

Another common way to represent graphs is to use **incidence matrices.** Let $G = (V, E)$ be an undirected graph. Suppose that $v_1, v_2, \ldots, v_n$ are the vertices and $e_1, e_2, \ldots, e_m$ are the edges of G. Then the incidence matrix with respect to this ordering of V and E is the $n \times m$ matrix $\mathbf{M} = [m_{ij}]$, where

$$m_{ij} = \begin{cases} 1 & \text{when edge } e_j \text{ is incident with } v_i, \\ 0 & \text{otherwise.} \end{cases}$$

Example 6   Represent the graph shown in Figure 6 with an incidence matrix.

Solution: The incidence matrix is

$$\begin{array}{c} \\ v_1 \\ v_2 \\ v_3 \\ v_4 \\ v_5 \end{array} \begin{array}{cccccc} e_1 & e_2 & e_3 & e_4 & e_5 & e_6 \\ \left[\begin{array}{cccccc} 1 & 1 & 0 & 0 & 0 & 0 \\ 0 & 0 & 1 & 1 & 0 & 1 \\ 0 & 0 & 0 & 0 & 1 & 1 \\ 1 & 0 & 1 & 0 & 0 & 0 \\ 0 & 1 & 0 & 1 & 1 & 0 \end{array}\right]. \end{array}$$

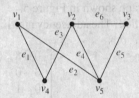

Figure 6   An Undirected Graph.

Incidence matrices can also be used to represent multiple edges and loops. Multiple edges are represented in the incidence matrix using columns with identical entries, because these edges are incident with the same pair of vertices. Loops are represented using a column with exactly one entry equal to 1, corresponding to the vertex that is incident with this loop.

Example 7   Represent the pseudograph shown in Figure 7 using an incidence matrix.

Solution: The incidence matrix for this graph is

$$\begin{array}{c} \\ v_1 \\ v_2 \\ v_3 \\ v_4 \\ v_5 \end{array} \begin{array}{cccccccc} e_1 & e_2 & e_3 & e_4 & e_5 & e_6 & e_7 & e_8 \\ \left[\begin{array}{cccccccc} 1 & 1 & 1 & 0 & 0 & 0 & 0 & 0 \\ 0 & 1 & 1 & 1 & 0 & 1 & 1 & 0 \\ 0 & 0 & 0 & 1 & 1 & 0 & 0 & 0 \\ 0 & 0 & 0 & 0 & 0 & 0 & 1 & 1 \\ 0 & 0 & 0 & 0 & 1 & 1 & 0 & 0 \end{array}\right]. \end{array}$$

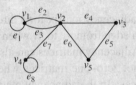

Figure 7   A Pseudograph.

Isomorphism of Graphs

We often need to know whether it is possible to draw two graphs in the same way. For instance, in chemistry, graphs are used to model compounds. Different compounds can have the same molecular formula but can differ in structure. Such compounds will be represented by graphs that cannot be drawn in the same way. The graphs representing previously known compounds can be used to determine whether a supposedly new compound has been studied before.

There is a useful terminology for graphs with the same structure.

Definition 1   The simple graphs $G_1 = (V_1, E_1)$ and $G_2 = (V_2, E_2)$ are *isomorphic* if there is a one-to-one and onto function f from V_1 to V_2 with the property that a and b are adjacent in G_1 if and only if $f(a)$ and $f(b)$ are adjacent in G_2, for all a and b in V_1. Such a function f is called an *isomorphism.*[*]

In other words, when two simple graphs are isomorphic, there is a one-to-one correspondence between vertices of the two graphs that preserves the adjacency relationship. Isomorphism of simple graphs is an equivalence relation. (We leave the verification of this as Exercise 22 at the end of this section.)

Example 8   Show that the graphs $G = (V, E)$ and $H = (W, F)$, displayed in Figure 8, are isomorphic.

Solution: The function f with $f(u_1) = v_1$, $f(u_2) = v_4$, $f(u_3) = v_3$, and $f(u_4) = v_2$ is a one-to-one correspondence between V and W. To see that this correspondence preserves adjacency, note that adjacent vertices in G are u_1 and u_2, u_1 and u_3, u_2 and u_4, and u_3 and u_4, and each of the pairs $f(u_1) = v_1$ and $f(u_2) = v_4$, $f(u_1) = v_1$ and $f(u_3) = v_3$, $f(u_2) = v_4$ and $f(u_4) = v_2$, and $f(u_3) = v_3$ and $f(u_4) = v_2$ are adjacent in H.   ◄

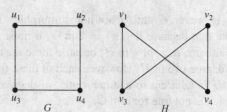

Figure 8   The Graphs G and H.

It is often difficult to determine whether two simple graphs are isomorphic. There are $n!$ possible one-to-one correspondences between the vertex sets of two simple graphs with n vertices. Testing each such correspondence to see whether it preserves adjacency and nonadjacency is impractical if n is at all large.

Sometimes it is not hard to show that two graphs are not isomorphic. In particular, we can show that two graphs are not isomorphic if we can find a property only one of the two graphs has, but that is preserved by isomorphism. A property preserved by isomorphism of graphs is called a **graph invariant.** For instance, isomorphic simple graphs must have the same number of vertices, because there is a one-to-one correspondence between the sets of vertices of the graphs.

Isomorphic simple graphs also must have the same number of edges, because the one-to-one correspondence between vertices establishes a one-to-one correspondence between edges. In addition, the degrees of the vertices in isomorphic simple graphs must be the same. That is, a vertex v of degree d in G must correspond to a vertex $f(v)$ of degree d in H, because a vertex w in G is adjacent to v if and only if $f(v)$ and $f(w)$ are adjacent in H.

Example 9   Show that graphs displayed in Figure 9 are not isomorphic.

Solution: Both G and H have five vertices and six edges. However, H has a vertex of degree one, namely, e, whereas G has no vertices of degree one. It follows that G and H are not isomorphic.◄

The number of vertices, the number of edges, and the number of vertices of each degree are all invariants under isomorphism. If any of these quantities differ in two simple graphs, these graphs cannot be isomorphic. However, when these invariants are the same, it does not necessarily mean that the two graphs are isomorphic. There are no useful sets of invariants currently known that can be used to determine whether simple graphs are isomorphic.

Example 10   Determine whether the graphs shown in Figure 10 are isomorphic.

Solution: The graphs G and H both have eight vertices and 10 edges. They also both have four vertices of degree two and four of degree three. Because these invariants all agree, it is still conceivable that these graphs are isomorphic.

---

[*]The word *isomorphism* comes from the Greek roots *isos* for "equal" and *morphe* for "form."

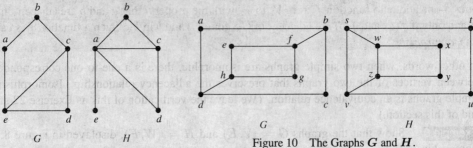

Figure 9   The Graphs G and H.

Figure 10   The Graphs G and H.

However, G and H are not isomorphic. To see this, note that because $\deg(a) = 2$ in G, a must correspond to either t, u, x, or y in H, because these are the vertices of degree two in H. However, each of these four vertices in H is adjacent to another vertex of degree two in H, which is not true for a in G.

Another way to see that G and H are not isomorphic is to note that the subgraphs of G and H made up of vertices of degree three and the edges connecting them must be isomorphic if these two graphs are isomorphic (the reader should verify this). However, these subgraphs, shown in Figure 11, are not isomorphic.   ◄

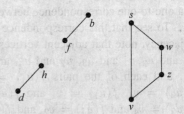

Figure 11   The Subgraphs of G and H Made Up of Vertices of Degree Three and the Edges Connecting Them.

To show that a function f from the vertex set of a graph G to the vertex set of a graph H is an isomorphism, we need to show that f preserves the presence and absence of edges. One helpful way to do this is to use adjacency matrices. In particular, to show that f is an isomorphism, we can show that the adjacency matrix of G is the same as the adjacency matrix of H, when rows and columns are labeled to correspond to the images under f of the vertices in G that are the labels of these rows and columns in the adjacency matrix of G. We illustrate how this is done in Example 11.

Example 11   Determine whether the graphs G and H displayed in Figure 12 are isomorphic.

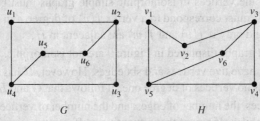

Figure 12   Graphs G and H.

Solution: Both G and H have six vertices and seven edges. Both have four vertices of degree two and two vertices of degree three. It is also easy to see that the subgraphs of G and H consisting of all vertices of degree two and the edges connecting them are isomorphic (as the reader should verify). Because G and H agree with respect to these invariants, it is reasonable to try to find an isomorphism f.

We now will define a function f and then determine whether it is an isomorphism. Because $\deg(u_1) = 2$ and because u_1 is not adjacent to any other vertex of degree two, the image of u_1 must be either v_4 or v_6, the only vertices of degree two in H not adjacent to a vertex of degree two. We arbitrarily set $f(u_1) = v_6$. [If we found that this choice did not lead to isomorphism, we would then try $f(u_1) = v_4$.] Because u_2 is adjacent to u_1, the possible images of u_2 are v_3 and v_5. We arbitrarily set $f(u_2) = v_3$. Continuing in this way, using adjacency of vertices and degrees as a guide, we set $f(u_3) = v_4$, $f(u_4) = v_5$, $f(u_5) = v_1$, and $f(u_6) = v_2$. We now have a one-to-one correspondence between the vertex set of G and the vertex set of H, namely, $f(u_1) = v_6$, $f(u_2) = v_3$, $f(u_3) = v_4$, $f(u_4) = v_5$, $f(u_5) = v_1$, $f(u_6) = v_2$. To see whether f preserves edges, we examine the adjacency matrix of G,

$$
\mathbf{A}_G = \begin{array}{c} \\ u_1 \\ u_2 \\ u_3 \\ u_4 \\ u_5 \\ u_6 \end{array}
\begin{array}{c} \begin{array}{cccccc} u_1 & u_2 & u_3 & u_4 & u_5 & u_6 \end{array} \\
\left[\begin{array}{cccccc}
0 & 1 & 0 & 1 & 0 & 0 \\
1 & 0 & 1 & 0 & 0 & 1 \\
0 & 1 & 0 & 1 & 0 & 0 \\
1 & 0 & 1 & 0 & 1 & 0 \\
0 & 0 & 0 & 1 & 0 & 1 \\
0 & 1 & 0 & 0 & 1 & 0
\end{array}\right]
\end{array}.
$$

and the adjacency matrix of H with the rows and columns labeled by the images of the corresponding vertices in G,

$$
\mathbf{A}_H = \begin{array}{c} \\ u_6 \\ u_3 \\ u_4 \\ u_5 \\ u_1 \\ u_2 \end{array}
\begin{array}{c} \begin{array}{cccccc} u_6 & u_3 & u_4 & u_5 & u_1 & u_2 \end{array} \\
\left[\begin{array}{cccccc}
0 & 1 & 0 & 1 & 0 & 0 \\
1 & 0 & 1 & 0 & 0 & 1 \\
0 & 1 & 0 & 1 & 0 & 0 \\
1 & 0 & 1 & 0 & 1 & 0 \\
0 & 0 & 0 & 1 & 0 & 1 \\
0 & 1 & 0 & 0 & 1 & 0
\end{array}\right]
\end{array}.
$$

Because $\mathbf{A}_G = \mathbf{A}_H$, it follows that f preserves edges. We conclude that f is an isomorphism, so G and H are isomorphic. Note that if f turned out not to be an isomorphism, we would *not* have established that G and H are not isomorphic, because another correspondence of the vertices in G and H may be an isomorphism.   ◄

The best algorithms known for determining whether two graphs are isomorphic have exponential worst-case time complexity (in the number of vertices of the graphs). However, linear average-case time complexity algorithms are known that solve this problem, and there is some hope that an algorithm with polynomial worst-case time complexity for determining whether two graphs are isomorphic can be found. The best practical algorithm, called NAUTY, can be used to determine whether two graphs with as many as 100 vertices are isomorphic in less than 1 second on a modern PC. The software for NAUTY can be downloaded over the Internet and experimented with.

Exercises

In Exercises 1–2 use an adjacency list to represent the given graph.

1.

2.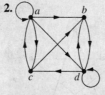

3. Represent the graph in Exercise 1 with an adjacency matrix.
4. Represent the graph in Exercise 2 with an adjacency matrix.

5. Represent each of these graphs with an adjacency matrix.

a) K_4 b) $K_{1,4}$ c) $K_{2,3}$ d) C_4 e) W_4 f) Q_3

In Exercise 6 draw a graph with the given adjacency matrix.

6. $\begin{bmatrix} 0 & 0 & 1 & 1 \\ 0 & 0 & 1 & 0 \\ 1 & 1 & 0 & 1 \\ 1 & 1 & 1 & 0 \end{bmatrix}$

In Exercises 7–8 represent the given graph using an adjacency matrix.

7.

8.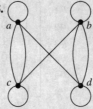

In Exercise 9 draw an undirected graph represented by the given adjacency matrix.

9. $\begin{bmatrix} 1 & 2 & 0 & 1 \\ 2 & 0 & 3 & 0 \\ 0 & 3 & 1 & 1 \\ 1 & 0 & 1 & 0 \end{bmatrix}$

In Exercises 10–11 find the adjacency matrix of the given directed multigraph.

10.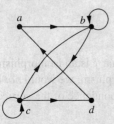

11.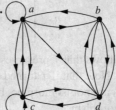

In Exercise 12 draw the graph represented by the given adjacency matrix.

12. $\begin{bmatrix} 1 & 2 & 1 \\ 2 & 0 & 0 \\ 0 & 2 & 2 \end{bmatrix}$

13. Is every zero–one square matrix that is symmetric and has zeros on the diagonal the adjacency matrix of a simple graph?

14. Use an incidence matrix to represent the graphs in Exercises 7–8.

*__15.__ What is the sum of the entries in a column of the adjacency matrix for an undirected graph? For a directed graph?

16. What is the sum of the entries in a column of the incidence matrix for an undirected graph?

In Exercises 17–21 determine whether the given pair of graphs is isomorphic. Exhibit an isomorphism or provide a rigorous argument that none exists.

17.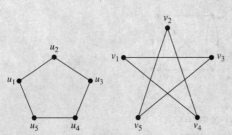

18.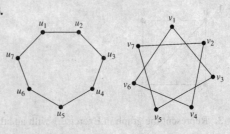

19.

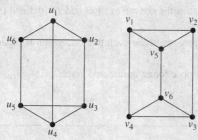

20.

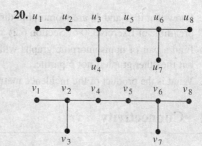

21.

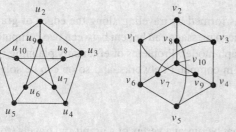

22. Show that isomorphism of simple graphs is an equivalence relation.

23. Describe the row and column of an adjacency matrix of a graph corresponding to an isolated vertex.

24. Show that the vertices of a bipartite graph with two or more vertices can be ordered so that its adjacency matrix has the form

$$\begin{bmatrix} \mathbf{0} & \mathbf{A} \\ \mathbf{B} & \mathbf{0} \end{bmatrix},$$

where the four entries shown are rectangular blocks.

A simple graph G is called **self-complementary** if G and $\overline{G}$ are isomorphic.

25. Find a self-complementary simple graph with five vertices.

26. For which integers n is C_n self-complementary?

27. How many nonisomorphic simple graphs are there with five vertices and three edges?

28. Are the simple graphs with the following adjacency matrices isomorphic?

a) $\begin{bmatrix} 0 & 0 & 1 \\ 0 & 0 & 1 \\ 1 & 1 & 0 \end{bmatrix}$, $\begin{bmatrix} 0 & 1 & 1 \\ 1 & 0 & 0 \\ 1 & 0 & 0 \end{bmatrix}$

b) $\begin{bmatrix} 0 & 1 & 0 & 1 \\ 1 & 0 & 0 & 1 \\ 0 & 0 & 0 & 1 \\ 1 & 1 & 1 & 0 \end{bmatrix}$, $\begin{bmatrix} 0 & 1 & 1 & 1 \\ 1 & 0 & 0 & 1 \\ 1 & 0 & 0 & 1 \\ 1 & 1 & 1 & 0 \end{bmatrix}$

c) $\begin{bmatrix} 0 & 1 & 1 & 0 \\ 1 & 0 & 0 & 1 \\ 1 & 0 & 0 & 1 \\ 0 & 1 & 1 & 0 \end{bmatrix}$, $\begin{bmatrix} 0 & 1 & 0 & 1 \\ 1 & 0 & 0 & 0 \\ 0 & 0 & 0 & 1 \\ 1 & 0 & 1 & 0 \end{bmatrix}$

29. Extend the definition of isomorphism of simple graphs to undirected graphs containing loops and multiple edges.

In Exercises 30–31 determine whether the given pair of directed graphs are isomorphic.

30.

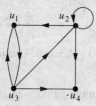

31.

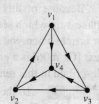

32. Show that if G and H are isomorphic directed graphs, then the converses of G and H (defined in the preamble of Exercise 30 of Section 6.2) are also isomorphic.

33. Find a pair of nonisomorphic graphs with the same degree sequence such that one graph is bipartite, but the other graph is not bipartite.

*__34.__ What is the product of the incidence matrix and its transpose for an undirected graph?

6.4   Connectivity

Introduction

Many problems can be modeled with paths formed by traveling along the edges of graphs. For instance, the problem of determining whether a message can be sent between two computers using intermediate links can be studied with a graph model. Problems of efficiently planning routes for mail delivery, garbage pickup, diagnostics in computer networks, and so on can be solved using models that involve paths in graphs.

Paths

Informally, a **path** is a sequence of edges that begins at a vertex of a graph and travels from vertex to vertex along edges of the graph.

A formal definition of paths and related terminology is given in Definition 1.

Definition 1   Let n be a nonnegative integer and G an undirected graph. A *path* of *length* n from u to v in G is a sequence of n edges $e_1, \ldots, e_n$ of G such that e_1 is associated with $\{x_0, x_1\}$, e_2 is associated with $\{x_1, x_2\}$, and so on, with e_n associated with $\{x_{n-1}, x_n\}$, where $x_0 = u$ and $x_n = v$. When the graph is simple, we denote this path by its vertex sequence $x_0, x_1, \ldots, x_n$ (because listing these vertices uniquely determines the path). The path is a *circuit* if it begins and ends at the same vertex, that is, if $u = v$, and has length greater than zero. The path or circuit is said to *pass through* the vertices $x_1, x_2, \ldots, x_{n-1}$ or *traverse* the edges $e_1, e_2, \ldots, e_n$. A path or circuit is *simple* if it does not contain the same edge more than once.

When it is not necessary to distinguish between multiple edges, we will denote a path $e_1, e_2, \ldots, e_n$, where e_i is associated with $\{x_{i-1}, x_i\}$ for $i = 1, 2, \ldots, n$ by its vertex sequence $x_0, x_1, \ldots, x_n$. This notation identifies a path only up to the vertices it passes through. There may be more than one path that passes through this sequence of vertices. Note that a path of length zero consists of a single vertex.

Remark: There is considerable variation of terminology concerning the concepts defined in Definition 1. For instance, in some books, the term **walk** is used instead of *path*, where a walk is defined to be an alternating sequence of vertices and edges of a graph, $v_0, e_1, v_1, e_2, \ldots, v_{n-1}, e_n, v_n$, where v_{i-1} and v_i are the endpoints of e_i for $i = 1, 2, \ldots, n$. When this terminology is used, **closed walk** is used instead of *circuit* to indicate a walk that begins and ends at the same vertex, and **trail** is used to denote a walk that has no repeated edge (replacing the term *simple path*). When this terminology is used, the terminology **path** is often used for a trail with no repeated vertices, conflicting with the terminology in Definition 1. Because of this variation in terminology, you will need to make sure which set of definitions are used in a particular book or article when you read about traversing edges of a graph. The text [GrYe06] is a good reference for the alternative terminology described in this remark.

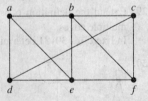

Figure 1   A Simple Graph.

Example 1   In the simple graph shown in Figure 1, a, d, c, f, e is a simple path of length 4, because $\{a, d\}$, $\{d, c\}$, $\{c, f\}$, and $\{f, e\}$ are all edges. However, d, e, c, a is not a path, because

$\{e, c\}$ is not an edge. Note that b, c, f, e, b is a circuit of length 4 because $\{b, c\}, \{c, f\}, \{f, e\}$, and $\{e, b\}$ are edges, and this path begins and ends at b. The path a, b, e, d, a, b, which is of length 5, is not simple because it contains the edge $\{a, b\}$ twice. ◄

Paths and circuits in directed graphs were introduced in Chapter 5. We now provide more general definitions.

Definition 2 Let n be a nonnegative integer and G a directed graph. A *path* of length n from u to v in G is a sequence of edges $e_1, e_2, \ldots, e_n$ of G such that e_1 is associated with (x_0, x_1), e_2 is associated with (x_1, x_2), and so on, with e_n associated with (x_{n-1}, x_n), where $x_0 = u$ and $x_n = v$. When there are no multiple edges in the directed graph, this path is denoted by its vertex sequence $x_0, x_1, x_2, \ldots, x_n$. A path of length greater than zero that begins and ends at the same vertex is called a *circuit* or *cycle*. A path or circuit is called *simple* if it does not contain the same edge more than once.

Remark: Terminology other than that given in Definition 2 is often used for the concepts defined there. In particular, the alternative terminology that uses *walk, closed walk, trail,* and *path* (described in the remarks following Definition 1) may be used for directed graphs. See [GrYe06] for details.

Note that the terminal vertex of an edge in a path is the initial vertex of the next edge in the path. When it is not necessary to distinguish between multiple edges, we will denote a path $e_1, e_2, \ldots, e_n$, where e_i is associated with (x_{i-1}, x_i) for $i = 1, 2, \ldots, n$ by its vertex sequence $x_0, x_1, \ldots, x_n$. The notation identifies a path only up to the vertices it passes through. There may be more than one path that passes through this sequence of vertices.

Paths represent useful information in many graph models, as Examples 2–4 demonstrate.

Example 2 **Paths in Acquaintanceship Graphs** In an acquaintanceship graph there is a path between two people if there is a chain of people linking these people, where two people adjacent in the chain know one another. For example, in Figure 7 in Section 6.1, there is a chain of six people linking Kamini and Ching. Many social scientists have conjectured that almost every pair of people in the world are linked by a small chain of people, perhaps containing just five or fewer people. This would mean that almost every pair of vertices in the acquaintanceship graph containing all people in the world is linked by a path of length not exceeding four. The play *Six Degrees of Separation* by John Guare is based on this notion. ◄

Example 3 **Paths in Collaboration Graphs** In a collaboration graph two vertices a and b, which represent authors, are connected by a path when there is a sequence of authors beginning at a and ending at b such that the two authors represented by the endpoints of each edge have written a joint paper. In the collaboration graph of all mathematicians, the **Erdős number** of a mathematician m (defined in terms of relations in Supplementary Exercise 14 in Chapter 5) is the length of the shortest path between m and the vertex representing the extremely prolific mathematician Paul Erdős (who died in 1996). That is, the Erdős number of a mathematician is the length of the shortest chain of mathematicians that begins with Paul Erdős and ends with this mathematician, where each adjacent pair of mathematicians have written a joint paper. The number of mathematicians with each Erdős number as of early 2006, according to the Erdős Number Project, is shown in Table 1. ◄

Example 4 **Paths in the Hollywood Graph** In the Hollywood graph (see Example 4 in Section 6.1) two vertices a and b are linked when there is a chain of actors linking a and b, where every two actors adjacent in the chain have acted in the same movie. In the Hollywood graph, the **Bacon number** of an actor c is defined to be the length of the shortest path connecting c and the well-known actor Kevin Bacon. As new movies are made, including new ones with Kevin Bacon, the Bacon number of actors can change. In Table 2 we show the number of actors with each Bacon number as of early 2006 using data from the Oracle of Bacon website. ◄

TABLE 1 The Number of Mathematicians with a Given Erdős Number (as of early 2006).	
Erdős Number	*Number of People*
0	1
1	504
2	6,593
3	33,605
4	83,642
5	87,760
6	40,014
7	11,591
8	3,146
9	819
10	244
11	68
12	23
13	5

TABLE 2 The Number of Actors with a Given Bacon Number (as of early 2006).	
Bacon Number	*Number of People*
0	1
1	1,902
2	160,463
3	457,231
4	111,310
5	8,168
6	810
7	81
8	14

Connectedness In Undirected Graphs

When does a computer network have the property that every pair of computers can share information, if messages can be sent through one or more intermediate computers? When a graph is used to represent this computer network, where vertices represent the computers and edges represent the communication links, this question becomes: When is there always a path between two vertices in the graph?

Definition 3   An undirected graph is called *connected* if there is a path between every pair of distinct vertices of the graph.

Thus, any two computers in the network can communicate if and only if the graph of this network is connected.

Example 5   The graph G_1 in Figure 2 is connected, because for every pair of distinct vertices there is a path between them (the reader should verify this). However, the graph G_2 in Figure 2 is not connected. For instance, there is no path in G_2 between vertices a and d.   ◄

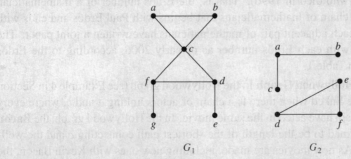

Figure 2   The Graphs G_1 and G_2.

We will need the following theorem in Chapter 7.

Theorem 1   There is a simple path between every pair of distinct vertices of a connected undirected graph.

Proof: Let u and v be two distinct vertices of the connected undirected graph $G = (V, E)$. Because G is connected, there is at least one path between u and v. Let $x_0, x_1, \ldots, x_n$, where $x_0 = u$ and $x_n = v$, be the vertex sequence of a path of least length. This path of least length is simple. To see this, suppose it is not simple. Then $x_i = x_j$ for some i and j with $0 \leqslant i < j$. This means that there is a path from u to v of shorter length with vertex sequence $x_0, x_1, \ldots, x_{i-1}, x_j, \ldots, x_n$ obtained by deleting the edges corresponding to the vertex sequence $x_i, \ldots, x_{j-1}$.   ◁

A **connected component** of a graph G is a connected subgraph of G that is not a proper subgraph of another connected subgraph of G. That is, a connected component of a graph G is a maximal connected subgraph of G. A graph G that is not connected has two or more connected components that are disjoint and have G as their union.

Example 6   What are the connected components of the graph H shown in Figure 3?

Solution: The graph H is the union of three disjoint connected subgraphs H_1, H_2, and H_3, shown in Figure 3. These three subgraphs are the connected components of H.   ◀

Example 7   **Connected Components of Call Graphs** Two vertices x and y are in the same component of a telephone call graph (see Example 7 in Section 6.1) when there is a sequence of telephone calls beginning at x and ending at y. When a call graph for telephone calls made during a particular day in the AT&T network was analyzed, this graph was found to have 53,767,087 vertices, more than 170 million edges, and more than 3.7 million connected components. Most of these components were small; approximately three-fourths consisted of two vertices representing pairs of telephone numbers that called only each other. This graph has one huge connected component with 44,989,297 vertices comprising more than 80% of the total. Furthermore, every vertex in this component can be linked to any other vertex by a chain of no more than 20 calls.   ◀

Sometimes the removal of a vertex and all edges incident with it produces a subgraph with more connected components than in the original graph. Such vertices are called **cut vertices** (or **articulation points**). The removal of a cut vertex from a connected graph produces a subgraph that is not connected. Analogously, an edge whose removal produces a graph with more connected components than in the original graph is called a **cut edge** or **bridge**.

Example 8   Find the cut vertices and cut edges in the graph G shown in Figure 4.

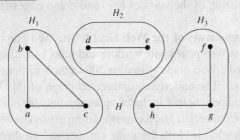

Figure 3   The Graph H and Its Connected Components H_1, H_2, and H_3.

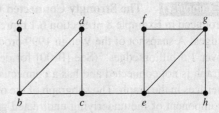

Figure 4   The Graph G.

Solution: The cut vertices of G are b, c, and e. The removal of one of these vertices (and its adjacent edges) disconnects the graph. The cut edges are $\{a, b\}$ and $\{c, e\}$. Removing either one of these edges disconnects G.   ◀

Connectedness in Directed Graphs

There are two notions of connectedness in directed graphs, depending on whether the directions of the edges are considered.

Definition 4   A directed graph is *strongly connected* if there is a path from a to b and from b to a whenever a and b are vertices in the graph.

For a directed graph to be strongly connected there must be a sequence of directed edges from any vertex in the graph to any other vertex. A directed graph can fail to be strongly connected but still be in "one piece." Definition 5 makes this notion precise.

Definition 5   A directed graph is *weakly connected* if there is a path between every two vertices in the underlying undirected graph.

That is, a directed graph is weakly connected if and only if there is always a path between two vertices when the directions of the edges are disregarded. Clearly, any strongly connected directed graph is also weakly connected.

Example 9   Are the directed graphs G and H shown in Figure 5 strongly connected? Are they weakly connected?

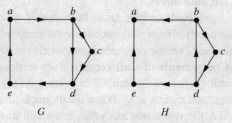

Figure 5   The Directed Graphs G and H.

Solution: G is strongly connected because there is a path between any two vertices in this directed graph (the reader should verify this). Hence, G is also weakly connected. The graph H is not strongly connected. There is no directed path from a to b in this graph. However, H is weakly connected, because there is a path between any two vertices in the underlying undirected graph of H (the reader should verify this).   ◄

The subgraphs of a directed graph G that are strongly connected but not contained in larger strongly connected subgraphs, that is, the maximal strongly connected subgraphs, are called the **strongly connected components** or **strong components** of G.

Example 10   The graph H in Figure 5 has three strongly connected components, consisting of the vertex a; the vertex e; and the graph consisting of the vertices b, c, and d and edges (b, c), (c, d), and (d, b).   ◄

Example 11   **The Strongly Connected Components of the Web Graph** The Web graph introduced in Example 8 of Section 6.1 represents Web pages with vertices and links with directed edges. A snapshot of the Web in 1999 produced a Web graph with over 200 million vertices and over 1.5 billion edges. (See [Br00] for details.) The underlying undirected graph of this Web graph is not connected and has a connected component that includes approximately 90% of the vertices in the graph. The subgraph of the original directed graph corresponding to this connected component of the underlying undirected graph (that is, with the same vertices and all directed edges connecting vertices in this graph) has one very large strongly connected component and many small ones. The former is called the **giant strongly connected component (GSCC)** of the directed graph. A Web page in this component can be reached following links starting at any other page in this component. The GSCC in the Web graph produced by this study was found to have over 53 million vertices. The remaining vertices in the large connected component of the undirected graph represent three different types of Web pages: pages that can be reached from a page in the GSCC, but do not link back to these pages following a series of links; pages that link back to pages in the GSCC following a series of links, but cannot be reached by following links on pages in the GSCC; and pages that cannot reach pages in the GSCC and cannot be reached from pages in the GSCC following a series of links. In this study, each of these three other sets was found to have approximately 44 million vertices. (It is rather surprising that these three sets are close to the same size.)   ◄

Paths and Isomorphism

There are several ways that paths and circuits can help determine whether two graphs are isomorphic. For example, the existence of a simple circuit of a particular length is a useful invariant that can be used to show that two graphs are not isomorphic. In addition, paths can be used to construct mappings that may be isomorphisms.

As we mentioned, a useful isomorphic invariant for simple graphs is the existence of a simple circuit of length k, where k is a positive integer greater than 2. Example 12 illustrates how this invariant can be used to show that two graphs are not isomorphic.

Example 12   Determine whether the graphs G and H shown in Figure 6 are isomorphic.

Solution: Both G and H have six vertices and eight edges. Each has four vertices of degree three, and two vertices of degree two. So, the three invariants—number of vertices, number of edges, and degrees of vertices—all agree for the two graphs. However, H has a simple circuit of length three, namely, v_1, v_2, v_6, v_1, whereas G has no simple circuit of length three, as can be determined by inspection (all simple circuits in G have length at least four). Because the existence of a simple circuit of length three is an isomorphic invariant, G and H are not isomorphic.   ◄

We have shown how the existence of a type of path, namely, a simple circuit of a particular length, can be used to show that two graphs are not isomorphic. We can also use paths to find mappings that are potential isomorphisms.

Example 13   Determine whether the graphs G and H shown in Figure 7 are isomorphic.

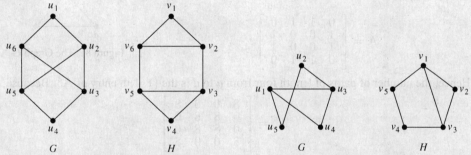

Figure 6 The Graphs **G** and **H**.	Figure 7 The Graphs **G** and **H**.

Solution: Both G and H have five vertices and six edges, both have two vertices of degree three and three vertices of degree two, and both have a simple circuit of length three, a simple circuit of length four, and a simple circuit of length five. Because all these isomorphic invariants agree, G and H may be isomorphic. To find a possible isomorphism, we can follow paths that go through all vertices so that the corresponding vertices in the two graphs have the same degree. For example, the paths u_1, u_4, u_3, u_2, u_5 in G and v_3, v_2, v_1, v_5, v_4 in H both go through every vertex in the graph; start at a vertex of degree three; go through vertices of degrees two, three, and two, respectively; and end at a vertex of degree two. By following these paths through the graphs, we define the mapping f with $f(u_1) = v_3$, $f(u_4) = v_2$, $f(u_3) = v_1$, $f(u_2) = v_5$, and $f(u_5) = v_4$. The reader can show that f is an isomorphism, so G and H are isomorphic, either by showing that f preserves edges or by showing that with the appropriate orderings of vertices the adjacency matrices of G and H are the same.   ◄

Counting Paths Between Vertices

The number of paths between two vertices in a graph can be determined using its adjacency matrix.

Theorem 2 Let G be a graph with adjacency matrix $\mathbf{A}$ with respect to the ordering $v_1, v_2, \ldots, v_n$ (with directed or undirected edges, with multiple edges and loops allowed). The number of different paths of length r from v_i to v_j, where r is a positive integer, equals the (i, j)th entry of $\mathbf{A}^r$.

Proof: The theorem will be proved using mathematical induction. Let G be a graph with adjacency matrix $\mathbf{A}$ (assuming an ordering $v_1, v_2, \ldots, v_n$ of the vertices of G). The number of paths from v_i to v_j of length 1 is the (i, j)th entry of $\mathbf{A}$, because this entry is the number of edges from v_i to v_j.

Assume that the (i, j)th entry of $\mathbf{A}^r$ is the number of different paths of length r from v_i to v_j. This is the induction hypothesis. Because $\mathbf{A}^{r+1} = \mathbf{A}^r \mathbf{A}$, the (i, j)th entry of $\mathbf{A}^{r+1}$ equals

$$b_{i1}a_{1j} + b_{i2}a_{2j} + \cdots + b_{in}a_{nj},$$

where b_{ik} is the (i, k)th entry of $\mathbf{A}^r$. By the induction hypothesis, b_{ik} is the number of paths of length r from v_i to v_k.

A path of length $r + 1$ from v_i to v_j is made up of a path of length r from v_i to some intermediate vertex v_k, and an edge from v_k to v_j. By the product rule for counting, the number of such paths is the product of the number of paths of length r from v_i to v_k, namely, b_{ik}, and the number of edges from v_k to v_j, namely, a_{kj}. When these products are added for all possible intermediate vertices v_k, the desired result follows by the sum rule for counting. ◁

Example 14 How many paths of length four are there from a to d in the simple graph G in Figure 8?

Solution: The adjacency matrix of G (ordering the vertices as a, b, c, d) is

$$\mathbf{A} = \begin{bmatrix} 0 & 1 & 1 & 0 \\ 1 & 0 & 0 & 1 \\ 1 & 0 & 0 & 1 \\ 0 & 1 & 1 & 0 \end{bmatrix}.$$

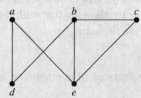

Figure 8   The Graph G.

Hence, the number of paths of length four from a to d is the $(1, 4)$th entry of $\mathbf{A}^4$. Because

$$\mathbf{A}^4 = \begin{bmatrix} 8 & 0 & 0 & 8 \\ 0 & 8 & 8 & 0 \\ 0 & 8 & 8 & 0 \\ 8 & 0 & 0 & 8 \end{bmatrix},$$

there are exactly eight paths of length four from a to d. By inspection of the graph, we see that a, b, a, b, d; a, b, a, c, d; a, b, d, b, d; a, b, d, c, d; a, c, a, b, d; a, c, a, c, d; a, c, d, b, d; and a, c, d, c, d are the eight paths from a to d. ◀

Theorem 2 can be used to find the length of the shortest path between two vertices of a graph, and it can also be used to determine whether a graph is connected (see Exercise 25).

Exercises

1. Does each of these lists of vertices form a path in the following graph? Which paths are simple? Which are circuits? What are the lengths of those that are paths?

   a) a, e, b, c, b b) a, e, a, d, b, c, a c) e, b, a, d, b, e d) c, b, d, a, e, c

In Exercises 2–3 determine whether the given graph is connected.

2.

3.

4. What do the connected components of acquaintanceship graphs represent?

5. Explain why in the collaboration graph of mathematicians a vertex representing a mathematician is in the same connected component as the vertex representing Paul Erdős if and only if that mathematician has a finite Erdős number.

6. Determine whether each of these graphs is strongly connected and if not, whether it is weakly connected.

a)
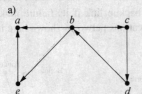

b)
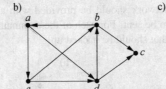

c)

7. What do the strongly connected components of a telephone call graph represent?

8. Find the strongly connected components of each of these graphs.

a)
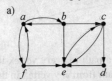

b)
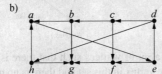

c)
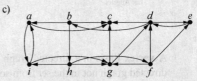

9. Find the number of paths of length n between two different vertices in K_4 if n is

a) 2.   b) 3.   c) 4.   d) 5.

10. Use paths either to show that these graphs are not isomorphic or to find an isomorphism between them.

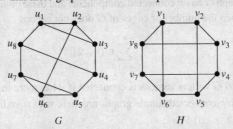

11. Use paths either to show that these graphs are not isomorphic or to find an isomorphism between them.

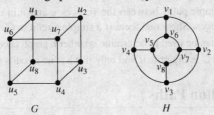

12. Find the number of paths of length n between any two nonadjacent vertices in $K_{3,3}$ for the values of n in Exercise 9.

13. Let $G = (V, E)$ be a simple graph. Let R be the relation on V consisting of pairs of vertices (u, v) such that there is a path from u to v or such that $u = v$. Show that R is an equivalence relation.

In Exercises 14–15 find all the cut vertices of the given graph.

14.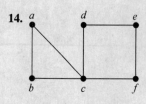

15.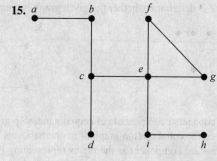

*16. Suppose that v is an endpoint of a cut edge. Prove that v is a cut vertex if and only if this vertex is not pendant.

*17. Show that a simple graph with at least two vertices has at least two vertices that are not cut vertices.

18. A communications link in a network should be provided with a backup link if its failure makes it impossible for some message to be sent. For each of the communications networks shown here in (a) and (b), determine those links that should be backed up.

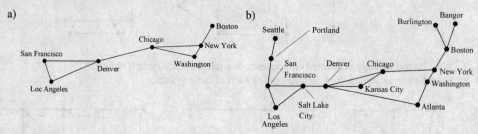

A **vertex basis** in a directed graph is a set of vertices such that there is a path to every vertex in the directed graph not in the set from some vertex in this set and there is no path from any vertex in the set to another vertex in the set.

19. What is the significance of a vertex basis in an influence graph (described in Example 3 of Section 6.1)? Find a vertex basis in the influence graph in this example.

*20. Show that if a simple graph G has k connected components and these components have $n_1, n_2, \ldots, n_k$ vertices, respectively, then the number of edges of G does not exceed

$$\sum_{i=1}^{k} C(n_i, 2).$$

*21. Show that a simple graph G with n vertices is connected if it has more than $(n-1)(n-2)/2$ edges.

22. How many nonisomorphic connected simple graphs are there with n vertices when n is

   a) 2?   b) 3?   c) 4?   d) 5?

23. Use Theorem 2 to find the length of the shortest path between a and f in the graph in Figure 1.

24. Let P_1 and P_2 be two simple paths between the vertices u and v in the simple graph G that do not contain the same set of edges. Show that there is a simple circuit in G.

25. Explain how Theorem 2 can be used to determine whether a graph is connected.

26. Show that a simple graph G is bipartite if and only if it has no circuits with an odd number of edges.

6.5   Euler and Hamilton Paths

Introduction

Can we travel along the edges of a graph starting at a vertex and returning to it by traversing each edge of the graph exactly once? Similarly, can we travel along the edges of a graph starting at a vertex and returning to it while visiting each vertex of the graph exactly once? Although these questions seem to be similar, the first question, which asks whether a graph has an *Euler circuit,* can be easily answered simply by examining the degrees of the vertices of the graph, while the second question, which asks whether a graph has a *Hamilton circuit,* is quite difficult to solve for most graphs. In this section we will study these questions and discuss the difficulty of solving them. Although both questions have many practical applications in many different areas, both arose in old puzzles. We will learn about these old puzzles as well as modern practical applications.

Euler Paths and Circuits

The town of Königsberg, Prussia (now called Kaliningrad and part of the Russian republic), was divided into four sections by the branches of the Pregel River. These four sections included the two regions on the banks of the Pregel, Kneiphof Island, and the region between the two branches of the Pregel. In the eighteenth century seven bridges connected these regions. Figure 1 depicts these regions and bridges.

The townspeople took long walks through town on Sundays. They wondered whether it was possible to start at some location in the town, travel across all the bridges without crossing any bridge twice, and return to the starting point.

The Swiss mathematician Leonhard Euler solved this problem. His solution, published in 1736, may be the first use of graph theory. Euler studied this problem using the multigraph obtained when the four regions are represented by vertices and the bridges by edges. This multigraph is shown in Figure 2.

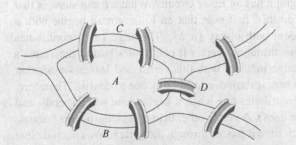

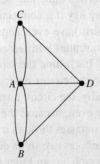

Figure 1   The Seven Bridges of Königsberg.   Figure 2   Multigraph Model of the Town of
                                                                      Königsberg.

The problem of traveling across every bridge without crossing any bridge more than once can be rephrased in terms of this model. The question becomes: Is there a simple circuit in this multigraph that contains every edge?

> **Definition 1**   An *Euler circuit* in a graph G is a simple circuit containing every edge of G. An *Euler path* in G is a simple path containing every edge of G.

Examples 1 and 2 illustrate the concept of Euler circuits and paths.

Example 1   Which of the undirected graphs in Figure 3 have an Euler circuit? Of those that do not, which have an Euler path?

Solution: The graph G_1 has an Euler circuit, for example, a, e, c, d, e, b, a. Neither of the graphs G_2 or G_3 has an Euler circuit (the reader should verify this). However, G_3 has an Euler path, namely, a, c, d, e, b, d, a, b. G_2 does not have an Euler path (as the reader should verify).   ◄

Example 2   Which of the directed graphs in Figure 4 have an Euler circuit? Of those that do not, which have an Euler path?

Solution: The graph H_2 has an Euler circuit, for example, $a, g, c, b, g, e, d, f, a$. Neither H_1 nor H_3 has an Euler circuit (as the reader should verify). H_3 has an Euler path, namely, $c, a, b, c, d, b,$

but H_1 does not (as the reader should verify).

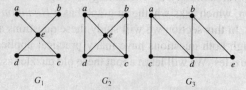

Figure 3   The Undirected Graphs G_1, G_2, and G_3.

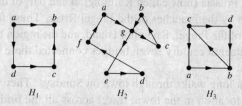

Figure 4   The Directed Graphs H_1, H_2, and H_3.

Necessary and Sufficient Conditions for Euler Circuits and Paths   There are simple criteria for determining whether a multigraph has an Euler circuit or an Euler path. Euler discovered them when he solved the famous Königsberg bridge problem. We will assume that all graphs discussed in this section have a finite number of vertices and edges.

What can we say if a connected multigraph has an Euler circuit? What we can show is that every vertex must have even degree. To do this, first note that an Euler circuit begins with a vertex a and continues with an edge incident with a, say $\{a, b\}$. The edge $\{a, b\}$ contributes one to $\deg(a)$. Each time the circuit passes through a vertex it contributes two to the vertex's degree, because the circuit enters via an edge incident with this vertex and leaves via another such edge. Finally, the circuit terminates where it started, contributing one to $\deg(a)$. Therefore, $\deg(a)$ must be even, because the circuit contributes one when it begins, one when it ends, and two every time it passes through a (if it ever does). A vertex other than a has even degree because the circuit contributes two to its degree each time it passes through the vertex. We conclude that if a connected graph has an Euler circuit, then every vertex must have even degree.

Is this necessary condition for the existence of an Euler circuit also sufficient? That is, must an Euler circuit exist in a connected multigraph if all vertices have even degree? This question can be settled affirmatively with a construction.

Suppose that G is a connected multigraph with at least two vertices and the degree of every vertex of G is even. We will form a simple circuit that begins at an arbitrary vertex a of G. Let $x_0 = a$. First, we arbitrarily choose an edge $\{x_0, x_1\}$ incident with a which is possible because G is connected. We continue by building a simple path $\{x_0, x_1\}, \{x_1, x_2\}, \ldots, \{x_{n-1}, x_n\}$, adding edges to the path until we cannot add another edge to the path. This happens when we reach a vertex for which we have already included all edges incident with that vertex in the path. For instance, in the graph G in Figure 5 we begin at a and choose in succession the edges $\{a, f\}$, $\{f, c\}$, $\{c, b\}$, and $\{b, a\}$.

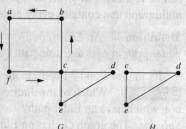

Figure 5   Constructing an Euler Circuit in G.

The path we have constructed must terminate because the graph has a finite number of edges, so we are guaranteed to eventually reach a vertex for which no edges are available to add to the path. The path begins at a with an edge of the form $\{a, x\}$, and we now show that it must terminate at a with an edge of the form $\{y, a\}$. To see that the path must terminate at a, note that each time the path goes through a vertex with even degree, it uses only one edge to enter this vertex, so because the degree must be at least two, at least one edge remains for the path to leave the vertex. Furthermore, every time we enter and leave a vertex of even degree, there are an even number of edges incident with this vertex that we have not yet used in our path. Consequently, as we form the path, every time we enter a vertex other than a, we can leave it. This means that path can end only at a. Next, note that the path we have constructed may use all the edges of the graph, or it may not if we have returned to a for the last time before using all the edges.

An Euler circuit has been constructed if all the edges have been used. Otherwise, consider the subgraph H obtained from G by deleting the edges already used and vertices that are not incident with any remaining edges. When we delete the circuit a, f, c, b, a from the graph in Figure 5, we obtain the subgraph labeled as H.

Because G is connected, H has at least one vertex in common with the circuit that has been deleted. Let w be such a vertex. (In our example, c is the vertex.)

Every vertex in H has even degree (because in G all vertices had even degree, and for each vertex, pairs of edges incident with this vertex have been deleted to form H). Note that H may not be connected. Beginning at w, construct a simple path in H by choosing edges as long as possible, as was done in G. This path must terminate at w. For instance, in Figure 5, c, d, e, c is a path in H. Next, form a circuit in G by splicing the circuit in H with the original circuit in G (this can be done because w is one of the vertices in this circuit). When this is done in the graph in Figure 5, we obtain the circuit a, f, c, d, e, c, b, a.

Continue this process until all edges have been used. (The process must terminate because there are only a finite number of edges in the graph.) This produces an Euler circuit. The construction shows that if the vertices of a connected multigraph all have even degree, then the graph has an Euler circuit.

We summarize these results in Theorem 1.

Theorem 1 A connected multigraph with at least two vertices has an Euler circuit if and only if each of its vertices has even degree.

We can now solve the Königsberg bridge problem. Because the multigraph representing these bridges, shown in Figure 2, has four vertices of odd degree, it does not have an Euler circuit. There is no way to start at a given point, cross each bridge exactly once, and return to the starting point.

Algorithm 1 gives the constructive procedure for finding Euler circuits given in the discussion preceding Theorem 1. (Because the circuits in the procedure are chosen arbitrarily, there is some ambiguity. We will not bother to remove this ambiguity by specifying the steps of the procedure more precisely.)

Algorithm 1 Constructing Euler Circuits.

procedure *Euler* (G: connected multigraph with all vertices of even degree)
circuit := a circuit in G beginning at an arbitrarily chosen vertex with edges successively added to form a path that returns to this vertex
$H := G$ with the edges of this circuit removed
while H has edges
begin
      subcircuit := a circuit in H beginning at a vertex in H that also is an endpoint of an edge of *circuit*
    $H := H$ with edges of *subcircuit* and all isolated vertices removed
      circuit := *circuit* with *subcircuit* inserted at the appropriate vertex
end {*circuit* is an Euler circuit}

Example 3 shows how Euler paths and circuits can be used to solve a type of puzzle.

Example 3   Many puzzles ask you to draw a picture in a continuous motion without lifting a pencil so that no part of the picture is retraced. We can solve such puzzles using Euler circuits and paths. For example, can *Mohammed's scimitars,* shown in Figure 6, be drawn in this way, where the drawing begins and ends at the same point?

Solution: We can solve this problem because the graph G shown in Figure 6 has an Euler circuit. It has such a circuit because all its vertices have even degree. We will use Algorithm 1 to construct an Euler circuit. First, we form the circuit $a, b, d, c, b, e, i, f, e, a$. We obtain the subgraph H by deleting the edges in this circuit and all vertices that become isolated when these edges are removed. Then we form the circuit $d, g, h, j, i, h, k, g, f, d$ in H. After forming this circuit we have used all edges in G. Splicing this new circuit into the first circuit at the appropriate place produces the Euler circuit $a, b, d, g, h, j, i, h, k, g, f, d, c, b, e, i, f, e, a$. This circuit gives a way to draw the scimitars without lifting the pencil or retracing part of the picture.   ◀

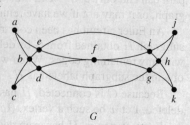

Figure 6   Mohammed's Scimitars.

Another algorithm for constructing Euler circuits, called Fleury's algorithm, is described in the exercises at the end of this section.

We will now show that a connected multigraph has an Euler path (and not an Euler circuit) if and only if it has exactly two vertices of odd degree. First, suppose that a connected multigraph does have an Euler path from a to b, but not an Euler circuit. The first edge of the path contributes one to the degree of a. A contribution of two to the degree of a is made every time the path passes through a. The last edge in the path contributes one to the degree of b. Every time the path goes through b there is a contribution of two to its degree. Consequently, both a and b have odd degree. Every other vertex has even degree, because the path contributes two to the degree of a vertex whenever it passes through it.

Now consider the converse. Suppose that a graph has exactly two vertices of odd degree, say a and b. Consider the larger graph made up of the original graph with the addition of an edge $\{a, b\}$. Every vertex of this larger graph has even degree, so there is an Euler circuit. The removal of the new edge produces an Euler path in the original graph. Theorem 2 summarizes these results.

Theorem 2   A connected multigraph has an Euler path but not an Euler circuit if and only if it has exactly two vertices of odd degree.

Example 4   Which graphs shown in Figure 7 have an Euler path?

Solution: G_1 contains exactly two vertices of odd degree, namely, b and d. Hence, it has an Euler path that must have b and d as its endpoints. One such Euler path is d, a, b, c, d, b. Similarly, G_2 has exactly two vertices of odd degree, namely, b and d. So it has an Euler path that must have b and d as endpoints. One such Euler path is $b, a, g, f, e, d, c, g, b, c, f, d$. G_3 has no Euler path because it has six vertices of odd degree.   ◀

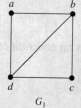

G_1

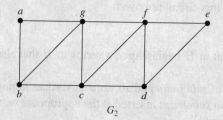

G_2

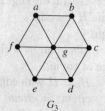

G_3

Figure 7   Three Undirected Graphs.

Returning to eighteenth-century Königsberg, is it possible to start at some point in the town, travel across all the bridges, and end up at some other point in town? This question can be answered by determining whether there is an Euler path in the multigraph representing the bridges in Königsberg. Because there are four vertices of odd degree in this multigraph, there is no Euler path, so such a trip is impossible.

Necessary and sufficient conditions for Euler paths and circuits in directed graphs are discussed in the exercises at the end of this section.

Euler paths and circuits can be used to solve many practical problems. For example, many applications ask for a path or circuit that traverses each street in a neighborhood, each road in a transportation network, each connection in a utility grid, or each link in a communications network exactly once. Finding an Euler path or circuit in the appropriate graph model can solve such problems. For example, if a postman can find an Euler path in the graph that represents the streets the postman needs to cover, this path produces a route that traverses each street of the route exactly once. If no Euler path exists, some streets will have to be traversed more than once. This problem is known as the *Chinese postman problem* in honor of Guan Meigu, who posed it in 1962. See [MiRo91] for more information on the solution of the Chinese postman problem when no Euler path exists.

Among the other areas where Euler circuits and paths are applied is in layout of circuits, in network multicasting, and in molecular biology, where Euler paths are used in the sequencing of DNA.

Hamilton Paths and Circuits

We have developed necessary and sufficient conditions for the existence of paths and circuits that contain every edge of a multigraph exactly once. Can we do the same for simple paths and circuits that contain every vertex of the graph exactly once?

Definition 2 A simple path in a graph G that passes through every vertex exactly once is called a *Hamilton path*, and a simple circuit in a graph G that passes through every vertex exactly once is called a *Hamilton circuit*. That is, the simple path $x_0, x_1, \ldots, x_{n-1}, x_n$ in the graph $G = (V, E)$ is a Hamilton path if $V = \{x_0, x_1, \ldots, x_{n-1}, x_n\}$ and $x_i \neq x_j$ for $0 \leqslant i < j \leqslant n$, and the simple circuit $x_0, x_1, \ldots, x_{n-1}, x_n, x_0$ (with $n > 0$) is a Hamilton circuit if $x_0, x_1, \ldots, x_{n-1}, x_n$ is a Hamilton path.

This terminology comes from a game, called the *Icosian puzzle*, invented in 1857 by the Irish mathematician Sir William Rowan Hamilton. It consisted of a wooden dodecahedron [a polyhedron with 12 regular pentagons as faces, as shown in Figure 8(a)], with a peg at each vertex of the dodecahedron, and string. The 20 vertices of the dodecahedron were labeled with different cities in the world. The object of the puzzle was to start at a city and travel along the edges of the dodecahedron, visiting each of the other 19 cities exactly once, and end back at the first city. The circuit traveled was marked off using the strings and pegs.

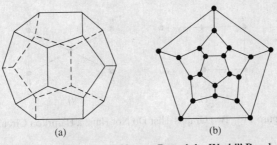

(a)   (b)

Figure 8   Hamilton's "A Voyage Round the World" Puzzle.

Because the author cannot supply each reader with a wooden solid with pegs and string, we will consider the equivalent question: Is there a circuit in the graph shown in Figure 8(b) that passes through each vertex exactly once? This solves the puzzle because this graph is isomorphic to the graph consisting of the vertices and edges of the dodecahedron. A solution of Hamilton's puzzle is shown in Figure 9.

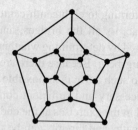

Figure 9   A Solution to the "A Voyage Round the World" Puzzle.

Example 5   Which of the simple graphs in Figure 10 have a Hamilton circuit or, if not, a Hamilton path?

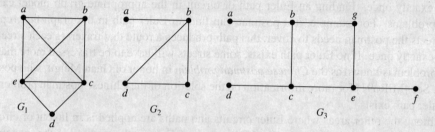

Figure 10   Three Simple Graphs.

Solution: G_1 has a Hamilton circuit: a, b, c, d, e, a. There is no Hamilton circuit in G_2 (this can be seen by noting that any circuit containing every vertex must contain the edge $\{a, b\}$ twice), but G_2 does have a Hamilton path, namely, a, b, c, d. G_3 has neither a Hamilton circuit nor a Hamilton path, because any path containing all vertices must contain one of the edges $\{a, b\}$, $\{e, f\}$, and $\{c, d\}$ more than once.   ◄

Is there a simple way to determine whether a graph has a Hamilton circuit or path? At first, it might seem that there should be an easy way to determine this, because there is a simple way to answer the similar question of whether a graph has an Euler circuit. Surprisingly, there are no known simple necessary and sufficient criteria for the existence of Hamilton circuits. However, many theorems are known that give sufficient conditions for the existence of Hamilton circuits. Also, certain properties can be used to show that a graph has no Hamilton circuit. For instance, a graph with a vertex of degree one cannot have a Hamilton circuit, because in a Hamilton circuit, each vertex is incident with two edges in the circuit. Moreover, if a vertex in the graph has degree two, then both edges that are incident with this vertex must be part of any Hamilton circuit. Also, note that when a Hamilton circuit is being constructed and this circuit has passed through a vertex, then all remaining edges incident with this vertex, other than the two used in the circuit, can be removed from consideration. Furthermore, a Hamilton circuit cannot contain a smaller circuit within it.

Example 6   Show that neither graph displayed in Figure 11 has a Hamilton circuit.

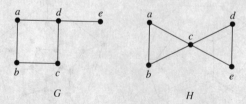

Figure 11   Two Graphs That Do Not Have a Hamilton Circuit.

Solution: There is no Hamilton circuit in G because G has a vertex of degree one, namely, e. Now consider H. Because the degrees of the vertices a, b, d, and e are all two, every edge incident with these vertices must be part of any Hamilton circuit. It is now easy to see that no Hamilton circuit can exist in H, for any Hamilton circuit would have to contain four edges incident with c, which is impossible.   ◄

Example 7   Show that K_n has a Hamilton circuit whenever $n \geqslant 3$.

Solution: We can form a Hamilton circuit in K_n beginning at any vertex. Such a circuit can be built by visiting vertices in any order we choose, as long as the path begins and ends at the same vertex and visits each other vertex exactly once. This is possible because there are edges in K_n between any two vertices.   ◄

Although no useful necessary and sufficient conditions for the existence of Hamilton circuits are known, quite a few sufficient conditions have been found. Note that the more edges a graph has, the more likely it is to have a Hamilton circuit. Furthermore, adding edges (but not vertices) to a graph with a Hamilton circuit produces a graph with the same Hamilton circuit. So as we add edges to a graph, especially when we make sure to add edges to each vertex, we make it increasingly likely that a Hamilton circuit exists in this graph. Consequently, we would expect there to be sufficient conditions for the existence of Hamilton circuits that depend on the degrees of vertices being sufficiently large. We state two of the most important sufficient conditions here. These conditions were found by Gabriel A. Dirac in 1952 and Oystein Ore in 1960.

Theorem 3   Dirac's Theorem   If G is a simple graph with n vertices with $n \geqslant 3$ such that the degree of every vertex in G is at least $n/2$, then G has a Hamilton circuit.

Theorem 4   Ore's Theorem   If G is a simple graph with n vertices with $n \geqslant 3$ such that $\deg(u) + \deg(v) \geqslant n$ for every pair of nonadjacent vertices u and v in G, then G has a Hamilton circuit.

The proof of Ore's Theorem is outlined in Exercise 27 at the end of this section. Dirac's Theorem can be proved as a corollary to Ore's Theorem because the conditions of Dirac's Theorem imply those of Ore's Theorem.

Both Ore's Theorem and Dirac's Theorem provide sufficient conditions for a connected simple graph to have a Hamilton circuit. However, these theorems do not provide necessary conditions for the existence of a Hamilton circuit. For example, the graph C_5 has a Hamilton circuit but does not satisfy the hypotheses of either Ore's Theorem or Dirac's Theorem, as the reader can verify. The best algorithms known for finding a Hamilton circuit in a graph or determining that no such circuit exists have exponential worst-case time complexity (in the number of vertices of the graph). Finding an algorithm that solves this problem with polynomial worst-case time complexity would be a major accomplishment because it has been shown that this problem is NP-complete. Consequently, the existence of such an algorithm would imply that many other seemingly intractable problems could be solved using algorithms with polynomial worst-case time complexity.

Hamilton paths and circuits can be used to solve practical problems. For example, many applications ask for a path or circuit that visits each road intersection in a city, each place pipelines intersect in a utility grid, or each node in a communications network exactly once. Finding a Hamilton path or circuit in the appropriate graph model can solve such problems. The famous **traveling salesman problem** asks for the shortest route a traveling salesman should take to visit a set of cities. This problem reduces to finding a Hamilton circuit in a complete graph such that the total weight of its edges is as small as possible. We will return to this question in Section 6.6.

We now describe a less obvious application of Hamilton circuits to coding.

Example 8   **Gray Codes**   The position of a rotating pointer can be represented in digital form. One way to do this is to split the circle into 2^n arcs of equal length and to assign a bit string of length n to each arc. Two ways to do this using bit strings of length three are shown in Figure 12. The digital representation of the position of the pointer can be determined using a set of n

contacts. Each contact is used to read one bit in the digital representation of the position. This is illustrated in Figure 13 for the two assignments from Figure 12.

When the pointer is near the boundary of two arcs, a mistake may be made in reading its position. This may result in a major error in the bit string read. For instance, in the coding scheme in Figure 12(a), if a small error is made in determining the position of the pointer, the bit string 100 is read instead of

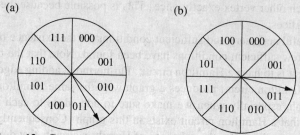

(a)   (b)

Figure 12   Converting the Position of a Pointer into Digital Form.

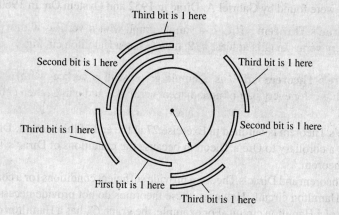

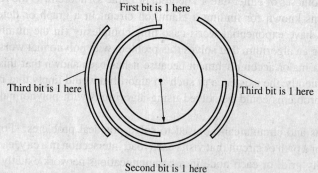

Figure 13   The Digital Representation of the Position of the Pointer.

011. All three bits are incorrect! To minimize the effect of an error in determining the position of the pointer, the assignment of the bit strings to the 2^n arcs should be made so that only one bit is different in the bit strings represented by adjacent arcs. This is exactly the situation in the coding scheme in Figure 12(b). An error in determining the position of the pointer gives the bit string 010 instead of 011. Only one bit is wrong.

A **Gray code** is a labeling of the arcs of the circle such that adjacent arcs are labeled with bit strings that differ in exactly one bit. The assignment in Figure 12(b) is a Gray code. We can find a Gray code by listing all bit strings of length n in such a way that each string differs in exactly one position from the preceding bit string, and the last string differs from the first in exactly one position. We can model this problem using the n-cube Q_n. What is needed to solve this problem is a Hamilton circuit in Q_n. Such Hamilton circuits are easily found. For instance, a Hamilton circuit for Q_3 is displayed in Figure 14. The sequence of bit strings differing in exactly one bit produced by this Hamilton circuit is 000, 001, 011, 010, 110, 111, 101, 100.

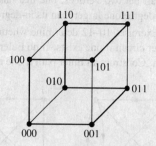

Figure 14 A Hamilton Circuit for Q_3.

Gray codes are named after Frank Gray, who invented them in the 1940s at AT&T Bell Laboratories to minimize the effect of errors in transmitting digital signals. ◄

Exercises

In Exercises 1–4 determine whether the given graph has an Euler circuit. Construct such a circuit when one exists. If no Euler circuit exists, determine whether the graph has an Euler path and construct such a path if one exists.

1.

2.

3.
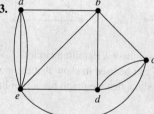

4.
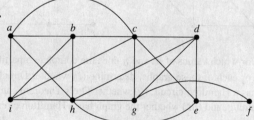

5. In Kaliningrad (the Russian name for Königsberg) there are two additional bridges, besides the seven that were present in the eighteenth century. These new bridges connect regions B and C and regions B and D, respectively. Can someone cross all nine bridges in Kaliningrad exactly once and return to the starting point?

6. When can the centerlines of the streets in a city be painted without traveling a street more than once? (Assume that all the streets are two-way streets.)

In Exercises 7–8 determine whether the picture shown can be drawn with a pencil in a continuous motion without lifting the pencil or retracing part of the picture.

7.

8.

*9. Show that a directed multigraph having no isolated vertices has an Euler path but not an Euler circuit if and only if the graph is weakly connected and the in-degree and out-degree of each vertex are equal for all but two vertices, one that has in-degree one larger than its out-degree and the other that has out-degree one larger than its in-degree.

In Exercises 10–12 determine whether the directed graph shown has an Euler circuit. Construct an Euler circuit if one exists. If no Euler circuit exists, determine whether the directed graph has an Euler path. Construct an Euler path if one exists.

10. **11.** 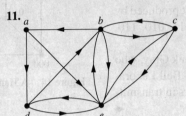 **12.**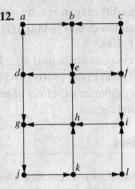

13. Devise an algorithm for constructing Euler paths in directed graphs.

14. Find the least number of times it is necessary to lift a pencil from the paper when drawing each of the graphs in Exercises 1–4 without retracing any part of the graph.

In Exercises 15–17 determine whether the given graph has a Hamilton circuit. If it does, find such a circuit. If it does not, give an argument to show why no such circuit exists.

15. 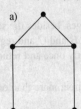 **16.** 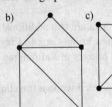 **17.**

18. For which values of m and n does the complete bipartite graph $K_{m,n}$ have a Hamilton circuit?

19. For each of these graphs, determine (i) whether Dirac's Theorem can be used to show that the graph has a Hamilton circuit, (ii) whether Ore's Theorem can be used to show that the graph has a Hamilton circuit, and (iii) whether the graph has a Hamilton circuit.

a)   b)   c)   d)

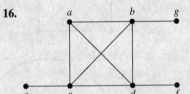

*20. Show that there is a Gray code of order n whenever n is a positive integer, or equivalently, show that the n-cube Q_n, $n > 1$, always has a Hamilton circuit. [*Hint:* Use mathematical induction. Show how to produce a Gray code of order n from one of order $n - 1$.]

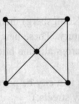

Fleury's algorithm for constructing Euler circuits begins with an arbitrary vertex of a connected multigraph and forms a circuit by choosing edges successively. Once an edge is chosen, it is removed. Edges are chosen successively so that each edge begins where the last edge ends, and so that this edge is not a cut edge unless there is no alternative.

*21. Express Fleury's algorithm in pseudocode.

*22. Give a variant of Fleury's algorithm to produce Euler paths.

23. Show that a bipartite graph with an odd number of vertices does not have a Hamilton circuit.

A **knight** is a chess piece that can move either two spaces horizontally and one space vertically or one space horizontally and two spaces vertically. That is, a knight on square (x, y) can move to any of the eight squares $(x \pm 2, y \pm 1)$, $(x \pm 1, y \pm 2)$, if these squares are on the chessboard, as illustrated here.

 A **knight's tour** is a sequence of legal moves by a knight starting at some square and visiting each square exactly once. A knight's tour is called **reentrant** if there is a legal move that takes the knight from the last square of the tour back to where the tour began. We can model knight's tours using the graph that has a vertex for each square on the board, with an edge connecting two vertices if a knight can legally move between the squares represented by these vertices.

24. Draw the graph that represents the legal moves of a knight on a 3×4 chessboard.

*25. Show that there is a knight's tour on a 3×4 chessboard.

*26. Show that there is no knight's tour on a 4×4 chessboard.

27. The parts of this exercise outline a proof of Ore's Theorem. Suppose that G is a simple graph with n vertices, $n \geqslant 3$, and $\deg(x) + \deg(y) \geqslant n$ whenever x and y are nonadjacent vertices in G. Ore's Theorem states that under these conditions, G has a Hamilton circuit.

a) Show that if G does not have a Hamilton circuit, then there exists another graph H with the same vertices as G, which can be constructed by adding edges to G such that the addition of a single edge would produce a Hamilton circuit in H. [*Hint:* Add as many edges as possible at each successive vertex of G without producing a Hamilton circuit.]

b) Show that there is a Hamilton path in H.

c) Let $v_1, v_2, \ldots, v_n$ be a Hamilton path in H. Show that $\deg(v_1) + \deg(v_n) \geqslant n$ and that there are at most $\deg(v_1)$ vertices not adjacent to v_n (including v_n itself).

d) Let S be the set of vertices preceding each vertex adjacent to v_1 in the Hamilton path. Show that S contains $\deg(v_1)$ vertices and $v_n \notin S$.

e) Show that S contains a vertex v_k, which is adjacent to v_n, implying that there are edges connecting v_1 and v_{k+1} and v_k and v_n.

f) Show that part (e) implies that $v_1, v_2, \ldots, v_{k-1}, v_k, v_n, v_{n-1}, \ldots, v_{k+1}, v_1$ is a Hamilton circuit in G. Conclude from this contradiction that Ore's Theorem holds.

6.6 Shortest-Path Problems

Introduction

Many problems can be modeled using graphs with weights assigned to their edges. As an illustration, consider how an airline system can be modeled. We set up the basic graph model by representing cities by vertices and flights by edges. Problems involving distances can be modeled by assigning distances between cities to the edges. Problems involving flight time can be modeled by assigning flight times to edges. Problems involving fares can be modeled by assigning fares to the edges. Figure 1 displays three different assignments of weights to the edges of a graph representing distances, flight times, and fares, respectively.

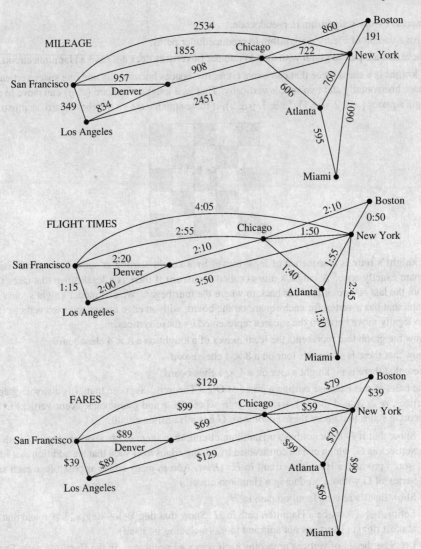

Figure 1   Weighted Graphs Modeling an Airline System.

Graphs that have a number assigned to each edge are called **weighted graphs.** Weighted graphs are used to model computer networks. Communications costs (such as the monthly cost of leasing a telephone line), the response times of the computers over these lines, or the distance between computers, can all be studied using weighted graphs. Figure 2 displays weighted graphs that represent three ways to assign weights to the edges of a graph of a computer network, corresponding to distance, response time, and cost.

Several types of problems involving weighted graphs arise frequently. Determining a path of least length between two vertices in a network is one such problem. To be more specific, let the **length** of a path in a weighted graph be the sum of the weights of the edges of this path. (The reader should note that this use of the term *length* is different from the use of *length* to denote the number of edges in a path in a graph without weights.) The question is: What is a shortest path, that is, a path of least length, between two given vertices? For instance, in the airline system represented by the weighted graph shown in Figure 1, what is a shortest path in air distance between Boston and Los Angeles? What combinations of flights has the smallest total flight time (that is, total time in the air, not including time between flights) between Boston and Los Angeles? What is the cheapest fare between these two cities? In the computer network shown in Figure 2, what is a least expensive set of telephone lines needed to connect the computers in San Francisco with those in New York? Which set of telephone lines gives a fastest response time for communications between San Francisco and New York? Which set of lines has a shortest overall distance?

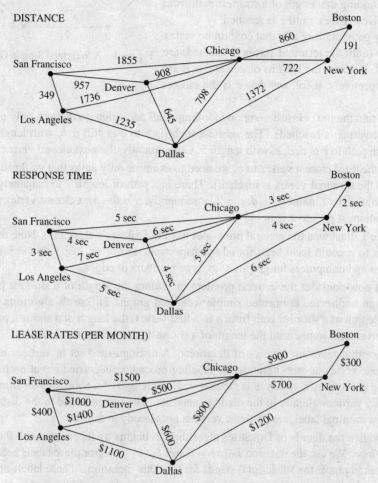

Figure 2   Weighted Graphs Modeling a Computer Network.

Another important problem involving weighted graphs asks for a circuit of shortest total length that visits every vertex of a complete graph exactly once. This is the famous *traveling salesman problem,* which asks for an order in which a salesman should visit each of the cities on his route exactly once so that he travels the minimum total distance. We will discuss the traveling salesman problem later in this section.

A Shortest-Path Algorithm

There are several different algorithms that find a shortest path between two vertices in a weighted graph. We will present an algorithm discovered by the Dutch mathematician Edsger Dijkstra in 1959. The version we will describe solves this problem in undirected weighted graphs where all the weights are positive. It is easy to adapt it to solve shortest-path problems in directed graphs.

Before giving a formal presentation of the algorithm, we will give a motivating example.

Example 1   What is the length of a shortest path between a and z in the weighted graph shown in Figure 3?

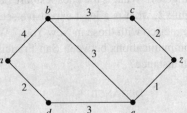

Solution: Although a shortest path is easily found by inspection, we will develop some ideas useful in understanding Dijkstra's algorithm. We will solve this problem by finding the length of a shortest path from a to successive vertices, until z is reached.

The only paths starting at a that contain no vertex other than a (until the terminal vertex is reached) are a, b and a, d. Because the lengths of a, b and a, d are 4 and 2, respectively, it follows that d is the closest vertex to a.

Figure 3   A Weighted Simple Graph.

We can find the next closest vertex by looking at all paths that go through only a and d (until the terminal vertex is reached). The shortest such path to b is still a, b, with length 4, and the shortest such path to e is a, d, e, with length 5. Consequently, the next closest vertex to a is b.

To find the third closest vertex to a, we need to examine only paths that go through only a, d, and b (until the terminal vertex is reached). There is a path of length 7 to c, namely, a, b, c, and a path of length 6 to z, namely, a, d, e, z. Consequently, z is the next closest vertex to a, and the length of a shortest path to z is 6.   ◀

Example 1 illustrates the general principles used in Dijkstra's algorithm. Note that a shortest path from a to z could have been found by inspection. However, inspection is impractical for both humans and computers for graphs with large numbers of edges.

We will now consider the general problem of finding the length of a shortest path between a and z in an undirected connected simple weighted graph. Dijkstra's algorithm proceeds by finding the length of a shortest path from a to a first vertex, the length of a shortest path from a to a second vertex, and so on, until the length of a shortest path from a to z is found.

The algorithm relies on a series of iterations. A distinguished set of vertices is constructed by adding one vertex at each iteration. A labeling procedure is carried out at each iteration. In this labeling procedure, a vertex w is labeled with the length of a shortest path from a to w that contains only vertices already in the distinguished set. The vertex added to the distinguished set is one with a minimal label among those vertices not already in the set.

We now give the details of Dijkstra's algorithm. It begins by labeling a with 0 and the other vertices with ∞. We use the notation $L_0(a) = 0$ and $L_0(v) = \infty$ for these labels before any iterations have taken place (the subscript 0 stands for the "0th" iteration). These labels are the lengths of shortest paths from a to the vertices, where the paths contain only the vertex a. (Because no path from a to a vertex different from a exists, ∞ is the length of a shortest path between a and this vertex.)

Dijkstra's algorithm proceeds by forming a distinguished set of vertices. Let S_k denote this set after k iterations of the labeling procedure. We begin with $S_0 = \emptyset$. The set S_k is formed from S_{k-1} by adding a vertex u not in S_{k-1} with the smallest label. Once u is added to S_k, we update the labels of all vertices not in S_k, so that $L_k(v)$, the label of the vertex v at the kth stage, is the length of a shortest path from a to v that contains vertices only in S_k (that is, vertices that were already in the distinguished set together with u).

Let v be a vertex not in S_k. To update the label of v, note that $L_k(v)$ is the length of a shortest path from a to v containing only vertices in S_k. The updating can be carried out efficiently when this observation is used: A shortest path from a to v containing only elements of S_k is either a shortest path from a to v that contains only elements of S_{k-1} (that is, the distinguished vertices not including u), or it is a shortest path from a to u at the $(k-1)$st stage with the edge (u, v)

added. In other words,

$$L_k(a, v) = \min\{L_{k-1}(a, v), L_{k-1}(a, u) + w(u, v)\}.$$

This procedure is iterated by successively, adding vertices to the distinguished set until z is added. When z is added to the distinguished set, its label is the length of a shortest path from a to z. Dijkstra's algorithm is given in Algorithm 1. Later we will give a proof that this algorithm is correct.

Algorithm Dijkstra's Algorithm.

procedure *Dijkstra* (G: weighted connected simple graph, with all weights positive)
$\{G$ has vertices $a = v_0, v_1, \ldots, v_n = z$ and weights $w(v_i, v_j)$ where $w(v_i, v_j) = \infty$ if $\{v_i, v_j\}$ is not an edge in $G\}$
for $i := 1$ **to** n
        $L(v_i) := \infty$
$L(a) := 0$
$S := \emptyset$
{the labels are now initialized so that the label of a is 0 and all other labels are ∞, and S is the empty set}
while $z \notin S$
begin
        $u :=$ a vertex not in S with $L(u)$ minimal
        $S := S \cup \{u\}$
        for all vertices v not in S
                if $L(u) + w(u, v) < L(v)$ **then** $L(v) := L(u) + w(u, v)$
        {this adds a vertex to S with minimal label and updates the labels of vertices not in S}
end $\{L(z) = $ length of a shortest path from a to $z\}$

Example 2 illustrates how Dijkstra's algorithm works. Afterward, we will show that this algorithm always produces the length of a shortest path between two vertices in a weighted graph.

Example 2   Use Dijkstra's algorithm to find the length of a shortest path between the vertices a and z in the weighted graph displayed in Figure 4(a).

Solution: The steps used by Dijkstra's algorithm to find a shortest path between a and z are shown in Figure 4. At each iteration of the algorithm the vertices of the set S_k are circled. A shortest path from a to each vertex containing only vertices in S_k is indicated for each iteration. The algorithm terminates when z is circled. We find that a shortest path from a to z is a, c, b, d, e, z, with length 13.   ◄

Remark: In performing Dijkstra's algorithm it is sometimes more convenient to keep track of labels of vertices in each step using a table instead of redrawing the graph for each step.

Next, we use an inductive argument to show that Dijkstra's algorithm produces the length of a shortest path between two vertices a and z in an undirected connected weighted graph. Take as the induction hypothesis the following assertion: At the kth iteration

   (i) the label of every vertex v in S is the length of a shortest path from a to this vertex, and
   (ii) the label of every vertex not in S is the length of a shortest path from a to this vertex that contains only (besides the vertex itself) vertices in S.

When $k = 0$, before any iterations are carried out, $S = \emptyset$, so the length of a shortest path from a to a vertex other than a is ∞. Hence, the basis case is true.

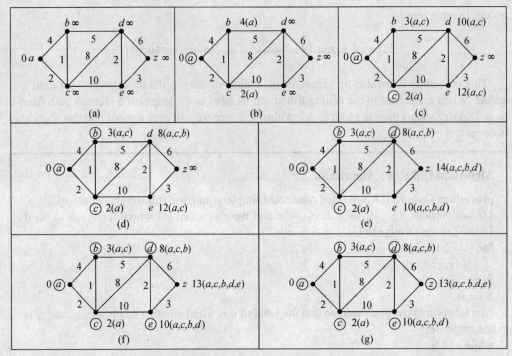

Figure 4   Using Dijkstra's Algorithm to Find a Shortest Path from a to z.

Assume that the inductive hypothesis holds for the kth iteration. Let v be the vertex added to S at the $(k+1)$st iteration, so v is a vertex not in S at the end of the kth iteration with the smallest label (in the case of ties, any vertex with smallest label may be used).

From the inductive hypothesis we see that the vertices in S before the $(k + 1)$st iteration are labeled with the length of a shortest path from a. Also, v must be labeled with the length of a shortest path to it from a. If this were not the case, at the end of the kth iteration there would be a path of length less than $L_k(v)$ containing a vertex not in S [because $L_k(v)$ is the length of a shortest path from a to v containing only vertices in S after the kth iteration]. Let u be the first vertex not in S in such a path. There is a path with length less than $L_k(v)$ from a to u containing only vertices of S. This contradicts the choice of v. Hence, (i) holds at the end of the $(k + 1)$st iteration.

Let u be a vertex not in S after $k + 1$ iterations. A shortest path from a to u containing only elements of S either contains v or it does not. If it does not contain v, then by the inductive hypothesis its length is $L_k(u)$. If it does contain v, then it must be made up of a path from a to v of shortest possible length containing elements of S other than v, followed by the edge from v to u. In this case, its length would be $L_k(v) + w(v, u)$. This shows that (ii) is true, because $L_{k+1}(u) = \min\{L_k(u), L_k(v) + w(v, u)\}$.

Theorem 1 has been proved.

Theorem 1   Dijkstra's algorithm finds the length of a shortest path between two vertices in a connected simple undirected weighted graph.

We can now estimate the computational complexity of Dijkstra's algorithm (in terms of additions and comparisons). The algorithm uses no more than $n - 1$ iterations, because one vertex is added to the distinguished set at each iteration. We are done if we can estimate the number of operations used for each iteration. We can identify the vertex not in S_k with the smallest label using no more than $n - 1$ comparisons. Then we use an addition and a comparison to update the label of each vertex not in S_k. It follows that no more than $2(n - 1)$ operations are used at each iteration, because there are no more than $n - 1$ labels to update at each iteration. Because we use no more than $n - 1$ iterations, each using no more than $2(n - 1)$ operations, we have Theorem 2.

Theorem 2 Dijkstra's algorithm uses $O(n^2)$ operations (additions and comparisons) to find the length of a shortest path between two vertices in a connected simple undirected weighted graph with n vertices.

The Traveling Salesman Problem

We now discuss an important problem involving weighted graphs. Consider the following problem: A traveling salesman wants to visit each of n cities exactly once and return to his starting point. For example, suppose that the salesman wants to visit Detroit, Toledo, Saginaw, Grand Rapids, and Kalamazoo (see Figure 5). In which order should he visit these cities to travel the minimum total distance? To solve this problem we can assume the salesman starts in Detroit (because this must be part of the circuit) and examine all possible ways for him to visit the other four cities and then return to Detroit (starting elsewhere will produce the same circuits). There are a total of 24 such circuits, but because we travel the same distance when we travel a circuit in reverse order, we need only consider 12 different circuits to find the minimum total distance he must travel. We list these 12 different circuits and the total distance traveled for each circuit. As can be seen from the list, the minimum total distance of 458 miles is traveled using the circuit Detroit–Toledo–Kalamazoo–Grand Rapids–Saginaw–Detroit (or its reverse).

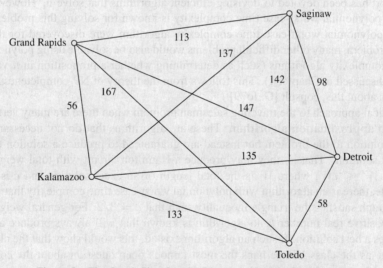

Figure 5 The Graph Showing the Distances between Five Cities.

We just described an instance of the **traveling salesman problem.** The traveling salesman problem asks for the circuit of minimum total weight in a weighted, complete, undirected graph that visits each vertex exactly once and returns to its starting point. This is equivalent to asking for a Hamilton circuit with minimum total weight in the complete graph, because each vertex is visited exactly once in the circuit.

The most straightforward way to solve an instance of the traveling salesman problem is to examine all possible Hamilton circuits and select one of minimum total length. How many circuits do we have to examine to solve the problem if there are n vertices in the graph? Once a starting point is chosen, there are $(n - 1)!$ different Hamilton circuits to examine, because there are $n - 1$ choices for the second vertex, $n - 2$ choices for the third vertex, and so on. Because a Hamilton circuit can be traveled in reverse order, we need only examine $(n - 1)!/2$ circuits to find our

Route	Total Distance (miles)
Detroit-Toledo-Grand Rapids-Saginaw-Kalamazoo-Detroit	610
Detroit-Toledo-Grand Rapids-Kalamazoo-Saginaw-Detroit	516
Detroit-Toledo-Kalamazoo-Saginaw-Grand Rapids-Detroit	588
Detroit-Toledo-Kalamazoo-Grand Rapids-Saginaw-Detroit	458
Detroit-Toledo-Saginaw-Kalamazoo-Grand Rapids-Detroit	540
Detroit-Toledo-Saginaw-Grand Rapids-Kalamazoo-Detroit	504
Detroit-Saginaw-Toledo-Grand Rapids-Kalamazoo-Detroit	598
Detroit-Saginaw-Toledo-Kalamazoo-Grand Rapids-Detroit	576
Detroit-Saginaw-Kalamazoo-Toledo-Grand Rapids-Detroit	682
Detroit-Saginaw-Grand Rapids-Toledo-Kalamazoo-Detroit	646
Detroit-Grand Rapids-Saginaw-Toledo-Kalamazoo-Detroit	670
Detroit-Grand Rapids-Toledo-Saginaw-Kalamazoo-Detroit	728

answer. Note that $(n-1)!/2$ grows extremely rapidly. Trying to solve a traveling salesman problem in this way when there are only a few dozen vertices is impractical. For example, with 25 vertices, a total of $24!/2$ (approximately 3.1×10^{23}) different Hamilton circuits would have to be considered. If it took just one nanosecond (10^{-9} second) to examine each Hamilton circuit, a total of approximately ten million years would be required to find a minimum-length Hamilton circuit in this graph by exhaustive search techniques.

Because the traveling salesman problem has both practical and theoretical importance, a great deal of effort has been devoted to devising efficient algorithms that solve it. However, no algorithm with polynomial worst-case time complexity is known for solving this problem. Furthermore, if a polynomial worst-case time complexity algorithm were discovered for the traveling salesman problem, many other difficult problems would also be solvable using polynomial worst-case time complexity algorithms (such as determining whether a proposition in n variables is a tautology, discussed in Chapter 1). This follows from the theory of NP-completeness. (For more information about this, consult [GaJo79].)

A practical approach to the traveling salesman problem when there are many vertices to visit is to use an **approximation algorithm.** These are algorithms that do not necessarily produce the exact solution to the problem but instead are guaranteed to produce a solution that is close to an exact solution. That is, they may produce a Hamilton circuit with total weight W' such that $W \leq W' \leq cW$, where W is the total length of an exact solution and c is a constant. For example, there is an algorithm with polynomial worst-case time complexity that works if the weighted graph satisfies the triangle inequality such that $c = 3/2$. For general weighted graphs for every positive real number k no algorithm is known that will always produce a solution at most k times a best solution. If such an algorithm existed, this would show that the class P would be the same as the class NP, perhaps the most famous open question about the complexity of algorithms.

In practice, algorithms have been developed that can solve traveling salesman problems with as many as 1000 vertices within 2% of an exact solution using only a few minutes of computer time. For more information about the traveling salesman problem, including history, applications, and algorithms, see the chapter on this topic in *Applications of Discrete Mathematics* [MiRo91] also available on the website for this book.

Exercises

1. For each of these problems about a subway system, describe a weighted graph model that can be used to solve the problem.
   a) What is the least amount of time required to travel between two stops?
   b) What is the minimum distance that can be traveled to reach a stop from another stop?

c) What is the least fare required to travel between two stops if fares between stops are added to give the total fare?

In Exercise 2 find the length of a shortest path between a and z in the given weighted graph.

2.

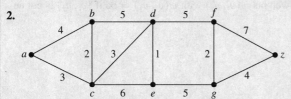

3. Find a shortest path between a and z in each of the weighted graphs in Exercise 2.

4. Find a shortest route (in distance) between computer centers in each of these pairs of cities in the communications network shown in Figure 2.
   a) Boston and Los Angeles   b) New York and San Francisco
   c) Dallas and San Francisco   d) Denver and New York

5. Find a least expensive route, in monthly lease charges, between the pairs of computer centers in Exercise 4 using the lease charges given in Figure 2.

6. Extend Dijkstra's algorithm for finding the length of a shortest path between two vertices in a weighted simple connected graph so that the length of a shortest path between the vertex a and every other vertex of the graph is found.

7. The weighted graphs in the figures here show some major roads in New Jersey. Part (a) shows the distances between cities on these roads; part (b) shows the tolls.

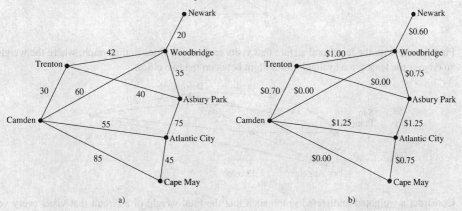

a) Find a shortest route in distance between Newark and Camden, and between Newark and Cape May, using these roads.

b) Find a least expensive route in terms of total tolls using the roads in the graph between the pairs of cities in part (a) of this exercise.

8. What are some applications where it is necessary to find the length of a longest simple path between two vertices in a weighted graph?

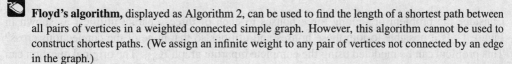 **Floyd's algorithm,** displayed as Algorithm 2, can be used to find the length of a shortest path between all pairs of vertices in a weighted connected simple graph. However, this algorithm cannot be used to construct shortest paths. (We assign an infinite weight to any pair of vertices not connected by an edge in the graph.)

9. Use Floyd's algorithm to find the distance between all pairs of vertices in the weighted graph in Figure 4(a).

*10. Give a big-O estimate of the number of operations (comparisons and additions) used by Floyd's algorithm to determine the shortest distance between every pair of vertices in a weighted simple graph with n vertices.

Algorithm 2 Floyd's Algorithm.

procedure *Floyd*(*G*: weighted simple graph)
{*G* has vertices $v_1, v_2, \ldots, v_n$ and weights $w(v_i, v_j)$ with $w(v_i, v_j) = \infty$ if (v_i, v_j) is not an edge}
  for $i := 1$ **to** n
    for $j := 1$ **to** n
      $d(v_i, v_j) := w(v_i, v_j)$
  for $i := 1$ **to** n
    for $j := 1$ **to** n
      for $k := 1$ **to** n
        if $d(v_j, v_i) + d(v_i, v_k) < d(v_j, v_k)$
          then $d(v_j, v_k) :=$
            $d(v_j, v_i) + d(v_i, v_k)$
{$d(v_i, v_j)$ is the length of a shortest path between v_i and v_j}

11. Solve the traveling salesman problem for this graph by finding the total weight of all Hamilton circuits and determining a circuit with minimum total weight.

12. Find a route with the least total airfare that visits each of the cities in this graph, where the weight on an edge is the least price available for a flight between the two cities.

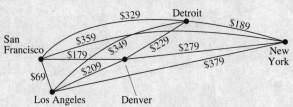

13. Construct a weighted undirected graph such that the total weight of a circuit that visits every vertex at least once is minimized for a circuit that visits some vertices more than once. [*Hint:* There are examples with three vertices.]

6.7   Planar Graphs

Introduction

Consider the problem of joining three houses to each of three separate utilities, as shown in Figure 1. Is it possible to join these houses and utilities so that none of the connections cross? This problem can be modeled using the complete bipartite graph $K_{3,3}$. The original question can be rephrased as: Can $K_{3,3}$ be drawn in the plane so that no two of its edges cross?

In this section we will study the question of whether a graph can be drawn in the plane without edges crossing. In particular, we will answer the houses-and-utilities problem.

There are always many ways to represent a graph. When is it possible to find at least one way to represent this graph in a plane without any edges crossing?

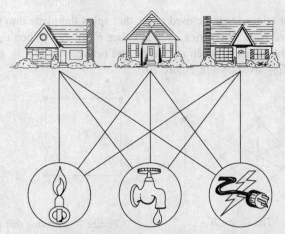

Figure 1   Three Houses and Three Utilities.

Definition 1   A graph is called *planar* if it can be drawn in the plane without any edges crossing (where a crossing of edges is the intersection of the lines or arcs representing them at a point other than their common endpoint). Such a drawing is called a *planar representation* of the graph.

A graph may be planar even if it is usually drawn with crossings, because it may be possible to draw it in a different way without crossings.

Example 1   Is K_4 (shown in Figure 2 with two edges crossing) planar?

Solution: K_4 is planar because it can be drawn without crossings, as shown in Figure 3.   ◄

Figure 2   The Graph K_4.

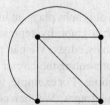

Figure 3 K_4 Drawn with No Crossings.

Example 2   Is Q_3, shown in Figure 4, planar?

Solution: Q_3 is planar, because it can be drawn without any edges crossing, as shown in Figure 5.   ◄

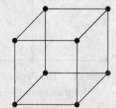

Figure 4   The Graph Q_3.

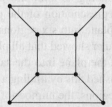

Figure 5   A Planar Representation of Q_3.

We can show that a graph is planar by displaying a planar representation. It is harder to show that a graph is nonplanar. We will give an example to show how this can be done in an ad hoc fashion. Later we will develop some general results that can be used to do this.

Example 3   Is $K_{3,3}$, shown in Figure 6, planar?

Solution: Any attempt to draw $K_{3,3}$ in the plane with no edges crossing is doomed. We now show why. In any planar representation of $K_{3,3}$, the vertices v_1 and v_2 must be connected to both

v_4 and v_5. These four edges form a closed curve that splits the plane into two regions, R_1 and R_2, as shown in Figure 7(a). The vertex v_3 is in either R_1 or R_2. When v_3 is in R_2, the inside of the closed curve, the edges between v_3 and v_4 and between v_3 and v_5 separate R_2 into two subregions, R_{21} and R_{22}, as shown in Figure 7(b).

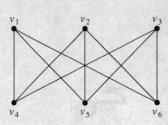

Figure 6   The Graph $K_{3,3}$.

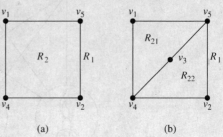

(a)   (b)

Figure 7   Showing that $K_{3,3}$ Is Nonplanar.

Next, note that there is no way to place the final vertex v_6 without forcing a crossing. For if v_6 is in R_1, then the edge between v_6 and v_3 cannot be drawn without a crossing. If v_6 is in R_{21}, then the edge between v_2 and v_6 cannot be drawn without a crossing. If v_6 is in R_{22}, then the edge between v_1 and v_6 cannot be drawn without a crossing.

A similar argument can be used when v_3 is in R_1. The completion of this argument is left for the reader. It follows that $K_{3,3}$ is not planar.   ◄

Example 3 solves the utilities-and-houses problem that was described at the beginning of this section. The three houses and three utilities cannot be connected in the plane without a crossing. A similar argument can be used to show that K_5 is nonplanar. (See Exercise 6 at the end of this section.)

Planarity of graphs plays an important role in the design of electronic circuits. We can model a circuit with a graph by representing components of the circuit by vertices and connections between them by edges. We can print a circuit on a single board with no connections crossing if the graph representing the circuit is planar. When this graph is not planar, we must turn to more expensive options. For example, we can partition the vertices in the graph representing the circuit into planar subgraphs. We then construct the circuit using multiple layers. We can construct the circuit using insulated wires whenever connections cross. In this case, drawing the graph with the fewest possible crossings is important.

Euler's Formula

A planar representation of a graph splits the plane into **regions,** including an unbounded region. For instance, the planar representation of the graph shown in Figure 8 splits the plane into six regions. These are labeled in the figure. Euler showed that all planar representations of a graph split the plane into the same number of regions. He accomplished this by finding a relationship among the number of regions, the number of vertices, and the number of edges of a planar graph.

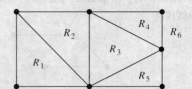

Figure 8   The Regions of the Planar Representation of a Graph.

Theorem 1   Euler's Formula   Let G be a connected planar simple graph with e edges and v vertices. Let r be the number of regions in a planar representation of G. Then $r = e - v + 2$.

Proof: First, we specify a planar representation of G. We will prove the theorem by constructing a sequence of subgraphs $G_1, G_2, \ldots, G_e = G$, successively adding an edge at each stage. This is done using the following inductive definition. Arbitrarily pick one edge of G to obtain G_1. Obtain G_n from G_{n-1} by arbitrarily adding an edge that is incident with a vertex already in G_{n-1}, adding the other vertex incident with this edge if it is not already in G_{n-1}. This construction is possible because G is connected. G is obtained after e edges are added. Let r_n, e_n, and v_n represent the number of regions, edges, and vertices of the planar representation of G_n induced by the planar representation of G, respectively.

The proof will now proceed by induction. The relationship $r_1 = e_1 - v_1 + 2$ is true for G_1, because $e_1 = 1$, $v_1 = 2$, and $r_1 = 1$. This is shown in Figure 9.

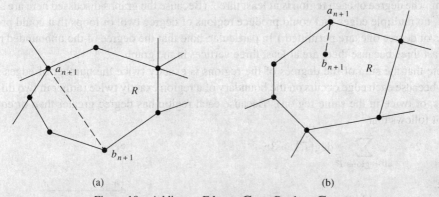

Figure 9   The Basis Case of the Proof of Euler's Formula.

Now assume that $r_n = e_n - v_n + 2$. Let $\{a_{n+1}, b_{n+1}\}$ be the edge that is added to G_n to obtain G_{n+1}. There are two possibilities to consider. In the first case, both a_{n+1} and b_{n+1} are already in G_n. These two vertices must be on the boundary of a common region R, or else it would be impossible to add the edge $\{a_{n+1}, b_{n+1}\}$ to G_n without two edges crossing (and G_{n+1} is planar). The addition of this new edge splits R into two regions. Consequently, in this case, $r_{n+1} = r_n + 1$, $e_{n+1} = e_n + 1$, and $v_{n+1} = v_n$. Thus, each side of the formula relating the number of regions, edges, and vertices increases by exactly one, so this formula is still true. In other words, $r_{n+1} = e_{n+1} - v_{n+1} + 2$. This case is illustrated in Figure 10(a).

(a)   (b)

Figure 10   Adding an Edge to G_n to Produce G_{n+1}.

In the second case, one of the two vertices of the new edge is not already in G_n. Suppose that a_{n+1} is in G_n but that b_{n+1} is not. Adding this new edge does not produce any new regions, because b_{n+1} must be in a region that has a_{n+1} on its boundary. Consequently, $r_{n+1} = r_n$. Moreover, $e_{n+1} = e_n + 1$ and $v_{n+1} = v_n + 1$. Each side of the formula relating the number of regions, edges, and vertices remains the same, so the formula is still true. In other words, $r_{n+1} = e_{n+1} - v_{n+1} + 2$. This case is illustrated in Figure 10(b).

We have completed the induction argument. Hence, $r_n = e_n - v_n + 2$ for all n. Because the original graph is the graph G_e, obtained after e edges have been added, the theorem is true.   ◁

Euler's formula is illustrated in Example 4.

Example 4   Suppose that a connected planar simple graph has 20 vertices, each of degree 3. Into how many regions does a representation of this planar graph split the plane?

Solution: This graph has 20 vertices, each of degree 3, so $v = 20$. Because the sum of the degrees of the vertices, $3v = 3 \cdot 20 = 60$, is equal to twice the number of edges, $2e$, we have $2e = 60$, or $e = 30$. Consequently, from Euler's formula, the number of regions is

$$r = e - v + 2 = 30 - 20 + 2 = 12.$$ ◀

Euler's formula can be used to establish some inequalities that must be satisfied by planar graphs. One such inequality is given in Corollary 1.

Corollary 1　If G is a connected planar simple graph with e edges and v vertices, where $v \geqslant 3$, then $e \leqslant 3v - 6$.

Before we prove Corollary 1 we will use it to prove the following useful result.

Corollary 2　If G is a connected planar simple graph, then G has a vertex of degree not exceeding five.

Proof: If G has one or two vertices, the result is true. If G has at least three vertices, by Corollary 1 we know that $e \leqslant 3v - 6$, so $2e \leqslant 6v - 12$. If the degree of every vertex were at least six, then because $2e = \sum_{v \in V} \deg(v)$ (by the Handshaking Theorem), we would have $2e \geqslant 6v$. But this contradicts the inequality $2e \leqslant 6v - 12$. It follows that there must be a vertex with degree no greater than five. ◁

The proof of Corollary 1 is based on the concept of the **degree** of a region, which is defined to be the number of edges on the boundary of this region. When an edge occurs twice on the boundary (so that it is traced out twice when the boundary is traced out), it contributes two to the degree. The degrees of the regions of the graph shown in Figure 11 are displayed in the figure.

The proof of Corollary 1 can now be given.

Proof: A connected planar simple graph drawn in the plane divides the plane into regions, say r of them. The degree of each region is at least three. (Because the graphs discussed here are simple graphs, no multiple edges that could produce regions of degree two, or loops that could produce regions of degree one, are permitted.) In particular, note that the degree of the unbounded region is at least three because there are at least three vertices in the graph.

Note that the sum of the degrees of the regions is exactly twice the number of edges in the graph, because each edge occurs on the boundary of a region exactly twice (either in two different regions, or twice in the same region). Because each region has degree greater than or equal to three, it follows that

$$2e = \sum_{\text{all regions } R} \deg(R) \geqslant 3r.$$

Hence,

$$(2/3)e \geqslant r.$$

Using $r = e - v + 2$ (Euler's formula), we obtain

$$e - v + 2 \leqslant (2/3)e.$$

It follows that $e/3 \leqslant v - 2$. This shows that $e \leqslant 3v - 6$. ◁

This corollary can be used to demonstrate that K_5 is nonplanar.

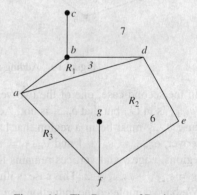

Figure 11　The Degrees of Regions.

Example 5　Show that K_5 is nonplanar using Corollary 1.

Solution: The graph K_5 has five vertices and 10 edges. However, the inequality $e \leqslant 3v - 6$ is not satisfied for this graph because $e = 10$ and $3v - 6 = 9$. Therefore, K_5 is not planar. ◀

It was previously shown that $K_{3,3}$ is not planar. Note, however, that this graph has six vertices and nine edges. This means that the inequality $e = 9 \leqslant 12 = 3 \cdot 6 - 6$ is satisfied. Consequently, the fact that the inequality $e \leqslant 3v - 6$ is satisfied does *not* imply that a graph is planar. However, the following corollary of Theorem 1 can be used to show that $K_{3,3}$ is nonplanar.

Corollary 3　If a connected planar simple graph has e edges and v vertices with $v \geqslant 3$ and no circuits of length three, then $e \leqslant 2v - 4$.

The proof of Corollary 3 is similar to that of Corollary 1, except that in this case the fact that there are no circuits of length three implies that the degree of a region must be at least four. The details of this proof are left for the reader (see Exercise 8 at the end of this section).

Example 6   Use Corollary 3 to show that $K_{3,3}$ is nonplanar.

Solution: Because $K_{3,3}$ has no circuits of length three (this is easy to see because it is bipartite), Corollary 3 can be used. $K_{3,3}$ has six vertices and nine edges. Because $e = 9$ and $2v - 4 = 8$, Corollary 3 shows that $K_{3,3}$ is nonplanar.   ◀

Kuratowski's Theorem

We have seen that $K_{3,3}$ and K_5 are not planar. Clearly, a graph is not planar if it contains either of these two graphs as a subgraph. Surprisingly, all nonplanar graphs must contain a subgraph that can be obtained from $K_{3,3}$ or K_5 using certain permitted operations.

If a graph is planar, so will be any graph obtained by removing an edge $\{u, v\}$ and adding a new vertex w together with edges $\{u, w\}$ and $\{w, v\}$. Such an operation is called an **elementary subdivision.** The graphs $G_1 = (V_1, E_1)$ and $G_2 = (V_2, E_2)$ are called **homeomorphic** if they can be obtained from the same graph by a sequence of elementary subdivisions.

Example 7   Show that the graphs G_1, G_2, and G_3 displayed in Figure 12 are all homeomorphic.

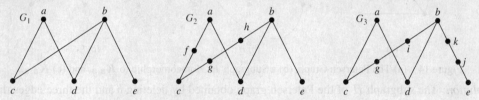

Figure 12   Homeomorphic Graphs.

Solution: These three graphs are homeomorphic because all three can be obtained from G_1 by elementary subdivisions. G_1 can be obtained from itself by an empty sequence of elementary subdivisions. To obtain G_2 from G_1 we can use this sequence of elementary subdivisions: (*i*) remove the edge $\{a, c\}$, add the vertex f, and add the edges $\{a, f\}$ and $\{f, c\}$; (*ii*) remove the edge $\{b, c\}$, add the vertex g, and add the edges $\{b, g\}$ and $\{g, c\}$; and (*iii*) remove the edge $\{b, g\}$, add the vertex h, and add the edges $\{g, h\}$ and $\{b, h\}$. We leave it to the reader to determine the sequence of elementary subdivisions needed to obtain G_3 from G_1.   ◀

The Polish mathematician Kazimierz Kuratowski established Theorem 2 in 1930, which characterizes planar graphs using the concept of graph homeomorphism.

Theorem 2   A graph is nonplanar if and only if it contains a subgraph homeomorphic to $K_{3,3}$ or K_5.

It is clear that a graph containing a subgraph homeomorphic to $K_{3,3}$ or K_5 is nonplanar. However, the proof of the converse, namely that every nonplanar graph contains a subgraph homeomorphic to $K_{3,3}$ or K_5, is complicated and will not be given here. Examples 8 and 9 illustrate how Kuratowski's Theorem is used.

Example 8   Determine whether the graph G shown in Figure 13 is planar.

Solution: G has a subgraph H homeomorphic to K_5. H is obtained by deleting h, j, and k and all edges incident with these vertices. H is homeomorphic to K_5 because it can be obtained from K_5 (with vertices a, b, c, g, and i) by a sequence of elementary subdivisions, adding the vertices d, e, and f. (The reader should construct such a sequence of elementary subdivisions.) Hence, G is nonplanar.   ◀

Example 9   Is the Petersen graph, shown in Figure 14(a), planar? (The Danish mathematician Julius Petersen studied this graph in 1891; it is often used to illustrate various theoretical properties of graphs.)

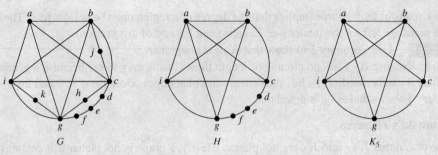

Figure 13   The Undirected Graph G, a Subgraph H Homeomorphic to K_5, and K_5.

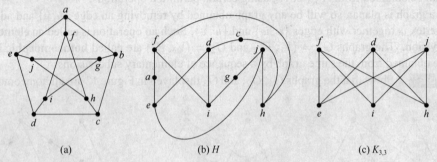

| (a) | (b) H | (c) $K_{3,3}$ |

Figure 14   (a) The Petersen Graph, (b) a Subgraph H Homeomorphic to $K_{3,3}$, and (c) $K_{3,3}$.

Solution: The subgraph H of the Petersen graph obtained by deleting b and the three edges that have b as an endpoint, shown in Figure 14(b), is homeomorphic to $K_{3,3}$, with vertex sets $\{f, d, j\}$ and $\{e, i, h\}$, because it can be obtained by a sequence of elementary subdivisions, deleting $\{d, h\}$ and adding $\{c, h\}$ and $\{c, d\}$, deleting $\{e, f\}$ and adding $\{a, e\}$ and $\{a, f\}$, and deleting $\{i, j\}$ and adding $\{g, i\}$ and $\{g, j\}$. Hence, the Petersen graph is not planar.   ◀

Exercises

1. Can five houses be connected to two utilities without connections crossing?

In Exercise 2 draw the given planar graph without any crossings.

2.

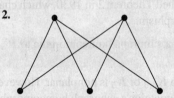

In Exercises 3–5 determine whether the given graph is planar. If so, draw it so that no edges cross.

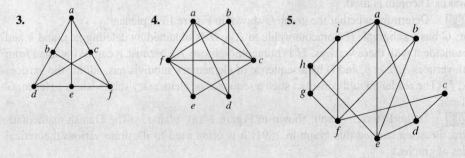

3.   **4.**   **5.**

6. Show that K_5 is nonplanar using an argument similar to that given in Example 3.
7. Suppose that a connected planar graph has six vertices, each of degree four. Into how many regions is the plane divided by a planar representation of this graph?
8. Prove Corollary 3.
*9. Suppose that a connected planar simple graph with e edges and v vertices contains no simple circuits of length 4 or less. Show that $e \leqslant (5/3)v - (10/3)$ if $v \geqslant 4$.
10. Which of these nonplanar graphs have the property that the removal of any vertex and all edges incident with that vertex produces a planar graph?
   a) K_5 b) K_6 c) $K_{3,3}$ d) $K_{3,4}$

In Exercise 11 determine whether the given graph is homeomorphic to $K_{3,3}$.

11.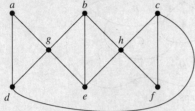

In Exercises 12–13 use Kuratowski's Theorem to determine whether the given graph is planar.

12.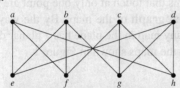

13.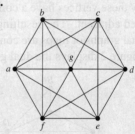

 The **crossing number** of a simple graph is the minimum number of crossings that can occur when this graph is drawn in the plane where no three arcs representing edges are permitted to cross at the same point.

**14. Find the crossing numbers of each of these nonplanar graphs.
   a) K_5 b) K_6 c) K_7 d) $K_{3,4}$ e) $K_{4,4}$ f) $K_{5,5}$
**15. Show that if m and n are even positive integers, the crossing number of $K_{m,n}$ is less than or equal to $mn(m-2)(n-2)/16$. [*Hint:* Place m vertices along the x-axis so that they are equally spaced and symmetric about the origin and place n vertices along the y-axis so that they are equally spaced and symmetric about the origin. Now connect each of the m vertices on the x-axis to each of the vertices on the y-axis and count the crossings.]

The **thickness** of a simple graph G is the smallest number of planar subgraphs of G that have G as their union.
*16. Find the thickness of the graphs in Exercise 14.
*17. Draw $K_{3,3}$ on the surface of a torus so that no edges cross.

6.8   Graph Coloring

Introduction

Problems related to the coloring of maps of regions, such as maps of parts of the world, have generated many results in graph theory. When a map* is colored, two regions with a common

---

* We will assume that all regions in a map are connected. This eliminates any problems presented by such geographical entities as Michigan.

border are customarily assigned different colors. One way to ensure that two adjacent regions never have the same color is to use a different color for each region. However, this is inefficient, and on maps with many regions it would be hard to distinguish similar colors. Instead, a small number of colors should be used whenever possible. Consider the problem of determining the least number of colors that can be used to color a map so that adjacent regions never have the same color. For instance, for the map shown on the left in Figure 1, four colors suffice, but three colors are not enough. (The reader should check this.) In the map on the right in Figure 1, three colors are sufficient (but two are not).

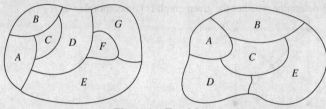

Figure 1   Two Maps.

Each map in the plane can be represented by a graph. To set up this correspondence, each region of the map is represented by a vertex. Edges connect two vertices if the regions represented by these vertices have a common border. Two regions that touch at only one point are not considered adjacent. The resulting graph is called the **dual graph** of the map. By the way in which dual graphs of maps are constructed, it is clear that any map in the plane has a planar dual graph. Figure 2 displays the dual graphs that correspond to the maps shown in Figure 1.

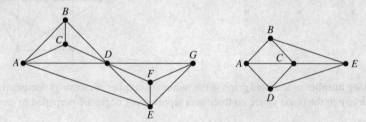

Figure 2   Dual Graphs of the Maps in Figure 1.

The problem of coloring the regions of a map is equivalent to the problem of coloring the vertices of the dual graph so that no two adjacent vertices in this graph have the same color. We now define a graph coloring.

Definition 1   A *coloring* of a simple graph is the assignment of a color to each vertex of the graph so that no two adjacent vertices are assigned the same color.

A graph can be colored by assigning a different color to each of its vertices. However, for most graphs a coloring can be found that uses fewer colors than the number of vertices in the graph. What is the least number of colors necessary?

Definition 2   The *chromatic number* of a graph is the least number of colors needed for a coloring of this graph. The chromatic number of a graph G is denoted by $\chi(G)$. (Here χ is the Greek letter *chi*.)

Note that asking for the chromatic number of a planar graph is the same as asking for the minimum number of colors required to color a planar map so that no two adjacent regions are assigned the same color. This question has been studied for more than 100 years. The answer is provided by one of the most famous theorems in mathematics.

Theorem 1   The Four Color Theorem   The chromatic number of a planar graph is no greater than four.

The Four Color Theorem was originally posed as a conjecture in the 1850s. It was finally proved by the American mathematicians Kenneth Appel and Wolfgang Haken in 1976. Prior to 1976, many incorrect proofs were published, often with hard-to-find errors. In addition, many futile attempts were made to construct counterexamples by drawing maps that require more than four colors. (Proving the Five Color Theorem is not that difficult.)

Perhaps the most notorious fallacious proof in all of mathematics is the incorrect proof of the Four Color Theorem published in 1879 by a London barrister and amateur mathematician, Alfred Kempe. Mathematicians accepted his proof as correct until 1890, when Percy Heawood found an error that made Kempe's argument incomplete. However, Kempe's line of reasoning turned out to be the basis of the successful proof given by Appel and Haken. Their proof relies on a careful case-by-case analysis carried out by computer. They showed that if the Four Color Theorem were false, there would have to be a counterexample of one of approximately 2000 different types, and they then showed that none of these types exists. They used over 1000 hours of computer time in their proof. This proof generated a large amount of controversy, because computers played such an important role in it. For example, could there be an error in a computer program that led to incorrect results? Was their argument really a proof if it depended on what could be unreliable computer output?

Note that the Four Color Theorem applies only to planar graphs. Nonplanar graphs can have arbitrarily large chromatic numbers, as will be shown in Example 2.

Two things are required to show that the chromatic number of a graph is k. First, we must show that the graph can be colored with k colors. This can be done by constructing such a coloring. Second, we must show that the graph cannot be colored using fewer than k colors. Examples 1–4 illustrate how chromatic numbers can be found.

Example 1   What are the chromatic numbers of the graphs G and H shown in Figure 3?

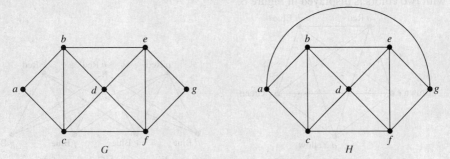

Figure 3   The Simple Graphs G and H.

Solution: The chromatic number of G is at least three, because the vertices a, b, and c must be assigned different colors. To see if G can be colored with three colors, assign red to a, blue to b, and green to c. Then, d can (and must) be colored red because it is adjacent to b and c. Furthermore, e can (and must) be colored green because it is adjacent only to vertices colored red and blue, and f can (and must) be colored blue because it is adjacent only to vertices colored red and green. Finally, g can (and must) be colored red because it is adjacent only to vertices colored blue and green. This produces a coloring of G using exactly three colors. Figure 4 displays such a coloring.

The graph H is made up of the graph G with an edge connecting a and g. Any attempt to color H using three colors must follow the same reasoning as that used to color G, except at the last stage, when all vertices other than g have been colored. Then, because g is adjacent (in H) to vertices colored red, blue, and green, a fourth color, say brown, needs to be used. Hence, H has a chromatic number equal to 4. A coloring of H is shown in Figure 4. ◄

370 Chapter 6 Graphs

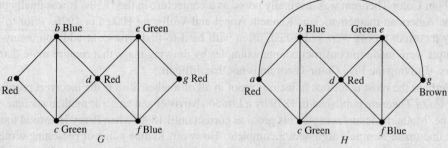

Figure 4   Colorings of the Graphs G and H.

Example 2   What is the chromatic number of K_n?

Solution: A coloring of K_n can be constructed using n colors by assigning a different color to each vertex. Is there a coloring using fewer colors? The answer is no. No two vertices can be assigned the same color, because every two vertices of this graph are adjacent. Hence, the chromatic number of $K_n = n$. That is, $\chi(K_n) = n$. (Recall that K_n is not planar when $n \geqslant 5$, so this result does not contradict the Four Color Theorem.) A coloring of K_5 using five colors is shown in Figure 5.   ◄

Example 3   What is the chromatic number of the complete bipartite graph $K_{m,n}$, where m and n are positive integers?

Solution: The number of colors needed may seem to depend on m and n. However, as Theorem 4 in Section 6.2 tells us, only two colors are needed, because $K_{m,n}$ is a bipartite graph. Hence, $\chi(K_{m,n}) = 2$. This means that we can color the set of m vertices with one color and the set of n vertices with a second color. Because edges connect only a vertex from the set of m vertices and a vertex from the set of n vertices, no two adjacent vertices have the same color. A coloring of $K_{3,4}$ with two colors is displayed in Figure 6.   ◄

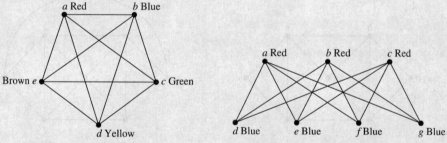

Figure 5   A Coloring of K_5.

Figure 6   A Coloring of $K_{3,4}$.

Example 4   What is the chromatic number of the graph C_n, where $n \geqslant 3$? (Recall that C_n is the cycle with n vertices.)

Solution: We will first consider some individual cases. To begin, let $n = 6$. Pick a vertex and color it red. Proceed clockwise in the planar depiction of C_6 shown in Figure 7. It is necessary to assign a second color, say blue, to the next vertex reached. Continue in the clockwise direction; the third vertex can be colored red, the fourth vertex blue, and the fifth vertex red. Finally, the sixth vertex, which is adjacent to the first, can be colored blue. Hence, the chromatic number of C_6 is 2. Figure 7 displays the coloring constructed here.

Next, let $n = 5$ and consider C_5. Pick a vertex and color it red. Proceeding clockwise, it is necessary to assign a second color, say blue, to the next vertex reached. Continuing in the clockwise direction, the third vertex can be colored red, and the fourth vertex can be colored blue. The fifth vertex cannot be colored either red or blue, because it is adjacent to the fourth vertex and the first vertex. Consequently, a third color is required for this vertex. Note that we would have also needed three colors if we had colored vertices in the counterclockwise direction. Thus, the chromatic number of C_5 is 3. A coloring of C_5 using three colors is displayed in Figure 7.

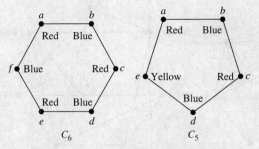

Figure 7   Colorings of C_5 and C_6.

In general, two colors are needed to color C_n when n is even. To construct such a coloring, simply pick a vertex and color it red. Proceed around the graph in a clockwise direction (using a planar representation of the graph) coloring the second vertex blue, the third vertex red, and so on. The nth vertex can be colored blue, because the two vertices adjacent to it, namely the $(n-1)$st and the first vertices, are both colored red.

When n is odd and $n > 1$, the chromatic number of C_n is 3. To see this, pick an initial vertex. To use only two colors, it is necessary to alternate colors as the graph is traversed in a clockwise direction. However, the nth vertex reached is adjacent to two vertices of different colors, namely, the first and $(n-1)$st. Hence, a third color must be used.

We have shown that $\chi(C_n) = 2$ if n is an even positive integer with $n \geqslant 4$ and $\chi(C_n) = 3$ if n is an odd positive integer with $n \geqslant 3$.   ◄

The best algorithms known for finding the chromatic number of a graph have exponential worst-case time complexity (in the number of vertices of the graph). Even the problem of finding an approximation to the chromatic number of a graph is difficult. It has been shown that if there were an algorithm with polynomial worst-case time complexity that could approximate the chromatic number of a graph up to a factor of 2 (that is, construct a bound that was no more than double the chromatic number of the graph), then an algorithm with polynomial worst-case time complexity for finding the chromatic number of the graph would also exist.

Applications of Graph Colorings

Graph coloring has a variety of applications to problems involving scheduling and assignments. (Note that because no efficient algorithm is known for graph coloring, this does not lead to efficient algorithms for scheduling and assignments.) Examples of such applications will be given here. The first application deals with the scheduling of final exams.

Example 5   Scheduling Final Exams   How can the final exams at a university be scheduled so that no student has two exams at the same time?

Solution: This scheduling problem can be solved using a graph model, with vertices representing courses and with an edge between two vertices if there is a common student in the courses they represent. Each time slot for a final exam is represented by a different color. A scheduling of the exams corresponds to a coloring of the associated graph.

For instance, suppose there are seven finals to be scheduled. Suppose the courses are numbered 1 through 7. Suppose that the following pairs of courses have common students: 1 and 2, 1 and 3, 1 and 4, 1 and 7, 2 and 3, 2 and 4, 2 and 5, 2 and 7, 3 and 4, 3 and 6, 3 and 7, 4 and 5, 4 and 6, 5 and 6, 5 and 7, and 6 and 7. In Figure 8 the graph associated with this set of classes is shown. A scheduling consists of a coloring of this graph.

Because the chromatic number of this graph is 4 (the reader should verify this), four time slots are needed. A coloring of the graph using four colors and the associated schedule are shown in Figure 9.   ◄

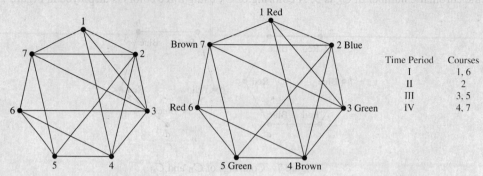

Figure 8   The Graph Representing   Figure 9   Using a Coloring to Schedule Final Exams.
the Scheduling of Final Exams.

Now consider an application to the assignment of television channels.

Example 6   **Frequency Assignments**   Television channels 2 through 13 are assigned to stations in North America so that no two stations within 150 miles can operate on the same channel. How can the assignment of channels be modeled by graph coloring?

Solution: Construct a graph by assigning a vertex to each station. Two vertices are connected by an edge if they are located within 150 miles of each other. An assignment of channels corresponds to a coloring of the graph, where each color represents a different channel.   ◄

An application of graph coloring to compilers is considered in Example 7.

Example 7   **Index Registers**   In efficient compilers the execution of loops is speeded up when frequently used variables are stored temporarily in index registers in the central processing unit, instead of in regular memory. For a given loop, how many index registers are needed? This problem can be addressed using a graph coloring model. To set up the model, let each vertex of a graph represent a variable in the loop. There is an edge between two vertices if the variables they represent must be stored in index registers at the same time during the execution of the loop. Thus, the chromatic number of the graph gives the number of index registers needed, because different registers must be assigned to variables when the vertices representing these variables are adjacent in the graph.   ◄

Exercises

In Exercises 1–2 construct the dual graph for the map shown. Then find the number of colors needed to color the map so that no two adjacent regions have the same color.

1.   **2.**
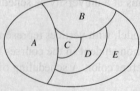   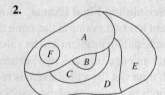

In Exercises 3–6 find the chromatic number of the given graph.

3.   **4.**
                          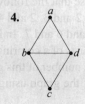

5.   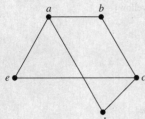   6.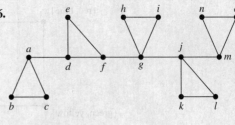

7. Which graphs have a chromatic number of 1?

8. What is the chromatic number of W_n?

9. Schedule the final exams for Math 115, Math 116, Math 185, Math 195, CS 101, CS 102, CS 273, and CS 473, using the fewest number of different time slots, if there are no students taking both Math 115 and CS 473, both Math 116 and CS 473, both Math 195 and CS 101, both Math 195 and CS 102, both Math 115 and Math 116, both Math 115 and Math 185, and both Math 185 and Math 195, but there are students in every other combination of courses.

10. The mathematics department has six committees each meeting once a month. How many different meeting times must be used to ensure that no member is scheduled to attend two meetings at the same time if the committees are $C_1 = \{$Arlinghaus, Brand, Zaslavsky$\}$, $C_2 = \{$Brand, Lee, Rosen$\}$, $C_3 = \{$Arlinghaus, Rosen, Zaslavsky$\}$, $C_4 = \{$Lee, Rosen, Zaslavsky$\}$, $C_5 = \{$Arlinghaus, Brand$\}$, and $C_6 = \{$Brand, Rosen, Zaslavsky$\}$?

 An **edge coloring** of a graph is an assignment of colors to edges so that edges incident with a common vertex are assigned different colors. The **edge chromatic number** of a graph is the smallest number of colors that can be used in an edge coloring of the graph.

11. Find the edge chromatic number of each of the graphs in Exercises 3–6.

12. Seven variables occur in a loop of a computer program. The variables and the steps during which they must be stored are t: steps 1 through 6; u: step 2; v: steps 2 through 4; w: steps 1, 3, and 5; x: steps 1 and 6; y: steps 3 through 6; and z: steps 4 and 5. How many different index registers are needed to store these variables during execution?

13. Construct a coloring of the graph shown using this algorithm.

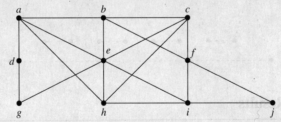

*14. Show that the coloring produced in this algorithm may use more colors than are necessary to color a graph.

A connected graph G is called **chromatically k-critical** if the chromatic number of G is k, but for every edge e of G, the chromatic number of the graph obtained by deleting this edge from G is $k - 1$.

15. Show that W_n is chromatically 4-critical whenever n is an odd integer, $n \geqslant 3$.

16. Show that if G is a chromatically k-critical graph, then the degree of every vertex of G is at least $k - 1$.

A **k-tuple coloring** of a graph G is an assignment of a set of k different colors to each of the vertices of G such that no two adjacent vertices are assigned a common color. We denote by $\chi_k(G)$ the smallest positive integer n such that G has a k-tuple coloring using n colors. For example, $\chi_2(C_4) = 4$. To see this, note that using only four colors we can assign two colors to each vertex of C_4, as illustrated, so that no two adjacent vertices are assigned the same color. Furthermore, no fewer than four colors suffice because the vertices v_1 and v_2 each must be assigned two colors, and a common color cannot be assigned to both v_1 and v_2. (For more information about k-tuple coloring, see [MiRo91].)

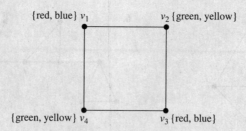

*17. Let G and H be the graphs displayed in Figure 3. Find
   a) $\chi_2(G)$.   b) $\chi_2(H)$.   c) $\chi_3(G)$.   d) $\chi_3(H)$.

18. Frequencies for mobile radio (or cellular) telephones are assigned by zones. Each zone is assigned a set of frequencies to be used by vehicles in that zone. The same frequency cannot be used in zones where interference is a problem. Explain how a k-tuple coloring can be used to assign k frequencies to each mobile radio zone in a region.

The famous Art Gallery Problem asks how many guards are needed to see all parts of an art gallery, where the gallery is the interior and boundary of a polygon with n sides. To state this problem more precisely, we need some terminology. A point x inside or on the boundary of a simple polygon P **covers** or **sees** a point y inside or on P if all points on the line segment xy are in the interior or on the boundary of P. We say that a set of points is a **guarding set** of a simple polygon P if for every point y inside P or on the boundary of P there is a point x in this guarding set that sees y. Denote by $G(P)$ the minimum number of points needed to guard the simple polygon P. The **Art Gallery Problem** asks for the function $g(n)$, which is the maximum value of $G(P)$ over all simple polygons with n vertices. That is, $g(n)$ is the minimum positive integer for which it is guaranteed that a simple polygon with n vertices can be guarded with $g(n)$ or fewer guards.

*19. Show that $g(5) = 1$. That is, show that all pentagons can be guarded using one point. [*Hint:* Show that there are either 0, 1, or 2 vertices with an interior angle greater than 180 degrees and that in each case, one guard suffices.]

*20. Show that $g(n) \geqslant \lfloor n/3 \rfloor$. [*Hint:* Consider the polygon with $3k$ vertices that resembles a comb with k prongs, such as the polygon with 15 sides shown here.]

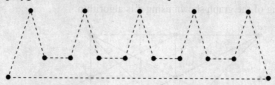

Key Terms and Results

TERMS

undirected edge: an edge associated to a set $\{u, v\}$, where u and v are vertices

directed edge: an edge associated to an ordered pair (u, v), where u and v are vertices

multiple edges: distinct edges connecting the same vertices

multiple directed edges: distinct directed edges associated with the same ordered pair (u,v), where u and v are vertices

loop: an edge connecting a vertex with itself

undirected graph: a set of vertices and a set of undirected edges each of which is associated with a set of one or two of these vertices

simple graph: an undirected graph with no multiple edges or loops

multigraph: an undirected graph that may contain multiple edges but no loops

pseudograph: an undirected graph that may contain multiple edges and loops

directed graph: a set of vertices together with a set of directed edges each of which is associated with an ordered pair of vertices

directed multigraph: a graph with directed edges that may contain multiple directed edges

simple directed graph: a directed graph without loops or multiple directed edges

adjacent: two vertices are adjacent if there is an edge between them

incident: an edge is incident with a vertex if the vertex is an endpoint of that edge

$\deg(v)$ (degree of the vertex v in an undirected graph): the number of edges incident with v with loops counted twice

$\deg^-(v)$ (the in-degree of the vertex v in a graph with directed edges): the number of edges with v as their terminal vertex

$\deg^+(v)$ (the out-degree of the vertex v in a graph with directed edges): the number of edges with v as their initial vertex

underlying undirected graph of a graph with directed edges: the undirected graph obtained by ignoring the directions of the edges

K_n (complete graph on n vertices): the undirected graph with n vertices where each pair of vertices is connected by an edge

bipartite graph: a graph with vertex set that can be partitioned into subsets V_1 and V_2 such that each edge connects a vertex in V_1 and a vertex in V_2

$K_{m,n}$ (complete bipartite graph): the graph with vertex set partitioned into a subset of m elements and a subset of n elements such that two vertices are connected by an edge if and only if one is in the first subset and the other is in the second subset

C_n (cycle of size n), $n \geqslant 3$: the graph with n vertices $v_1, v_2, \ldots, v_n$ and edges $\{v_1, v_2\}$, $\{v_2, v_3\}$, $\ldots$, $\{v_{n-1}, v_n\}$, $\{v_n, v_1\}$

W_n (wheel of size n), $n \geqslant 3$: the graph obtained from C_n by adding a vertex and edges from this vertex to the original vertices in C_n

Q_n (n-cube), $n \geqslant 1$: the graph that has the 2^n bit strings of length n as its vertices and edges connecting every pair of bit strings that differ by exactly one bit

isolated vertex: a vertex of degree zero

pendant vertex: a vertex of degree one

regular graph: a graph where all vertices have the same degree

subgraph of a graph $G = (V, E)$: a graph (W, F), where W is a subset of V and F is a subset of E

$G_1 \cup G_2$ (union of G_1 and G_2): the graph $(V_1 \cup V_2, E_1 \cup E_2)$, where $G_1 = (V_1, E_1)$ and $G_2 = (V_2, E_2)$

adjacency matrix: a matrix representing a graph using the adjacency of vertices

incidence matrix: a matrix representing a graph using the incidence of edges and vertices

isomorphic simple graphs: the simple graphs $G_1 = (V_1, E_1)$ and $G_2 = (V_2, E_2)$ are isomorphic if there is a one-to-one correspondence f from V_1 to V_2 such that $\{f(v_1), f(v_2)\} \in E_2$ if and only if $\{v_1, v_2\} \in E_1$ for all v_1 and v_2 in V_1

invariant: a property that isomorphic graphs either both have or both do not have

path from u to v in an undirected graph: a sequence of edges $e_1, e_2, \ldots, e_n$, where e_i is associated to $\{x_i, x_{i+1}\}$ for $i = 0, 1, \ldots, n$, where $x_0 = u$ and $x_{n+1} = v$

path from u to v in a graph with directed edges: a sequence of edges $e_1, e_2, \ldots, e_n$, where e_i is associated to (x_i, x_{i+1}) for $i = 0, 1, \ldots, n$, where $x_0 = u$ and $x_{n+1} = v$

simple path: a path that does not contain an edge more than once

circuit: a path of length $n \geqslant 1$ that begins and ends at the same vertex

connected graph: an undirected graph with the property that there is a path between every pair of vertices

connected component of a graph G: a maximal connected subgraph of G

strongly connected directed graph: a directed graph with the property that there is a directed path from every vertex to every vertex

strongly connected component of a directed graph G: a maximal strongly connected subgraph of G

Euler circuit: a circuit that contains every edge of a graph exactly once

Euler path: a path that contains every edge of a graph exactly once

Hamilton path: a path in a simple graph that passes through each vertex exactly once

Hamilton circuit: a circuit in a simple graph that passes through each vertex exactly once

weighted graph: a graph with numbers assigned to its edges

shortest-path problem: the problem of determining the path in a weighted graph such that the sum of the weights of the edges in this path is a minimum over all paths between specified vertices

traveling salesman problem: the problem that asks for the circuit of shortest total length that visits every vertex of the graph exactly once

planar graph: a graph that can be drawn in the plane with no crossings

regions of a representation of a planar graph: the regions the plane is divided into by the planar representation of the graph

elementary subdivision: the removal of an edge $\{u, v\}$ of an undirected graph and the addition of a new vertex w together with edges $\{u, w\}$ and $\{w, v\}$

homeomorphic: two undirected graphs are homeomorphic if they can be obtained from the same graph by a sequence of elementary subdivisions

graph coloring: an assignment of colors to the vertices of a graph so that no two adjacent vertices have the same color

chromatic number: the minimum number of colors needed in a coloring of a graph

RESULTS

There is an Euler circuit in a connected multigraph if and only if every vertex has even degree.

There is an Euler path in a connected multigraph if and only if at most two vertices have odd degree.

Dijkstra's algorithm: a procedure for finding a shortest path between two vertices in a weighted graph (see Section 6.6).

Euler's formula: $r = e - v + 2$ where r, e, and v are the number of regions of a planar representation, the number of edges, and the number of vertices, respectively, of a planar graph.

Kuratowski's Theorem: A graph is nonplanar if and only if it contains a subgraph homeomorphic to $K_{3,3}$ or K_5. (Proof beyond scope of this book.)

The Four Color Theorem: Every planar graph can be colored using no more than four colors. (Proof far beyond the scope of this book!)

Review Questions

1. a) Define a simple graph, a multigraph, a pseudograph, a directed graph, and a directed multigraph.

    b) Use an example to show how each of the types of graph in part (a) can be used in modeling. For example, explain how to model different aspects of a computer network or airline routes.

2. Give at least four examples of how graphs are used in modeling.

3. What is the relationship between the sum of the degrees of the vertices in an undirected graph and the number of edges in this graph? Explain why this relationship holds.

4. Why must there be an even number of vertices of odd degree in an undirected graph?

5. What is the relationship between the sum of the in-degrees and the sum of the out-degrees of the vertices in a directed graph? Explain why this relationship holds.

6. Describe the following families of graphs.

    a) K_n, the complete graph on n vertices   b) $K_{m,n}$, the complete bipartite graph on m and n vertices

    c) C_n, the cycle with n vertices   d) W_n, the wheel of size n e) Q_n, the n-cube

7. How many vertices and how many edges are there in each of the graphs in the families in Question 6?

8. a) What is a bipartite graph?

    b) Which of the graphs K_n, C_n, and W_n are bipartite?

    c) How can you determine whether an undirected graph is bipartite?

9. a) Describe three different methods that can be used to represent a graph.

    b) Draw a simple graph with at least five vertices and eight edges. Illustrate how it can be represented using the methods you described in part (a).

10. a) What does it mean for two simple graphs to be isomorphic?

b) What is meant by an invariant with respect to isomorphism for simple graphs? Give at least five examples of such invariants.

c) Give an example of two graphs that have the same numbers of vertices, edges, and degrees of vertices, but that are not isomorphic.

d) Is a set of invariants known that can be used to efficiently determine whether two simple graphs are isomorphic?

11. a) What does it mean for a graph to be connected?

b) What are the connected components of a graph?

12. a) Explain how an adjacency matrix can be used to represent a graph.

b) How can adjacency matrices be used to determine whether a function from the vertex set of a graph G to the vertex set of a graph H is an isomorphism?

c) How can the adjacency matrix of a graph be used to determine the number of paths of length r, where r is a positive integer, between two vertices of a graph?

13. a) Define an Euler circuit and an Euler path in an undirected graph.

b) Describe the famous Königsberg bridge problem and explain how to rephrase it in terms of an Euler circuit.

c) How can it be determined whether an undirected graph has an Euler path?

d) How can it be determined whether an undirected graph has an Euler circuit?

14. a) Define a Hamilton circuit in a simple graph.

b) Give some properties of a simple graph that imply that it does not have a Hamilton circuit.

15. Give examples of at least two problems that can be solved by finding the shortest path in a weighted graph.

16. a) Describe Dijkstra's algorithm for finding the shortest path in a weighted graph between two vertices.

b) Draw a weighted graph with at least 10 vertices and 20 edges. Use Dijkstra's algorithm to find the shortest path between two vertices of your choice in the graph.

17. a) What does it mean for a graph to be planar?

b) Give an example of a nonplanar graph.

18. a) What is Euler's formula for planar graphs?

b) How can Euler's formula for planar graphs be used to show that a simple graph is nonplanar?

19. State Kuratowski's Theorem on the planarity of graphs and explain how it characterizes which graphs are planar.

20. a) Define the chromatic number of a graph.

b) What is the chromatic number of the graph K_n when n is a positive integer?

c) What is the chromatic number of the graph C_n when n is a positive integer greater than 2?

d) What is the chromatic number of the graph $K_{m,n}$ when m and n are positive integers?

21. State the Four Color Theorem. Are there graphs that cannot be colored with four colors?

22. Explain how graph coloring can be used in modeling. Use at least two different examples.

Supplementary Exercises

1. How many edges does a 50-regular graph with 100 vertices have?

2. How many nonisomorphic subgraphs does K_3 have?

In Exercises 3–5 determine whether the given pair of graphs is isomorphic.

3.

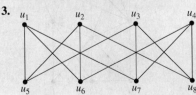 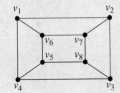

4.

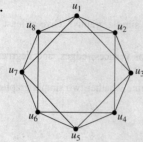

*5.

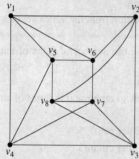

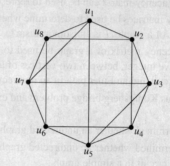

The **complete m-partite graph $K_{n_1,n_2,\ldots,n_m}$** has vertices partitioned into m subsets of $n_1, n_2, \ldots, n_m$ elements each, and vertices are adjacent if and only if they are in different subsets in the partition.

6. Draw these graphs.

   a) $K_{1,2,3}$ b) $K_{2,2,2}$ c) $K_{1,2,2,3}$

*7. How many vertices and how many edges does the complete m-partite graph $K_{n_1,n_2,\ldots,n_m}$ have?

*8. a) Prove or disprove that there are always two vertices with the same degree in a finite simple graph having at least two vertices.

   b) Do the same as in part (a) for finite multigraphs.

Let $G = (V, E)$ be a simple graph. The **subgraph induced** by a subset W of the vertex set V is the graph (W, F), where the edge set F contains an edge in E if and only if both endpoints of this edge are in W.

9. Consider the graph shown in Figure 3 of Section 6.4. Find the subgraphs induced by

   a) $\{a, b, c\}$.   b) $\{a, e, g\}$.   c) $\{b, c, f, g, h\}$.

10. Let n be a positive integer. Show that a subgraph induced by a nonempty subset of the vertex set of K_n is a complete graph.

A **clique** in a simple undirected graph is a complete subgraph that is not contained in any larger complete subgraph. In Exercises 11–13 find all cliques in the graph shown.

11.

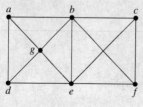

12.

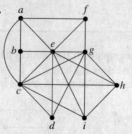

13.

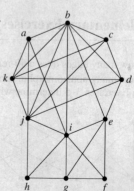

A **dominating set** of vertices in a simple graph is a set of vertices such that every other vertex is adjacent to at least one vertex of this set. A dominating set with the least number of vertices is called a **minimum dominating set.** In Exercises 14–16 find a minimum dominating set for the given graph.

14. 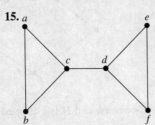   **15.**   **16.**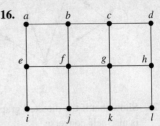

A simple graph can be used to determine the minimum number of queens on a chessboard that control the entire chessboard. An $n \times n$ chessboard has n^2 squares in an $n \times n$ configuration. A queen in a given position controls all squares in the same row, the same column, and on the two diagonals containing this square, as illustrated. The appropriate simple graph has n^2 vertices, one for each square, and two vertices are adjacent if a queen in the square represented by one of the vertices controls the square represented by the other vertex.

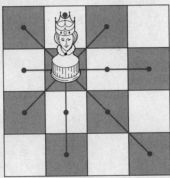

The Squares
Controlled
by a Queen

17. Construct the simple graph representing the $n \times n$ chessboard with edges representing the control of squares by queens for

a) $n = 3$.   b) $n = 4$.

18. Explain how the concept of a minimum dominating set applies to the problem of determining the minimum number of queens controlling an $n \times n$ chessboard.

∗∗19. Find the minimum number of queens controlling an $n \times n$ chessboard for

a) $n = 3$.   b) $n = 4$.   c) $n = 5$.

20. Suppose that G_1 and H_1 are isomorphic and that G_2 and H_2 are isomorphic. Prove or disprove that $G_1 \cup G_2$ and $H_1 \cup H_2$ are isomorphic.

21. Show that each of these properties is an invariant that isomorphic simple graphs either both have or both do not have.

a) connectedness   b) the existence of a Hamilton circuit   c) the existence of an Euler circuit

d) having crossing number C e) having n isolated vertices   f) being bipartite

22. How can the adjacency matrix of $\overline{G}$ be found from the adjacency matrix of G, where G is a simple graph?

23. How many nonisomorphic connected bipartite simple graphs are there with four vertices?

∗24. How many nonisomorphic simple connected graphs with five vertices are there

a) with no vertex of degree more than two?

b) with chromatic number equal to four?

c) that are nonplanar?

A directed graph is **self-converse** if it is isomorphic to its converse.

25. Determine whether the following graphs are self-converse.

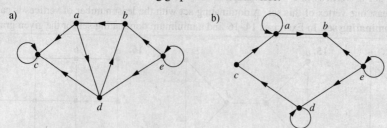

a)   b)

26. Show that if the directed graph G is self-converse and H is a directed graph isomorphic to G, then H is also self-converse.

An **orientation** of an undirected simple graph is an assignment of directions to its edges such that the resulting directed graph is strongly connected. When an orientation of an undirected graph exists, this graph is called **orientable**. In Exercises 27–29 determine whether the given simple graph is orientable.

27. 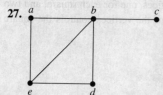   **28.**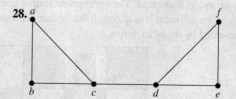

29.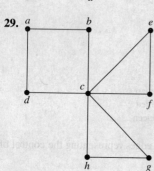

30. Because traffic is growing heavy in the central part of a city, traffic engineers are planning to change all the streets, which are currently two-way, into one-way streets. Explain how to model this problem.

*__31.__ Show that a graph is not orientable if it has a cut edge.

A **tournament** is a simple directed graph such that if u and v are distinct vertices in the graph, exactly one of (u, v) and (v, u) is an edge of the graph.

32. How many different tournaments are there with n vertices?

33. What is the sum of the in-degree and out-degree of a vertex in a tournament?

*__34.__ Show that every tournament has a Hamilton path.

35. Given two chickens in a flock, one of them is dominant. This defines the **pecking order** of the flock. How can a tournament be used to model pecking order?

36. Suppose that G is a connected multigraph with $2k$ vertices of odd degree. Show that there exist k subgraphs that have G as their union, where each of these subgraphs has an Euler path and where no two of these subgraphs have an edge in common. [*Hint:* Add k edges to the graph connecting pairs of vertices of odd degree and use an Euler circuit in this larger graph.]

*__37.__ Let G be a simple graph with n vertices. The **band width** of G, denoted by $B(G)$, is the minimum, over all permutations, $a_1, a_2, \ldots, a_n$ of the vertices of G, of $\max\{|i - j| \; a_i \text{ and } a_j \text{ are adjacent}\}$. That is, the band width is the minimum over all listings of the vertices of the maximum difference in the indices assigned to adjacent vertices. Find the band widths of these graphs.

a) K_5 b) $K_{1,3}$ c) $K_{2,3}$ d) $K_{3,3}$ e) Q_3 f) C_5

*38. The **distance** between two distinct vertices v_1 and v_2 of a connected simple graph is the length (number of edges) of the shortest path between v_1 and v_2. The **radius** of a graph is the minimum overall vertices v of the maximum distance from v to another vertex. The **diameter** of a graph is the maximum distance between two distinct vertices. Find the radius and diameter of

    a) K_6.   b) $K_{4,5}$.   c) Q_3.   d) C_6.

*39. a) Show that if the diameter of the simple graph G is at least four, then the diameter of its complement $\overline{G}$ is no more than two.

    b) Show that if the diameter of the simple graph G is at least three, then the diameter of its complement $\overline{G}$ is no more than three.

*40. Suppose that a multigraph has $2m$ vertices of odd degree. Show that any circuit that contains every edge of the graph must contain at least m edges more than once.

41. Find the second shortest path between the vertices a and z in Figure 3 of Section 6.6.

42. Devise an algorithm for finding the second shortest path between two vertices in a simple connected weighted graph.

43. Find the shortest path between the vertices a and z that passes through the vertex e in the weighted graph in Figure 4 in Section 6.6.

44. Devise an algorithm for finding the shortest path between two vertices in a simple connected weighted graph that passes through a specified third vertex.

*45. Show that if G is a simple graph with at least 11 vertices, then either G or $\overline{G}$, the complement of G, is nonplanar.

A set of vertices in a graph is called **independent** if no two vertices in the set are adjacent. The **independence number** of a graph is the maximum number of vertices in an independent set of vertices for the graph.

* 46. What is the independence number of

    a) K_n?   b) C_n?   c) Q_n?   d) $K_{m,n}$?

47. Show that the number of vertices in a simple graph is less than or equal to the product of the independence number and the chromatic number of the graph.

48. Show that the chromatic number of a graph is less than or equal to $v - i + 1$, where v is the number of vertices in the graph and i is the independence number of this graph.

49. Suppose that to generate a random simple graph with n vertices we first choose a real number p with $0 \leqslant p \leqslant 1$. For each of the $C(n, 2)$ pairs of distinct vertices we generate a random number x between 0 and 1. If $0 \leqslant x \leqslant p$, we connect these two vertices with an edge; otherwise these vertices are not connected.

    a) What is the probability that a graph with m edges where $0 \leqslant m \leqslant C(n, 2)$ is generated?

    b) What is the expected number of edges in a randomly generated graph with n vertices if each edge is included with probability p?

    c) Show that if $p = 1/2$ then every simple graph with n vertices is equally likely to be generated.

A property retained whenever additional edges are added to a simple graph (without adding vertices) is called **monotone increasing,** and a property that is retained whenever edges are removed from a simple graph (without removing vertices) is called **monotone decreasing.**

50. For each of these properties, determine whether it is monotone increasing and determine whether it is monotone decreasing.

    a) The graph G is connected.   b) The graph G is not connected.

    c) The graph G has an Euler circuit.   d) The graph G has a Hamilton circuit.

    e) The graph G is planar.   f) The graph G has chromatic number four.

    g) The graph G has radius three.   h) The graph G has diameter three.

51. Show that the graph property P is monotone increasing if and only if the graph property Q is monotone decreasing where Q is the property of not having property P.

**52. Suppose that P is a monotone increasing property of simple graphs. Show that the probability a random graph with n vertices has property P is a monotonic nondecreasing function of p, the probability an edge is chosen to be in the graph.

Computer Projects

Write programs with these input and output.

1. Given the vertex pairs associated to the edges of an undirected graph, find the degree of each vertex.
2. Given the ordered pairs of vertices associated to the edges of a directed graph, determine the in-degree and out-degree of each vertex.
3. Given the list of edges of a simple graph, determine whether the graph is bipartite.
4. Given the vertex pairs associated to the edges of a graph, construct an adjacency matrix for the graph. (Produce a version that works when loops, multiple edges, or directed edges are present.)
5. Given an adjacency matrix of a graph, list the edges of this graph and give the number of times each edge appears.
6. Given the vertex pairs associated to the edges of an undirected graph and the number of times each edge appears, construct an incidence matrix for the graph.
7. Given an incidence matrix of an undirected graph, list its edges and give the number of times each edge appears.
8. Given a positive integer n, generate an undirected graph by producing an adjacency matrix for the graph so that all simple graphs are equally likely to be generated.
9. Given a positive integer n, generate a directed graph by producing an adjacency matrix for the graph so that all directed graphs are equally likely to be generated.
10. Given the lists of edges of two simple graphs with no more than six vertices, determine whether the graphs are isomorphic.
11. Given an adjacency matrix of a graph and a positive integer n, find the number of paths of length n between two vertices. (Produce a version that works for directed and undirected graphs.)
*12. Given the list of edges of a simple graph, determine whether it is connected and find the number of connected components if it is not connected.
13. Given the vertex pairs associated to the edges of a multigraph, determine whether it has an Euler circuit and, if not, whether it has an Euler path. Construct an Euler path or circuit if it exists.
* 14. Given the ordered pairs of vertices associated to the edges of a directed multigraph, construct an Euler path or Euler circuit, if such a path or circuit exists.
**15. Given the list of edges of a simple graph, produce a Hamilton circuit, or determine that the graph does not have such a circuit.
**16. Given the list of edges of a simple graph, produce a Hamilton path, or determine that the graph does not have such a path.
17. Given the list of edges and weights of these edges of a weighted connected simple graph and two vertices in this graph, find the length of a shortest path between them using Dijkstra's algorithm. Also, find a shortest path.
18. Given the list of edges of an undirected graph, find a coloring of this graph using the algorithm given in the exercise set of Section 6.8.
19. Given a list of students and the courses that they are enrolled in, construct a schedule of final exams.
20. Given the distances between pairs of television stations, assign frequencies to these stations.

Computations and Explorations

Use a computational program or programs you have written to do these exercises.

1. Display all the simple graphs with four vertices.
2. Display a full set of nonisomorphic simple graphs with six vertices.
3. Display a full set of nonisomorphic directed graphs with four vertices.
4. Generate at random 10 different simple graphs each with 20 vertices so that each such graph is equally likely to be generated.
5. Construct a Gray code where the code words are bit strings of length six.

6. Construct knight's tours on chessboards of various sizes.
7. Determine whether each of the graphs you generated in Exercise 4 of this set is planar. If you can, determine the thickness of each of the graphs that are not planar.
8. Determine whether each of the graphs you generated in Exercise 4 of this set is connected. If a graph is not connected, determine the number of connected components of the graph.
9. Generate at random simple graphs with 10 vertices. Stop when you have constructed one with an Euler circuit. Display an Euler circuit in this graph.
10. Generate at random simple graphs with 10 vertices. Stop when you have constructed one with a Hamilton circuit. Display a Hamilton circuit in this graph.
11. Find the chromatic number of each of the graphs you generated in Exercise 4 of this set.
**12. Find the shortest path a traveling salesperson can take to visit each of the capitals of the 50 states in the United States, traveling by air between cities in a straight line.
*13. Estimate the probability that a randomly generated simple graph with n vertices is connected for each positive integer n not exceeding ten by generating a set of random simple graphs and determining whether each is connected.
**14. Work on the problem of determining whether the crossing number of $K(7, 7)$ is 77, 79, or 81. It is known that it equals one of these three values.

Writing Projects

Respond to these questions with essays using outside sources.

1. Describe the origins and development of graph theory prior to the year 1900.
2. Discuss the applications of graph theory to the study of ecosystems.
3. Discuss the applications of graph theory to sociology and psychology.
4. Discuss what can be learned by investigating the properties of the Web graph.
5. Describe algorithms for drawing a graph on paper or on a display given the vertices and edges of the graph. What considerations arise in drawing a graph so that it has the best appearance for understanding its properties?
6. What are some of the capabilities that a software tool for inputting, displaying, and manipulating graphs should have? Which of these capabilities do available tools have?
7. Describe some of the algorithms available for determining whether two graphs are isomorphic and the computational complexity of these algorithms. What is the most efficient such algorithm currently known?
8. Describe how Euler paths can be used to help determine DNA sequences.
9. Define *de Bruijn sequences* and discuss how they arise in applications. Explain how de Bruijn sequences can be constructed using Euler circuits.
10. Describe the *Chinese postman problem* and explain how to solve this problem.
11. Describe some of the different conditions that imply that a graph has a Hamilton circuit.
12. Describe some of the strategies and algorithms used to solve the traveling salesman problem.
13. Describe several different algorithms for determining whether a graph is planar. What is the computational complexity of each of these algorithms?
14. In modeling, very large scale integration (VLSI) graphs are sometimes embedded in a book, with the vertices on the spine and the edges on pages. Define the *book number* of a graph and find the book number of various graphs including K_n for $n = 3, 4, 5$, and 6.
15. Discuss the history of the Four Color Theorem.
16. Describe the role computers played in the proof of the Four Color Theorem. How can we be sure that a proof that relies on a computer is correct?
17. Describe and compare several different algorithms for coloring a graph, in terms of whether they produce a coloring with the least number of colors possible and in terms of their complexity.
18. Explain how graph multicolorings can be used in a variety of different models.
19. Explain how the theory of random graphs can be used in nonconstructive existence proofs of graphs with certain properties.

Chapter 7

Trees

A connected graph that contains no simple circuits is called a tree. Trees were used as long ago as 1857, when the English mathematician Arthur Cayley used them to count certain types of chemical compounds. Since that time, trees have been employed to solve problems in a wide variety of disciplines, as the examples in this chapter will show.

Trees are particularly useful in computer science, where they are employed in a wide range of algorithms. For instance, trees are used to construct efficient algorithms for locating items in a list. They can be used in algorithms, such as Huffman coding, that construct efficient codes saving costs in data transmission and storage. Trees can be used to study games such as checkers and chess and can help determine winning strategies for playing these games. Trees can be used to model procedures carried out using a sequence of decisions. Constructing these models can help determine the computational complexity of algorithms based on a sequence of decisions, such as sorting algorithms.

Procedures for building trees containing every vertex of a graph, including depth-first search and breadth-first search, can be used to systematically explore the vertices of a graph. Exploring the vertices of a graph via depth-first search, also known as backtracking, allows for the systematic search for solutions to a wide variety of problems, such as determining how eight queens can be placed on a chessboard so that no queen can attack another.

We can assign weights to the edges of a tree to model many problems. For example, using weighted trees we can develop algorithms to construct networks containing the least expensive set of telephone lines linking different network nodes.

7.1 Introduction to Trees

In Chapter 6 we showed how graphs can be used to model and solve many problems. In this chapter we will focus on a particular type of graph called a **tree**, so named because such graphs resemble trees. For example, *family trees* are graphs that represent genealogical charts. Family trees use vertices to represent the members of a family and edges to represent parent–child relationships. The family tree of the male members of the Bernoulli family of Swiss mathematicians is shown in Figure 1. The undirected graph representing a family tree (restricted to people of just one gender and with no inbreeding) is an example of a tree.

Definition 1   A *tree* is a connected undirected graph with no simple circuits.

Because a tree cannot have a simple circuit, a tree cannot contain multiple edges or loops. Therefore any tree must be a simple graph.

Example 1   Which of the graphs shown in Figure 2 are trees?

Solution: G_1 and G_2 are trees, because both are connected graphs with no simple circuits. G_3 is not a tree because e, b, a, d, e is a simple circuit in this graph. Finally, G_4 is not a tree because it is not connected. ◄

Any connected graph that contains no simple circuits is a tree. What about graphs containing no simple circuits that are not necessarily connected? These graphs are called **forests** and have the property that each of their connected components is a tree. Figure 3 displays a forest.

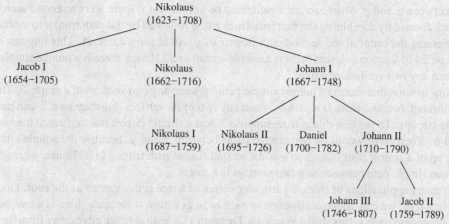

Figure 1   The Bernoulli Family of Mathematicians.

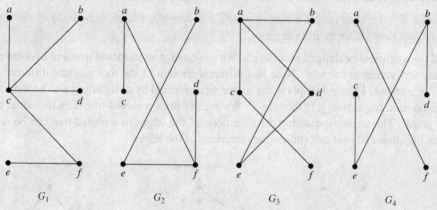

Figure 2   Examples of Trees and Graphs That Are Not Trees.

Trees are often defined as undirected graphs with the property that there is a unique simple path between every pair of vertices. Theorem 1 shows that this alternative definition is equivalent to our definition.

Theorem 1   An undirected graph is a tree if and only if there is a unique simple path between any two of its vertices.

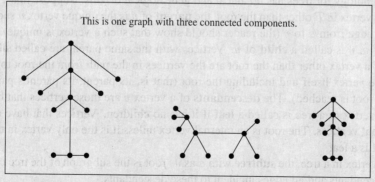

Figure 3   Example of a Forest.

Proof: First assume that T is a tree. Then T is a connected graph with no simple circuits. Let x and y be two vertices of T. Because T is connected, by Theorem 1 of Section 6.4 there is a simple path between x and y. Moreover, this path must be unique, for if there were a second such path, the path formed by combining the first path from x to y followed by the path from y to x obtained by reversing the order of the second path from x to y would form a circuit. This implies, using Exercise 24 of Section 6.4, that there is a simple circuit in T. Hence, there is a unique simple path between any two vertices of a tree.

Now assume that there is a unique simple path between any two vertices of a graph T. Then T is connected, because there is a path between any two of its vertices. Furthermore, T can have no simple circuits. To see that this is true, suppose T had a simple circuit that contained the vertices x and y. Then there would be two simple paths between x and y, because the simple circuit is made up of a simple path from x to y and a second simple path from y to x. Hence, a graph with a unique simple path between any two vertices is a tree.   ◁

In many applications of trees, a particular vertex of a tree is designated as the **root.** Once we specify a root, we can assign a direction to each edge as follows. Because there is a unique path from the root to each vertex of the graph (by Theorem 1), we direct each edge away from the root. Thus, a tree together with its root produces a directed graph called a **rooted tree.**

Definition 2   A *rooted tree* is a tree in which one vertex has been designated as the root and every edge is directed away from the root.

Rooted trees can also be defined recursively. We can change an unrooted tree into a rooted tree by choosing any vertex as the root. Note that different choices of the root produce different rooted trees. For instance, Figure 4 displays the rooted trees formed by designating a to be the root and c to be the root, respectively, in the tree T. We usually draw a rooted tree with its root at the top of the graph. The arrows indicating the directions of the edges in a rooted tree can be omitted, because the choice of root determines the directions of the edges.

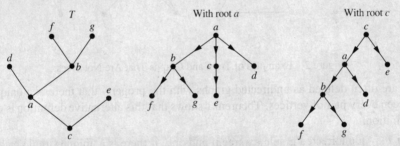

Figure 4   A Tree and Rooted Trees Formed by Designating Two Roots.

The terminology for trees has botanical and genealogical origins. Suppose that T is a rooted tree. If v is a vertex in T other than the root, the **parent** of v is the unique vertex u such that there is a directed edge from u to v (the reader should show that such a vertex is unique). When u is the parent of v, v is called a **child** of u. Vertices with the same parent are called **siblings.** The **ancestors** of a vertex other than the root are the vertices in the path from the root to this vertex, excluding the vertex itself and including the root (that is, its parent, its parent's parent, and so on, until the root is reached). The **descendants** of a vertex v are those vertices that have v as an ancestor. A vertex of a tree is called a **leaf** if it has no children. Vertices that have children are called **internal vertices.** The root is an internal vertex unless it is the only vertex in the graph, in which case it is a leaf.

If a is a vertex in a tree, the **subtree** with a as its root is the subgraph of the tree consisting of a and its descendants and all edges incident to these descendants.

Example 2   In the rooted tree T (with root a) shown in Figure 5, find the parent of c, the children of g, the siblings of h, all ancestors of e, all descendants of b, all internal vertices, and all leaves. What is the subtree rooted at g?

Solution: The parent of c is b. The children of g are h, i, and j. The siblings of h are i and j. The ancestors of e are c, b, and a. The descendants of b are c, d, and e. The internal vertices are a, b, c, g, h, and j. The leaves are d, e, f, i, k, l, and m. The subtree rooted at g is shown in Figure 6.   ◀

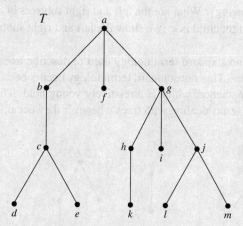
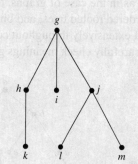

Figure 5   A Rooted Tree T.   Figure 6   The Subtree Rooted at g.

Rooted trees with the property that all of their internal vertices have the same number of children are used in many different applications. Later in this chapter we will use such trees to study problems involving searching, sorting, and coding.

Definition 3   A rooted tree is called an *m-ary tree* if every internal vertex has no more than m children. The tree is called a *full m-ary tree* if every internal vertex has exactly m children. An m-ary tree with $m = 2$ is called a *binary tree*.

Example 3   Are the rooted trees in Figure 7 full m-ary trees for some positive integer m?

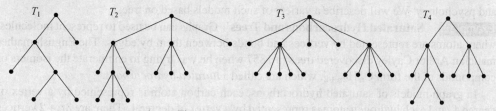

Figure 7   Four Rooted Trees.

Solution: T_1 is a full binary tree because each of its internal vertices has two children. T_2 is a full 3-ary tree because each of its internal vertices has three children. In T_3 each internal vertex has five children, so T_3 is a full 5-ary tree. T_4 is not a full m-ary tree for any m because some of its internal vertices have two children and others have three children.   ◀

An **ordered rooted tree** is a rooted tree where the children of each internal vertex are ordered. Ordered rooted trees are drawn so that the children of each internal vertex are shown in order from left to right. Note that a representation of a rooted tree in the conventional way determines an ordering for its edges. We will use such orderings of edges in drawings without explicitly mentioning that we are considering a rooted tree to be ordered.

In an ordered binary tree (usually called just a **binary tree**), if an internal vertex has two children, the first child is called the **left child** and the second child is called the **right child**. The tree rooted at the left child of a vertex is called the **left subtree** of this vertex, and the tree rooted at the right child of a vertex is called the **right subtree** of the vertex. The reader should note that for some applications every vertex of a binary tree, other than the root, is designated as a right or a left child of its parent. This is done even when some vertices have only one child. We will make such designations whenever it is necessary, but not otherwise.

Ordered rooted trees can be defined recursively.

Example 4   What are the left and right children of d in the binary tree T shown in Figure 8(a) (where the order is that implied by the drawing)? What are the left and right subtrees of c? *Solution*: The left child of d is f and the right child is g. We show the left and right subtrees of c in Figures 8(b) and 8(c), respectively.   ◀

Just as in the case of graphs, there is no standard terminology used to describe trees, rooted trees, ordered rooted trees, and binary trees. This nonstandard terminology occurs because trees are used extensively throughout computer science, which is a relatively young field. The reader should carefully check meanings given to terms dealing with trees whenever they occur.

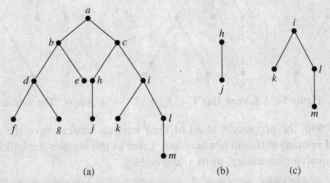

(a)   (b)   (c)

Figure 8   A Binary Tree T and Left and Right Subtrees of the Vertex c.

Trees as Models

Trees are used as models in such diverse areas as computer science, chemistry, geology, botany, and psychology. We will describe a variety of such models based on trees.

Example 5   **Saturated Hydrocarbons and Trees**   Graphs can be used to represent molecules, where atoms are represented by vertices and bonds between them by edges. The English mathematician Arthur Cayley discovered trees in 1857 when he was trying to enumerate the isomers of compounds of the form C_nH_{2n+2}, which are called *saturated hydrocarbons*.

In graph models of saturated hydrocarbons, each carbon atom is represented by a vertex of degree 4, and each hydrogen atom is represented by a vertex of degree 1. There are $3n+2$ vertices in a graph representing a compound of the form C_nH_{2n+2}. The number of edges in such a graph is half the sum of the degrees of the vertices. Hence, there are $(4n + 2n + 2)/2 = 3n + 1$ edges in this graph. Because the graph is connected and the number of edges is one less than the number of vertices, it must be a tree.

The nonisomorphic trees with n vertices of degree 4 and $2n + 2$ of degree 1 represent the different isomers of C_nH_{2n+2}. For instance, when $n = 4$, there are exactly two nonisomorphic trees of this type (the reader should verify this). Hence, there are exactly two different isomers of C_4H_{10}. Their structures are displayed in Figure 9. These two isomers are called butane and isobutane.   ◀

Example 6   **Representing Organizations**   The structure of a large organization can be modeled using a rooted tree. Each vertex in this tree represents a position in the organization. An edge from one vertex to another indicates that the person represented by the initial vertex is the (direct) boss of the person represented by the terminal vertex. The graph shown in Figure 10 displays such a tree. In the organization represented by this tree, the Director of Hardware Development works directly for the Vice President of R&D.   ◀

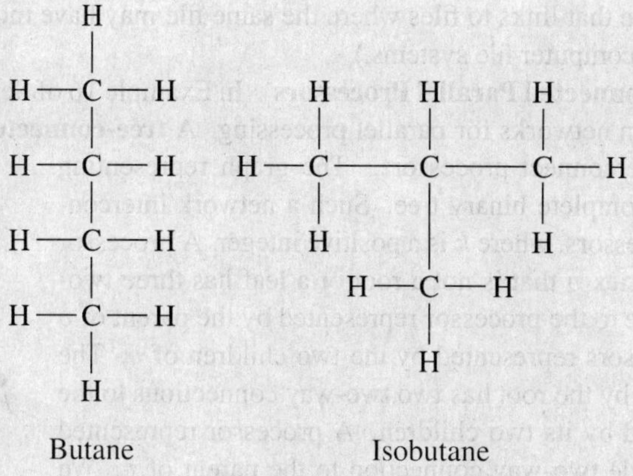

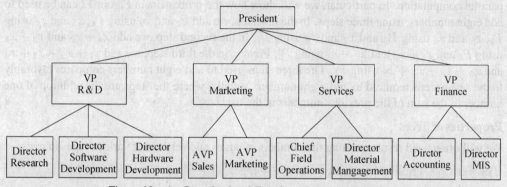

Figure 9   The Two Isomers of Butane.

Figure 10   An Organizational Tree for a Computer Company.

Example 7   **Computer File Systems**   Files in computer memory can be organized into directories. A directory can contain both files and subdirectories. The root directory contains the entire file system. Thus, a file system may be represented by a rooted tree, where the root represents the root directory, internal vertices represent subdirectories, and leaves represent ordinary files or empty directories. One such file system is shown in Figure 11. In this system, the file khr is in

The root is the root directory /
Internal vertices are directories
Leaves are files

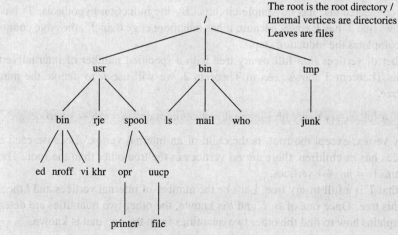

Figure 11   A Computer File System.

the directory rje. (Note that links to files where the same file may have more than one pathname can lead to circuits in computer file systems.)   ◄

Example 8   Tree-Connected Parallel Processors   In Example 16 of Section 6.2 we described several interconnection networks for parallel processing. A **tree-connected network** is another important way to interconnect processors. The graph representing such a network is a complete binary tree. Such a network intercon- nects $n = 2^k - 1$ processors, where k is a positive integer. A processor represented by the vertex v that is not a root or a leaf has three two- way connections—one to the processor represented by the parent of v and two to the processors represented by the two children of v. The processor represented by the root has two two-way connections to the processors represented by its two children. A processor represented by a leaf v has a single two-way connection to the parent of v. We display a tree-connected network with seven processors in Figure 12.

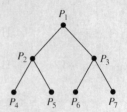

Figure 12   A Tree-Connected Network of Seven Processors.

We will illustrate how a tree-connected network can be used for parallel computation. In particular, we will show how the processors in Figure 12 can be used to add eight numbers, using three steps. In the first step, we add x_1 and x_2 using P_4, x_3 and x_4 using P_5, x_5 and x_6 using P_6, and x_7 and x_8 using P_7. In the second step, we add $x_1 + x_2$ and $x_3 + x_4$ using P_2 and $x_5 + x_6$ and $x_7 + x_8$ using P_3. Finally, in the third step, we add $x_1 + x_2 + x_3 + x_4$ and $x_5 + x_6 + x_7 + x_8$ using P_1. The three steps used to add eight numbers compares favorably to the seven steps required to add eight numbers serially, where the steps are the addition of one number to the sum of the previous numbers in the list.   ◄

Properties of Trees

We will often need results relating the numbers of edges and vertices of various types in trees.

Theorem 2   A tree with n vertices has $n - 1$ edges.

Proof: We will use mathematical induction to prove this theorem. Note that for all the trees here we can choose a root and consider the tree rooted.
BASIS STEP: When $n = 1$, a tree with $n = 1$ vertex has no edges. It follows that the theorem is true for $n = 1$.
INDUCTIVE STEP: The induction hypothesis states that every tree with k vertices has $k - 1$ edges, where k is a positive integer. Suppose that a tree T has $k + 1$ vertices and that v is a leaf of T (which must exist because the tree is finite), and let w be the parent of v. Removing from T the vertex v and the edge connecting w to v produces a tree T' with k vertices, because the resulting graph is still connected and has no simple circuits. By the induction hypothesis, T' has $k - 1$ edges. It follows that T has k edges because it has one more edge than T', the edge connecting v and w. This completes the induction step.   ◁

The number of vertices in a full m-ary tree with a specified number of internal vertices is determined, as Theorem 3 shows. As in Theorem 2, we will use n to denote the number of vertices in a tree.

Theorem 3   A full m-ary tree with i internal vertices contains $n = mi + 1$ vertices.

Proof: Every vertex, except the root, is the child of an internal vertex. Because each of the i internal vertices has m children, there are mi vertices in the tree other than the root. Therefore, the tree contains $n = mi + 1$ vertices.   ◁

Suppose that T is a full m-ary tree. Let i be the number of internal vertices and l the number of leaves in this tree. Once one of n, i, and l is known, the other two quantities are determined. Theorem 4 explains how to find the other two quantities from the one that is known.

Theorem 4 A full m-ary tree with
   (i) n vertices has $i = (n-1)/m$ internal vertices and $l = [(m-1)n+1]/m$ leaves,
   (ii) i internal vertices has $n = mi + 1$ vertices and $l = (m-1)i + 1$ leaves,
   (iii) l leaves has $n = (ml-1)/(m-1)$ vertices and $i = (l-1)/(m-1)$ internal vertices.

Proof: Let n represent the number of vertices, i the number of internal vertices, and l the number of leaves. The three parts of the theorem can all be proved using the equality given in Theorem 3, that is, $n = mi + 1$, together with the equality $n = l + i$, which is true because each vertex is either a leaf or an internal vertex. We will prove part (i) here. The proofs of parts (ii) and (iii) are left as exercises for the reader.

Solving for i in $n = mi + 1$ gives $i = (n-1)/m$. Then inserting this expression for i into the equation $n = l + i$ shows that $l = n - i = n - (n-1)/m = [(m-1)n+1]/m$.   ◁

Example 9 illustrates how Theorem 4 can be used.

Example 9   Suppose that someone starts a chain letter. Each person who receives the letter is asked to send it on to four other people. Some people do this, but others do not send any letters. How many people have seen the letter, including the first person, if no one receives more than one letter and if the chain letter ends after there have been 100 people who read it but did not send it out? How many people sent out the letter?

Solution: The chain letter can be represented using a 4-ary tree. The internal vertices correspond to people who sent out the letter, and the leaves correspond to people who did not send it out. Because 100 people did not send out the letter, the number of leaves in this rooted tree is $l = 100$. Hence, part (iii) of Theorem 4 shows that the number of people who have seen the letter is $n = (4 \cdot 100 - 1)/(4-1) = 133$. Also, the number of internal vertices is $133 - 100 = 33$, so 33 people sent out the letter.   ◀

It is often desirable to use rooted trees that are "balanced" so that the subtrees at each vertex contain paths of approximately the same length. Some definitions will make this concept clear. The **level** of a vertex v in a rooted tree is the length of the unique path from the root to this vertex. The level of the root is defined to be zero. The **height** of a rooted tree is the maximum of the levels of vertices. In other words, the height of a rooted tree is the length of the longest path from the root to any vertex.

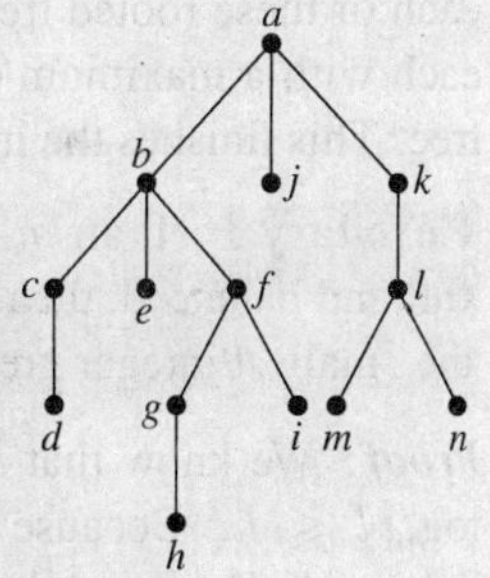

Figure 13   A Rooted Tree.

Example 10   Find the level of each vertex in the rooted tree shown in Figure 13. What is the height of this tree?

Solution: The root a is at level 0. Vertices b, j, and k are at level 1. Vertices c, e, f, and l are at level 2. Vertices d, g, i, m, and n are at level 3. Finally, vertex h is at level 4. Because the largest level of any vertex is 4, this tree has height 4.   ◀

A rooted m-ary tree of height h is **balanced** if all leaves are at levels h or $h - 1$.

Example 11   Which of the rooted trees shown in Figure 14 are balanced?

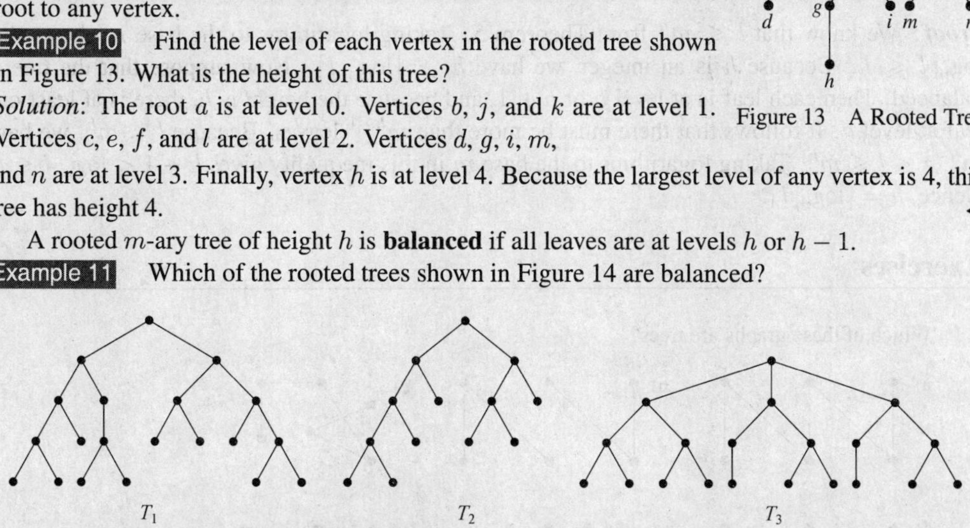

T_1 T_2 T_3

Figure 14   Some Rooted Trees.

Solution: T_1 is balanced, because all its leaves are at levels 3 and 4. However, T_2 is not balanced, because it has leaves at levels 2, 3, and 4. Finally, T_3 is balanced, because all its leaves are at level 3.   ◄

The results in Theorem 5 relate the height and the number of leaves in m-ary trees.

Theorem 5   There are at most m^h leaves in an m-ary tree of height h.

Proof: The proof uses mathematical induction on the height. First, consider m-ary trees of height 1. These trees consist of a root with no more than m children, each of which is a leaf. Hence, there are no more than $m^1 = m$ leaves in an m-ary tree of height 1. This is the basis step of the inductive argument.

Now assume that the result is true for all m-ary trees of height less than h; this is the inductive hypothesis. Let T be an m-ary tree of height h. The leaves of T are the leaves of the subtrees of T obtained by deleting the edges from the root to each of the vertices at level 1, as shown in Figure 15.

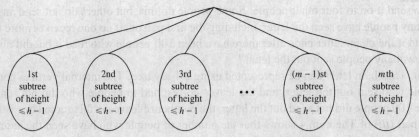

Figure 15   The Inductive Step of the Proof.

Each of these subtrees has height less than or equal to $h - 1$. So by the inductive hypothesis, each of these rooted trees has at most m^{h-1} leaves. Because there are at most m such subtrees, each with a maximum of m^{h-1} leaves, there are at most $m \cdot m^{h-1} = m^h$ leaves in the rooted tree. This finishes the inductive argument.   ◄

Corollary 1   If an m-ary tree of height h has l leaves, then $h \geqslant \lceil \log_m l \rceil$. If the m-ary tree is full and balanced, then $h = \lceil \log_m l \rceil$. (We are using the ceiling function here. Recall that $\lceil x \rceil$ is the smallest integer greater than or equal to x.)

Proof: We know that $l \leqslant m^h$ from Theorem 5. Taking logarithms to the base m shows that $\log_m l \leqslant h$. Because h is an integer, we have $h \geqslant \lceil \log_m l \rceil$. Now suppose that the tree is balanced. Then each leaf is at level h or $h - 1$, and because the height is h, there is at least one leaf at level h. It follows that there must be more than m^{h-1} leaves. Because $l \leqslant m^h$, we have $m^{h-1} < l \leqslant m^h$. Taking logarithms to the base m in this inequality gives $h - 1 < \log_m l \leqslant h$. Hence, $h = \lceil \log_m l \rceil$.   ◄

Exercises

1. Which of these graphs are trees?

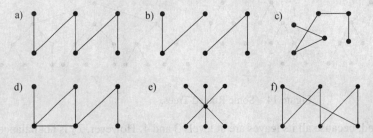

2. Answer these questions about the rooted tree illustrated.

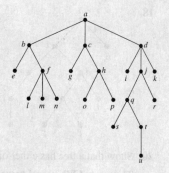

   a) Which vertex is the root?

   b) Which vertices are internal?

   c) Which vertices are leaves?

   d) Which vertices are children of j?

   e) Which vertex is the parent of h?

   f) Which vertices are siblings of o?

   g) Which vertices are ancestors of m?

   h) Which vertices are descendants of b?

3. Is the rooted tree in Exercise 2 a full m-ary tree for some positive integer m?

4. What is the level of each vertex of the rooted tree in Exercise 2?

5. Draw the subtree of the tree in Exercise 2 that is rooted at

   a) a.   b) c.   c) e.

6. a) How many nonisomorphic unrooted trees are there with three vertices?

   b) How many nonisomorphic rooted trees are there with three vertices (using isomorphism for directed graphs)?

7. a) How many nonisomorphic unrooted trees are there with five vertices?

   b) How many nonisomorphic rooted trees are there with five vertices (using isomorphism for directed graphs)?

8. How many edges does a tree with 10,000 vertices have?

9. How many edges does a full binary tree with 1000 internal vertices have?

10. Suppose 1000 people enter a chess tournament. Use a rooted tree model of the tournament to determine how many games must be played to determine a champion, if a player is eliminated after one loss and games are played until only one entrant has not lost. (Assume there are no ties.)

11. A chain letter starts with a person sending a letter out to 10 others. Each person is asked to send the letter out to 10 others, and each letter contains a list of the previous six people in the chain. Unless there are fewer than six names in the list, each person sends one dollar to the first person in this list, removes the name of this person from the list, moves up each of the other five names one position, and inserts his or her name at the end of this list. If no person breaks the chain and no one receives more than one letter, how much money will a person in the chain ultimately receive?

12. Either draw a full m-ary tree with 84 leaves and height 3, where m is a positive integer, or show that no such tree exists.

   A **complete m-ary tree** is a full m-ary tree, where every leaf is at the same level.

13. Construct a complete binary tree of height 4 and a complete 3-ary tree of height 3.

14. Prove

   a) part (ii) of Theorem 4.   b) part (iii) of Theorem 4.

15. How many edges are there in a forest of t trees containing a total of n vertices?

16. How many different isomers do these saturated hydrocarbons have?

   a) C_3H_8 b) C_5H_{12} c) C_6H_{14}

17. Let n be a power of 2. Show that n numbers can be added in $\log n$ steps using a tree-connected network of $n - 1$ processors.

   The **eccentricity** of a vertex in an unrooted tree is the length of the longest simple path beginning at this vertex. A vertex is called a **center** if no vertex in the tree has smaller eccentricity than this vertex. In Exercises 18–19 find every vertex that is a center in the given tree.

18.
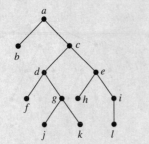

19.
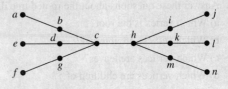

20. Show that a tree has either one center or two centers that are adjacent.

The **rooted Fibonacci trees** T_n are defined recursively in the following way. T_1 and T_2 are both the rooted tree consisting of a single vertex, and for $n = 3, 4, \ldots$, the rooted tree T_n is constructed from a root with T_{n-1} as its left subtree and T_{n-2} as its right subtree.

21. Draw the first seven rooted Fibonacci trees.

22. What is wrong with the following "proof" using mathematical induction of the statement that every tree with n vertices has a path of length $n-1$. *Basis step:* Every tree with one vertex clearly has a path of length 0. *Inductive step:* Assume that a tree with n vertices has a path of length $n-1$, which has u as its terminal vertex. Add a vertex v and the edge from u to v. The resulting tree has $n+1$ vertices and has a path of length n. This completes the induction step.

7.2   Applications of Trees

Introduction

We will discuss three problems that can be studied using trees. The first problem is: How should items in a list be stored so that an item can be easily located? The second problem is: What series of decisions should be made to find an object with a certain property in a collection of objects of a certain type? The third problem is: How should a set of characters be efficiently coded by bit strings?

Binary Search Trees

Searching for items in a list is one of the most important tasks that arises in computer science. Our primary goal is to implement a searching algorithm that finds items efficiently when the items are totally ordered. This can be accomplished through the use of a **binary search tree,** which is a binary tree in which each child of a vertex is designated as a right or left child, no vertex has more than one right child or left child, and each vertex is labeled with a key, which is one of the items. Furthermore, vertices are assigned keys so that the key of a vertex is both larger than the keys of all vertices in its left subtree and smaller than the keys of all vertices in its right subtree.

This recursive procedure is used to form the binary search tree for a list of items. Start with a tree containing just one vertex, namely, the root. The first item in the list is assigned as the key of the root. To add a new item, first compare it with the keys of vertices already in the tree, starting at the root and moving to the left if the item is less than the key of the respective vertex if this vertex has a left child, or moving to the right if the item is greater than the key of the respective vertex if this vertex has a right child. When the item is less than the respective vertex and this vertex has no left child, then a new vertex with this item as its key is inserted as a new left child. Similarly, when the item is greater than the respective vertex and this vertex has no right child, then a new vertex with this item as its key is inserted as a new right child. We illustrate this procedure with Example 1.

Example 1   Form a binary search tree for the words *mathematics, physics, geography, zoology, meteorology, geology, psychology,* and *chemistry* (using alphabetical order).

Solution: Figure 1 displays the steps used to construct this binary search tree. The word *mathematics* is the key of the root. Because *physics* comes after *mathematics* (in alphabetical order), add a right child of the root with key *physics*. Because *geography* comes before *mathematics*, add a left child of the root with key *geography*. Next, add a right child of the vertex with key *physics*, and assign it the key *zoology*, because *zoology* comes after *mathematics* and after *physics*. Similarly, add a left child of the vertex with key *physics* and assign this new vertex the key *meteorology*. Add a right child of the vertex with key *geography* and assign this new vertex the key *geology*. Add a left child of the vertex with key *zoology* and assign it the key *psychology*. Add a left child of the vertex with key *geography* and assign it the key *chemistry*. (The reader should work through all the comparisons needed at each step.)   ◄

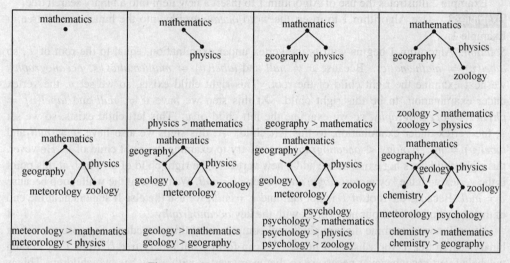

Figure 1   Constructing a Binary Search Tree.

Once we have a binary search tree, we need a way to locate items in the binary search tree, as well as a way to add new items. Algorithm 1, an insertion algorithm, actually does both of these tasks, even though it may appear that it is only designed to add vertices to a binary search tree. That is, Algorithm 1 is a procedure that locates an item x in a binary search tree if it is present, and adds a new vertex with x as its key if x is not present. In the pseudocode, v is the vertex currently under examination and $label(v)$ represents the key of this vertex. The algorithm begins by examining the root. If the x equals the key of v, then the algorithm has found the location of x and terminates; if x is less than the key of v, we move to the left child of v and repeat the procedure; and if x is greater than the key of v, we move to the right child of v and repeat the procedure. If at any step we attempt to move to a child that is not present, we know that x is not present in the tree, and we add a new vertex as this child with x as its key.

Algorithm 1   Locating and Adding Items to a Binary Search Tree.

procedure *insertion*(T: binary search tree, x: item)
$v := $ root of T
{a vertex not present in T has the value *null* }
while $v \neq null$ and $label(v) \neq x$
begin
   if $x < label(v)$ **then**
      if left child of $v \neq null$ **then** $v := $ left child of v

> **else** add *new vertex* as a left child of v and set $v := null$
> **else**
>   **if** right child of $v \neq null$ **then** $v :=$ right child of v
>   **else** add *new vertex* as a right child of v to T and set $v := null$
> **end**
> **if** root of $T = null$ **then** add a vertex v to the tree and label it with x
> **else if** v is null or $label(v) \neq x$ **then** label *new vertex* with x and let v be this new vertex
> $\{v = \text{location of } x\}$

Example 2 illustrates the use of Algorithm 1 to insert a new item into a binary search tree.

Example 2   Use Algorithm 1 to insert the word *oceanography* into the binary search tree in Example 1.

Solution: Algorithm 1 begins with v, the vertex under examination, equal to the root of T, so $label(v) = mathematics$. Because $v \neq null$ and $label(v) = mathematics < oceanography$, we next examine the right child of the root. This right child exists, so we set v, the vertex under examination, to be this right child. At this step we have $v \neq null$ and $label(v) = physics > oceanography$, so we examine the left child of v. This left child exists, so we set v, the vertex under examination, to this left child. At this step, we also have $v \neq null$ and $label(v) = metereology < oceanography$, so we try to examine the right child of v. However, this right child does not exist, so we add a new vertex as the right child of v (which at this point is the vertex with the key *metereology*) and we set $v := null$. We now exit the **while** loop because $v = null$. Because the root of T is not *null* and $v = null$, we use the **else if** statement at the end of the algorithm to label our new vertex with the key *oceanography*.   ◄

We will now determine the computational complexity of this procedure. Suppose we have a binary search tree T for a list of n items. We can form a full binary tree U from T by adding unlabeled vertices whenever necessary so that every vertex with a key has two children. This is illustrated in Figure 2. Once we have done this, we can easily locate or add a new item as a key without adding a vertex.

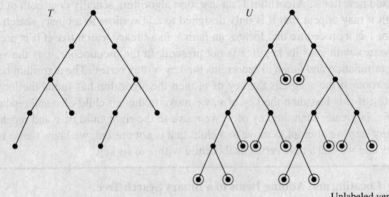

Unlabeled vertices circled

Figure 2   Adding Unlabeled Vertices to Make a Binary Search Tree Full.

The most comparisons needed to add a new item is the length of the longest path in U from the root to a leaf. The internal vertices of U are the vertices of T. It follows that U has n internal vertices. We can now use part (*ii*) of Theorem 4 in Section 7.1 to conclude that U has $n + 1$ leaves. Using Corollary 1 of Section 7.1, we see that the height of U is greater than or equal to $h = \lceil \log(n + 1) \rceil$. Consequently, it is necessary to perform at least $\lceil \log(n + 1) \rceil$ comparisons to add some item. Note that if U is balanced, its height is $\lceil \log(n + 1) \rceil$ (by Corollary 1 of Section

7.1). Thus, if a binary search tree is balanced, locating or adding an item requires no more than $\lceil \log(n+1) \rceil$ comparisons. A binary search tree can become unbalanced as items are added to it. Because balanced binary search trees give optimal worst-case complexity for binary searching, algorithms have been devised that rebalance binary search trees as items are added. The interested reader can consult references on data structures for the description of such algorithms.

Decision Trees

Rooted trees can be used to model problems in which a series of decisions leads to a solution. For instance, a binary search tree can be used to locate items based on a series of comparisons, where each comparison tells us whether we have located the item, or whether we should go right or left in a subtree. A rooted tree in which each internal vertex corresponds to a decision, with a subtree at these vertices for each possible outcome of the decision, is called a **decision tree.** The possible solutions of the problem correspond to the paths to the leaves of this rooted tree. Example 3 illustrates an application of decision trees.

Example 3   Suppose there are seven coins, all with the same weight, and a counterfeit coin that weighs less than the others. How many weighings are necessary using a balance scale to determine which of the eight coins is the counterfeit one? Give an algorithm for finding this counterfeit coin.

Solution: There are three possibilities for each weighing on a balance scale. The two pans can have equal weight, the first pan can be heavier, or the second pan can be heavier. Consequently, the decision tree for the sequence of weighings is a 3-ary tree. There are at least eight leaves in the decision tree because there are eight possible outcomes (because each of the eight coins can be the counterfeit lighter coin), and each possible outcome must be represented by at least one leaf. The largest number of weighings needed to determine the counterfeit coin is the height of the decision tree. From Corollary 1 of Section 7.1 it follows that the height of the decision tree is at least $\lceil \log_3 8 \rceil = 2$. Hence, at least two weighings are needed.

It is possible to determine the counterfeit coin using two weighings. The decision tree that illustrates how this is done is shown in Figure 3.   ◄

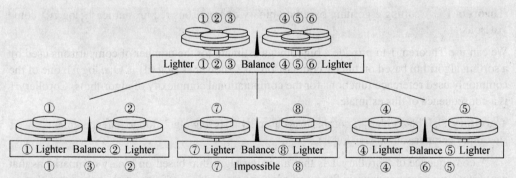

Figure3   A Decision Tree for Locating a Counterfeit Coin. The counterfeit coin is shown in color below each final weighing.

The Complexity of Sorting Algorithms   Many different sorting algorithms have been developed. To decide whether a particular sorting algorithm is efficient, its complexity is determined. Using decision trees as models, a lower bound for the worst-case complexity of sorting algorithms can be found.

We can use decision trees to model sorting algorithms and to determine an estimate for the worst-case complexity of these algorithms. Note that given n elements, there are $n!$ possible orderings of these elements, because each of the $n!$ permutations of these elements can be the correct order. The sorting algorithms studied in this book, and most commonly used sorting algorithms, are based on binary comparisons, that is, the comparison of two elements at a time. The result of each such comparison narrows down the set of possible orderings. Thus, a sorting algorithm based on binary comparisons can be represented by a binary decision tree in which each internal vertex represents a comparison of two elements. Each leaf represents one of the $n!$ permutations of n elements.

Example 4   We display in Figure 4 a decision tree that orders the elements of the list a, b, c. ◄

The complexity of a sort based on binary comparisons is measured in terms of the number of such comparisons used. The largest number of binary comparisons ever needed to sort a list with n elements gives the worst-case performance of the algorithm. The most comparisons used equals the longest path length in the decision tree representing the sorting procedure. In other words, the largest number of comparisons ever needed is equal to the height of the decision tree. Because the height of a binary tree with $n!$ leaves is at least $\lceil \log n! \rceil$ (using Corollary 1 in Section 7.1), at least $\lceil \log n! \rceil$ comparisons are needed, as stated in Theorem 1.

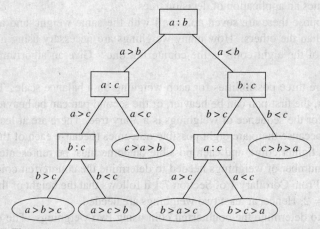

Figure 4   A Decision Tree for Sorting Three Distinct Elements.

Theorem 1   A sorting algorithm based on binary comparisons requires at least $\lceil \log n! \rceil$ comparisons.

We can use Theorem 1 to provide a big-Omega estimate for the number of comparisons used by a sorting algorithm based on binary comparison. We know that $\lceil \log n! \rceil$ is $\Theta(n \log n)$, one of the commonly used reference functions for the computational complexity of algorithms. Corollary 1 is a consequence of this estimate.

Corollary 1   The number of comparisons used by a sorting algorithm to sort n elements based on binary comparisons is $\Omega(n \log n)$.

A consequence of Corollary 1 is that a sorting algorithm based on binary comparisons that uses $\Theta(n \log n)$ comparisons, in the worst case, to sort n elements is optimal, in the sense that no other such algorithm has better worst-case complexity. We see that the merge sort algorithm is optimal in this sense.

We can also establish a similar result for the average-case complexity of sorting algorithms. The average number of comparisons used by a sorting algorithm based on binary comparisons is the average depth of a leaf in the decision tree representing the sorting algorithm. We know that the average depth of a leaf in a binary tree with N vertices is $\Omega(\log N)$. We obtain the following estimate when we let $N = n!$ and note that a function that is $\Omega(\log n!)$ is also $\Omega(n \log n)$ because $\log n!$ is $\Theta(n \log n)$.

Theorem 2   The average number of comparisons used by a sorting algorithm to sort n elements based on binary comparisons is $\Omega(n \log n)$.

Prefix Codes

Consider the problem of using bit strings to encode the letters of the English alphabet (where no distinction is made between lowercase and uppercase letters). We can represent each letter with a bit string of length five, because there are only 26 letters and there are 32 bit strings of length five. The total number of bits used to encode data is five times the number of characters in the text when each character is encoded with five bits. Is it possible to find a coding scheme of these letters such that, when data are coded, fewer bits are used? We can save memory and reduce transmittal time if this can be done.

Consider using bit strings of different lengths to encode letters. Letters that occur more frequently should be encoded using short bit strings, and longer bit strings should be used to encode rarely occurring letters. When letters are encoded using varying numbers of bits, some method must be used to determine where the bits for each character start and end. For instance, if e were encoded with 0, a with 1, and t with 01, then the bit string 0101 could correspond to *eat, tea, eaea,* or *tt.*

One way to ensure that no bit string corresponds to more than one sequence of letters is to encode letters so that the bit string for a letter never occurs as the first part of the bit string for another letter. Codes with this property are called **prefix codes.** For instance, the encoding of e as 0, a as 10, and t as 11 is a prefix code. A word can be recovered from the unique bit string that encodes its letters. For example, the string 10110 is the encoding of *ate.* To see this, note that the initial 1 does not represent a character, but 10 does represent a (and could not be the first part of the bit string of another letter). Then, the next 1 does not represent a character, but 11 does represent t. The final bit, 0, represents e.

A prefix code can be represented using a binary tree, where the characters are the labels of the leaves in the tree. The edges of the tree are labeled so that an edge leading to a left child is assigned a 0 and an edge leading to a right child is assigned a 1. The bit string used to encode a character is the sequence of labels of the edges in the unique path from the root to the leaf that has this character as its label. For instance, the tree in Figure 5 represents the encoding of e by 0, a by 10, t by 110, n by 1110, and s by 1111.

The tree representing a code can be used to decode a bit string. For instance, consider the word encoded by 11111011100 using the code in Figure 5. This bit string can be decoded by starting at the root, using the sequence of bits to form a path that stops when a leaf is reached. Each 0 bit takes the path down the edge leading to the left child of the last vertex in the path, and each 1 bit corresponds to the right child of this vertex. Consequently, the initial 1111 corresponds to the path starting at the root, going right four times, leading to a leaf in the graph that has s as its label, because the string 1111 is the code for s. Continuing with the fifth bit, we reach a leaf next after going right then left, when the vertex labeled with a, which is encoded by 10, is visited. Starting with the seventh bit, we reach a leaf next after going right three times and then left, when the vertex labeled with n, which is encoded by 1110, is visited. Finally, the last bit, 0, leads to the leaf that is labeled with e. Therefore, the original word is *sane.*

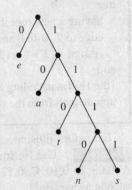

Figure 5   The Binary Tree with a Prefix Code.

We can construct a prefix code from any binary tree where the left edge at each internal vertex is labeled by 0 and the right edge by a 1 and where the leaves are labeled by characters. Characters are encoded with the bit string constructed using the labels of the edges in the unique path from the root to the leaves.

Huffman Coding   We now introduce an algorithm that takes as input the frequencies (which are the probabilities of occurrences) of symbols in a string and produces as output a prefix code that encodes the string using the fewest possible bits, among all possible binary prefix codes for these symbols. This algorithm, known as **Huffman coding,** was developed by David Huffman in a term paper he wrote in 1951 while a graduate student at MIT. (Note that this algorithm assumes that we already know how many times each symbol occurs in the string, so we can compute the frequency of each symbol by dividing the number of times this symbol occurs by the length of the string.) Huffman coding is a fundamental algorithm in *data compression,* the subject devoted to reducing the number of bits required to represent information. Huffman coding is extensively used to compress bit strings representing text and it also plays an important role in compressing audio and image files.

Algorithm 2 presents the Huffman coding algorithm. Given symbols and their frequencies, our goal is to construct a rooted binary tree where the symbols are the labels of the leaves. The algorithm begins with a forest of trees each consisting of one vertex, where each vertex has a symbol as its label and where the weight of this vertex equals the frequency of the symbol that is its label. At each step, we combine two trees having the least total weight into a single tree by introducing a new root and placing the tree with larger weight as its left subtree and the tree with smaller weight as its right subtree. Furthermore, we assign the sum of the weights of the two subtrees of this tree as the total weight of the tree. (Although procedures for breaking ties by choosing between trees with equal weights can be specified, we will not specify such procedures here.) The algorithm is finished when it has constructed a tree, that is, when the forest is reduced to a single tree.

Algorithm 2   Huffman Coding.

procedure *Huffman*(C: symbols a_i with frequencies w_i, $i = 1, \ldots, n$)
$F :=$ forest of n rooted trees, each consisting of the single vertex a_i and assigned weight w_i
while F is not a tree
begin
    Replace the rooted trees T and T' of least weights from F with $w(T) \geqslant w(T')$ with a tree
        having a new root that has T as its left subtree and T' as its right subtree. Label the new edge to T with 0 and the new edge to T' with 1.
        Assign $w(T) + w(T')$ as the weight of the new tree.
end
{the Huffman coding for the symbol a_i is the concatenation of the labels of the edges in the unique path from the root to the vertex a_i}

Example 5 illustrates how Algorithm 2 is used to encode a set of five symbols.

Example 5   Use Huffman coding to encode the following symbols with the frequencies listed: A: 0.08, B: 0.10, C: 0.12, D: 0.15, E: 0.20, F: 0.35. What is the average number of bits used to encode a character?

Solution: Figure 6 displays the steps used to encode these symbols. The encoding produced encodes A by 111, B by 110, C by 011, D by 010, E by 10, and F by 00. The average number of bits used to encode a symbol using this encoding is $3 \cdot 0.08 + 3 \cdot 0.10 + 3 \cdot 0.12 + 3 \cdot 0.15 + 2 \cdot 0.20 + 2 \cdot 0.35 = 2.45$. ◄

Note that Huffman coding is a greedy algorithm. Replacing the two subtrees with the smallest weight at each step leads to an optimal code in the sense that no binary prefix code for these symbols can encode these symbols using fewer bits.

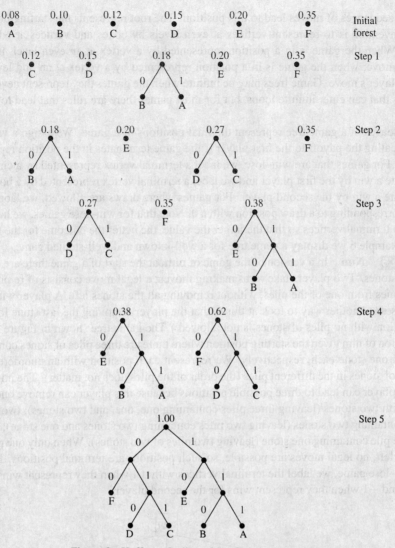

Figure 6   Huffman Coding of Symbols in Example 4.

There are many variations of Huffman coding. For example, instead of encoding single symbols, we can encode blocks of symbols of a specified length, such as blocks of two symbols. Doing so may reduce the number of bits required to encode the string. We can also use more than two symbols to encode the original symbols in the string. Furthermore, a variation known as adaptive Huffman coding (see [Sa00]) can be used when the frequency of each symbol in a string is not known in advance, so that encoding is done at the same time the string is being read.

Game Trees

Trees can be used to analyze certain types of games such as tic-tac-toe, nim, checkers, and chess. In each of these games, two players take turns making moves. Each player knows the moves made by the other player and no element of chance enters into the game. We model such games using **game trees;** the vertices of these trees represent the positions that a game can be in as it progresses; the edges represent legal moves between these positions. Because game trees are usually large, we simplify game trees by representing all symmetric positions of a game by the same vertex. However, the same position of a game may be represented by different vertices if different sequences of moves lead to this position. The root represents the starting position. The usual convention is to represent vertices at even levels by boxes and vertices at odd levels by circles. When the game is in a position represented by a vertex at an even level, it is the first player's move; when the game is in a position represented by a vertex at an odd level, it is the second player's move. Game trees may be infinite when the games they represent never end, such as games that can enter infinite loops, but for most games there are rules that lead to finite game trees.

The leaves of a game tree represent the final positions of a game. We assign a value to each leaf indicating the payoff to the first player if the game terminates in the position represented by this leaf. For games that are win–lose, we label a terminal vertex represented by a circle with a 1 to indicate a win by the first player and we label a terminal vertex represented by a box with a −1 to indicate a win by the second player. For games where draws are allowed, we label a terminal vertex corresponding to a draw position with a 0. Note that for win–lose games, we have assigned values to terminal vertices so that the larger the value, the better the outcome for the first player.

In Example 6 we display a game tree for a well-known and well-studied game.

Example 6   **Nim**   In a version of the game of **nim,** at the start of a game there are a number of piles of stones. Two players take turns making moves; a legal move consists of removing one or more stones from one of the piles, without removing all the stones left. A player without a legal move loses. (Another way to look at this is that the player removing the last stone loses because the position with no piles of stones is not allowed.) The game tree shown in Figure 7 represents this version of nim given the starting position where there are three piles of stones containing two, two, and one stone each, respectively. We represent each position with an unordered list of the number of stones in the different piles (the order of the piles does not matter). The initial move by the first player can lead to three possible positions because this player can remove one stone from a pile with two stones (leaving three piles containing one, one, and two stones); two stones from a pile containing two stones (leaving two piles containing two stones and one stone); or one stone from the pile containing one stone (leaving two piles of two stones). When only one pile with one stone is left, no legal moves are possible, so such positions are terminal positions. Because nim is a win–lose game, we label the terminal vertices with +1 when they represent wins for the first player and −1 when they represent wins for the second player.   ◀

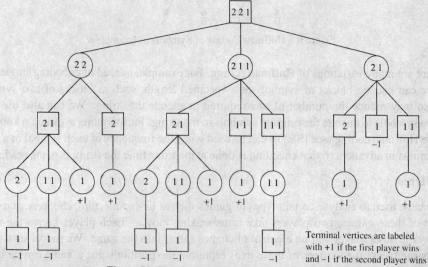

Terminal vertices are labeled
with +1 if the first player wins
and −1 if the second player wins

Figure 7   The Game Tree for a Game of Nim.

Example 7   **Tic-tac-toe**   The game tree for tic-tac-toe is extremely large and cannot be drawn here, although a computer could easily build such a tree. We show a portion of the game tic-tac-toe in Figure 8(a). Note that by considering symmetric positions equivalent, we need only consider three possible initial moves, as shown in Figure 8(a). We also show a subtree of this game tree leading to terminal positions in Figure 8(b), where a player who can win makes a winning move.

◀

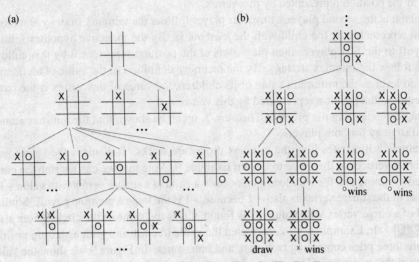

Figure 8   Some of the Game Tree for Tic-Tac-Toe.

We can recursively define the values of all vertices in a game tree in a way that enables us to determine the outcome of this game when both players follow optimal strategies. By a **strategy** we mean a set of rules that tells a player how to select moves to win the game. An optimal strategy for the first player is a strategy that maximizes the payoff to this player and for the second player is a strategy that minimizes this payoff. We now recursively define the value of a vertex.

Definition 1   The *value of a vertex in a game tree* is defined recursively as:
  (*i*) the value of a leaf is the payoff to the first player when the game terminates in the position represented by this leaf.
  (*ii*) the value of an internal vertex at an even level is the maximum of the values of its children, and the value of an internal vertex at an odd level is the minimum of the values of its children.

The strategy where the first player moves to a position represented by a child with maximum value and the second player moves to a position of a child with minimum value is called the **minmax strategy.** We can determine who will win the game when both players follow the minmax strategy by calculating the value of the root of the tree; this value is called the **value** of the tree. This is a consequence of Theorem 3.

Theorem 3   The value of a vertex of a game tree tells us the payoff to the first player if both players follow the minmax strategy and play starts from the position represented by this vertex.

Proof: We will use induction to prove this theorem.
BASIS STEP: If the vertex is a leaf, by definition the value assigned to this vertex is the payoff to the first player.
INDUCTIVE STEP: The inductive hypothesis is the assumption that the values of the children of a vertex are the payoffs to the first player, assuming that play starts at each of the positions represented by these vertices. We need to consider two cases, when it is the first player's turn and when it is the second player's turn.

When it is the first player's turn, this player follows the minmax strategy and moves to the position represented by the child with the largest value. By the inductive hypothesis, this value is the payoff to the first player when play starts at the position represented by this child and follows the minmax strategy. By the recursive step in the definition of the value of an internal vertex at an even level (as the maximum value of its children), the value of this vertex is the payoff when play begins at the position represented by this vertex.

When it is the second player's turn, this player follows the minmax strategy and moves to the position represented by the child with the least value. By the inductive hypothesis, this value is the payoff to the first player when play starts at the position represented by this child and both players follow the minmax strategy. By the recursive definition of the value of an internal vertex at an odd level as the minimum value of its children, the value of this vertex is the payoff when play begins at the position represented by this vertex.   ◁

Remark: By extending the proof of Theorem 3, it can be shown that the minmax strategy is the optimal strategy for both players.

Example 8 illustrates how the minmax procedure works. It displays the values assigned to the internal vertices in the game tree from Example 6. Note that we can shorten the computation required by noting that for win–lose games, once a child of a square vertex with value $+1$ is found, the value of the square vertex is also $+1$ because $+1$ is the largest possible payoff. Similarly, once a child of a circle vertex with value -1 is found, this is the value of the circle vertex also.

Example 8   In Example 6 we constructed the game tree for nim with a starting position where there are three piles containing two, two, and one stones. In Figure 9 we show the values of the vertices of this game tree. The values of the vertices are computed using the values of the leaves and working one level up at a time. In the right margin of this figure we indicate whether we use the maximum or minimum of the values of the children to find the value of an internal vertex at each level. For example, once we have found the values of the three children of the root, which are 1, -1, and -1, we find the value of the root by computing $\max(1, -1, -1) = 1$. Because the value of the root is 1, it follows that the first player wins when both players follow a minmax strategy.   ◁

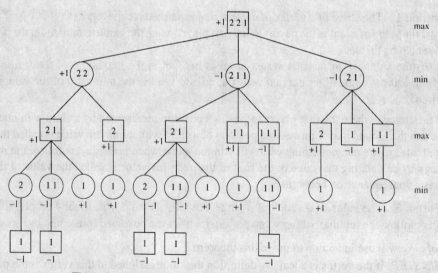

Figure 9   Showing the Values of Vertices in the Game of Nim.

Game trees for some well-known games can be extraordinarily large, because these games have many different possible moves. For example, the game tree for chess has been estimated to have as many as 10^{100} vertices! It may be impossible to use Theorem 3 directly to study a game because of the size of the game tree. Therefore, various approaches have been devised to help determine good strategies and to determine the outcome of such games. One useful technique, called *alpha-beta pruning,* eliminates much computation by pruning portions of the game tree that cannot affect the values of ancestor vertices. (For information about alpha-beta pruning, consult [Gr90].) Another useful approach is to use *evaluation functions,* which estimate the value of internal vertices in the game tree when it is not feasible to compute these values exactly. For example, in the game of tic-tac-toe, as an evaluation function for a position, we may use the number of files (rows, columns, and diagonals) containing no Os (used to indicate moves of the second player) minus the number of files containing no Xs (used to indicate moves of the first player). This evaluation function provides some indication of which player has the advantage in the game. Once the values of an evaluation function are inserted, the value of the game can be computed following the rules used for the minmax strategy. Computer programs created to play chess, such as the famous Deep Blue program, are based on sophisticated evaluation functions. For more information about how computers play chess see [Le91].

Exercises

1. Build a binary search tree for the words *banana, peach, apple, pear, coconut, mango,* and *papaya* using alphabetical order.

2. How many comparisons are needed to locate or to add each of these words in the search tree for Exercise 1, starting fresh each time?

   a) *pear*   b) *banana*   c) *kumquat*   d) *orange*

3. Using alphabetical order, construct a binary search tree for the words in the sentence "*The quick brown fox jumps over the lazy dog.*"

4. How many weighings of a balance scale are needed to find a counterfeit coin among four coins if the counterfeit coin may be either heavier or lighter than the others? Describe an algorithm to find the counterfeit coin using this number of weighings.

*5. How many weighings of a balance scale are needed to find a counterfeit coin among 12 coins if the counterfeit coin is lighter than the others? Describe an algorithm to find the lighter coin using this number of weighings.

6. Find the least number of comparisons needed to sort four elements and devise an algorithm that sorts these elements using this number of comparisons.

   The **tournament sort** is a sorting algorithm that works by building an ordered binary tree. We represent the elements to be sorted by vertices that will become the leaves. We build up the tree one level at a time as we would construct the tree representing the winners of matches in a tournament. Working left to right, we compare pairs of consecutive elements, adding a parent vertex labeled with the larger of the two elements under comparison. We make similar comparisons between labels of vertices at each level until we reach the root of the tree that is labeled with the largest element. The tree constructed by the tournament sort of 22, 8, 14, 17, 3, 9, 27, 11 is illustrated in part (a) of the figure. Once the largest element has been determined, the leaf with this label is relabeled by $-\infty$, which is defined to be less than every element. The labels of all vertices on the path from this vertex up to the root of the tree are recalculated, as shown in part (b) of the figure. This produces the second largest element. This process continues until the entire list has been sorted.

7. Complete the tournament sort of the list 22, 8, 14, 17, 3, 9, 27, 11. Show the labels of the vertices at each step.

8. Describe the tournament sort using pseudocode.

9. How many comparisons does the tournament sort use to find the second largest, the third largest, and so on, up to the $(n-1)$st largest (or second smallest) element?

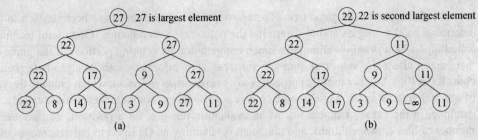

(a)   (b)

10. Which of these codes are prefix codes?

    a) a: 11, e: 00, t: 10, s: 01   b) a: 0, e: 1, t: 01, s: 001

    c) a: 101, e: 11, t: 001, s: 011, n: 010

    d) a: 010, e: 11, t: 011, s: 1011, n: 1001, i: 10101

11. What are the codes for a, e, i, k, o, p, and u if the coding scheme is represented by this tree?

12. Use Huffman coding to encode these symbols with given frequencies: a: 0.20, b: 0.10, c: 0.15, d: 0.25, e: 0.30. What is the average number of bits required to encode a character?

13. Construct two different Huffman codes for these symbols and frequencies: t: 0.2, u: 0.3, v: 0.2, w: 0.3.

14. Construct a Huffman code for the letters of the English alphabet where the frequencies of letters in typical English text are as shown in this table.

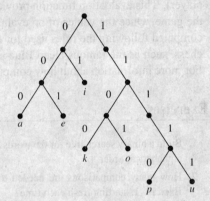

Letter	Frequency	Letter	Frequency
A	0.0817	N	0.0662
B	0.0145	O	0.0781
C	0.0248	P	0.0156
D	0.0431	Q	0.0009
E	0.1232	R	0.0572
F	0.0209	S	0.0628
G	0.0182	T	0.0905
H	0.0668	U	0.0304
I	0.0689	V	0.0102
J	0.0010	W	0.0264
K	0.0080	X	0.0015
L	0.0397	Y	0.0211
M	0.0277	Z	0.0005

Suppose that m is a positive integer with $m \geqslant 2$. An m-ary Huffman code for a set of N symbols can be constructed analogously to the construction of a binary Huffman code. At the initial step, $((N-1) \bmod (m-1)) + 1$ trees consisting of a single vertex with least weights are combined into a rooted tree with these vertices as leaves. At each subsequent step, the m trees of least weight are combined into an m-ary tree.

15. Using the symbols 0, 1, and 2 use ternary $(m = 3)$ Huffman coding to encode these letters with the given frequencies: A: 0.25, E: 0.30, N: 0.10, R: 0.05, T: 0.12, Z: 0.18.

16. Given $n + 1$ symbols $x_1, x_2, \ldots, x_n, x_{n+1}$ appearing 1, $f_1, f_2, \ldots, f_n$ times in a symbol string, respectively, where f_j is the jth Fibonacci number, what is the maximum number of bits used to encode a symbol when all possible tie-breaking selections are considered at each stage of the Huffman coding algorithm?

17. Draw a game tree for nim if the starting position consists of two piles with two and three stones, respectively. When drawing the tree represent by the same vertex symmetric positions that result from the same move. Find the value of each vertex of the game tree. Who wins the game if both players follow an optimal strategy?

18. Suppose that we vary the payoff to the winning player in the game of nim so that the payoff is n dollars when n is the number of legal moves made before a terminal position is reached. Find the payoff to the first player if the initial position consists of
a) two piles with one and three stones, respectively.

b) two piles with two and four stones, respectively.

c) three piles with one, two, and three stones, respectively.

19. Draw the subtree of the game tree for tic-tac-toe beginning at each of these positions. Determine the value of each of these subtrees.

a)

O	X	X
X	O	O
	X	

b)

X	O	X
O	X	X
	O	

c)

X		O
O	O	
X		X

d)

	O	X
	X	O
	X	O

20. Show that if a game of nim begins with two piles containing the same number of stones, as long as this number is at least two, then the second player wins when both players follow optimal strategies.

21. How many children does the root of the game tree for checkers have? How many grandchildren does it have?

22. Draw the game tree for the game of tic-tac-toe for the levels corresponding to the first two moves. Assign the value of the evaluation function mentioned in the text that assigns to a position the number of files containing no Os minus the number of files containing no Xs as the value of each vertex at this level and compute the value of the tree for vertices as if the evaluation function gave the correct values for these vertices.

7.3 Tree Traversal

Introduction

Ordered rooted trees are often used to store information. We need procedures for visiting each vertex of an ordered rooted tree to access data. We will describe several important algorithms for visiting all the vertices of an ordered rooted tree. Ordered rooted trees can also be used to represent various types of expressions, such as arithmetic expressions involving numbers, variables, and operations. The different listings of the vertices of ordered rooted trees used to represent expressions are useful in the evaluation of these expressions.

Universal Address Systems

Procedures for traversing all vertices of an ordered rooted tree rely on the orderings of children. In ordered rooted trees, the children of an internal vertex are shown from left to right in the drawings representing these directed graphs.

We will describe one way we can totally order the vertices of an ordered rooted tree. To produce this ordering, we must first label all the vertices. We do this recursively:

1. Label the root with the integer 0. Then label its k children (at level 1) from left to right with $1, 2, 3, \ldots, k$.

2. For each vertex v at level n with label A, label its k_v children, as they are drawn from left to right, with $A.1, A.2, \ldots, A.k_v$.

Following this procedure, a vertex v at level n, for $n \geqslant 1$, is labeled $x_1.x_2.\ldots.x_n$, where the unique path from the root to v goes through the x_1st vertex at level 1, the x_2nd vertex at level 2, and so on. This labeling is called the **universal address system** of the ordered rooted tree.

We can totally order the vertices using the lexicographic ordering of their labels in the universal address system. The vertex labeled $x_1.x_2.\ldots.x_n$ is less than the vertex labeled $y_1.y_2.\ldots.y_m$ if there is an i, $0 \leqslant i \leqslant n$, with $x_1 = y_1$, $x_2 = y_2, \ldots, x_{i-1} = y_{i-1}$, and $x_i < y_i$; or if $n < m$ and $x_i = y_i$ for $i = 1, 2, \ldots, n$.

Example 1   We display the labelings of the universal address system next to the vertices in the ordered rooted tree shown in Figure 1. The lexicographic ordering of the labelings is

$$0 \; <1 < 1.1 < 1.2 < 1.3 < 2 < 3 < 3.1 < 3.1.1 < 3.1.2 < 3.1.2.1 < 3.1.2.2$$
$$< 3.1.2.3 < 3.1.2.4 < 3.1.3 < 3.2 < 4 < 4.1 < 5 < 5.1 < 5.1.1 < 5.2 < 5.3$$

◀

Traversal Algorithms

Procedures for systematically visiting every vertex of an ordered rooted tree are called **traversal algorithms.** We will describe three of the most commonly used such algorithms, **preorder traversal, inorder traversal,** and **postorder traversal.** Each of these algorithms can be defined recursively. We first define preorder traversal.

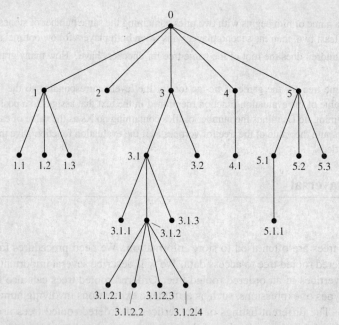

Figure 1   The Universal Address System of an Ordered Rooted Tree.

Definition 1   Let T be an ordered rooted tree with root r. If T consists only of r, then r is the *preorder traversal* of T. Otherwise, suppose that $T_1, T_2, \ldots, T_n$ are the subtrees at r from left to right in T. The *preorder traversal* begins by visiting r. It continues by traversing T_1 in preorder, then T_2 in preorder, and so on, until T_n is traversed in preorder.

The reader should verify that the preorder traversal of an ordered rooted tree gives the same ordering of the vertices as the ordering obtained using a universal address system. Figure 2 indicates how a preorder traversal is carried out.

Example 2 illustrates preorder traversal.

Example 2   In which order does a preorder traversal visit the vertices in the ordered rooted tree T shown in Figure 3?

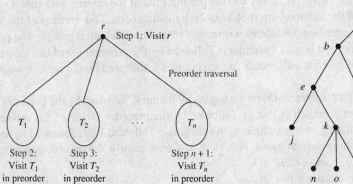

Figure 2   Preorder Traversal.

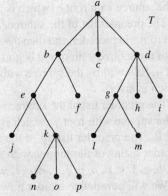

Figure 3   The Ordered Rooted Tree T.

Solution: The steps of the preorder traversal of T are shown in Figure 4. We traverse T in preorder by first listing the root a, followed by the preorder list of the subtree with root b, the preorder list

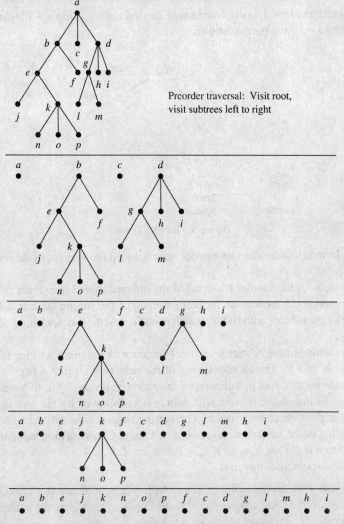

Figure 4   The Preorder Traversal of T.

of the subtree with root c (which is just c) and the preorder list of the subtree with root d.

The preorder list of the subtree with root b begins by listing b, then the vertices of the subtree with root e in preorder, and then the subtree with root f in preorder (which is just f). The preorder list of the subtree with root d begins by listing d, followed by the preorder list of the subtree with root g, followed by the subtree with root h (which is just h), followed by the subtree with root i (which is just i).

The preorder list of the subtree with root e begins by listing e, followed by the preorder listing of the subtree with root j (which is just j), followed by the preorder listing of the subtree with root k. The preorder listing of the subtree with root g is g followed by l, followed by m. The preorder listing of the subtree with root k is k, n, o, p. Consequently, the preorder traversal of T is a, b, e, j, k, n, o, p, f, c, d, g, l, m, h, i. ◄

We will now define inorder traversal.

Definition 2 Let T be an ordered rooted tree with root r. If T consists only of r, then r is the *inorder traversal* of T. Otherwise, suppose that $T_1, T_2, \ldots, T_n$ are the subtrees at r from left to right. The *inorder traversal* begins by traversing T_1 in inorder, then visiting r. It continues by traversing T_2 in inorder, then T_3 in inorder, $\ldots$, and finally T_n in inorder.

Figure 5 indicates how inorder traversal is carried out. Example 3 illustrates how inorder traversal is carried out for a particular tree.

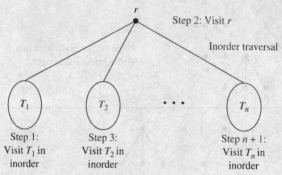

Figure 5   Inorder Traversal.

Example 3   In which order does an inorder traversal visit the vertices of the ordered rooted tree T in Figure 3?

Solution: The steps of the inorder traversal of the ordered rooted tree T are shown in Figure 6. The inorder traversal begins with an inorder traversal of the subtree with root b, the root a, the inorder listing of the subtree with root c, which is just c, and the inorder listing of the subtree with root d.

The inorder listing of the subtree with root b begins with the inorder listing of the subtree with root e, the root b, and f. The inorder listing of the subtree with root d begins with the inorder listing of the subtree with root g, followed by the root d, followed by h, followed by i.

The inorder listing of the subtree with root e is j, followed by the root e, followed by the inorder listing of the subtree with root k. The inorder listing of the subtree with root g is l, g, m. The inorder listing of the subtree with root k is n, k, o, p. Consequently, the inorder listing of the ordered rooted tree is j, e, n, k, o, p, b, f, a, c, l, g, m, d, h, i. ◄

We now define postorder traversal.

Definition 3 Let T be an ordered rooted tree with root r. If T consists only of r, then r is the *postorder traversal* of T. Otherwise, suppose that $T_1, T_2, \ldots, T_n$ are the subtrees at r from left to right. The *postorder traversal* begins by traversing T_1 in postorder, then T_2 in postorder, $\ldots$, then T_n in postorder, and ends by visiting r.

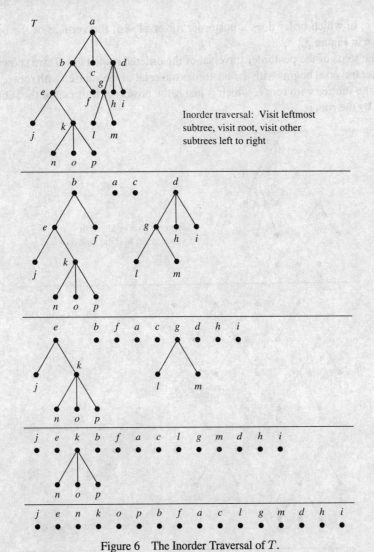

Inorder traversal: Visit leftmost
subtree, visit root, visit other
subtrees left to right

Figure 6   The Inorder Traversal of T.

Figure 7 illustrates how postorder traversal is done. Example 4 illustrates how postorder traversal works.

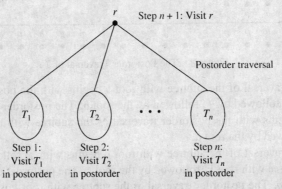

Step $n + 1$: Visit r

Postorder traversal

Step 1:   Step 2:   Step n:
Visit T_1 Visit T_2 Visit T_n
in postorder   in postorder   in postorder

Figure 7   Postorder Traversal.

Example 4   In which order does a postorder traversal visit the vertices of the ordered rooted tree T shown in Figure 3?

Solution: The steps of the postorder traversal of the ordered rooted tree T are shown in Figure 8. The postorder traversal begins with the postorder traversal of the subtree with root b, the postorder traversal of the subtree with root c, which is just c, the postorder traversal of the subtree with root d, followed by the root a.

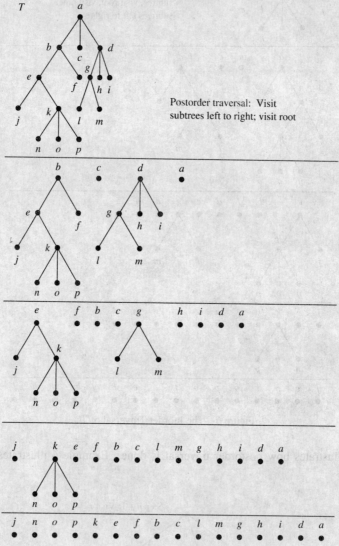

Postorder traversal: Visit subtrees left to right; visit root

Figure 8   The Postorder Traversal of T.

The postorder traversal of the subtree with root b begins with the postorder traversal of the subtree with root e, followed by f, followed by the root b. The postorder traversal of the rooted tree with root d begins with the postorder traversal of the subtree with root g, followed by h, followed by i, followed by the root d.

The postorder traversal of the subtree with root e begins with j, followed by the postorder traversal of the subtree with root k, followed by the root e. The postorder traversal of the subtree with root g is l, m, g. The postorder traversal of the subtree with root k is n, o, p, k. Therefore, the postorder traversal of T is j, n, o, p, k, e, f, b, c, l, m, g, h, i, d, a. ◄

There are easy ways to list the vertices of an ordered rooted tree in preorder, inorder, and postorder. To do this, first draw a curve around the ordered rooted tree starting at the root, moving along the edges, as shown in the example in Figure 9. We can list the vertices in preorder by listing each vertex the first time this curve passes it. We can list the vertices in inorder by listing a leaf the first time the curve passes it and listing each internal vertex the second time the curve passes it. We can list the vertices in postorder by listing a vertex the last time it is passed on the way back up to its parent. When this is done in the rooted tree in Figure 9, it follows that the preorder traversal gives $a, b, d, h, e, i, j, c, f, g, k$, the inorder traversal gives $h, d, b, i, e, j, a, f, c, k, g$; and the postorder traversal gives $h, d, i, j, e, b, f, k, g, c, a$.

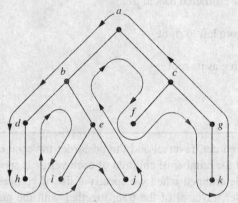

Figure 9   A Shortcut for Traversing an Ordered Rooted Tree in Preorder, Inorder, and Postorder.

Algorithms for traversing ordered rooted trees in preorder, inorder, or postorder are most easily expressed recursively.

Algorithm 1   Preorder Traversal.

procedure *preorder*(T: ordered rooted tree)
r := root of T
list r
for each child c of r from left to right
begin
    $T(c)$:= subtree with c as its root
    preorder($T(c)$)
end

Algorithm 2   Inorder Traversal.

procedure *inorder*(T: ordered rooted tree)
r := root of T
if r is a leaf **then** list r
else
begin
    l := first child of r from left to right
    $T(l)$:= subtree with l as its root
    inorder($T(l)$)

list r
for each child c of r except for l from left to right
   $T(c) :=$ subtree with c as its root
   inorder$(T(c))$
end

Algorithm 3   Postorder Traversal.

procedure *postorder*(T: ordered rooted tree)
$r :=$ root of T
for each child c of r from left to right
begin
   $T(c) :=$ subtree with c as its root
   postorder$(T(c))$
end
list r

Note that both the preorder traversal and the postorder traversal encode the structure of an ordered rooted tree when the number of children of each vertex is specified. That is, an ordered rooted tree is uniquely determined when we specify a list of vertices generated by a preorder traversal or by a postorder traversal of the tree, together with the number of children of each vertex (see Exercise 13). In particular, both a preorder traversal and a postorder traversal encode the structure of a full ordered m-ary tree. However, when the number of children of vertices is not specified, neither a preorder traversal nor a postorder traversal encodes the structure of an ordered rooted tree (see Exercise 14).

Infix, Prefix, and Postfix Notation

We can represent complicated expressions, such as compound propositions, combinations of sets, and arithmetic expressions using ordered rooted trees. For instance, consider the representation of an arithmetic expression involving the operators + (addition), − (subtraction), ∗ (multiplication), / (division), and ↑ (exponentiation). We will use parentheses to indicate the order of the operations. An ordered rooted tree can be used to represent such expressions, where the internal vertices represent operations, and the leaves represent the variables or numbers. Each operation operates on its left and right subtrees (in that order).

Example 5   What is the ordered rooted tree that represents the expression $((x + y) \uparrow 2) + ((x - 4)/3)$?

Solution: The binary tree for this expression can be built from the bottom up. First, a subtree for the expression $x + y$ is constructed. Then this is incorporated as part of the larger subtree representing $(x + y) \uparrow 2$. Also, a subtree for $x - 4$ is constructed, and then this is incorporated into a subtree representing $(x - 4)/3$. Finally the subtrees representing $(x+y) \uparrow 2$ and $(x - 4)/3$ are combined to form the ordered rooted tree representing $((x+y) \uparrow 2)+((x-4)/3)$. These steps are shown in Figure 10. ◄

An inorder traversal of the binary tree representing an expression produces the original expression with the elements and operations in the same order as they originally occurred, except for unary operations, which instead immediately follow their operands. For instance, inorder traversals of the binary trees in Figure 11, which represent the expressions $(x + y)/(x + 3)$, $(x + (y/x)) + 3$, and $x + (y/(x + 3))$, all lead to the infix expression $x + y/x + 3$. To make such expressions unambiguous it is necessary to include parentheses in the inorder traversal whenever we encounter an operation. The fully parenthesized expression obtained in this way is said to be in **infix form.**

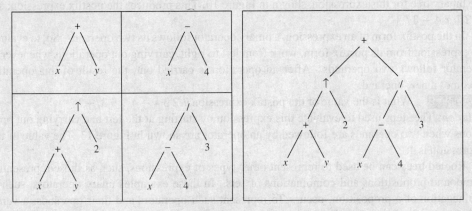

Figure 10   A Binary Tree Representing $((x + y) \uparrow 2) + ((x - 4)/3)$.

We obtain the **prefix form** of an expression when we traverse its rooted tree in preorder. Expressions written in prefix form are said to be in **Polish notation,** which is named after the Polish logician Jan Łukasiewicz. An expression in prefix notation (where each operation has a specified number of operands), is unambiguous, so no parentheses are needed in such an expression. The verification of this is left as an exercise for the reader.

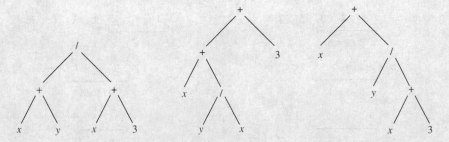

Figure 11   Rooted Trees Representing $(x + y)/(x + 3)$, $(x + (y/x)) + 3$, and $x + (y/(x + 3))$.

Example 6   What is the prefix form for $((x + y) \uparrow 2) + ((x - 4)/3)$?
Solution: We obtain the prefix form for this expression by traversing the binary tree that represents it, shown in Figure 10. This produces $+ \uparrow + x\, y\, 2 / - x\, 4\, 3$. ◄

In the prefix form of an expression, a binary operator, such as $+$, precedes its two operands. Hence, we can evaluate an expression in prefix form by working from right to left. When we encounter an operator, we perform the corresponding operation with the two operands immediately to the right of this operand. Also, whenever an operation is performed, we consider the result a new operand.

Example 7   What is the value of the prefix expression $+ - * 2\, 3\, 5/ \uparrow 2\, 3\, 4$?
Solution: The steps used to evaluate this expression by working right to left, and performing operations using the operands on the right, are shown in Figure 12. The value of this expression is 3. ◄

We obtain the **postfix form** of an expression by traversing its binary tree in postorder. Expressions written in postfix form are said to be in **reverse Polish notation.** Expressions in reverse Polish notation are unambiguous, so parentheses are not needed. The verification of this is left to the reader.

Example 8   What is the postfix form of the expression $((x + y) \uparrow 2) + ((x - 4)/3)$?
Solution: The postfix form of the expression is obtained by carrying out a postorder traversal of the binary tree for this expression, shown in Figure 10. This produces the postfix expression: $x\, y + 2 \uparrow x\, 4 - 3\, / +$. ◀

In the postfix form of an expression, a binary operator follows its two operands. So, to evaluate an expression from its postfix form, work from left to right, carrying out operations whenever an operator follows two operands. After an operation is carried out, the result of this operation becomes a new operand.

Example 9   What is the value of the postfix expression $7\, 2\, 3\, * - 4 \uparrow 9\, 3\, /+$?
Solution: The steps used to evaluate this expression by starting at the left and carrying out operations when two operands are followed by an operator are shown in Figure 13. The value of this expression is 4. ◀

Rooted trees can be used to represent other types of expressions, such as those representing compound propositions and combinations of sets. In these examples unary operators, such as the negation of a proposition, occur. To represent such operators and their operands, a vertex representing the operator and a child of this vertex representing the operand are used.

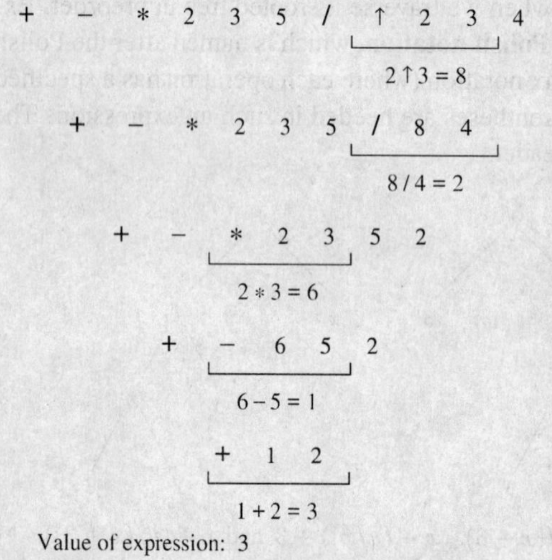

Figure 12   Evaluating a Prefix Expression. 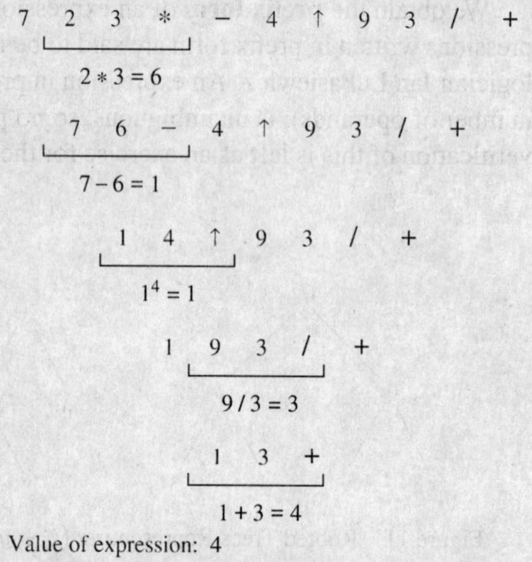   Figure 13   Evaluating a Postfix Expression.

Example 10   Find the ordered rooted tree representing the compound proposition $(\neg(p \wedge q)) \leftrightarrow (\neg p \vee \neg q)$. Then use this rooted tree to find the prefix, postfix, and infix forms of this expression.
Solution: The rooted tree for this compound proposition is constructed from the bottom up. First, subtrees for $\neg p$ and $\neg q$ are formed (where $\neg$ is considered a unary operator). Also, a subtree for $p \wedge q$ is formed. Then subtrees for $\neg(p \wedge q)$ and $(\neg p) \vee (\neg q)$ are constructed. Finally, these two subtrees are used to form the final rooted tree. The steps of this procedure are shown in Figure 14.

The prefix, postfix, and infix forms of this expression are found by traversing this rooted tree in preorder, postorder, and inorder (including parentheses), respectively. These traversals give $\leftrightarrow \neg \wedge pq \vee \neg p \neg q$, $pq \wedge \neg p \neg q \neg \vee \leftrightarrow$, and $(\neg(p \wedge q)) \leftrightarrow ((\neg p) \vee (\neg q))$, respectively. ◀

Because prefix and postfix expressions are unambiguous and because they can be evaluated easily without scanning back and forth, they are used extensively in computer science. Such expressions are especially useful in the construction of compilers.

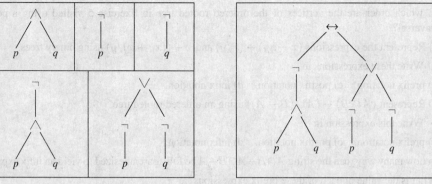

Figure 14   Constructing the Rooted Tree for a Compound Proposition.

Exercises

In Exercises 1–2 construct the universal address system for the given ordered rooted tree. Then use this to order its vertices using the lexicographic order of their labels.

1.

2.

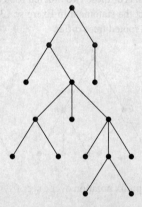

3. Suppose that the vertex with the largest address in an ordered rooted tree T has address 2.3.4.3.1. Is it possible to determine the number of vertices in T?

In Exercises 4–5 determine the order in which a preorder traversal visits the vertices of the given ordered rooted tree.

4.

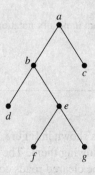

5.

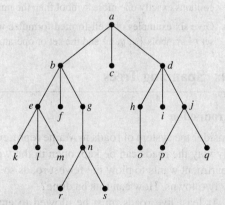

6. In which order are the vertices of the ordered rooted tree in Exercise 4 visited using a postorder traversal?

7. In which order are the vertices of the ordered rooted tree in Exercise 5 visited using a postorder traversal?

8. a) Represent the expressions $(x + xy) + (x/y)$ and $x + ((xy + x)/y)$ using binary trees.

   Write these expressions in

   b) prefix notation.   c) postfix notation.   d) infix notation.

9. a) Represent $(A \cap B) - (A \cup (B - A))$ using an ordered rooted tree.

   Write this expression in

   b) prefix notation.   c) postfix notation.   d) infix notation.

*10. In how many ways can the string $A \cap B - A \cap B - A$ be fully parenthesized to yield an infix expression?

11. What is the value of each of these prefix expressions?

   a) $- * 2 / 8 4 3$ b) $\uparrow - * 3 3 * 4 2 5$ c) $+ - \uparrow 3 2 \uparrow 2 3 / 6 - 4 2$ d) $* + 3 + 3 \uparrow 3 + 3 3 3$

12. Construct the ordered rooted tree whose preorder traversal is $a, b, f, c, g, h, i, d, e, j, k, l$, where a has four children, c has three children, j has two children, b and e have one child each, and all other vertices are leaves.

*13. Show that an ordered rooted tree is uniquely determined when a list of vertices generated by a postorder traversal of the tree and the number of children of each vertex are specified.

14. Show that postorder traversals of these two ordered rooted trees produce the same list of vertices. Note that this does not contradict the statement in Exercise 13, because the numbers of children of internal vertices in the two ordered rooted trees differ.

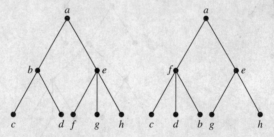

Well-formed formulae in prefix notation over a set of symbols and a set of binary operators are defined recursively by these rules:

   (*i*) if x is a symbol, then x is a well-formed formula in prefix notation;

   (*ii*) if X and Y are well-formed formulae and $*$ is an operator, then $* X Y$ is a well-formed formula.

*15. Show that any well-formed formula in prefix notation over a set of symbols and a set of binary operators contains exactly one more symbol than the number of operators.

16. Give six examples of well-formed formulae with three or more operators in postfix notation over the set of symbols $\{x, y, z\}$ and the set of operators $\{+, \times, \circ\}$.

7.4   Spanning Trees

Introduction

Consider the system of roads in Maine represented by the simple graph shown in Figure 1(a). The only way the roads can be kept open in the winter is by frequently plowing them. The highway department wants to plow the fewest roads so that there will always be cleared roads connecting any two towns. How can this be done?

   At least five roads must be plowed to ensure that there is a path between any two towns. Figure 1(b) shows one such set of roads. Note that the subgraph representing these roads is a tree, because it is connected and contains six vertices and five edges.

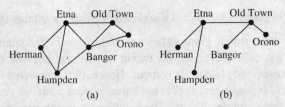

Figure 1   (a) A Road System and (b) a Set of Roads to Plow.

This problem was solved with a connected subgraph with the minimum number of edges containing all vertices of the original simple graph. Such a graph must be a tree.

Definition 1   Let G be a simple graph. A *spanning tree* of G is a subgraph of G that is a tree containing every vertex of G.

A simple graph with a spanning tree must be connected, because there is a path in the spanning tree between any two vertices. The converse is also true; that is, every connected simple graph has a spanning tree. We will give an example before proving this result.

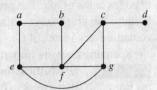

Figure 2   The Simple Graph G.

Example 1   Find a spanning tree of the simple graph G shown in Figure 2.

Solution: The graph G is connected, but it is not a tree because it contains simple circuits. Remove the edge $\{a, e\}$. This eliminates one simple circuit, and the resulting subgraph is still connected and still contains every vertex of G. Next remove the edge $\{e, f\}$ to eliminate a second simple circuit. Finally, remove edge $\{c, g\}$ to produce a simple graph with no simple circuits. This subgraph is a spanning tree, because it is a tree that contains every vertex of G. The sequence of edge removals used to produce the spanning tree is illustrated in Figure 3.

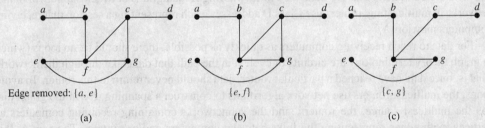

Figure 3   Producing a Spanning Tree for G by Removing Edges That Form Simple Circuits.

The tree shown in Figure 3 is not the only spanning tree of G. For instance, each of the trees shown in Figure 4 is a spanning tree of G.   ◄

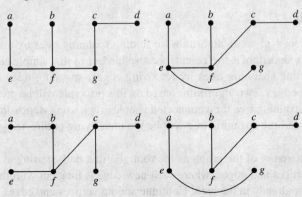

Figure 4   Spanning Trees of G.

Theorem 1   A simple graph is connected if and only if it has a spanning tree.

Proof: First, suppose that a simple graph G has a spanning tree T. T contains every vertex of G. Furthermore, there is a path in T between any two of its vertices. Because T is a subgraph of G, there is a path in G between any two of its vertices. Hence, G is connected.

Now suppose that G is connected. If G is not a tree, it must contain a simple circuit. Remove an edge from one of these simple circuits. The resulting subgraph has one fewer edge but still contains all the vertices of G and is connected. This subgraph is still connected because when two vertices are connected by a path containing the removed edge, they are connected by a path not containing this edge. We can construct such a path by inserting into the original path, at the point where the removed edge once was, the simple circuit with this edge removed. If this subgraph is not a tree, it has a simple circuit; so as before, remove an edge that is in a simple circuit. Repeat this process until no simple circuits remain. This is possible because there are only a finite number of edges in the graph. The process terminates when no simple circuits remain. A tree is produced because the graph stays connected as edges are removed. This tree is a spanning tree because it contains every vertex of G.   ◁

Spanning trees are important in data networking, as Example 2 shows.

Example 2   **IP Multicasting**   Spanning trees play an important role in multicasting over Internet Protocol (IP) networks. To send data from a source computer to multiple receiving computers, each of which is a subnetwork, data could be sent separately to each computer. This type of networking, called unicasting, is inefficient, because many copies of the same data are transmitted over the network. To make the transmission of data to multiple receiving computers more efficient, IP multicasting is used. With IP multicasting, a computer sends a single copy of data over the network, and as data reaches intermediate routers, the data are forwarded to one or more other routers so that ultimately all receiving computers in their various subnetworks receive these data. (Routers are computers that are dedicated to forwarding IP datagrams between subnetworks in a network. In multicasting, routers use Class D addresses, each representing a session that receiving computers may join.)

For data to reach receiving computers as quickly as possible, there should be no loops (which in graph theory terminology are circuits or cycles) in the path that data take through the network. That is, once data have reached a particular router, data should never return to this router. To avoid loops, the multicast routers use network algorithms to construct a spanning tree in the graph that has the multicast source, the routers, and the subnetworks containing receiving computers as vertices, with edges representing the links between computers and/or routers. The root of this spanning tree is the multicast source. The subnetworks containing receiving computers are leaves of the tree. (Note that subnetworks not containing receiving stations are not included in the graph.) This is illustrated in Figure 5.   ◄

Depth-First Search

The proof of Theorem 1 gives an algorithm for finding spanning trees by removing edges from simple circuits. This algorithm is inefficient, because it requires that simple circuits be identified. Instead of constructing spanning trees by removing edges, spanning trees can be built up by successively adding edges. Two algorithms based on this principle will be presented here.

We can build a spanning tree for a connected simple graph using **depth-first search.** We will form a rooted tree, and the spanning tree will be the underlying undirected graph of this rooted tree.

Arbitrarily choose a vertex of the graph as the root. Form a path starting at this vertex by successively adding vertices and edges, where each new edge is incident with the last vertex in the path and a vertex not already in the path. Continue adding vertices and edges to this path as long

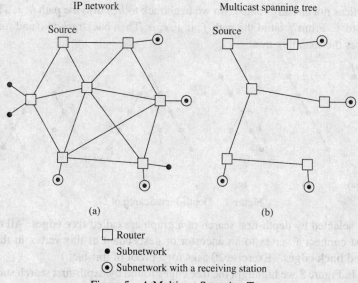

IP network   Multicast spanning tree

□ Router
● Subnetwork
◉ Subnetwork with a receiving station

Figure 5   A Multicast Spanning Tree.

as possible. If the path goes through all vertices of the graph, the tree consisting of this path is a spanning tree. However, if the path does not go through all vertices, more vertices and edges must be added. Move back to the next to last vertex in the path, and, if possible, form a new path starting at this vertex passing through vertices that were not already visited. If this cannot be done, move back another vertex in the path, that is, two vertices back in the path, and try again.

Repeat this procedure, beginning at the last vertex visited, moving back up the path one vertex at a time, forming new paths that are as long as possible until no more edges can be added. Because the graph has a finite number of edges and is connected, this process ends with the production of a spanning tree. Each vertex that ends a path at a stage of the algorithm will be a leaf in the rooted tree, and each vertex where a path is constructed starting at this vertex will be an internal vertex.

The reader should note the recursive nature of this procedure. Also, note that if the vertices in the graph are ordered, the choices of edges at each stage of the procedure are all determined when we always choose the first vertex in the ordering that is available. However, we will not always explicitly order the vertices of a graph.

Depth-first search is also called **backtracking**, because the algorithm returns to vertices previously visited to add paths. Example 3 illustrates backtracking.

Example 3   Use depth-first search to find a spanning tree for the graph G shown in Figure 6. *Solution*: The steps used by depth-first search to produce a spanning tree of G are shown in Figure 7. We arbitrarily start with the vertex f. A path is built by successively adding edges incident

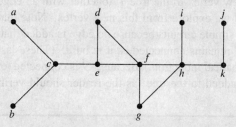

Figure 6   The Graph G.

with vertices not already in the path, as long as this is possible. This produces a path f, g, h, k, j (note that other paths could have been built). Next, backtrack to k. There is no path beginning at k

containing vertices not already visited. So we backtrack to h. Form the path h, i. Then backtrack to h, and then to f. From f build the path f, d, e, c, a. Then backtrack to c and form the path c, b. This produces the spanning tree. ◄

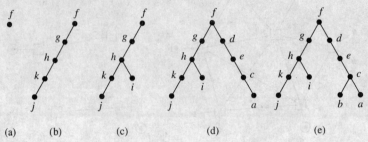

(a)   (b)   (c)   (d)   (e)

Figure 7   Depth-First Search of G.

The edges selected by depth-first search of a graph are called **tree edges.** All other edges of the graph must connect a vertex to an ancestor or descendant of this vertex in the tree. These edges are called **back edges.** (Exercise 20 asks for a proof of this fact.)

Example 4   In Figure 8 we highlight the tree edges found by depth-first search starting at vertex f by showing them with heavy colored lines. The back edges (e, f) and (f, h) are shown with thinner black lines. ◄

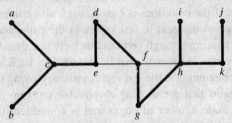

Figure 8   The Tree Edges and Back Edges of the Depth-First Search in Example 4.

We have explained how to find a spanning tree of a graph using depth-first search. However, our discussion so far has not brought out the recursive nature of depth-first search. To help make the recursive nature of the algorithm clear, we need a little terminology. We say that we *explore* from a vertex v when we carry out the steps of depth-first search beginning when v is added to the tree and ending when we have backtracked back to v for the last time. The key observation needed to understand the recursive nature of the algorithm is that when we add an edge connecting a vertex v to a vertex w, we finish exploring from w before we return to v to complete exploring from v.

In Algorithm 1 we construct the spanning tree of a graph G with vertices $v_1, \ldots, v_n$ by first selecting the vertex v_1 to be the root. We initially set T to be the tree with just this one vertex. At each step we add a new vertex to the tree T together with an edge from a vertex already in T to this new vertex and we explore from this new vertex. Note that at the completion of the algorithm, T contains no simple circuits because no edge is added that connects a vertex already in the tree. Moreover, T remains connected as it is built. (These last two observations can be easily proved via mathematical induction.) Because G is connected, every vertex in G is visited by the algorithm and is added to the tree (as the reader should verify). It follows that T is a spanning tree of G.

Algorithm 1   Depth-First Search.

procedure $DFS(G$: connected graph with vertices $v_1, v_2, \ldots, v_n)$

$T :=$ tree consisting only of the vertex v_1
$visit(v_1)$
procedure $visit(v$: vertex of $G)$
for each vertex w adjacent to v and not yet in T
begin
   add vertex w and edge $\{v, w\}$ to T
   $visit(w)$
end

We now analyze the computational complexity of the depth-first search algorithm. The key observation is that for each vertex v, the procedure $visit(v)$ is called when the vertex v is first encountered in the search and it is not called again. Assuming that the adjacency lists for G are available (see Section 6.3), no computations are required to find the vertices adjacent to v. As we follow the steps of the algorithm, we examine each edge at most twice to determine whether to add this edge and one of its endpoints to the tree. Consequently, the procedure *DFS* constructs a spanning tree using $O(e)$, or $O(n^2)$, steps where e and n are the number of edges and vertices in G, respectively. [Note that a step involves examining a vertex to see whether it is already in the spanning tree as it is being built and adding this vertex and the corresponding edge if the vertex is not already in the tree. We have also made use of the inequality $e \leqslant n(n-1)/2$, which holds for any simple graph.]

Depth-first search can be used as the basis for algorithms that solve many different problems. For example, it can be used to find paths and circuits in a graph, it can be used to determine the connected components of a graph, and it can be used to find the cut vertices of a connected graph. As we will see, depth-first search is the basis of backtracking techniques used to search for solutions of computationally difficult problems. (See [GrYe99], [Ma89], and [CoLeRiSt01] for a discussion of algorithms based on depth-first search.)

Breadth-First Search

We can also produce a spanning tree of a simple graph by the use of **breadth-first search.** Again, a rooted tree will be constructed, and the underlying undirected graph of this rooted tree forms the spanning tree. Arbitrarily choose a root from the vertices of the graph. Then add all edges incident to this vertex. The new vertices added at this stage become the vertices at level 1 in the spanning tree. Arbitrarily order them. Next, for each vertex at level 1, visited in order, add each edge incident to this vertex to the tree as long as it does not produce a simple circuit. Arbitrarily order the children of each vertex at level 1. This produces the vertices at level 2 in the tree. Follow the same procedure until all the vertices in the tree have been added. The procedure ends because there are only a finite number of edges in the graph. A spanning tree is produced because we have produced a tree containing every vertex of the graph. An example of breadth-first search is given in Example 5.

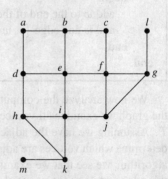

Figure 9   A Graph G.

Example 5   Use breadth-first search to find a spanning tree for the graph shown in Figure 9.

Solution: The steps of the breadth-first search procedure are shown in Figure 10. We choose the vertex e to be the root. Then we add edges incident with all vertices adjacent to e, so edges from e to b, d, f, and i are added. These four vertices are at level 1 in the tree. Next, add the edges from these vertices at level 1 to adjacent vertices not already in the tree. Hence, the edges from

b to a and c are added, as are edges from d to h, from f to j and g, and from i to k. The new vertices a, c, h, j, g, and k are at level 2. Next, add edges from these vertices to adjacent vertices not already in the graph. This adds edges from g to l and from k to m.   ◀

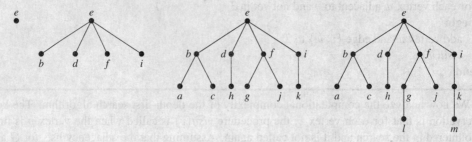

Figure 10   Breadth-First Search of G.

We describe breadth-first search in pseudocode as Algorithm 2. In this algorithm, we assume the vertices of the connected graph G are ordered as $v_1, v_2, \ldots, v_n$. In the algorithm we use the term "process" to describe the procedure of adding new vertices, and corresponding edges, to the tree adjacent to the current vertex being processed as long as a simple circuit is not produced.

Algorithm 2   Breadth-First Search.

procedure *BFS* (G: connected graph with vertices $v_1, v_2, \ldots, v_n$)
$T :=$ tree consisting only of vertex v_1
$L :=$ empty list
put v_1 in the list L of unprocessed vertices
while L is not empty
begin
   remove the first vertex, v, from L
   for each neighbor w of v
     if w is not in L and not in T **then**
     begin
        add w to the end of the list L
        add w and edge $\{v, w\}$ to T
     end
end

We now analyze the computational complexity of breadth-first search. For each vertex v in the graph we examine all vertices adjacent to v and we add each vertex not yet visited to the tree T. Assuming we have the adjacency lists for the graph available, no computation is required to determine which vertices are adjacent to a given vertex. As in the analysis of the depth-first search algorithm, we see that we examine each edge at most twice to determine whether we should add this edge and its endpoint not already in the tree. It follows that the breadth-first search algorithm uses $O(e)$ or $O(n^2)$ steps.

Backtracking Applications

There are problems that can be solved only by performing an exhaustive search of all possible solutions. One way to search systematically for a solution is to use a decision tree, where each internal vertex represents a decision and each leaf a possible solution. To find a solution via backtracking, first make a sequence of decisions in an attempt to reach a solution as long as this is possible. The sequence of decisions can be represented by a path in the decision tree. Once it is known that no solution can result from any further sequence of decisions, backtrack to the parent of the current vertex and work toward a solution with another series of decisions, if this is possible. The procedure continues until a solution is found, or it is established that no solution exists. Examples 6 to 8 illustrate the usefulness of backtracking.

Example 6 **Graph Colorings** How can backtracking be used to decide whether a graph can be colored using n colors?

Solution: We can solve this problem using backtracking in the following way. First pick some vertex a and assign it color 1. Then pick a second vertex b, and if b is not adjacent to a, assign it color 1. Otherwise, assign color 2 to b. Then go on to a third vertex c. Use color 1, if possible, for c. Otherwise use color 2, if this is possible. Only if neither color 1 nor color 2 can be used should color 3 be used. Continue this process as long as it is possible to assign one of the n colors to each additional vertex, always using the first allowable color in the list. If a vertex is reached that cannot be colored by any of the n colors, backtrack to the last assignment made and change the coloring of the last vertex colored, if possible, using the next allowable color in the list. If it is not possible to change this coloring, backtrack farther to previous assignments, one step back at a time, until it is possible to change a coloring of a vertex. Then continue assigning colors of additional vertices as long as possible. If a coloring using n colors exists, backtracking will produce it. (Unfortunately this procedure can be extremely inefficient.)

In particular, consider the problem of coloring the graph shown in Figure 11 with three colors. The tree shown in Figure 11 illustrates how backtracking can be used to construct a 3-coloring. In this procedure, red is used first, then blue, and finally green. This simple example can obviously be done without backtracking, but it is a good illustration of the technique.

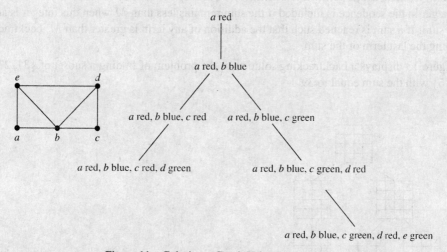

Figure 11 Coloring a Graph Using Backtracking.

In this tree, the initial path from the root, which represents the assignment of red to a, leads to a coloring with a red, b blue, c red, and d green. It is impossible to color e using any of the three colors when a, b, c, and d are colored in this way. So, backtrack to the parent of the vertex representing this coloring. Because no other color can be used for d, backtrack one more level. Then change the color of c to green. We obtain a coloring of the graph by then assigning red to d and green to e. ◄

Example 7 **The n-Queens Problem** The n-queens problem asks how n queens can be placed on an $n \times n$ chessboard so that no two queens can attack one another. How can backtracking be used to solve the n-queens problem?

Solution: To solve this problem we must find n positions on an $n \times n$ chessboard so that no two of these positions are in the same row, same column, or in the same diagonal [a diagonal consists of all positions (i, j) with $i + j = m$ for some m, or $i - j = m$ for some m]. We will use backtracking to solve the n-queens problem. We start with an empty chessboard. At stage $k + 1$ we attempt putting an additional queen on the board in the $(k + 1)$st column, where there are already queens in the first k columns. We examine squares in the $(k + 1)$st column starting with the square in the first row, looking for a position to place this queen so that it is not in the same row or on the same diagonal as a queen already on the board. (We already know it is not in the same column.) If it is impossible to find a position to place the queen in the $(k + 1)$st column, backtrack to the placement of the queen in the kth column, and place this queen in the next allowable row in this column, if such a row exists. If no such row exists, backtrack further.

In particular, Figure 12 displays a backtracking solution to the four-queens problem. In this solution, we place a queen in the first row and column. Then we put a queen in the third row of the second column. However, this makes it impossible to place a queen in the third column. So we backtrack and put a queen in the fourth row of the second column. When we do this, we can place a queen in the second row of the third column. But there is no way to add a queen to the fourth column. This shows that no solution results when a queen is placed in the first row and column. We backtrack to the empty chessboard, and place a queen in the second row of the first column. This leads to a solution as shown in Figure 12.   ◄

Example 8   **Sums of Subsets**   Consider this problem. Given a set of positive integers $x_1, x_2, \ldots, x_n$, find a subset of this set of integers that has M as its sum. How can backtracking be used to solve this problem?

Solution: We start with a sum with no terms. We build up the sum by successively adding terms. An integer in the sequence is included if the sum remains less than M when this integer is added to the sum. If a sum is reached such that the addition of any term is greater than M, backtrack by dropping the last term of the sum.

Figure 13 displays a backtracking solution to the problem of finding a subset of $\{31, 27, 15, 11, 7, 5\}$ with the sum equal to 39.   ◄

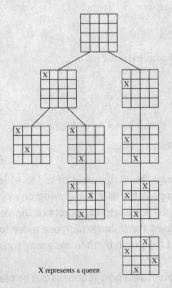

Figure 12   A Backtracking Solution
of the Four-Queens Problem.

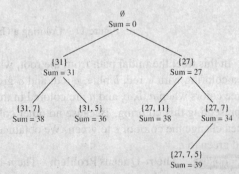

Figure 13   Find a Sum Equal to 39
Using Backtracking.

Depth-First Search in Directed Graphs

We can easily modify both depth-first search and breadth-first search so that they can run given a directed graph as input. However, the output will not necessarily be a spanning tree, but rather a spanning forest. In both algorithms we can add an edge only when it is directed away from the vertex that is being visited and to a vertex not yet added. If at a stage of either algorithm we find that no edge exists starting at a vertex already added to one not yet added, the next vertex added by the algorithm becomes the root of a new tree in the spanning forest. This is illustrated in Example 9.

Example 9   What is the output of depth-first search given the graph G shown in Figure 14(a) as input?

Solution: We begin the depth-first search at vertex a and add vertices b, c, and g and the corresponding edges where we are blocked. We backtrack to c but we are still blocked, and then backtrack to b, where we add vertices f and e and the corresponding edges. Backtracking takes us all the way back to a. We then start a new tree at d and add vertices h, l, k, and j and the corresponding edges. We backtrack to k, then l, then h, and back to d. Finally, we start a new tree at i, completing the depth-first search. The output is shown in Figure 14(b).   ◄

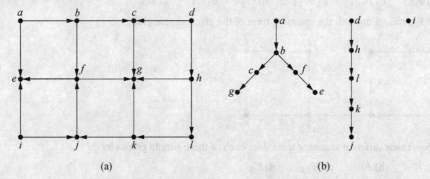

(a)   (b)

Figure 14   Depth-First Search of a Directed Graph.

Depth-first search in directed graphs is the basis of many algorithms (see [GrYe99], [Ma89], and [CoLeRiSt01]). It can be used to determine whether a directed graph has a circuit, it can be used to carry out a topological sort of a graph, and it can also be used to find the strongly connected components of a directed graph.

We conclude this section with an application of depth-first search and breadth-first search to search engines on the Web.

Example 10   **Web Spiders**   To index websites, search engines such as Yahoo systematically explore the Web starting at known sites. These search engines use programs called Web spiders (or crawlers or bots) to visit websites and analyze their contents. Web spiders use both depth-first searching and breadth-first searching to create indices. As described in Example 8 in Section 6.1, Web pages and links between them can be modeled by a directed graph called the Web graph. Web pages are represented by vertices and links are represented by directed edges. Using depth-first search, an initial Web page is selected, a link is followed to a second Web page (if there is such a link), a link on the second Web page is followed to a third Web page, if there is such a link, and so on, until a page with no new links is found. Backtracking is then used to examine links at the previous level to look for new links, and so on. (Because of practical limitations, Web spiders have limits to the depth they search in depth-first search.) Using breadth-first search, an initial Web page is selected and a link on this page is followed to a second Web page, then a second link on the initial page is followed (if it exists), and so on, until all links of the initial page have been followed. Then links on the pages one level down are followed, page by page, and so on.   ◄

Exercises

1. How many edges must be removed from a connected graph with n vertices and m edges to produce a spanning tree?

   In Exercises 2–3 find a spanning tree for the graph shown by removing edges in simple circuits.

2.
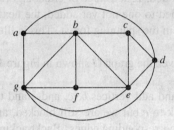

3.
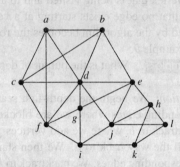

4. Find a spanning tree for each of these graphs.

   a) K_5 b) $K_{4,4}$ c) $K_{1,6}$ d) Q_3 e) C_5 f) W_5

   In Exercise 5 draw all the spanning trees of the given simple graphs.

5.
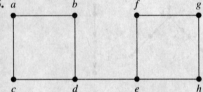

*6. How many different spanning trees does each of these simple graphs have?

   a) K_3 b) K_4 c) $K_{2,2}$ d) C_5

   In Exercises 7–8 use depth-first search to produce a spanning tree for the given simple graph. Choose a as the root of this spanning tree and assume that the vertices are ordered alphabetically.

7.
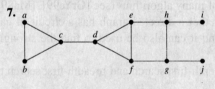

8.
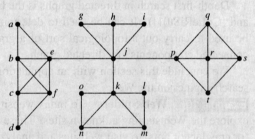

9. Use depth-first search to find a spanning tree of each of these graphs.

   a) W_6 (see Example 7 of Section 6.2), starting at the vertex of degree 6   b) K_5

   c) $K_{3,4}$, starting at a vertex of degree 3   d) Q_3

10. Describe the trees produced by breadth-first search and depth-first search of the wheel graph W_n, starting at the vertex of degree n, where n is an integer with $n \geq 3$. (See Example 7 of Section 6.2.) Justify your answers.

11. Describe the trees produced by breadth-first search and depth-first search of the complete bipartite graph $K_{m,n}$, starting at a vertex of degree m, where m and n are positive integers. Justify your answers.

12. Suppose that an airline must reduce its flight schedule to save money. If its original routes are as

illustrated here, which flights can be discontinued to retain service between all pairs of cities (where it may be necessary to combine flights to fly from one city to another)?

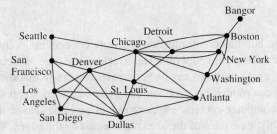

13. Which connected simple graphs have exactly one spanning tree?

*14. Show that the length of the shortest path between vertices v and u in a connected simple graph equals the level number of u in the breadth-first spanning tree of G with root v.

15. Use backtracking to solve the n-queens problem for these values of n.

    a) $n = 3$ b) $n = 5$ c) $n = 6$

16. Explain how backtracking can be used to find a Hamilton path or circuit in a graph.

A **spanning forest** of graph G is a forest that contains every vertex of G such that two vertices are in the same tree of the forest when there is a path in G between these two vertices.

17. Show that every finite simple graph has a spanning forest.

18. How many edges must be removed to produce the spanning forest of a graph with n vertices, m edges, and c connected components?

19. Devise an algorithm for constructing the spanning forest of a graph based on depth-first searching.

20. Let G be a connected graph. Show that if T is a spanning tree of G constructed using depth-first search, then an edge of G not in T must be a back edge, that is, it must connect a vertex to one of its ancestors or one of its descendants in T.

21. For which graphs do depth-first search and breadth-first search produce identical spanning trees no matter which vertex is selected as the root of the tree? Justify your answer.

22. Use mathematical induction to prove that breadth-first search visits vertices in order of their level in the resulting spanning tree.

23. Use pseudocode to describe a variation of breadth-first search that assigns the integer m to the mth vertex visited in the search.

24. Show that if G is a directed graph and T is a spanning tree constructed using depth-first search, then every edge not in the spanning tree is a **forward edge** connecting an ancestor to a descendant, a **back edge** connecting a descendant to an ancestor, or a **cross edge** connecting a vertex to a vertex in a previously visited subtree.

Let T_1 and T_2 be spanning trees of a graph. The **distance** between T_1 and T_2 is the number of edges in T_1 and T_2 that are not common to T_1 and T_2.

25. Find the distance between each pair of spanning trees shown in Figures 3(c) and 4 of the graph G shown in Figure 2.

**26. Suppose that T_1 and T_2 are spanning trees of a simple graph G. Moreover, suppose that e_1 is an edge in T_1 that is not in T_2. Show that there is an edge e_2 in T_2 that is not in T_1 such that T_1 remains a spanning tree if e_1 is removed from it and e_2 is added to it, and T_2 remains a spanning tree if e_2 is removed from it and e_1 is added to it.

A **rooted spanning tree** of a directed graph is a rooted tree containing edges of the graph such that every vertex of the graph is an endpoint of one of the edges in the tree.

27. For each of the directed graphs in Exercises 10–12 of Section 6.5 either find a rooted spanning tree of the graph or determine that no such tree exists.

*28. Give an algorithm to build a rooted spanning tree for connected directed graphs in which each vertex has the same in-degree and out-degree.

7.5   Minimum Spanning Trees

Introduction

A company plans to build a communications network connecting its five computer centers. Any pair of these centers can be linked with a leased telephone line. Which links should be made to ensure that there is a path between any two computer centers so that the total cost of the network is minimized? We can model this problem using the weighted graph shown in Figure 1, where vertices represent computer centers, edges represent possible leased lines, and the weights on edges are the monthly lease rates of the lines represented by the edges. We can solve this problem by finding a spanning tree so that the sum of the weights of the edges of the tree is minimized. Such a spanning tree is called a **minimum spanning tree.**

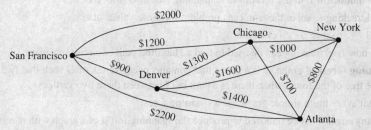

Figure 1   A Weighted Graph Showing Monthly Lease Costs for Lines in a Computer Network.

Algorithms for Minimum Spanning Trees

A wide variety of problems are solved by finding a spanning tree in a weighted graph such that the sum of the weights of the edges in the tree is a minimum.

Definition 1   A *minimum spanning tree* in a connected weighted graph is a spanning tree that has the smallest possible sum of weights of its edges.

We will present two algorithms for constructing minimum spanning trees. Both proceed by successively adding edges of smallest weight from those edges with a specified property that have not already been used. Both are greedy algorithms. Recall that a greedy algorithm is a procedure that makes an optimal choice at each of its steps. Optimizing at each step does not guarantee that the optimal overall solution is produced. However, the two algorithms presented in this section for constructing minimum spanning trees are greedy algorithms that do produce optimal solutions.

The first algorithm that we will discuss was given by Robert Prim in 1957, although the basic ideas of this algorithm have an earlier origin. To carry out **Prim's algorithm,** begin by choosing any edge with smallest weight, putting it into the spanning tree. Successively add to the tree edges of minimum weight that are incident to a vertex already in the tree and not forming a simple circuit with those edges already in the tree. Stop when $n-1$ edges have been added.

Later in this section, we will prove that this algorithm produces a minimum spanning tree for any connected weighted graph. Algorithm 1 gives a pseudocode description of Prim's algorithm.

Algorithm 1   Prim's Algorithm.

procedure *Prim*(G: weighted connected undirected graph with n vertices)
$T :=$ a minimum-weight edge
for $i := 1$ **to** $n-2$

> **begin**
> $e :=$ an edge of minimum weight incident to a vertex in T and not forming a
>   simple circuit in T if added to T
> $T := T$ with e added
> **end** $\{T$ is a minimum spanning tree of $G\}$

Note that the choice of an edge to add at a stage of the algorithm is not determined when there is more than one edge with the same weight that satisfies the appropriate criteria. We need to order the edges to make the choices deterministic. We will not worry about this in the remainder of the section. Also note that there may be more than one minimum spanning tree for a given connected weighted simple graph. (See Exercise 5.) Examples 1 and 2 illustrate how Prim's algorithm is used.

Example 1   Use Prim's algorithm to design a minimum-cost communications network connecting all the computers represented by the graph in Figure 1.

Solution: We solve this problem by finding a minimum spanning tree in the graph in Figure 1. Prim's algorithm is carried out by choosing an initial edge of minimum weight and successively adding edges of minimum weight that are incident to a vertex in the tree and that do not form simple circuits. The edges in color in Figure 2 show a minimum spanning tree produced by Prim's algorithm, with the choice made at each step displayed. ◄

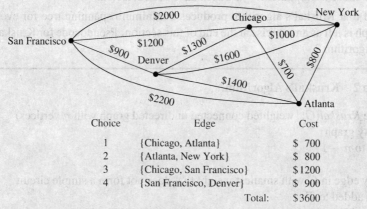

Choice	Edge	Cost
1	{Chicago, Atlanta}	$ 700
2	{Atlanta, New York}	$ 800
3	{Chicago, San Francisco}	$1200
4	{San Francisco, Denver}	$ 900
	Total:	$3600

Figure 2   A Minimum Spanning Tree for the Weighted Graph in Figure 1.

Example 2   Use Prim's algorithm to find a minimum spanning tree in the graph shown in Figure 3.

Solution: A minimum spanning tree constructed using Prim's algorithm is shown in Figure 4. The successive edges chosen are displayed. ◄

Figure 3   A Weighted Graph.

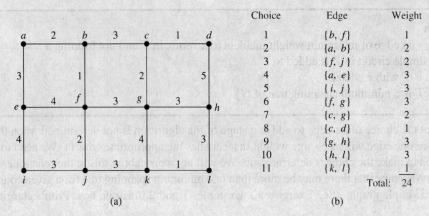

Choice	Edge	Weight
1	$\{b, f\}$	1
2	$\{a, b\}$	2
3	$\{f, j\}$	2
4	$\{a, e\}$	3
5	$\{i, j\}$	3
6	$\{f, g\}$	3
7	$\{c, g\}$	2
8	$\{c, d\}$	1
9	$\{g, h\}$	3
10	$\{h, l\}$	3
11	$\{k, l\}$	1
	Total:	24

(a)   (b)

Figure 4   A Minimum Spanning Tree Produced Using Prim's Algorithm.

The second algorithm we will discuss was discovered by Joseph Kruskal in 1956, although the basic ideas it uses were described much earlier. To carry out **Kruskal's algorithm,** choose an edge in the graph with minimum weight.

Successively add edges with minimum weight that do not form a simple circuit with those edges already chosen. Stop after $n - 1$ edges have been selected.

The proof that Kruskal's algorithm produces a minimum spanning tree for every connected weighted graph is left as an exercise at the end of this section. Pseudocode for Kruskal's algorithm is given in Algorithm 2.

Algorithm 2   Kruskal's Algorithm.

procedure *Kruskal*(G: weighted connected undirected graph with n vertices)
$T :=$ empty graph
for $i := 1$ **to** $n - 1$
begin
   $e :=$ any edge in G with smallest weight that does not form a simple circuit
      when added to T
   $T := T$ with e added
end $\{T$ is a minimum spanning tree of $G\}$

The reader should note the difference between Prim's and Kruskal's algorithms. In Prim's algorithm edges of minimum weight that are incident to a vertex already in the tree, and not forming a circuit, are chosen; whereas in Kruskal's algorithm edges of minimum weight that are not necessarily incident to a vertex already in the tree, and that do not form a circuit, are chosen. Note that as in Prim's algorithm, if the edges are not ordered, there may be more than one choice for the edge to add at a stage of this procedure. Consequently, the edges need to be ordered for the procedure to be deterministic. Example 3 illustrates how Kruskal's algorithm is used.

Example 3   Use Kruskal's algorithm to find a minimum spanning tree in the weighted graph shown in Figure 3.

Solution: A minimum spanning tree and the choices of edges at each stage of Kruskal's algorithm are shown in Figure 5.   ◄

We will now prove that Prim's algorithm produces a minimum spanning tree of a connected weighted graph.

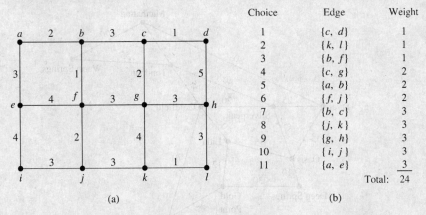

Choice	Edge	Weight
1	$\{c, d\}$	1
2	$\{k, l\}$	1
3	$\{b, f\}$	1
4	$\{c, g\}$	2
5	$\{a, b\}$	2
6	$\{f, j\}$	2
7	$\{b, c\}$	3
8	$\{j, k\}$	3
9	$\{g, h\}$	3
10	$\{i, j\}$	3
11	$\{a, e\}$	3
	Total:	24

(a)   (b)

Figure 5   A Minimum Spanning Tree Produced by Kruskal's Algorithm.

Proof: Let G be a connected weighted graph. Suppose that the successive edges chosen by Prim's algorithm are $e_1, e_2, \ldots, e_{n-1}$. Let S be the tree with $e_1, e_2, \ldots, e_{n-1}$ as its edges, and let S_k be the tree with $e_1, e_2, \ldots, e_k$ as its edges. Let T be a minimum spanning tree of G containing the edges $e_1, e_2, \ldots, e_k$, where k is the maximum integer with the property that a minimum spanning tree exists containing the first k edges chosen by Prim's algorithm. The theorem follows if we can show that $S = T$.

Suppose that $S \neq T$, so that $k < n - 1$. Consequently, T contains $e_1, e_2, \ldots, e_k$, but not e_{k+1}. Consider the graph made up of T together with e_{k+1}. Because this graph is connected and has n edges, too many edges to be a tree, it must contain a simple circuit. This simple circuit must contain e_{k+1} because there was no simple circuit in T. Furthermore, there must be an edge in the simple circuit that does not belong to S_{k+1} because S_{k+1} is a tree. By starting at an endpoint of e_{k+1} that is also an endpoint of one of the edges $e_1, \ldots, e_k$, and following the circuit until it reaches an edge not in S_{k+1}, we can find an edge e not in S_{k+1} that has an endpoint that is also an endpoint of one of the edges $e_1, e_2, \ldots, e_k$. By deleting e from T and adding e_{k+1}, we obtain a tree T' with $n - 1$ edges (it is a tree because it has no simple circuits). Note that the tree T' contains $e_1, e_2, \ldots, e_k, e_{k+1}$. Furthermore, because e_{k+1} was chosen by Prim's algorithm at the $(k + 1)$st step, and e was also available at that step, the weight of e_{k+1} is less than or equal to the weight of e. From this observation it follows that T' is also a minimum spanning tree, because the sum of the weights of its edges does not exceed the sum of the weights of the edges of T. This contradicts the choice of k as the maximum integer such that a minimum spanning tree exists containing $e_1, \ldots, e_k$. Hence, $k = n - 1$, and $S = T$. It follows that Prim's algorithm produces a minimum spanning tree.   ◁

It can be shown (see [CoLeRiSt01]) that to find a minimum spanning tree of a graph with e edges and v vertices, Kruskal's algorithm can be carried out using $O(e \log e)$ operations and Prim's algorithm can be carried out using $O(e \log v)$ operations. Consequently, it is preferable to use Kruskal's algorithm for graphs that are **sparse**, that is, where e is very small compared to $C(v, 2) = v(v - 1)/2$, the total number of possible edges in an undirected graph with v vertices. Otherwise, there is little difference in the complexity of these two algorithms.

Exercises

1. The roads represented by this graph are all unpaved. The lengths of the roads between pairs of towns are represented by edge weights. Which roads should be paved so that there is a path of paved roads between each pair of towns so that a minimum road length is paved? (*Note:* These towns are in Nevada.)

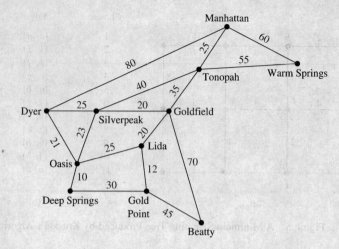

In Exercise 2 use Prim's algorithm to find a minimum spanning tree for the given weighted graph.

2.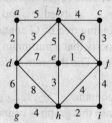

3. Use Kruskal's algorithm to design the communications network described at the beginning of the section.

4. Use Kruskal's algorithm to find a minimum spanning tree for the weighted graph in Exercise 2.

5. Find a connected weighted simple graph with the fewest edges possible that has more than one minimum spanning tree.

6. Devise an algorithm similar to Prim's algorithm for constructing a maximum spanning tree of a connected weighted graph.

*7. Devise an algorithm for finding the second shortest spanning tree in a connected weighted graph.

8. Show that there is a unique minimum spanning tree in a connected weighted graph if the weights of the edges are all different.

9. Find a spanning tree with minimal total weight containing the edges $\{e, i\}$ and $\{g, k\}$ in the weighted graph in Figure 3.

Sollin's algorithm produces a minimum spanning tree from a connected weighted simple graph $G = (V, E)$ by successively adding groups of edges. Suppose that the vertices in V are ordered. This produces an ordering of the edges where $\{u_0, v_0\}$ precedes $\{u_1, v_1\}$ if u_0 precedes u_1 or if $u_0 = u_1$ and v_0 precedes v_1. The algorithm begins by simultaneously choosing the edge of least weight incident to each vertex. The first edge in the ordering is taken in the case of ties. This produces a graph with no simple circuits, that is, a forest of trees (Exercise 24 asks for a proof of this fact). Next, simultaneously choose for each tree in the forest the shortest edge between a vertex in this tree and a vertex in a different tree. Again the first edge in the ordering is chosen in the case of ties. Continue the process of simultaneously adding edges connecting trees until $n - 1$ edges have been chosen. At this stage a minimum spanning tree has been constructed.

10. Use Sollin's algorithm to produce a minimum spanning tree for the weighted graph shown in

a) Figure 1.   b) Figure 3.

**11. Prove that Sollin's algorithm produces a minimum spanning tree in a connected undirected weighted graph.

*12. Show that if there are r trees in the forest at some intermediate step of Sollin's algorithm, then at least $\lceil r/2 \rceil$ edges are added by the next iteration of the algorithm.

*13. Show that Sollin's algorithm requires at most $\log n$ iterations to produce a minimum spanning tree from a connected undirected weighted graph with n vertices.

Key Terms and Results

TERMS

tree: a connected undirected graph with no simple circuits

forest: an undirected graph with no simple circuits

rooted tree: a directed graph with a specified vertex, called the root, such that there is a unique path to any other vertex from this root

subtree: a subgraph of a tree that is also a tree

parent of v in a rooted tree: the vertex u such that (u, v) is an edge of the rooted tree

child of a vertex v in a rooted tree: any vertex with v as its parent

sibling of a vertex v in a rooted tree: a vertex with the same parent as v

ancestor of a vertex v in a rooted tree: any vertex on the path from the root to v

descendant of a vertex v in a rooted tree: any vertex that has v as an ancestor

internal vertex: a vertex that has children

leaf: a vertex with no children

level of a vertex: the length of the path from the root to this vertex

height of a tree: the largest level of the vertices of a tree

m-ary tree: a tree with the property that every internal vertex has no more than m children

full m-ary tree: a tree with the property that every internal vertex has exactly m children

binary tree: an m-ary tree with $m = 2$ (each child may be designated as a left or a right child of its parent)

ordered tree: a tree in which the children of each internal vertex are linearly ordered

balanced tree: a tree in which every leaf is at level h or $h - 1$, where h is the height of the tree

binary search tree: a binary tree in which the vertices are labeled with items so that a label of a vertex is greater than the labels of all vertices in the left subtree of this vertex and is less than the labels of all vertices in the right subtree of this vertex

decision tree: a rooted tree where each vertex represents a possible outcome of a decision and the leaves represent the possible solutions

prefix code: a code that has the property that the code of a character is never a prefix of the code of another character

minmax strategy: the strategy where the first player and second player move to positions represented by a child with maximum and minimum value, respectively

value of a vertex in a game tree: for a leaf, the payoff to the first player when the game terminates in the position represented by this leaf; for an internal vertex, the maximum or minimum of the values of its children, for an internal vertex at an even or odd level, respectively

tree traversal: a listing of the vertices of a tree

preorder traversal: a listing of the vertices of an ordered rooted tree defined recursively—the root is listed, followed by the first subtree, followed by the other subtrees in the order they occur from left to right

inorder traversal: a listing of the vertices of an ordered rooted tree defined recursively—the first subtree is listed, followed by the root, followed by the other subtrees in the order they occur from left to right

postorder traversal: a listing of the vertices of an ordered rooted tree defined recursively—the subtrees are listed in the order they occur from left to right, followed by the root

infix notation: the form of an expression (including a full set of parentheses) obtained from an inorder traversal of the binary tree representing this expression

prefix (or Polish) notation: the form of an expression obtained from a preorder traversal of the tree representing this expression

postfix (or reverse Polish) notation: the form of an expression obtained from a postorder traversal of the tree representing this expression

spanning tree: a tree containing all vertices of a graph

minimum spanning tree: a spanning tree with smallest possible sum of weights of its edges

greedy algorithm: an algorithm that optimizes by making the optimal choice at each step

RESULTS

A graph is a tree if and only if there is a unique simple path between any of its vertices.

A tree with n vertices has $n - 1$ edges.

A full m-ary tree with i internal vertices has $mi + 1$ vertices.

The relationships among the numbers of vertices, leaves, and internal vertices in a full m-ary tree (see Theorem 4 in Section 7.1)

There are at most m^h leaves in an m-ary tree of height h.

If an m-ary tree has l leaves, its height h is at least $\lceil \log_m l \rceil$. If the tree is also full and balanced, then its height is $\lceil \log_m l \rceil$.

Huffman coding: a procedure for constructing an optimal binary code for a set of symbols, given the frequencies of these symbols

depth-first search, or backtracking: a procedure for constructing a spanning tree by adding edges that form a path until this is not possible, and then moving back up the path until a vertex is found where a new path can be formed

breadth-first search: a procedure for constructing a spanning tree that successively adds all edges incident to the last set of edges added, unless a simple circuit is formed

Prim's algorithm: a procedure for producing a minimum spanning tree in a weighted graph that successively adds edges with minimal weight among all edges incident to a vertex already in the tree such that no edge produces a simple circuit when it is added

Kruskal's algorithm: a procedure for producing a minimum spanning tree in a weighted graph that successively adds edges of least weight that are not already in the tree such that no edge produces a simple circuit when it is added

Review Questions

1. a) Define a tree.   b) Define a forest.
2. Can there be two different simple paths between the vertices of a tree?
3. Give at least three examples of how trees are used in modeling.
4. a) Define a rooted tree and the root of such a tree.
   b) Define the parent of a vertex and a child of a vertex in a rooted tree.
   c) What are an internal vertex, a leaf, and a subtree in a rooted tree?
   d) Draw a rooted tree with at least 10 vertices, where the degree of each vertex does not exceed 3. Identify the root, the parent of each vertex, the children of each vertex, the internal vertices, and the leaves.
5. a) How many edges does a tree with n vertices have?
   b) What do you need to know to determine the number of edges in a forest with n vertices?
6. a) Define a full m-ary tree.
   b) How many vertices does a full m-ary tree have if it has i internal vertices? How many leaves does the tree have?
7. a) What is the height of a rooted tree?   b) What is a balanced tree?
   c) How many leaves can an m-ary tree of height h have?
8. a) What is a binary search tree?   b) Describe an algorithm for constructing a binary search tree.
   c) Form a binary search tree for the words *vireo, warbler, egret, grosbeak, nuthatch,* and *kingfisher.*
9. a) What is a prefix code?   b) How can a prefix code be represented by a binary tree?

10. a) Define preorder, inorder, and postorder tree traversal.

   b) Give an example of preorder, postorder, and inorder traversal of a binary tree of your choice with at least 12 vertices.

11. a) Explain how to use preorder, inorder, and postorder traversals to find the prefix, infix, and postfix forms of an arithmetic expression.

   b) Draw the ordered rooted tree that represents $((x - 3) + ((x/4) + (x - y) \uparrow 3))$.

   c) Find the prefix and postfix forms of the expression in part (b).

12. Show that the number of comparisons used by a sorting algorithm is at least $\lceil \log n! \rceil$.

13. a) Describe the Huffman coding algorithm for constructing an optimal code for a set of symbols, given the frequency of these symbols.

   b) Use Huffman coding to find an optimal code for these symbols and frequencies: A: 0.2, B: 0.1, C: 0.3, D: 0.4.

14. Draw the game tree for nim if the starting position consists of two piles with one and four stones, respectively. Who wins the game if both players follow an optimal strategy?

15. a) What is a spanning tree of a simple graph?   b) Which simple graphs have spanning trees?

   c) Describe at least two different applications that require that a spanning tree of a simple graph be found.

16. a) Describe two different algorithms for finding a spanning tree in a simple graph.

   b) Illustrate how the two algorithms you described in (a) can be used to find the spanning tree of a simple graph, using a graph of your choice with at least eight vertices and 15 edges.

17. a) Explain how backtracking can be used to determine whether a simple graph can be colored using n colors.

   b) Show, with an example, how backtracking can be used to show that a graph with a chromatic number equal to 4 cannot be colored with three colors, but can be colored with four colors.

18. a) What is a minimum spanning tree of a connected weighted graph?

   b) Describe at least two different applications that require that a minimum spanning tree of a connected weighted graph be found.

19. a) Describe Kruskal's algorithm and Prim's algorithm for finding minimum spanning trees.

   b) Illustrate how Kruskal's algorithm and Prim's algorithm are used to find a minimum spanning tree, using a weighted graph with at least eight vertices and 15 edges.

Supplementary Exercises

*1. Show that a simple graph is a tree if and only if it contains no simple circuits and the addition of an edge connecting two nonadjacent vertices produces a new graph that has exactly one simple circuit (where circuits that contain the same edges are not considered different).

*2. How many nonisomorphic rooted trees are there with six vertices?

3. Show that every tree with at least one edge must have at least two pendant vertices.

4. Show that a tree with n vertices that has $n - 1$ pendant vertices must be isomorphic to $K_{1,n-1}$.

5. What is the sum of the degrees of the vertices of a tree with n vertices?

*6. Suppose that $d_1, d_2, \ldots, d_n$ are n positive integers with sum $2n - 2$. Show that there is a tree that has n vertices such that the degrees of these vertices are $d_1, d_2, \ldots, d_n$.

7. Show that every tree is a planar graph.

8. Show that every tree is bipartite.

9. Show that every forest can be colored using two colors.

 A **B-tree of degree** k is a rooted tree such that all its leaves are at the same level, its root has at least two and at most k children unless it is a leaf, and every internal vertex other than the root has at least $\lceil k/2 \rceil$, but no more than k, children. Computer files can be accessed efficiently when B-trees are used to represent them.

10. Draw three different B-trees of degree 3 with height 4.

*11. Give an upper bound and a lower bound for the number of leaves in a B-tree of degree k with height h.

*12. Give an upper bound and a lower bound for the height of a B-tree of degree k with n leaves.

The **binomial trees** B_i, $i = 0, 1, 2, \ldots$, are ordered rooted trees defined recursively:

Basis step: The binomial tree B_0 is the tree with a single vertex.

Recursive step: Let k be a nonnegative integer. To construct the binomial tree B_{k+1}, add a copy of B_k to a second copy of B_k by adding an edge that makes the root of the first copy of B_k the leftmost child of the second copy of B_k.

13. Draw B_k for $k = 0, 1, 2, 3, 4$.

14. How many vertices does B_k have? Prove that your answer is correct.

15. Find the height of B_k. Prove that your answer is correct.

16. How many vertices are there in B_k at depth j, where $0 \leqslant j \leqslant k$? Justify your answer.

17. What is the degree of the root of B_k? Prove that your answer is correct.

18. Show that the vertex of largest degree in B_k is the root.

A rooted tree T is called an S_k-**tree** if it satisfies this recursive definition. It is an S_0-tree if it has one vertex. For $k > 0$, T is an S_k-tree if it can be built from two S_{k-1}-trees by making the root of one the root of the S_k-tree and making the root of the other the child of the root of the first S_k-tree.

19. Draw an S_k-tree for $k = 0, 1, 2, 3, 4$.

20. Show that an S_k-tree has 2^k vertices and a unique vertex at level k. This vertex at level k is called the **handle**.

*21. Suppose that T is an S_k-tree with handle v. Show that T can be obtained from disjoint trees $T_0, T_1, \ldots,$ T_{k-1}, where v is not in any of these trees, where T_i is an S_i-tree for $i = 0, 1, \ldots, k-1$, by connecting v to r_0 and r_i to r_{i+1} for $i = 0, 1, \ldots, k-2$.

The listing of the vertices of an ordered rooted tree in **level order** begins with the root, followed by the vertices at level 1 from left to right, followed by the vertices at level 2 from left to right, and so on.

22. List the vertices of the ordered rooted trees in Figures 3 and 9 of Section 7.3 in level order.

23. Devise an algorithm for listing the vertices of an ordered rooted tree in level order.

*24. Devise an algorithm for determining if a set of universal addresses can be the addresses of the leaves of a rooted tree.

25. Devise an algorithm for constructing a rooted tree from the universal addresses of its leaves.

A **cut set** of a graph is a set of edges such that the removal of these edges produces a subgraph with more connected components than in the original graph, but no proper subset of this set of edges has this property.

26. Show that a cut set of a graph must have at least one edge in common with any spanning tree of this graph.

A **cactus** is a connected graph in which no edge is in more than one simple circuit not passing through any vertex other than its initial vertex more than once or its initial vertex other than at its terminal vertex (where two circuits that contain the same edges are not considered different).

27. Which of these graphs are cacti?

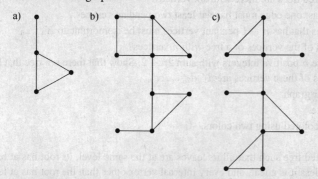

28. Is a tree necessarily a cactus?

29. Show that a cactus is formed if we add a circuit containing new edges beginning and ending at a vertex of a tree.

*30. Show that if every circuit not passing through any vertex other than its initial vertex more than once in a connected graph contains an odd number of edges, then this graph must be a cactus.

A **degree-constrained spanning tree** of a simple graph G is a spanning tree with the property that the degree of a vertex in this tree cannot exceed some specified bound. Degree-constrained spanning trees are useful in models of transportation systems where the number of roads at an intersection is limited, models of communications networks where the number of links entering a node is limited, and so on.

In Exercises 31–33 find a degree-constrained spanning tree of the given graph where each vertex has degree less than or equal to 3, or show that such a spanning tree does not exist.

31.   **32.**   **33.**

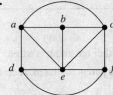   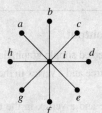   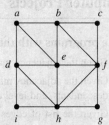

34. Show that a degree-constrained spanning tree of a simple graph in which each vertex has degree not exceeding 2 consists of a single Hamilton path in the graph.

35. A tree with n vertices is called **graceful** if its vertices can be labeled with the integers $1, 2, \ldots, n$ such that the absolute values of the difference of the labels of adjacent vertices are all different. Show that these trees are graceful.

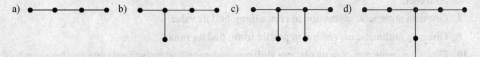

A **caterpillar** is a tree that contains a simple path such that every vertex not contained in this path is adjacent to a vertex in the path.

36. Which of the graphs in Exercise 35 are caterpillars?

37. How many nonisomorphic caterpillars are there with six vertices?

**38. a) Prove or disprove that all trees whose edges form a single path are graceful.

b) Prove or disprove that all caterpillars are graceful.

39. Suppose that in a long bit string the frequency of occurrence of a 0 bit is 0.9 and the frequency of a 1 bit is 0.1 and bits occur independently.

a) Construct a Huffman code for the four blocks of two bits, 00, 01, 10, and 11. What is the average number of bits required to encode a bit string using this code?

b) Construct a Huffman code for the eight blocks of three bits. What is the average number of bits required to encode a bit string using this code?

40. Suppose that G is a directed graph with no circuits. Describe how depth-first search can be used to carry out a topological sort of the vertices of G.

*41. Suppose that e is an edge in a weighted graph that is incident to a vertex v such that the weight of e does not exceed the weight of any other edge incident to v. Show that there exists a minimum spanning tree containing this edge.

42. Three couples arrive at the bank of a river. Each of the wives is jealous and does not trust her husband when he is with one of the other wives (and perhaps with other people), but not with her. How can six people cross to the other side of the river using a boat that can hold no more than two people so that no husband is alone with a woman other than his wife? Use a graph theory model.

*43. Show that if no two edges in a weighted graph have the same weight, then the edge with least weight incident to a vertex v is included in every minimum spanning tree.

44. Find a minimum spanning tree of each of these graphs where the degree of each vertex in the spanning tree does not exceed 2.

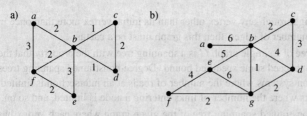

a)

b)

Computer Projects

Write programs with these input and output.

1. Given the adjacency matrix of an undirected simple graph, determine whether the graph is a tree.

2. Given the adjacency matrix of a rooted tree and a vertex in the tree, find the parent, children, ancestors, descendants, and level of this vertex.

3. Given the list of edges of a rooted tree and a vertex in the tree, find the parent, children, ancestors, descendants, and level of this vertex.

4. Given a list of items, construct a binary search tree containing these items.

5. Given a binary search tree and an item, locate or add this item to the binary search tree.

6. Given the ordered list of edges of an ordered rooted tree, find the universal addresses of its vertices.

7. Given the ordered list of edges of an ordered rooted tree, list its vertices in preorder, inorder, and postorder.

8. Given an arithmetic expression in prefix form, find its value.

9. Given an arithmetic expression in postfix form, find its value.

10. Given the frequency of symbols, use Huffman coding to find an optimal code for these symbols.

11. Given an initial position in the game of nim, determine an optimal strategy for the first player.

12. Given the adjacency matrix of a connected undirected simple graph, find a spanning tree for this graph using depth-first search.

13. Given the adjacency matrix of a connected undirected simple graph, find a spanning tree for this graph using breadth-first search.

14. Given a set of positive integers and a positive integer N, use backtracking to find a subset of these integers that have N as their sum.

*15. Given the adjacency matrix of an undirected simple graph, use backtracking to color the graph with three colors, if this is possible.

*16. Given a positive integer n, solve the n-queens problem using backtracking.

17. Given the list of edges and their weights of a weighted undirected connected graph, use Prim's algorithm to find a minimum spanning tree of this graph.

18. Given the list of edges and their weights of a weighted undirected connected graph, use Kruskal's algorithm to find a minimum spanning tree of this graph.

Computations and Explorations

Use a computational program or programs you have written to do these exercises.

1. Display all trees with six vertices.

2. Display a full set of nonisomorphic trees with seven vertices.

*3. Construct a Huffman code for the symbols with ASCII codes given the frequency of their occurrence in representative input.

4. Compute the number of different spanning trees of K_n for $n = 1, 2, 3, 4, 5, 6$. Conjecture a formula for the number of such spanning trees whenever n is a positive integer.

5. Compare the number of comparisons needed to sort lists of n elements for $n = 100$, 1000, and 10,000, where the elements are randomly selected positive integers, using the selection sort, the insertion sort, the merge sort, and the quick sort.

6. Compute the number of different ways n queens can be arranged on an $n \times n$ chessboard so that no two queens can attack each other for all positive integers n not exceeding 10.

*7. Find a minimum spanning tree of the graph that connects the capital cities of the 50 states in the United States to each other where the weight of each edge is the distance between the cities.

8. Draw the complete game tree for a game of checkers on a 4×4 board.

Writing Projects

Respond to these essays using outside sources.

1. Explain how Cayley used trees to enumerate the number of certain types of hydrocarbons.

2. Define AVL-trees (sometimes also known as *height-balanced trees*). Describe how and why AVL-trees are used in a variety of different algorithms.

3. Define *quad trees* and explain how images can be represented using them. Describe how images can be rotated, scaled, and translated by manipulating the corresponding quad tree.

4. Define a *heap* and explain how trees can be turned into heaps. Why are heaps useful in sorting?

5. Describe dynamic algorithms for data compression based on letter frequencies as they change as characters are successively read, such as adaptive Huffman coding.

6. Explain how *alpha-beta pruning* can be used to simplify the computation of the value of a game tree.

7. Describe the techniques used by chess-playing programs such as Deep Blue.

8. Define the type of graph known as a *mesh of trees*. Explain how this graph is used in applications to very large system integration and parallel computing.

9. Discuss the algorithms used in IP multicasting to avoid loops between routers.

10. Describe an algorithm based on depth-first search for finding the articulation points of a graph.

11. Describe an algorithm based on depth-first search to find the strongly connected components of a directed graph.

12. Describe the search techniques used by the crawlers and spiders in different search engines on the Web.

13. Describe an algorithm for finding the minimum spanning tree of a graph such that the maximum degree of any vertex in the spanning tree does not exceed a fixed constant k.

14. Compare and contrast some of the most important sorting algorithms in terms of their complexity and when they are used.

15. Discuss the history and origins of algorithms for constructing minimum spanning trees.

16. Describe algorithms for producing random trees.

华章数学经典原版

书名	书号	定价	出版年	作者
离散数学及其应用 （英文精编版. 第6版）	978-7-111-31329	55	2010	（美）Kenneth H. Rosen
初等数论及其应用（英文版 第6版）	978-7-111-31792	89	2010	（美）Kenneth H. Rosen
统计模型：理论和实践（英文版 第2版）	978-7-111-31797	38	2010	（美）David A. Freedman
概率论教程 （英文版 第3版）	978-7-111-30289	49	2010	（美）Kai LaiChung
数学建模（英文精编版 第4版）	978-7-111-28249	65	2009	（美）FrankR. Giordano
组合数学 （英文版 第5版）	978-7-111-26525	49	2009	（美）Richard A. Brualdi
复变函数及应用 （英文版 第8版）	978-7-111-25363	65	2009	（美）James Ward Brown
算法概论 （注释版）	978-7-111-25361	55	2009	（美）Sanjoy Dasgupts 钱枫注译
数学建模 方法与分析（英文版. 第3版）	978-7-111-25364	49	2008	（美）MarkM. Meerschaert
离散数学及其应用 （英文版. 第6版）	978-7-111-23935	89	2008	（美）Kenneth H. Rosen
线性代数（英文版. 第7版）	978-7-111-21198	58	2007	（美）Steven J. Leon
离散数学（英文版. 第5版）	978-7-111-20167	75	2006	（美）Lawrence E. Spence Charles Vanden Eynd
应用逻辑（英文版. 第2版）	978-7-111-19772	49	2006	（美）Anil Nerode Richard A. Shore
数论概论（英文版. 第3版）	978-7-111-19611	52	2006	（美）Joseph H. Silverman
高等微积分（英文版. 第2版）	978-7-111-19349	76	2006	（美）Patrick M. Fitzpatrick
实分析和概率论（英文版. 第2版）	978-7-111-19348	69	2006	（美）R. M. Dudley